DOG 83
EMPLOYERS

**DIRECTORY OF
OPPORTUNITIES FOR
GRADUATES**

VNU BUSINESS
PUBLICATIONS

Contents

Publisher:
Mark Lane
Editor:
Iris Rosier
Production manager:
Teresa Solomon
Advertisement manager:
Peter Luckraft
Art Director:
Chris Patton
Designer:
Grant Nelson

Typeset,
reproduced and printed by photolithography and
bound in Great Britain at The Pitman Press, Bath
Contents pages
Newtext Filmsetting Limited, London,
Cover printed
by Libra Scan, London

© **1982 VNU Business Publications**
53-55 Frith Street
London W1A 2HG

ISBN 0 86271 027 8 (paperback: DOG Employers)
ISBN 0 86271 028 6 (paperback: Further Studies)

Preparing for work

4 **Shaping up for the jobs jungle**
Anna Ewins helps you sort out the
priorities when assessing your career needs
and demands.

11 **A service to suit everyone**
Careers services will do as much or as
little as you want. Debbie Catt outlines their
aims and activities.

15 **Diary of an information officer**
Leila Roberts explains how you can
either help yourself or enlist the aid of experts
in the careers library.

21 **Work out which employer**
Bob Willott offers some guidelines on
making sure the organisation is right for you.

29 **Write no wrongs**
Filling in application forms can be
a real hassle. Iris Rosier eases you through
the process.

34 **A recruiter's life is not a happy one**
It all looks different from the other side
of the desk. Jim Hallam shares some less
than magical moments.

40 **Wheels within wheels**
As a disabled graduate himself,
Andrew Bruce shows how to be positive with
a handicap.

43 **Older and wiser**
Mature students have a lot to offer on
the job market. Bill Gothard identifies some of
your hidden assets.

Contents

Alternative strategies

49 **Branch away from the obvious**
Martin Higham points out the
value of flexible thinking when planning
your career.

52 **Time for some talent spotting**
You've more skills and abilities than
you probably think. Debbie Catt helps you
take a closer look.

56 **Brave new worlds of work**
Helen Wood challenges traditional
employment roles by suggesting ways round
the system.

63 **If at first you don't succeed**
You can make excellent use of
your time if you can't get a job straight-
away. Helen Nixon explores some less
obvious paths.

Focus on employment and training

67 **Employers** – present the key facts
about their jobs, training schemes,
salaries and prospects, and the sort of
graduates they wish to attract.

377 **Professional bodies** – set out
their membership requirements
and the contribution they can make to your
career.

387 **Working overseas** – the
employers who are recruiting for
overseas posts.

Indexes

399 The addresses and activities of
over 500 employers willing to accept
graduate applications

421 Occupations

437 Employer activity

447 Degree subject

465 Geographical

SHAPING UP FOR THE JOBS JUNGLE

ANNA EWINS CAREERS ADVISER FROM CITY UNIVERSITY SKETCHES OUT THE KEY PERSONAL AREAS WHICH WILL BUILD UP YOUR SKILLS INTO A CAREER PROFILE

SUSAN HELLARD

The key to approaching the career of your choice is knowing what you want and where you're going. Now that sounds very simple, but if you're one of the many thousands who have little idea of what to do when you leave college, and even less idea of how to find out, then it can seem a daunting task.

The answer is to start by thinking about your personal goals. That's not as easy as it sounds. You will have to be honest in your assessments; you will have to learn how to process the information you assemble and plan your priorities.

You may have a very ordered mind and find the task of assembling all the information a simple one. That makes you one of the lucky ones. Most people will need a little help and support in getting things together.

CONSIDER THE IMPORTANCE YOU WANT WORK TO ASSUME IN YOUR LIFE

Talking to a careers adviser or someone you respect will be invaluable in clarifying your goals. There are also a number of books available* which you can buy or which the careers service may be able to lend to you. They cover setting your goals, career decision-making and planning your life in general.

Some careers services run planning workshops where practical exercises help you to work with other students in moving closer to deciding the direction you would like your life to take.

Self-assessment will mean looking at the choices which are open to you and the different lifestyles which each could involve. You must also consider the kinds of people you want to be with and the importance you want work to assume in your life.

At this stage you may be thinking; what a waste of time. The choice of jobs, even the range of organisations within those jobs, seems so huge at first that it looks time-consuming and unproductive to wade through such preparation – particularly if you feel that you will not stand much chance of getting what you want, or don't fancy very much what's on offer anyway.

But exercising your imagination by planning your life is more than a mere flight of fancy. It can be a sound basis for helping to determine your goals, and writing a short autobiography is one way of identifying the important themes in your life.

Only some of your key needs and values may be apparent at the moment. You probably take the rest for granted or don't realise them at all. But you will gain useful indicators by considering how you have made choices in the past – positive and negative experiences – how you have managed your work as a student, how you spend your time and how you would like to spend it.

Consider not only your work related values, but those with implications for your personal life. Think about whether you want to work primarily with people or things; whether you would like to be engaged in directing and influencing others, intellectual problem-solving or practical work; what kind of work will fit in with your self-image; how ambitious you are; how important security is to you; how much risk or challenge you want and what conditions of work such as location or hours are important. In a few careers services, a computer aided decision programme, CDAS, is available to help you work out the importance of these criteria.

Most students consider their skills primarily in terms of performance on their present course. Even if they can recognise other skills, they discount experiences like those acquired in a social setting as irrelevant.

But when taking stock of what you have to offer an employer, you must consider all your experiences and activities in leisure time, voluntary and vacation work as well as academic skills. Examine the different roles in your life such as being a student, a good friend, a mother or father, official of a club or a voluntary worker.

Many careers publications have checklists to help in describing and working out your skills. They fall roughly into three categories: people, data and things. The former covers instructing, supervising, counselling, advising, leading and managing; data means listing numerical or organisational skills, and the latter section will include physical, mechanical or spatial abilities.

SKILLS ARE NOT JUST ACADEMIC – HOW YOU ORGANISE YOUR TIME OR HANDLE RELATIONSHIPS IS EQUALLY IMPORTANT

Of course it is not enough to know merely what you are good at, you also need to know how you can apply it to new situations. Not all skills are equally applicable. Some are very specific, relating to a highly technical subject; others are more general and can be transferred to other contexts, like analysing, researching, organising, designing, listening and supervising.

Another type of skill is concerned with how

you organise your time; how you handle relationships with others, how you use authority and responsibility, and so on. Transferable and self-management skills are most useful in adapting to and thriving in new situations. Employers seek these as basic skills (except in very degree related or highly technical jobs). Between 35 and 40% of first appointments for graduates are for those of any discipline (although communication skills and a reasonable degree of numeracy are specified in many cases, irrespective of degree discipline).

On the surface, the work of a lawyer may seem very different from a computer programmer, yet they use many of the same skills – analysing, manoeuvring and implementing plans. The differences are the problems or content knowledge of the work.

COMPUTER ASSISTED SYSTEMS CAN HELP IN YOUR CHOICE OF CAREER, BUT IT'S UP TO YOU TO MAKE THE FINAL DECISION

Cast your net as widely as possible at first. This may mean reconsidering options which you have previously rejected. Sources of information include your careers service and library. They will give a wide range of employer and occupational literature and directories, information on video cassettes, details of where previous graduates have gone and vacancy lists.

Two computer assisted systems, Gradscope and Cascaid HE, provide suggestions of occupations for graduates of any discipline. But although these programmes can help you narrow down the choices you have been considering, the main decisions will be made by you. At this stage you must consider the chances of success of each option, because this will influence your overall order of preference. One career may stand out above the rest and you may decide to invest most of your energies into it, and only act upon your second choice if the main one does not work out. On the other hand, several options may arise which you pursue simultaneously.

If you don't get any job offers in the areas of your choice, you will need to reconsider others either in the short term, with your first preference still in mind, or more seriously, as a longer term alternative.

The British National Oil Corporation

BNOC is a major operator in off-shore oil and gas developments in the North Sea, and one of the fastest-growing companies in Britain.

see also page 107

At interview or even after starting the job of your choice, you may decide it is not what you really want. Then you can simply go back into the decision-making process again, until you find the right job.

* Bibliography

Planning your future a workbook for personal goal-setting, by GA Ford and GL Lippitt, published by University Associates, California, 1972.

Where do I go from here with my life? a systematic life/work planning manual for students of all ages and career changers, by JC Crystal and RN Bolles, published by Ten Speed Press, California, 1974.

The Three Boxes of Life an introduction to life/work planning, by RN Bolles, published by Ten Speed Press, California, 1978.

Skills in life/career planning by K Barrsh and L Sandmeyer, published by Wadsworth, California, 1979.

The Inventurers excursion in life and career renewal, by J Hagberg and R Leider, published by Addison-Webley, 1978.

How to decide a workbook for women, published by College Entrance Examination Board, New York, 1975.

What colour is your parachute? a practical manual for job hunters and career changers, by RN Bolles, published by Ten Speed Press, California, 1978.

Values Clarification a handbook of practical strategies for teachers and students, by SR Simon, LW Howe, H Kirschenbaum, published by Hart, New York, 1972.

POINT•CHECKPOINT•CHECKPOINT•CHECK

AGCAS information sheets

AGCAS information sheets cover a wide range of career and job areas. They include information on qualifications, prospects, training courses, useful addresses and suggest other relevant publications/sources of information.

Applications & interviews	Patent work	Tourism
Accountancy	Personnel work	Town & country planning
Actuarial work	Police	Transport
Advertising	Postgraduate management education	Using languages
Banking	Postgraduate research & training	Work related to education
Careers with music for graduates	Production	Youth & community work
Computers	Professions related to medicine	
Industry	Public sector administration	**Opportunities for:**
Insurance	Purchasing	Graduates in any subject
Journalism	Radio, tv, theatre & cinema	Archaeologists
Legal profession in England & Wales	Research design & development	Biochemists
Leisure & recreation	Retailing	Biologists
Library information and archive work	Scientists in the health service	Chemical engineers
Local government	Secretarial work	Chemists
Management services	Selling & technical services	Civil engineers
Marketing	Social work	Economists
Market research	Study & employment overseas	Electrical & electronic engineers
Museums & art galleries	Surveying & valuation	Geographers
Notes for discontinuing students	Teaching in further & higher	Geologists
Notes for law students not joining the	education	Mathematicians
legal profession	Teaching overseas	Mechanical & production engineers
Nursing	Teaching in schools in the UK	Metallurgists/materials scientists
Offshore oil and related industries	Teaching in special schools	Physicists
Opportunities in agriculture,	The City	Psychologists
horticulture and fisheries	The publishing industry	Sociologists

Available at your university or polytechnic careers service.

Variety

Life at TI is varied – variety of product, technology, structure and management style. For graduates this means a really varied career. There's a role for you in TI.

Training

Training programmes are individually tailored to give you the competence and confidence to contribute early in your chosen function. We encourage you, where appropriate, to qualify for membership of a professional institution.

Diversity

TI consists of over 100 companies, employs 37,000 people and sells over £1 billion of goods a year. Yet each company maintains responsibility for its own decisions; business units small enough to give every graduate their own identity.

Opportunity

We need graduates in any discipline, but especially in Engineering and Technology, with specific traineeships provided in both Engineering and Finance – our Graduate Brochure, available from your Careers Service, will give you all the background.

**Graduate Recruitment & Training Officer,
TI Group plc,
Woodbourne Grange,
21 Woodbourne Road,
Birmingham B17 8BZ**

TIME RUNS OUT

ANDREW WILSON EXPLAINS THE MECHANICS OF CHOOSING A CAREER AND TAKING THE JOB PLUNGE

Before he went to university, Andrew Wilson knew that he wanted a career in business but hadn't defined his plans. "I decided to take a bachelor of commerce degree at Birmingham University with options in French and German, because my A levels seemed to be narrowing my career path. I knew I needed as many different skills as possible for a business career."

A spell at McDonalds after leaving school had sparked off some ideas about entering management. But Andrew only began to think seriously about his future at the end of his second year at university. "I visited my careers adviser and we threw around lots of ideas. We finally came up with marketing or sales."

"I wanted a job where I would be really involved in decision making, because in the long term I'm aiming for the top. So, I didn't want to become too specialised early on, and marketing seemed to offer the variety and

contact with a range of people to help me get the right experience." Andrew's careers adviser warned him that the fields he was considering were very competitive, but encouraged him to apply.

Andrew applied for short courses arranged by some of the larger companies during the Christmas vacation. "We were involved in role-playing exercises, management problem-solving and presentations. Staff from marketing, personnel and sales departments also joined in and explained their duties and the demands of the work." The experience was invaluable and "not only did it confirm my ideas, but it looked good on my CV," says Andrew.

Finally deciding to apply for marketing jobs in companies that fulfilled his requirements Andrew knew, "They had to be market leaders in their own fields, have a well organised graduate training scheme and be in fast moving consumer products." He picked out the appropriate companies by "reading their recruitment blurb, and discussing my findings with my careers adviser. But before I started form-filling I used the careers directories to check that I had the experience and qualities they were looking for." Andrew also read the weekly marketing magazines, "It impresses the interviewer when you can demonstrate you are aware of what's happening in the industry, but it also helped me clarify my ideas and gave me confidence for interviews."

Andrew also applied for sales vacancies "I thought I could gain some experience, and then move into marketing at a later stage. To find out a little more about sales work, Andrew spent two days on the road with a rep. "Although I enjoyed it, it seemed to be a very lonely job, and you've a long way from where the real policy decisions are made."

During his second interviews Andrew had the chance to look around several companies and talk to some recent graduates. He used this opportunity to answer his remaining doubts of, "Am I suited? Will I get on with the people I'll be working with," and most importantly, "How fast have new entrants progressed?"

Andrew finally accepted an offer from Thomson Holidays as marketing assistant. Happy with his choice, Andrew is "already making my own decisions and looking forward to the future".

Meet us and you'll know

Coopers & Lybrand

Peter Waine,
National Student Manager,
Abacus House,
Gutter Lane, Cheapside,
London EC2V 8AH.

chartered accountancy with C & L

see also page 140

A SERVICE TO SUIT EVERYONE

THERE'S MORE TO A CAREERS
SERVICE THAN MEETS
THE EYE. DEBBIE CATT
SHOWS YOU HOW TO
MAKE THE MOST OF IT

In these days of medical advances it's odd that no-one has yet found a cure for 'panicitis'. You don't see packets of pills on the chemist's counter, even though it's always about and at its worst in May and June. The symptoms – a dazed expression, a feeling of total confusion – are usually accompanied by voices saying such things as "When are you going to earn some money?" and "Well, have you got a job yet?"

Panicitis is curable. But don't ignore the warning signs too long. Advanced cases can result in the 'I've left it too late' syndrome, or even a year of 'unemploymentosis'. Calling in at

your university or polytechnic careers service should set you on the road to recovery. If the thought of it is worrying, you don't even have to speak to anyone there; just walk in and browse around. If you can't find what you want then you'll have to ask for help. But if you can't face officialdom at the enquiry desk there's bound to be one student who knows the ropes and can lead you to the material you want or some further contact points.

A splendid way to begin is to fix an appointment with a careers adviser. A discussion should really clear the air, because advisers are generally receptive to your ideas, however zany. They'll find out what stage you've reached in your career planning and help with the next step. It doesn't matter whether it's a further course, a permanent job or ideas on how best to spend a year off. It's not an inquisition – you don't have to explain your motives to a straight-faced human probe.

Careers services have been set up to reassure you and to offer constructive help. They can help you to draw up a curriculum vitae, put you on the right path with application forms or even set up a mock interview to give you some unbiased and constructive feedback.

For the retiring violets who don't fancy the idea of plunging straight in as the interview victim, many services arrange a variety of group sessions. These pack a lot of information into a very short time, and cover those topics most useful to the largest number of students. You may see posters, for example, advertising self-presentation workshops or mass-interest questionnaire sessions. If not, it's worth asking the careers staff to arrange one, specially if you can round up enough of your friends to participate. You may be given an interest questionnaire as part of your individual interview with a careers adviser. They're not aptitude tests, but they do throw out some suggestions of job areas. Whether you feel any of these careers are appropriate or not, most students agree it's a real cog-turning exercise for your brain.

If you've already plenty of ideas about what you're looking for you can explore the careers library. To the uninitiated, it's a bit like Willie Wonker's chocolate factory. For a start the files on occupational areas could keep you going till Kingdom come. If a new job title catches your interest ask about getting more details or the

Financial Training's method is no easier than the rest

Simply more effective

Financial Training has a wholly professional approach to education and training. Material and tutors are of the highest calibre, benefiting from years of experience in Chartered Accountancy tuition. Within this environment committed students thrive. Their confidence and that of the top firms who send them to us is soundly based on an incomparable success record – and success comes naturally with confidence.

f Financial Training

Birmingham
2nd Floor Tower Block
Centre City Hill Street
Birmingham B5 4UA
Tel: 021 632 5845

Newcastle
94/104 Grainger Road
Newcastle upon Tyne NE1 5JQ
Tel: 0632 329365

Sheffield
Pegasus House, 463a Glossop Road
Sheffield S10 2QD. Tel: 0742 669 265

Cardiff
8 Park Grove, Cardiff CF1 3BN
Tel: 0222 34141

Leeds
10a Central Road, Leeds LS1 6DE
Tel: 0532 457455

Liverpool & Manchester
64 Port Street, Manchester M1 2EG
Tel: 061 236 9646

London 136/142 Bramley Road, London W10 6SR. Tel: 01-960 4421

addresses to contact. The information sheets published by the Association of Graduate Careers Advisory Services (AGCAS) cover the most obvious work areas. Written by careers advisers with undecided students very much in mind, they can lead you on to dig a little deeper into topics previously considered 'old hat'.

Most careers services have video cassettes dealing with interviews, which can be a useful way of improving your technique. They also have videos produced by the larger companies to outline their recruitment slant. Once you are aware of the dangers of being misled by the slick patter of the brochures, you can read between the lines and pick out a few key facts. Few will actually disclose that they made drastic cuts in staff and output and there's rarely enough detail about what will happen to you when you join, like training appraisal schemes and so on. Indeed finding out what happened to last year's new entrants can be startling. This is best answered by talking to recent graduates at company open days or on visits arranged through careers services. It will take an effort to drag yourself up to some distant site but it should be well worth it.

NEWSPAPERS, TRADE JOURNALS AND VACANCY LISTS CAN GIVE YOU IDEAS ON EMPLOYERS WHO'LL WANT YOU

Specialist journals and the press are vastly underrated as sources of vacancy information. Dailies focus on specific employment areas on particular days like *The Guardian* education pages on Tuesdays and creative and media on Mondays; *The Times* on Tuesdays has a legal section and on Mondays public and local educational authorities, and *The Daily Telegraph* has an impressive number of vacancies each day. Regional newspapers are another obvious source; if you've got your eye on one spot in the country, it's worth getting a regular copy. Professional journals also provide a surprising amount of potential vacancy information chiefly in the form of advertisers, not necessarily in actual vacancy displays. Commercial local radio also carries job details; so find out if there's one which might help you home in on possible job chances.

But apart from this do-it-yourself investigation there are also direct ways of contacting employers, like vacancy lists and organised visits from recruiters.

The Central Services Unit (CSU), a national clearing house for graduate vacancies, issue a fortnightly list, *Current Vacancies*, throughout the year. It's circulated to all polytechnic and university careers services, and many services compile and publish their own local lists too. You can arrange to have the lists sent to you once you leave, so register early with the careers service. CSU and some individual careers services also publish regular lists, *Forward Vacancies*, which only include vacancies for the summer onwards. These appear around November and run till about Easter.

Live employer contact on the other hand can be made in two ways. Every spring term careers services play host to graduate recruiters who are interviewing final year students for permanent jobs. These first interviews are usually over by Easter and further sessions are arranged at company headquarters or at the site where you might hope to work. For those students who delay to the very last minute, convincing themselves it's best to concentrate on their exams rather than on job-hunting, a safety net is laid on at the end of the summer term. These Summer Fairs help recruiters with unfilled vacancies by jamboree mopping up operations, held in large city universities and polytechnics. Employers jostle eagerly with their colleagues for the attentions of unattached graduates. You may need to book an interview time.

As a last resort for some rather elusive opportunities you may even place yourself in the hands of a specialist employment agency.

This is all very well if you've decided to launch yourself into the job market, but there are other pathways to investigate. For instance, if you're thinking of adding a few more letters to your name, you need to check with *Graduate Studies* and *DOG Further Studies* to find the most appropriate course. The careers service can even advise on plans for a year abroad or voluntary work, and help weigh up all the angles.

"Enough, enough," you may scream. Yet realistically you need to process a good deal of all the information before taking any future step. But the fact that there's a team of friendly and informed people waiting to help you through it takes much of the pressure off. Take advantage of the services; they are only provided for your benefit and it's a lot less painful than replacing torn-out hair.

"It's noon in
Saudi Arabia.
It's as hot
as hell.
It's hard work.
It's the best
decision I ever
made." *Mike Gossip*

Field Technical Engineer 1

14

COLIN HADLEY

DIARY OF AN INFORMATION OFFICER

LEILA ROBERTS OF BRADFORD UNIVERSITY SHOWS HOW THE INFORMATION TEAM HELPS STUDENTS FIND THEIR WAY

A typical November day . . .

7.30 am Throw open window, breathe autumnal air, stride, singing to the shower. Return, refreshed and cheery, select simple but elegant outfit from wardrobe, douse self with Blasé and dress.

7.31 am Reject this fantasy as altogether too improbable, roll over in bed and wish it were Saturday.

9.00 am I have arrived at work, a breathing example of the walking undead. Two students are already ensconced in the careers library, pouring diligently over open files.

A ziggurat of papers, books and brochures blocks the light from one window: this monumental edifice represents the first job of the day – filing. Our receptionist, Lauraine, and my assistant, Chris, have already begun to organise themselves into a mini production line, punching, rubber stamping, sorting and busily inserting the material into library files. Much of it is from employers; recruitment literature, application forms, annual reports and vacancy information is put to one side to be advertised before being filed. Spare literature sits there waiting to be whisked off to our 'take-away' room. We are in the middle of the build up to employer visits, and need to take careful stock of the vast amount of literature which is pouring in. Grants and awards, prospectuses, articles for the overseas files are all in my pile as well as the most interesting, the information for the occupations files. Today's new arrivals include a booklet on the Sea Industry Authority (fish farming file) and a new set of regulations from the Institution of Chemical Engineers. I start on my daily chore of giving students an idea of just how much diverse information there is in this library and how to get at it.

9.30 am A few more students have shuffled into the library. Some are waiting to see careers advisers, some browse through files, some have a quick smoke while they read the newspapers. A hard core are furiously filling in application forms, chewing their pencils anxiously and bobbing up to the reception desk to borrow the dictionary.

As I file away bits of paper, I wonder if anyone will even read some of the items. The community work information sheet will certainly be read but what about the page of information on the horse racing industry, or the section on chiropractic?

10.00 am I hare to the snack bar, collect a cup of chocolate and a sticky bun and return in time for the ritual of the Post Session. At this tribal gathering of all members of the careers service we oversee the distribution of the day's post, and discuss briefly any problems or projects. I seize on any interesting items for inclusion in the *Vacancy Lists*, or my weekly *News Bulletin*, for students. As it's the autumn term it is also my chance to see the careers advisers, who spend a good deal of time in various academic departments working with groups of final year students. This group work is intended to develop self-presentation skills, ways of identifying aptitudes and abilities, or knowledge of jobs and the employment market. The careers library can be a useful tool to students for finding out about different types of jobs. Some have lots of ideas but if they haven't done any realistic self-appraisal, they strike me as being like those who put to sea without a compass. Then I have to find out at the Post Session what's going on in the general office, the careers service's engine room, about employer visits, the mailing list and collecting all those statistics.

10.30 am At last I manage to install myself at my desk and begin to sift through things which need immediate action. Letters need answering, I have to arrange a visit to a prison for some interested students, and I must write to a couple of employers who just might have graduate vacancies this year.

WE ARE IN THE BUSINESS OF EDUCATING PEOPLE TO MAKE INFORMED DECISIONS, NOT TAKING THE DECISIONS FOR THEM

11.00 am *Noises off*. At the reception desk Lauraine is imitating Gordon at Khartoum, she's beleaguered by students asking questions and wanting forms. I move in to ease the crush and in this way get my first 'lister' of the day.

The Ubiquitous List is one of the trials of an IO's life. Every day I am asked for all sorts of lists: of machine tool manufacturers, grant providers, research courses in palaeontology, marmalade manufacturers in Finland. Usually the question means 'have you got something that I can take home now, which will tell me what to do and absolve me from all further effort?' Sometimes I paraphrase it as 'I haven't got a clue what I want to do – help!' Mutter to myself 'why can't they say what they mean?'

The best list question I ever had was from a complete stranger who asked, 'Can I have a list of employers to apply to?' I was obliged to point out that there isn't such a thing as a graduate job which would fit all students or even all students graduating from the same course. And I told him in no uncertain terms that the careers service isn't simply a job-placing agency which forces a very unheterogeneous band of students

into uniform pin-stripes, adding, "we are in the business of educating people to make informed decisions, not taking the decisions for them."

However, just to show that you can't be right all the time, this 'lister' was an engineer who simply wanted to find out about oil companies involved in North Sea operations. I had just shown him the appropriate file when someone else popped up, this time with a question about postgraduate study in the USA. Questions about further study are always cropping up, but some people are only interested in it because they are stuck in the groove of defining themselves solely in terms of their academic discipline. If you are a mechanical engineer who wants to go into mechanical engineering I suppose its logical, but isn't quite so useful, if you have studied English or zoology. Usually I suggest that a careers adviser will not only outline the steps to be taken in applying for further study but will also cover other options.

11.10 am Retreating back to my desk I find the *New Scientist* propped on my phone. This is a hint from the indefatigable Chris that the *Vacancy List* goes to print today and I haven't finished scanning my allocation of newspapers and journals. Scanning is important, not only because we want to tell our final year students and recent graduates about the widest possible range of vacancies, but also so we keep our fingers on the pulse of the job market. How else could we help our students make a realistic assessment of the opportunities open to them?

12.00 noon Finish scanning and rejoin Lauraine manning the milkround barricades. A constant background of tinny music seeps through from one corner of the library where employers' video tapes are being played. The 20 Midland Bank forms which arrived this morning have gone already and we are running short of others. Inbetween answering enquiries the two of us write off busily for more supplies and check the level of recruitment literature in the 'take-away' room. November to March, the milkround season, is when we sail closest to the bureaucratic wind. There's always a certain amount of friction. We want to be as accommodating as possible to our students but we know we have to stick to certain procedures to make sure that anything gets done at all!

1.00 pm Lunch time! Release! Food! A quiet hour with my book, away from the inevitable phone calls.

2.00 pm A good start to the afternoon, a parcel arrives from the bookshop. I like parcels and I like books but I am disappointed to find that mostly it's full of worthy but dull tomes like the *Directory of Contractors* and *Willings Press Guide*. However, one looks promising, it's a slim paperback on career planning.

I dispose of the others quickly and settle down for an examination of the paperback. The rise in unemployment has led to a lot of rubbishy books being published on job hunting, on a par with the 'Cure Your Own Hangups', pop-psychology best sellers. It always surprises me that the one or two good books aren't more popular, and I'm amazed at the little attention many people left to their own devices are prepared to give to thinking seriously about their future. Perhaps its because they regard a job as a life sentence. Yesterday a cheerful soul said "No one really wants to work, do they?" Some students seem to expect everything to be as automatic as getting A levels and leaving the rest to UCCA. In fact knowing what you want and why can make you alive to all sorts of opportunities. It's not just a question of how now but also the future. That's why careers advisers are always advocating making the most of vacation and voluntary work as a testing ground for ideas. It does add weight to applications!

2.30 pm The library is fairly buzzing now. Suppressed giggles from one corner indicate that a form-filler has got to the section on 'the most important event of your life' and some wit is proposing increasingly rude or fantastic replies. I try to overhear, without success!

LATEST MILKROUND VACANCIES, NEWS OF VISITS, VIDEO TAPES AND VACATION COURSES ARE THE ORDER OF THE DAY

3.00 pm I settle down to work on my current special projects, updating the library files on voluntary work overseas and compiling a special package for unemployed graduates. It covers such things as writing a curriculum vitae, coping with depression, where to look for vacancies etc. One of the worst aspects of my job is seeing last year's graduates come into the library week after week and watching their confidence ebb away because they haven't found work.

3.30 pm I hear the voice of Anne, one of our regulars, at the reception desk and pop out to make a fuss of her bouncy and excitable guide

dog, Raglan, appropriately named as Anne wryly admits, after Lord Raglan of the Charge of the Light Brigade!

3.45 pm Another regular has dropped in, who has been letting his unsuccessful job hunt get him down. However, congratulations are in order because he has been accepted for pilot training by the RAF and is naturally overjoyed. Modestly he puts his success down to luck, but hard work, determination and ability have been factors too.

4.00 pm Wild hilarity in the office as my latest poster rolls off the photocopier to be revealed to a philistine world. It might be primitive but at least it attracts attention!

4.05 pm Time to begin composing the weekly *News Bulletin* which is sent out to final year students. On this page of cheap A4 paper I am required to cram such diverse snippets as extra milkround vacancies, news of visits and speakers, vacation courses, open days, postgraduate studentships, new books and video tapes and Civil Service closing dates. I have to think how to attract both those students who think disparagingly of a careers service as a forcing ground for chartered accountants and those who passionately want to be chartered accountants. The bulletin is finished and stencilled, tomorrow we can run it off on our temperamental, kick-it-and-scream duplicator.

4.40 pm Custer's Last Stand is taking place at the reception desk where Lauraine is surrounded by pressing hordes handing in application forms. Why is it everyone leaves everything to the last minute? I go to her aid. There's always a panic for forms the day before an employer's closing date and the general office has to process all the forms. When a large employer has nearly 100 applicants and there are 10 closing dates in one day, they are inundated. It's a time consuming job. Finally, we admit defeat and leave a pile of forms for tomorrow morning, a neat match for the heap of filing still sitting like a vulture in its corner!

5.00 pm The last student is turfed out of the library and we begin tidying the scattered books and files. I am interested to note that the 'alternative work' and 'technical writing' files have both been looked at. The last file is put back on the shelf, the lights are switched off. I make a mental note to order next year's edition of the *Directory of Co-operatives* but, tomorrow, as Scarlett O'Hara said, is another day.

Choosing only the best raw m

That's why some organisations perform better than the rest.

The best possible beginning for any business career is to qualify as a chartered accountant. A professional qualification says a great deal about you and your ambitions. In particular, it demonstrates that you have deliberately chosen to keep open the wider range of career options that our profession will undoubtedly give to you.

Only by training the best graduates to the highest standards can we provide the range and quality of services demanded by our clients. Our ability to meet these demands depends on our most important asset – our staff. We make it our business to ensure that you acquire the technical skills, management ability and business perception to make you stand out. In today's competitive world, it gives you an edge that could make all the difference.

terial makes all the difference

Fill in the coupon or write for further information to Philip Johnson, National Recruitment Manager, Deloitte Haskins & Sells, PO Box 142, 25 Bread Street, London EC4V 4AJ.

Please send me a copy of your graduate brochure, 'The difference is Deloitte Haskins & Sells'.

Name

Address

University

The Difference is **Deloitte Haskins+Sells**

see also page 153

Wouldn't you rather have been on David's side than Goliath's?

More of a challenge, wouldn't you say? And proof that biggest isn't always best.

Williams & Glyn's may be smaller than the Big Four, but we're big on informality and flexibility. Innovators and pioneers, we were the first bank, by two years, to place all branch accounting on line to computer and the first to introduce free banking for all personal customers with credit balances.

Graduates from every discipline are needed to join us in 1983, including those with a computer bias. Qualities we also seek are those which suggest an organised mind, ability to communicate and to maintain excellent working relationships at all levels. As a graduate with Williams & Glyn's, you will be on a development programme lasting an average of 2 years during which time you'll gain practical experience as well as attend a number of specialist/technical courses.

You can expect to receive a starting salary of around £7,000-£7,500 with other benefits which are normally associated with a major clearing bank, such as generous holidays and profit-share schemes.

We may be visiting your university during the Spring term, so we hope to meet you then. Otherwise, please write giving some details about your background and we will send you some information about us and, of course, an application form.

Michael Brookes,
Personnel Department,
Williams & Glyn's Bank,
New London Bridge House,
25 London Bridge Street,
London SE1 9SX.

WILLIAMS & GLYN'S BANK plc ❖

Where people come first.

WORK OUT WHICH EMPLOYER

BOB WILLOTT HAS ALL-ROUND EMPLOYER EXPERIENCE, HE HAS WORKED FOR A PUBLISHER AND A PROFESSIONAL BODY. NOW HE'S A PARTNER IN A CHARTERED ACCOUNTANCY PRACTICE

When all you hear about is new graduates being unemployed for a year or more, it's not surprising if you panic. Employment opportunities may not be very plentiful at the moment but you certainly shouldn't take the first available opening without a thought to what you really want. It is far better to stop and look out some career objectives rather than have no objectives at all. Enlightened employers recognise that graduate recruitment is a two-way decision-making process so they will be impressed by someone who has developed clear ideas about the type of career

path they are aiming for.

The potential choice of organisation is enormous, ranging through business and public service. When business alone offers everything from the large multinational corporations to professional partnerships, from manufacturing to service industries, it's a problem to define your requirements. Historically, service industries have sometimes been frowned upon as unproductive because it was considered more worthwhile to be a builder than to help someone else be a more efficient builder. While the need for more, and more successful, manufacturing business in Britain still exists, much of the growth in recent years has been in the service industries. It is always difficult to project future trends but the expansion, if any, in manufacturing business seems likely to be concentrated in higher technology. Among service industries, professional services, communications and leisure related pursuits may offer reasonable prospects.

What is the difference between the private and public sectors of business? In the early years of a graduate's work experience, it may be scarcely discernible. Shell, for instance, is classified as a private enterprise owned by its shareholders among the general public and institutions while BP was until recently owned substantially by the Government. The nature of the industry, the size of organisation and its management structure are probably far more important than the ownership. Unfortunately too many publicly owned enterprises have gained a reputation for being concentrated in declining industries. They're expected to be enormous in size and moribund in their approach to management. But these criticisms could be levelled equally at some of the companies in the private sector. So don't worry too much about whether a business is owned by private shareholders or by the Government, just make sure you build up a clear picture about its size, its prospects and management structure.

At the end of the day, one of the main distinctions between business and public service is in how the performance of the organisation is measured, and rightly so. Business is looking for profit. The public services are not. But both are usually concerned about quality. They look to the value given in relation to the resources available. The public

21

THIS IS A TWISTED NEMATIC LIQUID CRYSTAL
DISPLAY.   IT IS 14-WAY MULTIPLEXED AND
CONTAINS FOUR LINES OF FORTY CHARACTERS.
STANDARD TELECOMMUNICATION LABORATORIES.

APPLY NOW

Application is the key-word at STL

Not research for the sake of research. Rather the investigation, development and consolidation of novel ideas– materials, components, systems, technologies–that will revolutionise the way we live today–and tomorrow.

Viably, economically, efficiently.

If you're a graduate software specialist, electronic engineer, mathematician, physicist, materials or computer scientist with a practical approach, apply now.

Contact
Standard Telecommunication
Laboratories Limited,
London Road, Harlow,
Essex CM17 9NA.

Ideas that work

STL

A principal research centre of ITT.

services cannot ignore money any more than business can ignore the social consequences of its decisions. Nevertheless the distinction between objectives creates a difference in attitudes, priorities and even in management style. Where would you feel most at home?

It is impossible to generalise about what size of organisation is best? Size is only one factor. But many graduates are doubtful about mammoth organisations and sometimes those doubts are well justified. In a first job, the graduate should have the chance to try out a wide range of disciplines and make decisions. The more experience you can cram into the first few years, the better placed you'll be to judge your potential and exploit it.

SIZE OF EMPLOYER, TRAINING FACILITIES AND JOB INVOLVEMENT WILL ALL AFFECT YOUR CAREER CHOICE

The level of job satisfaction will depend to some extent on how involved you feel in your employer's activities. The structure and style of some very large organisations are better than others in achieving a sense of participation. Ideally the size of employer should allow you to combine good training facilities with breadth of experience and arouse a strong sense of involvement. But there's no magic size test you can apply. You have to ask pertinent questions, get third party opinions and then make your own judgment.

Training is important in virtually every type of employment. But even when it leads to an essential postgraduate qualification, the training is not an end in itself. Training programmes are designed to enable you to perform as effectively as possible, so it must interrelate with an adequate variety of work experience. And you need to have been involved in decision-making. It's important you check out the reputation of any training organisation and the value of its qualification. The ability of the trainers and the quality of their material are more important than external appearances. So ask other trainees what they think about the standard of training, if you get a chance.

Most employers who place a high value on recruiting good graduates will go to considerable lengths to impress you. So don't be over cynical about glossy brochures and

stage managed presentations, even though you must guard against the glowing rhetoric of false prospectuses which may be totally out of touch with reality. You can substantiate employers' claims by finding someone working in the same area of activity. Not only should you ask whether they would work for the employer concerned, but its worth quizzing them on the employer's growth record and on the reputation of their products or services. A meteoric rise in fortunes may be as hazardous as a more mundane performance. Fast growing businesses are often exciting to work for and offer above average opportunities for early responsibility and progress. Formal training facilities on the other hand may be limited. But try to discover whether such a business is vulnerable to changing fashions or increasing competition. It needs someone who understands accounts to give you a view on its financial stability like a friendly accountant, bank manager or stockbroker. If the company is listed on the Stock Exchange, a major business library will keep press cutting and financial information services (McCarthys, Moodies and Extel are some of the better known) which you may browse through for clues. Your careers service will also keep annual reports which can be revealing.

TALK TO EMPLOYEES AND FIND OUT ABOUT SALARIES AND MOBILITY BEFORE SIGNING THE CONTRACT

Far more important than the impact of glossy brochures is your own judgement after you have spoken to other graduates already working for the organisation. Usually you will be able to talk to them freely at second interview or perhaps at an exploratory visit. It's vital that you do meet other graduates before you accept an offer. Existing employees and customers (or their equivalent in the public services) often provide some of the most reliable testimonials.

The location of the company may be very important but there are two aspects to consider. It's not just the graduate's own preference for a specific location and the prospect of frequent travel. It's more in the nature of the job. If you are inflexible about where you want to work and not inclined to be mobile, your career

WHAT IS ENGINEERING?

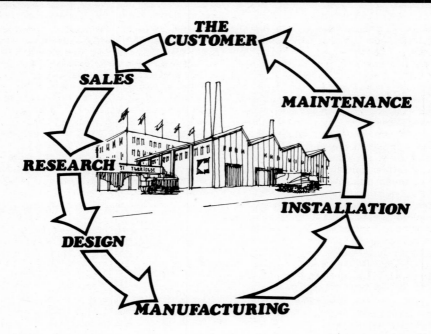

THE CUSTOMER

SALES

MAINTENANCE

RESEARCH

DESIGN

INSTALLATION

MANUFACTURING

Engineering Careers Information Service

Sponsored by
The Engineering Employers' Federation
The Confederation of Shipbuilding and
Engineering Unions
The Engineering Industry Training Board

British Engineering
A great career

see also page 48

development prospects will almost certainly suffer. You may rank the quality of life as far more important than career prospects and financial reward. But you must sort out your own priorities before signing up. Too often prospective employees mutter something vague at interview and then wonder why the employer is later disappointed when they're reluctant to move or travel when the job requires it.

Although it's controversial, I would not encourage a graduate to place too much emphasis on long term prospects at the outset of a career. Obviously, an employer is looking out for someone who wants to make a success of their working life and who is open-minded about where that success is achieved. But you will be doing yourself and your employer an injustice if you treat your first appointment as nothing more than a short-stay training ground. A certain amount of career logic must be applied. Most people joining the Civil Service for example are likely to remain there for the rest of their working lives but the nature of their work will probably vary enormously during that time.

On the other hand don't start out on your chosen career believing that you are committed to an unwavering course for up to 40 years. Life is just not like that. If you want some excitement and above-average job interest, be prepared to make sensible changes when an interesting opportunity arises. Provided all your other requirements from a prospective employer look good don't worry too much if you aren't offered at second interview the firm

prospect of a senior management post in five years time. Confidence in your own ability to succeed is infinitely more important.

But are you sure you want to work in business at all? Ten years ago there was a popular view among graduates that serving the community was more important and more fruitful than stooping to the dirty business of making money. Attitudes have changed. The generation of national wealth is recognised as essential to allocating that wealth, and consequently the black and white distinction between business and public service has dissolved.

It's all a question of thinking about the type of activity which will make best use of your personal talents. And even more important is defining what your talents really are, not what you would like them to be. Are you numerate, artistic, mechanical, or what? Do you like working in a group or on your own? Do you strike up good initial relationships with strangers or is it a long slog? Having a social conscience does not mean you should become a social worker.

After you have thought carefully about what you want from an employer, identified the type of work you would like, start preparing for the interview. Some ideas should have started to emerge and more will occur to you as you start to dig out more information. Remember you will be interviewing your future employer as much as the employer is interviewing you.

POINT•CHECKPOINT•CHECKPOINT•CHECK

Is there employer choice in 1982?
We asked careers advisers around the country to tell us what marked out the successful students in a tight employment market.

❝Students who get what they want have a good realisation of what they have to offer; they start early and don't wait till everyone else is applying. And they put a lot of effort into their attempts.❞ Bradford

❝Success seems to follow when students have clarified their goals and identified what they are prepared to do without. If you can go into an interview, feeling comfortable about what you have revealed of yourself in your application, and ready to cope with more

detailed questions, then you'll have improved your chances.❞ Sussex

❝Some students are easily put off by gloomy press reports about companies or work areas which are suffering from the cuts. So it's very important to have up to date accurate employer information before making any applications. Doing your homework on the firm is vital.❞ Cardiff

❝A lot of students are so worried about unemployment that they're ready to grab at any job. But unless they work out the fundamental elements of each job and try to slant their applications accordingly they can waste a lot of time.❞ Sheffield

FORD
The first choice for ambitious Graduates

Deciding on your first career move is a very important matter.

You'll certainly want to make sure that your first employer can offer you a real job from day one, genuine training and development, an exciting future, broad career options and, of course, excellent rewards.

If these are your criteria, make sure you talk to Ford.

As one of the world's most successful motor manufacturers, Ford is moving confidently into the future — designing, producing and marketing an advanced range of fuel efficient vehicles to meet the ever changing needs of tomorrow's world.

When you join the Ford team you'll enjoy immediate responsibility on a development programme which is widely recognised to be one of the most fertile breeding grounds for top management professionals. The graduates we appoint today will become the core of our management team in the future.

And apart from an exciting future in a progressive organisation, you'll also enjoy excellent rewards. Starting salaries will be at least £6,500 pa and will be further enhanced by a valuable range of fringe benefits.

So make Ford your first move to career success.

For more information contact your Careers Service, or the Manager, College Recruitment, Room 1/178, Ford Motor Company Limited, Eagle Way, Brentwood, Essex CM13 3BW.

26

see also page 169

SARAH KING

JOB TACTICS

A
FTER AN ECONOMICS DEGREE
AT BRISTOL UNIVERSITY,
PENELOPE DIXON WAS ABLE TO
TURN DOWN SECOND INTERVIEWS

"I think I'm reward oriented", says Penelope, so tackling the problem of career choice she set out to find a career that would be "a challenge, and related to consumers." Penelope didn't want to be cut off from the rest of the world, a creative job using her communication skills seemed the answer. The problem was in finding such a field.

At Bristol University's careers service she did a Gradscope interest questionnaire which suggested marketing, advertising and estate management. She had already discarded estate management since she had an unrelated degree. A careers service talk sparked off her interest in marketing; to follow this up she joined the CRAC Insight into Management course, which included case studies and simulations of marketing problems. This gave her a much clearer idea of the various demands of marketing.

The next step was to pick up the graduate job directories. "Certainly, for initial information the directories are great," says Penelope. From the indexes she compiled a list of companies recruiting graduates into marketing. "The way they presented their entries", influenced her a great deal. She ended up with about 13 big names on her list, all in consumer products.

Penelope's methodical approach to her career extended to the forms themselves: "I worked out very firmly what I had to offer. Filling in forms took so long, but I even looked at company reports." Her time was well spent because she was invited to 11 first interviews from 13 applications.

With all her interviews lined up, Penelope felt confident enough to eliminate some companies from her list. "I see interviews as a two-way affair, and if I felt they couldn't offer swift moves through their management structure I ruled them out."

Penelope realised she should check out advertising as well, since it fitted in with her requirements. "I'd done some research on advertising agencies for an economics essay," and she also looked at journals like *Campaign* and *The Economist*. She worked out which agencies had the most refreshing approach to advertising, which offered the most useful training, and who had landed which contract. Then she applied to them, whether or not they advertised vacancies.

Penelope finally rejected marketing, partly because "it's still difficult for women to succeed in marketing". One firm even told her that women would never rise very far with them. "It was reassuring to find that in advertising one's sex didn't matter," says Penelope. "Sexism in their advertising was one of the things that determined which agencies I chose." Penelope knew she had to respect the work of an agency to be able to work for them.

Second interviews in advertising were more productive. By her third interview Penelope had been offered two very similar jobs. "I decided to cancel the remaining interviews while I agonised between them." She phoned them both up and explained the situation. "They were both very helpful and invited me to look around. They still seemed equal in all the important things like opportunities and quality of work, but I liked the people more at Leo Burnett's so I chose them. I think I'll enjoy it."

You're working hard for your qualifications. Make the most of them

If you're taking a degree this summer, BHS have a training scheme that will make the most of your well earned qualifications. As one of the U.K.'s most progressive and profitable retailing organisations with an impressive record of growth, we offer tremendous scope and long term prospects to men and women with the right qualities and real ambition.

Store Management

is the key to our success. To reach our high standards, we will give you a thorough training in all aspects of management of a modern Retail Store. Our intensive and comprehensive Store Management Training Programme will develop you rapidly to take full advantage of the significant opportunities which we provide.

Your initial training will last a year, on successful completion of which you will be promoted to the position of Section Manager, and, will continue your development to become a Store Manager.

Salaries are highly competitive and our excellent range of benefits includes subsidised meals, 15% staff discount, free life assurance and share participation scheme after qualifying period.

Why not find out more? Write now for an application form quoting ref: TSM/DOG to:

BRITISH HOME STORES

Personnel Services Department, British Home Stores PLC, Marylebone House, 129/137 Marylebone Road, London NW1 5QD.

see also page 94

WRITE NO WRONGS

SOME OF THE MISTAKES MADE BY GRADUATES IN THEIR APPLICATIONS ARE EASILY AVOIDED. IRIS ROSIER TELLS YOU HOW TO AVOID THE MOST DAMAGING BLUNDERS

It's very galling when your friends are boasting about the pressures of fitting in yet another interview and you're getting rejection slips. You begin to wonder frantically about BO, tutors forecasting your failure in finals or why your face doesn't fit. The explanation is usually much simpler.

Here at VNU we receive several hundred applications from newly qualified graduates in a year. We tend to disregard the careless ones; those that come on scrappy file paper or are scribbled on sheets torn hastily from shorthand notebooks.

Some applications are memorable only for their illegibility. We haven't been able to decipher some typed CVs because we only rated the tenth copy. Incomplete photocopies are common; in one instance we literally had half the story.

TAKE TIME AND CARE WITH YOUR APPLICATIONS. PRESENTATION, SPELLING AND GRAMMAR ARE VITAL

No employer minds a handwritten letter or form so long as it doesn't require too much effort in decoding as well. If your handwriting is indecipherable then print your answers. Indeed it may be preferable to a badly typed form. If you're not a whiz kid typist, a complicated form can overtax your skill. By the way we're boringly conventional in our attitudes to spelling and grammar. And most other employers share exactly the same views on these tiresome but essential details.

Some postgraduates spoiled their chances simply because they were too idle, or too arrogant, to update their CVs. It was glaringly obvious that they'd been carefully constructed to win a place on perhaps a marketing or a language course rather than the jobs being advertised. Every application has to be tailored to the job.

So what are the best tactics, particularly if you dislike letter writing and those words 'Any other information' fill you with dread. If you've got the time, then you should try to make time to attend any session run by your careers service on applications. You're quite likely to find employers and advisers taking part, ready to regale you with horror stories about applications which omitted not only the name of the degree course but even that of the job desired. Alternatively you could prepare a CV or a specimen Standard Introduction Form (SIF) and ask your careers adviser to pass an expert eye over it.

But if you're going it alone, then you've got to allow yourself time. It'll take probably three times as long as you'd anticipated. An assembly job comes first. For an ordinary milk round interview you need to check whether you should use a company application form or an SIF. It means buying good quality paper, large envelopes, paper clips and a pocket file to store copies of all your applications. Will you need a dictionary? At the careers service, you want to study the company brochure carefully and then look at the annual report, if it's available. Before you leave, pick up a copy of the information sheet *Applications and Interviews* and any title about the sort of work you're applying for.

You still can't sit down and start writing frantically; it's a slow process. First make a list of closing dates, then work out the date on which you must have finished the form. Does it have to be entrusted to the Post Office or can it be handed in at the careers service? The next job is to read the instructions carefully and plan out what you must say and what you'd like to say if there's space. And if the form has been scrunched up in your case, either get another copy now or iron out the creases.

Photocopying the blank form is a good idea; it lets you work out how much you can write in those horrid little boxes. There's not much point in trying to squeeze every detail of the last twenty-one years in, personal and academic, if it looks an indigestible mass. This is a special problem for the mature student, who may have to go onto an additional sheet with essential

APPLICATION FORM

NAME OF EMPLOYER Research Services	JOB FUNCTION Admin Trainee
SURNAME (DR **MR** MRS MISS) Brownswood	FIRST NAME Eric
NATIONALITY British	DATE AND PLACE OF BIRTH Washington 9.3.62
DATES AVAILABLE FOR EMPLOYMENT July 1983	DATES AVAILABLE FOR INTERVIEW Up to 31.5.83 After 20.6.83
HOME ADDRESS 93 The Avenue Leek, Staffs. POSTCODE TELEPHONE BT13 3BJ 0533 913 DATES AT THIS ADDRESS 21.6.83 28.6.83 31.9.83 onwards	TERM ADDRESS Flat 19, Old Hall, College Road, Edinburgh POSTCODE TELEPHONE E1 93X DATES AT THIS ADDRESS Up to 20.6.83 Holidays all Easter

| SECONDARY/FURTHER EDUCATION (DATES)

East Forest High School 73-78
Leek Tertiary College   78-80
Dates don't tie up

'O' LEVEL OR EQUIVALENT WITH GRADES

1977 'O' E Lang, Art, Religious Knowledge,
Woodwork, General Studies, E Literature, Physics

No grades

'A' LEVEL OR EQUIVALENT

1980 'A' British Constitution (B), General Studies (C)
and English (B) | FIRST DEGREE
Institution, qualification dates, subjects studied.

Heriot-Watt University
October 80-July 83 BA *In what?*

General Humanities
Computer Application Module
Yr1 12 Modules

Which ones?
Then what? |

EDUCATION. Why you chose your course. Aspects of particular interest or satisfaction.

The subjects offered by the college at 'A' level were restricted so I valued the flexibility of a modular degree which allowed me to try out unknown disciplines.

But what did he get out of it?

ACTIVITIES AND INTERESTS — Both at school & college. Indicate to what level pursued.

Rock climbing, fellwalking.
Leader of Jambalaya Group — meets weekly

How often?
Where?

What on earth is this?

PREVIOUS WORK EXPERIENCE — Give dates. Include vac work, Industrial training. What have you gained from these?

Spelling

Worked as a labourer for Forestry Commission between leaving school and starting college which was both an enjoyable outdoor life and gave me an opportunity to contribute to the local conservation programme. I haven't been able to get a job since. Voluntary work in Edinburgh with deprived children.

No dates   *Why?*   *Useful — find out more*

CAREER CHOICE — Say why you think you are suited to this sort of work.

I want to work in a high technology industry, which will not be full of obsolescent routines and rules. Although I am interested in computer programming I should prefer a more general business training.

Where does this fit in?   *Not another revolutionary?*

WHY DO YOU WISH TO JOIN THIS ORGANISATION?

A medium sized company seems to give you the best of both worlds. It is flexible enough to give personal attention to individuals but offers scope for career development moves within the company.

Sensible viewpoint

ADDITIONAL INFORMATION — State restrictions in mobility. Any health problems. Questions you wish to raise at interview?

I have a clean driving licence. My health is excellent. I would prefer to work within twenty miles of home.

Why no questions?   *Tied to home?*

REFEREES — Give occupation

1 John Bull
College Tutor
Heriot-Watt University
Edinburgh

Which department?

POSTCODE ⟋   **TELEPHONE** *Careless!*

2 Rosemary Long
Ace Agency
Stoke-on-Trent
Staffs

No occupation
What sort of agency?

POSTCODE ⟋   **TELEPHONE**

PUBLIC FINANCE
making sure the pieces fit
fully paid accountancy training for honours graduates

Each year, local and national government together spend some £100 billion to provide the nation's essential services. Making sure that the money is raised efficiently and spent effectively is the task of Government Auditors.

This unusually creative financial role is not only challenging but also carries unrivalled advantages. For instance, where else can an honours graduate combine work of great public benefit with the pursuit of a professional qualification and outstanding career prospects?

One of the most diverse and rewarding career options available, Government Audit will involve you in every aspect of modern financial management and the promotion of peak efficiency at all levels. Far from desk-bound routine, it is the ideal challenge for anyone eager for day to day variety and real responsibility from the outset. Whilst fulfilling a very practical role you will be studying— on full pay, of course, with all study costs covered— for membership of the Chartered Institute of Public Finance and Accountancy. Opportunities exist in . . .

The Exchequer and Audit Department—which is concerned with the financial activities of central government (covering everything from agricultural subsidies to atomic energy), many quasi-governmental bodies (including the British Museum and the Civil Aviation Authority), and a number of international organisations such as UNESCO and the World Health Organisation. There are opportunities to travel in the UK and overseas.

The District Audit Service—which examines the financial activities of local authorities in England and Wales at all levels from the Greater London Council to district councils. The work covers all aspects of local government such as education, housing and social services and involves dealing with an extremely wide variety of professional and other administrative managers.

Training takes about three years, and combines periods of block-release at a polytechnic with practical on-the-job experience. Currently there are vacancies in London and a number of major provincial centres.

Candidates must have, or obtain in 1983, an honours degree in any discipline (normally at least 2nd class). Good communications skills, an analytical approach and the ability to work independently are further key requirements.

Starting salary at 20 (for example) £5270 with automatic promotion on qualifying to £7465. Further promotion may usually be expected within a year to the salary range £9230-£11265. Inner London salaries are £1087 higher.

For further details and an application form write to the Civil Service Commission, Alencon Link, Basingstoke, Hants, RG21 1JB, or telephone Basingstoke (0256) 68551 (answering service operates outside office hours). Please quote reference: G/680/D27.

Exchequer and Audit   District Audit

GOVERNMENT AUDITORS

see also pages 127, 311

details of past experience. But don't be too drastic in your pruning, an employer may positively need to know you have O level maths. Layout is as important as clarity in your use of English. If you are typing, double spacing could help your presentation enormously.

When you finish, check that you haven't left any blank spaces. An employer can read all sorts of dire things into an unexplained year gap. Tell them you're in good health, so they don't think you're trying to conceal a dread disease. Have you been strictly accurate and honest? An interview or a referee will often reveal the truth, if you've overplayed your hand. Naturally, you're being scrupulous about keeping your referees well informed about the sorts of jobs you are applying for. And you have checked their initials, their addresses and job titles. The checking process is deadly boring but absolutely necessary – it includes signing and dating the form.

Some employers like an accompanying letter, which need only be short, there's no point in rambling on about trivia. If you know the employer is preselecting from forms, then the whole application merits extra attention.

Before you send off the application, be sure you have a copy. There's nothing worse than being in a panic at an interview because you can't remember whether you angled this one for an accountancy or a marketing job.

MAKE SURE THE KEY FACTS ON YOUR CV STAND OUT AND EMPHASISE THEM IN THE COVERING LETTER

In these days of massive competition, you want to know how to stand out from the other 200 applicants. Some students search too wildly for gimmicks when a good description of their hobbies and interests might be more sensible; especially if it throws light on your practical capabilities and you have been the organiser for catering at the union or the trainer for the hang gliding club. But don't use clichés, choose your words carefully. You may be able to write fluently about a vac job, work experience or a sandwich placement. A very bald CV with one word answers could make you look like a boring type with very little to offer. It's no good being well qualified if you don't do yourself justice on paper.

Speculative applications present extra problems. Some employers don't want to know, while others, especially those in the media expect to be headhunted. They know they don't need to advertise, you have to take the initiative. The presentation of your CV is crucial. Make sure that the covering letter complements the CV rather than duplicates it. The letter should never take more than one sheet of A4. It's no good exaggerating your enthusiasm or overselling yourself; showing where you might be valuable to the organisation could be vastly more profitable. If you can afford it, sending a stamped addressed envelope shows willing. It doesn't guarantee a reply though.

SPARE A THOUGHT FOR THE RECRUITERS. TAILOR YOUR APPLICATION TO THEIR NEEDS AND PROBLEMS

These ideas don't just relate to VNU. We checked them out with careers advisers and then compared notes with other employers. One graduate recruiter for a very large company talked about the sort of application that makes him groan.

"If only students realised how small a clerical staff we have," he groused. "If you're faced with 3,500 applications you bless those that had the sense to use the company form. We're used to it and can pick out vital information more quickly than from the SIF. It saves us time, too, if applicants use the reference number on a vacancy.

"Don't try to pull the wool over our eyes by omitting important details like a change of course or repeating a year. It's better to be honest even if you're in the middle of a course which has turned out a bad mistake.

"When I first scan through a form I'm checking that the student meets the basic requirements of the training scheme for which they've applied." This recruiter likes to see course information on an A4 sheet. Your application must show clearly that you know what you want to do and that you have thought how you might fit into his organisation.

On pages 30 and 31 we show you an imaginary application form with some obvious errors and the reactions of a graduate recruiter.

A RECRUITER'S LOT IS NOT A HAPPY ONE

COLIN HADLEY

J IM HALLAM, EMPLOYMENT SERVICES MANAGER FOR BOOTS, RECALLS HIS INTERVIEWING BLUES TO HELP YOU AVOID SOME OF THE TRAPS

The milkround, sometimes called the graduate recruitment programme, is an important feature in the diary of events for most large companies. You probably see us as the grand inquisitors. Perhaps I can lift the veil. It's no mysterious process.

The milkround happens mainly between January and March, the most idyllic time of year in Britain to have a heavy travelling programme which could take you from Aberdeen to Canterbury and Plymouth to Belfast. In those three months, representatives of my company are faced by about 1,500 eager faces in an effort to recruit 70. For this we sacrifice family life for five weeks of hotel living, icy roads or the joys of British Rail.

It's worth it because we have to search out bright, resourceful graduates to fit into interesting and challenging jobs. We're all in competition looking for the cream of graduates. It's our job to spot in half an hour or so which candidates are worth introducing to our line management for final selection. So in that first session we aim simply to bring the application form to life and to clear up any points which seem vague. At the same time we can answer your questions about the company and feed in useful data about specific vacancies.

Have you ever thought what a pile of 1,500 application forms looks like? It's a pretty daunting sight to any personnel officer. From your angle, you know you must look good on paper if you've survived that first sift. Now you have to concentrate on presenting yourself so you live up to that image. You need to become a skilled interviewee who is as well prepared about school and leisure activities as about your course and career choice. Remember one

chemistry student seems very like another when talking about course and lab work, unless you have something outstanding to offer in project work. That's why relevant work experience can give your application such a boost, it's a good talking point. Your answers to questions will win our hearts if they display some real insight into working problems.

IT'S DEVASTATING IF ALL YOUR CANDIDATES TURN OUT TO BE LOW FAT RATHER THAN CREAM

We're obviously disappointed if our visit seems a waste of time and money. We expect one or two candidates not to live up to expectations. But it's devastating if all your candidates in any session turn out to be low fat yogurt rather than cream. To give you some idea of our grouses I've jotted down the gist of a conversation I had recently.

The set is in a senior common room in a large university. It's a snowy Monday in January and three graduate recruiters, Peter, Lesley and I, are reviewing our progress so far.

Peter's normally happy face looked strangely haggard. "Had a good morning?" I enquired half suspecting the reply. Peter winced at the question. It was obviously worse than I thought. As he settled himself down to lunch, part restored by two glasses of careers advisory service sherry, he moaned, "I don't know what I've done to deserve the candidates I had to see this morning. On paper they looked very good."

"What was the problem?"

"Oh, nothing new, you'll have come across the problems many times, it was just that they all seem to have come together in the same place at the same time. As ever – most of the students were poorly prepared, especially about the company and its activities. You'd have thought there was no information at all on the firm in the careers library. This lot certainly didn't know about it.

"We spend thousands every year on brochures, telling the careers advisers what we do and making sure our file in the careers library is bursting with facts and figures. I even checked it this morning before I started interviewing. As usual it was full of good background information."

Lesley broke in, "How students have the audacity to turn up for interview when they can't even answer the simplest questions about the business and its products, defeats me. You'd have thought in the present job situation they'd have made the effort to go beyond the file to find out about us."

Peter nodded in agreement, "I don't think I saw one student this morning who really knew what the career meant in practical terms. It should have been an interesting morning because I recruit for a wide variety of scientific and commercial positions. In theory I should have heard about very different skills, knowledge and experience. Not one candidate explained well, why they had chosen a particular career route. They'd hardly started on any form of self analysis, and those who had, didn't seem to have applied it to the jobs they were putting in for."

"The ones that bug me", I said, "are those that expect careers advisers to give them an idea of what might suit them and then think the job will fall into their lap. I know they've a lot on their plates just before finals but a wrong career choice now can set them back years."

"You're dead right," agreed Peter, "that lot this morning hadn't a clue about the challenges or the frustrations. They didn't seem to appreciate what skills would be needed, and they want to be professionals! To make matters worse, they hadn't even tried to anticipate my questions. From the look on their faces you could tell that the simplest questions took them quite by surprise."

"Usually when I come here," said Lesley, "you can tell those who've been to practice interview sessions. They're the ones who know how to field three quarters of my questions at first interview. You know the 'why have you chosen this career' and 'why with this company' type question. At least none of mine this morning turned up looking like they had slept under a hedge. I got so bored hearing them trot out hackneyed clichés to explain themselves. There wasn't one with an ounce of originality. And only one stood out as a good logical thinker, capable of presenting an argument in a lively well expressed manner. I swear I'll cheerfully strangle the next one who bleats 'I want to work with people' as their only motivation for wanting to join us!"

STUDENTS NEVER THINK ABOUT MARKETING THEMSELVES SO THEY STAND OUT FROM THE CROWD

It was nearly time for us to get ready for the afternoon's fray. As we moved off Peter delivered his final thought. He's not a marketing man but he hit the nail on the head by saying, "If only they had the vaguest conception of how competitive the whole thing is. They never think about marketing themselves so they stand out from the crowd. They haven't learned how to put over their strengths and experiences to make a lasting impression!"

It had been quite a pleasant lunch and at least Peter seemed able to face the afternoon.

My morning hadn't been quite so bad but the reason why this particular conversation over lunch stuck in my memory was because of Peter's final remark.

"By the way", he added with a wry smile, "two of the candidates I interviewed this morning mentioned they have interviews with you this afternoon."

Suddenly the sun went in.

![British Transport Police crest]

British Transport POLICE

A GREAT FORCE A GOOD CAREER

If you want a challenging career that offers you responsibility, security, good pay and conditions PLUS free and reduced rate rail travel for yourself and your dependants, the British Transport Police is well worth considering. We will give you much more — job satisfaction and a chance to belong to a great team (we are one of the oldest police forces in the world).

You'll need to be
* Bright   * Level-headed   * Decisive   * A bit above average
* Between 18½ and 30
* Over 5′ 9″ (175cm) if you're a man   * Over 5′ 6″ (168cm) if you're a woman
* Physically Fit with Good Eyesight   * A British Subject

Here is YOUR worthwhile career that will bring you between £6,213 (Provinces) and £8,778 (London) right from the start. Vacancies exist at most large centres.

For further details please write to:

Inspector A. C. Lamb, (Dept. Cup)
Force Careers Officer,
British Transport Police,
P.O. Box No. 260,
15, Tavistock Place,
London, WC1H 9SJ.

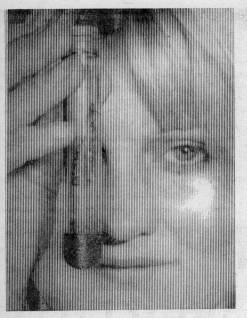

PANEL BEATING

CATHY HAMER HAS MOVED FROM PHD RESEARCH IN DRUG METABOLISM TO A MANAGEMENT JOB WITH AN OIL COMPANY

As the second year of her PhD progressed Cathy Hamer realised she was having doubts about a research job. "I was elected president of the postgraduate union and spent much of my time organising people and events, which I enjoyed." Cathy wanted to use these abilities in a job, and the careers service encouraged her to explore types of work outside research.

She began applying to oil companies on the milkround, for management services and marketing type jobs. "It was all a bit of a gamble because I was applying outside my field at the age of 26. Preparing for the interviews took quite a time, reading recruitment brochures and information sheets. I also made sure I'd read a copy of my application form so that my answers were fresh in my mind.

"First interviews were usually with a head office personnel officer so they weren't always able to answer my technical queries. Larger companies, though, often sent someone from the department to which I'd applied. Some asked very searching questions, but others seemed bored with the whole exercise. Most made me feel comfortable and relaxed. Once or twice I just had to use what was asked to wangle in all the information I wanted them to know. Obviously I had to prepare a good answer to the expected 'Why are you changing fields' question; but I hadn't anticipated all the questions for a half-hour interview. The recruiters were more interested in what I did in my spare time than in my academic background, which came as quite a surprise."

To prepare for the second interviews, Cathy read the *Financial Times*, "to find out what was happening in the oil industry, and to follow the commercial progress of the companies that I'd applied to." Second interviews usually meant a whole day and an over-night stay. Candidates met their interviewers and last year's graduates over cocktails or dinner. Although this was meant to be informal, Cathy felt "rather nervous having to eat, drink and chat with them."

The following day often started with another presentation before the panel interviews began. "The second interview is much more intense. I wasn't always sure what the five interviewers were even getting at."

Verbal reasoning and mathematical logic tests were just two of many Cathy had to face. Often they were followed by a group discussion with, in one instance, five other candidates. "They seemed to be looking for leaders who could argue without putting other people's backs up. It was often uncomfortable because all the other candidates seem better than you."

A 40 minute interview about the oil industry was Cathy's worst session, "It was the end of the morning, I was tired and hungry, and they were using unfamiliar technical language. Two would discuss something then throw it at me, so I never knew when they wanted me to answer." A look round the department with a recent graduate helped to give an impression of the company and the people, "because I could see current projects and get an idea of what I'd be doing if I joined. Sometimes I found it easy to talk to the people and felt at home. In other places I knew straight away I wouldn't be happy there." At least all her efforts paid off; Cathy has accepted a job in BP's Trade and Supply Department.

RECRUITMENT CODE

BRIAN GRIMWOOD

THE CODE OF PRACTICE, AGREED BY THE STANDING CONFERENCE OF EMPLOYERS OF GRADUATES, THE NATIONAL UNION OF STUDENTS AND THE ASSOCIATION OF GRADUATE CAREERS ADVISORY SERVICES

All three parties agree that the proposals below have been found to increase mutual confidence and can therefore be strongly recommended, though not rigidly enforced. These proposals are without prejudice to legal obligations which may operate in respect of these matters under Acts of Parliament or governmental regulations, such as the Race Relations Act, the 1978 Employment Protection (Consolidation) Act, Sex Discrimination Act etc.

Advisers, employers and students will respect the confidence in which information may be given, and disclose such information only to those qualified to receive it.

Graduate careers advisory services exist to help students and former students to decide on a career and type of employment.

A careers advisory service will:
1. Make careers information available to all its students and give proper publicity to all legally-recognised, named employers who ask for it.
2. Facilitate such employers' interviews without discrimination.
3. Wherever possible offer similar help to students and graduates of other institutions by mutual agreement.
4. Recognise that all students have the right to have their names put before any employers, although an interview with a particular employer cannot be guaranteed. (Employers are always responsible for any pre-selection.)
5. Deal with private agencies representing employers only if such representation shall clearly be in the interest of students. All agencies should state which employers they represent and should interview only on behalf of those employers.
6. Be impartial in its dealings with employers.

Employers will:
1. Provide enough up-to-date material to give students an objective picture of their organisations and the relevant jobs with them.
2. Avoid, in their literature or in their application forms for employment in the UK, any reference to the applicant's religious or political beliefs.
3. Notify careers advisory services, in advance, if a direct approach is being made to any department for recruitment purposes.
4. Recognise the problems created by autumn term interviews and, in particular, refrain from setting deadlines for the acceptance of offers which would prejudice interviews taking place in the second term.
5. Recognise that off-campus interviews involving unreasonable absence from academic or other commitments should be avoided, if possible, during term time.
● Give students the opportunity to alter their appointments if they conflict with other essential commitments.
● Avoid second interviews in the summer term for students preparing for their Finals, other than in very exceptional circumstances.
6. Normally pay expenses for off-campus interviews, always making it clear before interviews if such payment will not be offered.
7. Tell candidates the results of each stage of selection within a mutually agreed period; when preselection is used, promptly inform those candidates not selected for interview.
8. Agree referees with the candidate and indicate clearly what effect taking up references may have on an offer (ie whether it is

conditional or unconditional).

9. Spell out clearly terms of service in offer-letters and allow reasonable time for decision, taking into account both how early in the year the offer is made and how candidates on a reserve list may be affected.

10. Recognise that both the offer of a post and its acceptance (unless conditions are attached to either) form a contract, breach of which can result in legal action.

Students will:

1. When booking interviews, commit themselves to:
● Read the employer's material:
● Assess their suitability for the vacancies advertised:
● Fill in such forms as may be required:
● Be punctual:
● If unable to keep an appointment, make every effort to inform the careers service or employer in advance by telephone or letters:
● Tell employers if they decide to withdraw their applications at any stage:
● Avoid delay in replying to letters from

potential employers.

2. When attending interviews at employers' premises, seek only repayment of actual expenses incurred. If there is more than one interview on a trip, the students must explain matters and offer to divide claims among the employers concerned. (Claiming expenses twice over can result in legal proceedings, including criminal prosecution.)

3. Once an unconditional offer has been accepted, decline all other offers and cancel other applications immediately. They should inform the careers advisory service of the choice made. If candidates wish to qualify their acceptance in any way (and the possibility of a grant for postgraduate study represents a qualification) this must be clearly stated at the time of acceptance. Such qualification may affect the terms of the offer.

4. Recognise that both the offer of a post and its acceptance (unless conditions are attached to either) form a contract, breach of which can result in legal action.

POINT•CHECKPOINT•CHECKPOINT•CHECK

Interview checklist
BEFORE
● Re-read copy of your application form.
● Re-read company's recruitment literature and annual report.
● Find out about company's main competitors and the state of the industry generally.
● Read daily newspapers, especially *Financial Times*, for current affairs and industrial topics.
● Plan your journey and what you are going to wear.
● Arrange a mock interview at your careers service.
● Prepare questions to ask at the end of the interview. Could cover topics like: Is there an appraisal system? What happened to last year's graduate intake? What are the chances of support for further qualifications? (only if you're really interested). Are there any plans for the company to expand into other product areas? move location etc?

DURING
● Try not to fidget
● If there is more than one interviewer give

your answer to the person who asked the question. Don't try to include the whole panel when you speak.
● Be honest in your answers; it's a dangerous game trying to guess, what the interviewer wants to hear. It might just be a ploy to get you to commit yourself to something you can't back-up.
● If you don't understand a question, say so. There's no shame in asking for clarification, but you can easily make a fool of yourself if you only have a vague idea of what the interviewer is on about.
● Try to remember the questions you prepared for the end of the interview; even if it means bringing out a piece of paper with them written on. At least it shows you thought about the process.

AFTER
● Try to remember any topics/questions which caught you out. Talk them over with a careers adviser or do your own research.
● Don't brood about how you think you performed. Just try and sort out any problems before your next interview.

WHEELS WITHIN WHEELS

SUCCESSFUL AS A PERSONNEL MANAGER WITH SHELL, ANDREW BRUCE RECALLS THE TRAUMAS OF HIS JOB QUEST AS A DISABLED GRADUATE

Six years ago I was scanning DOG to find a few organisations that might possibly be interested in giving me a decent job. The only difference was that unlike most of my fellow students, I was, and still am, confined to a wheelchair. So what, you may ask? Well, that was my initial attitude anyway.

Unfortunately, it wasn't long before I became very clearly aware that I had to convince other people who didn't know me that being in a wheelchair need not be a disadvantage or an insurmountable obstacle to my employment. In addition to selling my academic and personal credentials like any graduate applicant, I had to demonstrate that my disability was incidental to my application and not the main component of it; hence the title of this article. Fortunately, I have succeeded in convincing recruitment officers of this on a couple of occasions. In other words I was offered employment.

My first job after graduating was with a government department, but I disliked the work and decided to leave. I am now working for Shell International in London as a remuneration and employee relations assistant in their personnel department. One of the things that pleases me is that I have been expected to hold down a full job at Shell, just like any other employee, and compete equally for vacancies too. This is the way it should be, but for some students the problem arises in getting a chance to prove yourself. Before I got this job, I made well over 50 written applications, from which I got only nine or ten first interviews. Such a ratio compared unfavourably with colleagues on my postgraduate diploma course in personnel management.

Just about the biggest problem to overcome is how to handle your disability on application forms. It was easy to list my O and A passes,

tell them I have a BA (Hons) Law degree and that my favourite hobby is amateur dramatics, but quite another thing to explain my physical condition to a stranger. And in a way which would not adversely affect my application.

To be honest, I found no foolproof way to approach this subject on the form, but mention it you must because no prospective employer will think much of you if you are not open to begin with. Personally, I think that the best bet is to describe concisely on the application form, exactly what form your disability takes. Then, you can follow this up immediately with a positive explanation of the ways in which you minimise the effects of your handicap. For example, I was able to write truthfully that 'I am fully mobile within the constraints of my wheelchair and take a very active part in interests such as amateur dramatics, etc'. It helps too if you can cite any previous job experience, even if it was only vacation work. In short, the more evidence you produce to illustrate your ability to overcome your handicap, the more likely the person assessing the application form will want to meet 'this out of the ordinary cripple who really does seem to be a cut above what one would expect'.

For those who have specific characteristics that may be seen as an obstacle to their employment such as being unable to climb stairs in an office block, or having problems with the clarity of their speech, I think it is very helpful to demonstrate to potential employers early on how such difficulties can be overcome. Anyone who has known me for some time is often genuinely surprised at the way I am able to innovate or adjust to situations that initially seem full of physical problems. In my experience, most disabled people are extremely good at adapting to awkward circumstances, which is one reason why they can become first class employees. Of necessity, they have to mould their jobs into time effective tasks that keep wasted effort to a minimum, otherwise they will be in danger of working a 60 hour week to do the same tasks as able-bodied people working only a 35–40 hour week. As someone who values his free time, I would dislike that situation intensely!

In addition to being flexible, disabled applicants need to have good sense of humour and a lot of patience. And they'll need plenty of determination if they are not to be fobbed off by employers, some of whom they may suspect of not treating them fairly. Of course you are often competing just like able-bodied colleagues with many others for a few vacancies. So you may not be invited to interviews for purely academic or personality reasons. This is all part of the job-hunting scene. Yet, on one or two occasions a certain regrettable word called discrimination crept into my mind. Nothing concrete ever surfaced but when one employer offered first interviews to all 19 other members of my course, and not to me, I couldn't help feeling pretty suspicious about it. I decided to pursue the issue, and after applying considerable pressure received an apology from the company concerned. They stated that I should have been advised personally that the job demanded a great deal of mobility and they had no option but to turn me down on this count. It was a clear case of not giving a disabled person a chance to prove themselves physically able to do the job. Consequently, I would strongly urge that you press employers for their reasons, if you feel unhappy about the way in which your application has been handled.

Fortunately, such incidents are not common, and regularly you have to look at and accept the realities of the situation. It may not be feasible or safe for some employers to accommodate you physically. You can't work on the third floor when there is no lift and you cannot walk. Since joining Shell, it has become clear to me that large organisations may be more suitable for many disabled graduates because they have a large range of jobs, and they're in modern, accessible buildings. Generally they also have the financial resources to make any necessary physical adaptations and facilities without recourse to the various Government schemes for grants to employers. My employers have been very positive on this front, installing, for instance, ramps and special toilets for the disabled in their London headquarters. To my knowledge several other large organisations in the public and private sectors have taken similar steps to accommodate disabled staff more easily. 'Small is beautiful' is not necessarily true for handicapped applicants.

RECRUITERS CAN BE UNSURE HOW TO HANDLE AN INTERVIEW WITH A DISABLED CANDIDATE

It's worth bearing in mind that the Companies Act requires all but the smallest employers to set out their policies towards the employment of the disabled in their annual reports. Have a look at a few before you start filling in application forms. Careers services will have copies.

Assuming that you cross the initial hurdle and are rewarded by a first interview, then I believe that 'disabled' applicants can sometimes use this to good advantage. For instance, I found one or two recruiters were unsure how to handle an interview with a disabled candidate. It showed in their uneasiness when they asked me about my disability. So I was able to seize the initiative and offer the information they wanted without them having to ask 'How mobile am I?' 'What can't I do?' and so on. This can make a good impression if you are open and friendly as well, because the selector can then relax and settle down to the main purpose of the interview; to find out if this candidate is better than the other fifty being seen. You will not necessarily get the job, of course, but at least you feel that you have been given a fair crack of the whip, vis-a-vis other applicants. In short, you have to be willing to sell yourself convincingly and not wait for only those questions which the interviewer feels are relevant. Mind you, be wary about over-selling, as I have learnt to my cost on more than one occasion.

Once I actually got a job, it wasn't long before I realised that I had another responsibility in the organisation, apart from doing my own work well. I am one of only a few disabled employees within a very large workforce. So whether I like it or not, I am a kind of 'ambassador' for many other handicapped people who would follow me and others like me into employment if only they had the opportunity. Regrettably, precious few disabled people are holding down responsible jobs inside industry, and in this time of economic gloom far too many are doomed to the dole queue. I believe that those disabled people like myself, who have stimulating and enjoyable jobs alongside and in competition with able-bodies employees, are extremely fortunate because we have achieved, in job terms at least, equality.

It is essential that many more of us get employment, and realise our special responsibility to demonstrate we can do the job at least as well, if not better than able-bodied colleagues. It needs a lot of patience, determination and flexibility. But above all it demands an ability to get on with others so that they not only like you as a person, but more importantly come to respect you as a working colleague. Only in this way will the disabled professional gain acceptance and integrate fully into an organisation. I do hope that you will do your bit to break down these barriers, because no amount of prospective legislation to protect the handicapped can change the attitudes of employers as much as a fully productive disabled employee.

POINT•CHECKPOINT•CHECKPOINT•CHECK

Who can help

There are over 500 Disablement Resettlement Officers (DROs) in post throughout the UK. They have considerable financial resources to help disabled people obtain and continue in employment. You don't have to be registered as a disabled person to use their services. This assistance can range from the provision of taxi fares for difficult journeys, to arranging for the installation of ramps and lifts to accommodate special wheelchairs and other equipment. First contact can be made through your local job centre. Many local authority careers services have specialist careers officers who work exclusively with handicapped clients. Your local careers office should be able to put you in touch with the nearest one.

Additional financial support is available to disabled students in the form of a disabled student allowance. An amount of not more than £500 can be drawn on for each student who incurs extra expenses because of their handicap while on a higher course once they already have a grant. This is entirely separate from the allowance given to disabled students on their first degree or diploma course.

The British Computer Society has a Committee for the Disabled; specialists from the profession offer help and advice to other disabled computer hopefuls.

The Association of Disabled Professionals however, provides an information and contacts service covering a wide range of employment areas. It can put you in touch with disabled people who have the experience to help you overcome some of the initial problems in their specialist area.

The National Bureau for Handicapped Students is mainly concerned with educational topics but they do produce some helpful literature about sources of funding and send their brochure *Students and Disabilities 1982/83*, free of charge.

Useful addresses
- The Spastics Society
12 Park Crescent, London W1N 4EQ
- Royal National Institute for the Blind
224 Great Portland Street, London W1N 6AA
- Royal National Institute for the Deaf
105 Gower Street, London WC1
- National Bureau for Handicapped Students
40 Brunswick Square, London WC1N 1AZ
- The Association of Disabled Professionals
Initial contact through Ms Marchant
The Stables, 73 Pound Road, Banstead, Surrey
SM7 2HU

OLDER AND WISER?

MATURE STUDENTS HAVE EXCEPTIONAL ASSETS, BILL GOTHARD OF READING UNIVERSITY SHOWS HOW THEY CAN BEST BE DISPLAYED TO ADVANTAGE IN THE JOB HUNT

Younger students tend to look guardedly at those strange creatures, often as old as their parents, who sit in the same classes and work alongside them. But mature students are a growing arm of higher education – and often a misunderstood one.

A mature student may be no more than 25 but employers are going to expect more from them than the younger student. In some occupations such as social work and teaching, experience in life can be an advantage; in others like retailing or banking, the competition from the newly fledged graduate will be much stiffer.

On the whole, employers are willing to consider mature students, but their

expectations are likely to be high. This is because they are less easy to fit into conventional graduate career structures. A sense of direction from someone who has entered higher education in their 30s or 40s is expected, so don't assume that an employer knows why you decided to leave your job to spend three years reading geography, although it may seem very obvious to you.

You must capitalise on your work experience. This is where you hold a clear advantage over younger students. If you sometimes feel your age working against you, remember that the graduate aged 21 usually feels very green and lacking in experience of the world.

MATURE STUDENTS NEED TO EXPLAIN THEIR ABILITIES, AND PROMOTE THE SKILLS THEY HAVE DEVELOPED THROUGH THEIR EXPERIENCES

Make a note of all the jobs you have done, and all the activities this work has involved. Looking back over several years may not be easy but you will find that this is time well spent. It gives you the opportunity to highlight the skills which you have developed over a number of years.

Don't list just obvious abilities such as typing or being able to produce technical drawings, but less tangible skills such as being able to influence or persuade people, or being able to improvise. Skills of all kinds can usually be transferred.

Employers seek people with particular qualities and you probably have more expertise than you credit yourself with at present. Indeed, you may take many of these skills for granted, but it will be to your advantage to make sure that employers realise fully what you have to offer.

The quick job hunting map* can be a great help in sorting out your abilities. It lists broad areas, each with a number of sub-skills. They are: manual or machine, athletic, outdoor, travelling, detail, follow-through, numerical, financial, influencing, communications (reading, writing, speaking), instructing, interpreting, guiding, learning and researching, analysing, evaluating.

This covers all the main areas and from it you

can produce a profile of your particular abilities. Individually, these skills can seem trivial but collectively, they can present you as a person with valuable experience and clear potential. The exercise can also be very helpful in answering questions like 'What do you have to offer this company?' which appear on so many application forms.

Some jobs have an upper age limit. If you are really keen on one of these occupations and you are over the age limit, it is still worthwhile applying. You will need to be persuasive and to show that you are really motivated towards that occupation rather than just wanting a job. There are certainly cases of people breaking through these barriers, but you have got to promote yourself.

YOUR MATURITY IS NOT ALWAYS REFLECTED IN THE STARTING SALARY BUT WILL BE USEFUL IN SPEEDING UP YOUR PROMOTION CHANCES

Another problem can be starting salary. Although older than the normal 21 year old graduate, you may have to settle for a similar starting salary. This is frustrating and often difficult, but it may be essential to get into the sort of occupation you want. Once employed, you are in a much stronger position to negotiate increases in salary and to get promotion.

Terry is a typical mature student. He was 30 when he graduated in applied physics from North Bank Polytechnic. Leaving school at 16, he joined a large local heavy engineering firm as a craft apprentice. He did well at technical college and became a design draughtsman.

Over the years frustration set in partly because of a lack of promotion; at the same time his trade union activities grew until he eventually became a shop steward. With his wife's encouragement he took the plunge and left his job for full time studies. Although hard-up, he enjoyed his time at college and obtained a lower second class honours degree.

But in his final year, he wasn't keen on entering an essentially technical job. He considered teaching but felt that he couldn't afford to be a student for another year. And his previous experience had put him off returning to industry.

In talks with a careers adviser, Terry's involvement with the students' union came up.

He had run the union, chosen and been responsible for a number of the staff. Terry was sceptical about the idea of industrial relations. Having been a shop steward, he found it difficult to imagine himself on the other side of the fence, especially as his previous employer had a poor record of industrial relations. But after being convinced that not all employers adopted the same attitude he applied to a number of companies highlighting his trade union activities and stressing his role in managing the students' union. After several interviews he was offered a post in the industrial relations department of an electronics company.

Similar success can be achieved equally by mature women students. Jill got her first job when she was 17, having completed a commercial course at school. She worked in three secretarial jobs until she was 23, when she had her first child. By the time her second child was at school, she decided to study for A levels at the local technical college.

A year later, fired with enthusiasm for studying, she applied for a place at a nearby university. She spent three years reading sociology and running her home. As her final year approached, she began to think about what she wanted to do but could only feel certain that she didn't want to return to secretarial work. But at 38, not very mobile and without a relevant degree, she wasn't optimistic about her chances of getting a satisfying job.

She considered teaching but was pessimistic about getting a job, especially with her particular discipline. Retailing appealed to her but her age and lack of mobility made this unlikely.

PREVIOUS WORKING EXPERIENCE SHOULD NEVER BE UNDERVALUED WHAT SEEMS IRRELEVANT AT FIRST SIGHT MAY REVEAL HIDDEN SKILLS

However, her teenage children and the course had aroused her interest in adolescents and she explored the opportunities in this field. She discovered a one year full time course to train careers officers at the local polytechnic and went to talk to her careers adviser about this.

Jill felt that her working experience was too dated and narrow to be of much relevance and

because she hadn't had the time to become involved in anything other than her work at university, she felt that this would count against her.

But her three jobs had been for quite different firms and had given her a good insight into a number of occupations. In her final job she had been given responsibility and had done a fair amount of administration.

IT'S UNWISE TO RULE OUT AN INDUSTRY OR A SECTOR OF EMPLOYMENT JUST BECAUSE OF ONE UNREWARDING EXPERIENCE

When she'd been a housewife, she had helped to set up and run a playgroup, which required a good deal of energy, drive and initiative. As her children grew older, she had trained and worked voluntarily as a marriage guidance counsellor, which had helped her to listen carefully and sympathetically to people.

Feeling more confident she applied to the course and was accepted. A grant from the training board provided financial support.

Both cases demonstrate some of the problems – and advantages – of being a mature student. Terry's union experience gave him invaluable insight into industrial relations which he could draw upon in another role. His activities in the students' union, although not of obvious relevance to Terry, could be put forward as

evidence of supervisory skills and management potential.

And his initial negative attitude to returning to industry reflects the attitude of many mature students. Their earlier working experience has often been unrewarding and has usually played a major part in encouraging them to enter higher education. This can lead to blanket dismissal of a key sector of employment, which could mean missing the opportunity of a satisfactory job.

Jill's case demonstrates how some mature students lack confidence in themselves because of an early lack of success in the education system, and sometimes as a result of having been restricted to relatively low-level jobs. They find it hard to envisage themselves as graduates, capable of doing responsible jobs. Jill clearly undervalued her working experience.

She also didn't see the relevance of her playgroup or marriage guidance experiences because they didn't relate to the age group with which she wanted to work. But her age, her experience as a mother, her voluntary activities as well as her employment experience were all to her advantage as a potential careers officer.

* *The quick job-hunting map* by Richard N Bolles. Published by Ten Speed Press.

POINT•CHECKPOINT•CHECKPOINT•CHECK

First approaches

If you are a mature student, you'll probably find that either you don't fit into the run of the mill new graduate vacancies or no-one's advertising the type of jobs you're looking for. Either way, you will need to take the initiative and approach employers rather than waiting for them to search you out.

It's important to have a well presented curriculum vitae full of information that stops the personnel officer from checking your age and then filing the form straight in the bin. There's usually masses of employment or education detail to wade through before you come up with facts that are directly relevant to your applications. You will probably find it saves time in the long run to compile several CVs to cope with different job areas or types of employers.

Some guidelines to make the task easier include:
- keep dates chronological,
- make sure any time gaps are accounted for,
- don't pack in every fact about yourself,
- be very selective,
- make sure the whole thing is easy to read.
- If you can't type accurately get your various CVs done professionally.
- A well expressed, hand written letter can put the finishing touch to your application. This should explain briefly why you are contacting the organisation. But the main purpose of the accompanying letter is to highlight those key points from your CV which will make the employer sit up and read on. It's a difficult technique to develop, but the overall length should stay short otherwise the reader will just switch off. Check out the finished product with a careers adviser.

Help shape the future

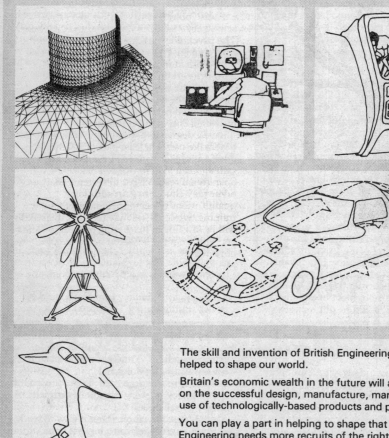

The skill and invention of British Engineering has helped to shape our world.

Britain's economic wealth in the future will also depend on the successful design, manufacture, marketing and use of technologically-based products and processes.

You can play a part in helping to shape that future. Engineering needs more recruits of the right calibre — young men and women who can research and develop, design and produce tomorrow's products — from micro-electronics to wind-power generators — from wrist-watch TV to automotive design.

If you would like more information about career opportunities in the British Engineering Industry, send for a variety of leaflets to: EITB Publications, PO Box 75, Stockport, Cheshire SK4 1PH.

Name ....
Address ....
....
....

British Engineering
HELPING TO SHAPE THE FUTURE

Engineering Careers Information Service
Sponsored by EITB, EEF and CSEU

BRANCH AWAY FROM THE OBVIOUS

EVIDENCE FROM RECRUITMENT MANAGER MARTIN HIGHAM SHOWS HOW A SHIFT IN CAREER CHOICE CAN BE EXCITING AND SUCCESSFUL

The demand for graduate chemical engineers dropped sharply a few years ago. It came as a shock because the supply had been growing for some time. As a result many chemical engineers had to follow arts graduates and start looking at other careers outside the normal ones associated with their degrees. Historians or English specialists for example expect few vacancies – apart from teaching; economists, or linguists will find a few more but no special arts graduate jobs. Two chemical engineers, faced with this problem, chose very different paths; one landed a job in marketing consumer goods;

the other eventually turned to accountancy. Both shrewdly assessed their personality, assets and liabilities and then looked for careers in line with their talents and temperaments.

A discipline like psychology which spans the arts-science faculties illustrates the problems. The psychology graduate who says 'I want to be a psychologist' has narrowed the choices to four. Both clinical and educational areas, require a certain class of degree and postgraduate training; academic work is only possible if the degree is good enough, and occupational psychology has an even more restricted entry. But if that graduate were to say 'I have a degree in psychology. Where can I best make use of at least part of it?' then the openings are far wider. Those skilled in statistics can look for jobs in market or operational research, or in systems analysis. Some may choose to gain additional qualifications in personnel management or training, while others may feel that their skills will be of value in marketing or selling – and so on. This example has been based on jobs obtained by psychology graduates in Rowntree Mackintosh.

If you wish, or have to seek a job outside your specifications, you will need to look first at what you have to offer, then at related careers.

No doubt you will have filled in a good many introduction or application forms, almost all calling for the same basic information. They all ask who you are and about your academic record and results. They want to know about vacation and other work and your success or otherwise on the games field, in the prefect's or committee room. What you do in your leisure time is often included in terms of hobbies and what you've done in the vacations. Some forms may even have asked you a lot of personal questions, about strengths, weaknesses, how others see you and so on. Despite what you could have made up to complete such personal probes, there's some value in looking back over the objective facts you have listed, and asking yourself a few questions. What are my best subjects, and which do I prefer? How far have my activities in school and in my degree course pointed in any direction, or none at all? What do my spare time activities tell me about myself?

To show you in practical terms – Dick Stringfellow took science A levels: his best

GRADUATES...
...A FUTURE TO STRETCH YOUR INTELLECT

Past experience has taught us a lot about graduate attitudes. Graduates deal in facts not flannel. They want them spelt out without the superlatives. What sort of training will they get? - Where will they be working? - How will their performance be assessed? - and precisely where can they expect to climb in the coming years?

All these questions are answered in our recruitment literature so read it and see what we offer.

BEFORE YOU DO - let us leave you with some further information...

The Royal ranks as one of the worlds largest and most successful

insurance companies. Graduates occupy key positions - in sales, underwriting, investment, computing, accounting, you name it. Many progress to senior positions gaining the extra responsibility to match the ability demonstrated through the results they have produced.

Anyway, send for our literature, speak to your careers service then make your own judgement whether Royal can offer what you want.

Contact: Judith Taylor, Management Development Unit, Group Personnel, Royal Insurance, New Hall Place, Liverpool.

Royal Insurance

subjects, but he was interested in and enjoyed arts ones as well; he'd been a prefect, played in some school teams, and enjoyed organising things. At that stage he intended to become a chemist and do research. At university he found other and wider interests, and soon realised that he was nowhere near dedicated enough to do chemical research. His chief interest seemed to reflect a wish to work with people. Fortunately he decided in time to change his degree course. Eventually he chose a career in personnel and works management, which proved the value of his self assessment.

LOOK BEYOND THE OBVIOUS JOBS AND TRY TO EXPLORE A WIDER RANGE OF RELATED ALTERNATIVES

Mary Sullivan took a degree in music – her first love. But she joined the police, because she had learnt to care for others. Mary preferred an outside life, and her skill in riding led to a job in the mounted police. Other students have found that their absorption in university life has given them a new perspective and, once they had broken out of the traditional pattern, a wider choice of career.

You probably know the puzzle of trying to draw four continuous straight lines through nine dots, arranged in three horizontal, parallel rows of three dots each. Few people can do it, because they organise the dots, perceptually, into a nine-dot square. If told that they can come outside the square the dots appear to form, most people see at once how it can be done. But the pattern otherwise inhibits them. In the same way students assume that certain types of job are associated with particular degree subjects, and they find it hard to come outside that pattern. Once they start to consider it, or are forced to do so by circumstances, they realise it may later prove to be a blessing in disguise. Some books on careers sensibly refer readers to 'related careers'; and there is a growing amount of information available at careers services on 'alternative work', which is treated in detail in this section of DOG.

If you've discarded the category of alternatives which include self-sufficient communes, VSO, CSV and similar occupations, your best plan is to look first at those firms listed in DOG who will accept graduates of any discipline. They appear in the Index under the heading of 'Any

degree subject'. You may have a little difficulty in explaining to a prospective employer why, with your degree, you want a career in one of the more unusual areas. But if you have done some self-assessment along the lines suggested above, you should be able to put up a convincing case for yourself.

Theo Clay started job hunting after six years at university. The post he was offered in personnel seemed a natural choice for a psychology graduate. But then he looked over what he had done. He'd started as a medical student, but after failing his second MB he'd switched to psychology and converted an ordinary degree into an honours one. His major interests during his course made him realise he was more cut out for selling and so he applied to in a firm taking graduates in any subject.

Theo's now an export sales manager dealing with the Far East. Janet Andrews on the other hand was working for a degree in catering and hotel management, but decided to try for marketing. Her success came in part because she was able to convince her interviewer that her decision was the right one, and that she had the capacity, as well as the interest to follow that career. As it happens, she first thought of it as a result of a careers talk in her final year; now she is a successful brand manager.

BE OPEN TO ALL SUGGESTIONS FROM CAREERS ADVISERS, WHO MAY RECOGNISE QUALITIES YOU'VE OVERLOOKED

Notice how a shift in career-choice can come about almost by chance; in Janet's case (as incidentally in my own) through a careers talk. They may seem to have no appeal, but it pays to go to them. Theo had read the literature available at his careers service, and talked to his adviser; his interviewer soon saw that someone who sold himself so well could probably also sell other products. Some interviewers may try to suggest possibilities you had not considered, if they believe you have the right qualities.

Both Theo and Janet had thought what they could do outside the usual run and had looked at their interests and achievements before deciding they fitted the requirements. And they could give good reasons for their decisions. They'd found a formula which rarely fails.

TIME FOR SOME TALENT SPOTTING

DEBBIE CATT OFFERS SOME DOWN TO EARTH STRATEGIES TO RE-CHARGE YOUR BATTERIES AND HELP YOU MAKE YOUR APPLICATIONS WORK FOR YOU

A slap in the face with a wet fish may produce much the same effect as discovering that there are no jobs of the sort you'd set your heart on. It might not make you feel any better after this rude awakening, but more and more students are having to face the same cruel reality. Admittedly the recession has been nibbling away at graduate jobs for some time. But it's only the last two or three years that have witnessed an almost panic situation. It seems specially unfair when students have chosen courses because they seem to be related to jobs. Obvious examples are teaching and some of the sciences, particularly biology.

But the difficulties have been far more widespread then anyone has had the courage to acknowledge. Traditionally, arts graduates have had a desperate struggle to find jobs in anything vaguely requiring their academic subject as a background. But there are still geographers, linguists, historians and English graduates who believe that they will be able to get jobs that make use of their specialist knowledge. For the vast majority this is not the case. A few may be able to use their subject after considerable experience, and perhaps a further qualification. Many are disillusioned because they can't walk into the media, museums or other holy grail type employment areas. Yet many of them, even if reluctantly, found work in areas relatively close to their first choice. Those who planned their moves carefully enough could find a backdoor route to their original goal. Unfortunately many of these related jobs have disappeared as well and jobs for graduates of any discipline as a whole are diminishing leaving a lot of very frustrated students high and dry.

Now to compound the problem, other subjects have been sucked up into the confusion. Engineers, that previously exalted group, are now beginning to experience similar difficulties with only the field of electronics keeping its head very high above water. And after an unseemly burst of popularity, computer scientists are now flooding onto a barren employment market.

STUDENTS NEED TO EXAMINE THEIR MOTIVES FOR FOLLOWING A COURSE AND MAKING A SUBSEQUENT JOB CHOICE

But not only are students from particular subject areas finding the going tough, actual job areas are being squeezed as well, like social work, marketing and teaching. Teaching is still declining. And no other discipline has brought home more strongly the need for students to examine their motives for following a course and their subsequent job choice than this profession. Re-evaluating yourself at the end of three or maybe four years of hard grind is neither a pleasant nor an easy task.

Talking over the problem and any of your own plans with a careers adviser is a good start. You may in fact already have an idea where your re-appraisal of the situation will lead. But you still have to convince the employer that his/her job is not second best for you even though it's not what you originally planned. Of course there's got to be a certain amount of honesty in the exchange, because trying to tell a hard bitten personnel officer that you took an archaeology degree just so that you could go into production management isn't going to ring true however accomplished your white lies.

MOST COURSES EQUIP YOU WITH A RANGE OF SKILLS WHICH MAY NOT BE IMMEDIATELY OBVIOUS

Employers don't make things any easier. Some have a very clear idea of the type of candidate they are after, but a large number have some vague concept of the good applicant and leave the rest to you. This is fine if you know how to sell yourself or if indeed you know what your plus points are. But by highlighting your transferrable skills you can show an employer how versatile your academic training has been, and indicate where you would make the best contribution to an organisation. Identifying these skills is not just important to impress employers. It helps you to take a closer look at yourself and make sure your abilities will be well used.

Most courses equip you with a range of skills which may not be immediately obvious. This doesn't just apply to vocational subjects: everyone picks up expertise in any learning situation. Geographers for example often forget that their appreciation of statistics and methods of graphical representation can be invaluable in many work situations. An ability to handle and interpret figures is essential in any financially oriented business including insurance, purchasing and any branch of retailing. Like many other subjects, geography is rarely associated with computing techniques, yet computers often play a key role in the curriculum. An economic geography option provides a data base for marketing, air and commodity broking and other commercially oriented activities.

In case you still haven't quite tuned in to the message let's look at some more examples.

Scientists have to have a methodical approach to their studies, most of which are of a fairly practical nature. But the subsequent report writing and planning follow-up schemes requires certain organised thought processes and logical ability.

Historians on the other hand specialise in research methods and pruning down vast amounts of information to extract the vital facts. The techniques they develop will be equally acceptable in an employment context, because the actual material involved is irrelevant. So any job which involves the dissemination of information, like market research, consumer advice, legal work or advertising could be considered. Librarians too can apply their information retrieval techniques to a variety of work. Most companies keep records of one type or another and coping with the mass of paper and facts is always a headache.

Teaching courses also provide some very marketable skills, in fact so many they need to be divided into three groups. Firstly there are the interpersonal ones of empathic listening, advising, persuading and of course training and demonstrating. Then come the management and organisational skills in planning, monitoring, evaluating, and motivating, not to mention leadership and control. Finally come communication skills concerned with collecting, analysing and presenting information.

HIGHER EDUCATION DEVELOPS SELF-MOTIVATING AND ORGANISATIONAL ABILITY BY THROWING STUDENTS ON THEIR OWN RESOURCES

But these skills are by no means exclusive to teaching. The process of higher education generally develops a self-motivating and organisational ability by throwing students on their own resources. An engineering training promotes logical thought and develops a rational approach to problem solving. Again the actual problem matter is not important; it's the ability to tackle any problem that is of such value.

Courses with the same name can, just like people, be startlingly different. A little probing here and there can unearth some impressive details to add weight to your application. Options, projects and field-work or the use you made of results could provide a valuable source of material. Even if a particular scheme backfired or did not produce the expected outcome the very fact that you planned an experiment or project as competently as possible suggests a range of qualities to an employer.

Once you've analysed these qualities they need to be matched to jobs that are available. You don't have to try to accomplish the whole thing on your own. Test out a few ideas with a careers adviser.

SOME INDIVIDUALS USE SKILLS AND ABILITIES WHICH WOULD NOT NORMALLY BE ASSOCIATED WITH THEIR ACADEMIC BACKGROUNDS

As well as being a biologist, mathematician or whatever, you are a person. Now that may appear a crass statement but you would be surprised how many candidates believe themselves to have taken on the persona of their subject and abandoned all aspects of their previous existence. If you've never given much thought to your personality and attitudes, then finding your basic human qualities is going to be quite a struggle.

Recent examples of direction-changes include a life scientist who has become a diving instructor with a firm of international aqua sports makers and a sociologist who joined a firm of consulting engineers as a trainee technician. These individuals used skills and abilities which would not normally be associated with their academic backgrounds. They felt it would be more satisfying to make use of their other abilities and concentrate on personal ambitions when choosing a job. And you can draw your own conclusions about the teacher who became a bunny girl.

Occasionally there's an exciting spin-off that couldn't have been anticipated. You never know, you may actually enjoy the change of job direction. A fill-in job as a supervisor of waitresses in a plush London hotel turned out very well for a recent languages graduate. Although she only started there for the money, she found to her amazement that not only did she like the work, but the organisation liked her. She is now well up the management ladder.

Let's face it, how many of you really know what working in the job you'd planned for would really have been like? The recession, bad though its effects generally are, may have saved you from a fate worse than death. Success stories abound, and your careers adviser can show you where other graduates have ended up. Don't be dismayed by the figures of unemployed. Remember they did not have the chance to read, and take appropriate action from this article.

POINT•CHECKPOINT•CHECKPOINT•CHECK

Test it out
If you're all geared up to look at alternative job areas but don't know where to start, there are several free questionnaires you can tackle which should help throw up a few ideas.

Gradscope is a computer aided pencil and paper exercise widely used by graduate careers advisory services. It compares your answers to 50 questions on different aspects of work, with profiles of more than 100 occupations. Between eight and 12 occupations are suggested which come closest to meeting your stated priorities.

Some students have found the results disappointing if the job titles include ones they dislike or would not be prepared to consider. Yet if the capabilities and purpose of the exercise are explained clearly at the beginning,

expectations would be more realistic. In fact the best use can be made of the process if it's regarded as a cog-turning one, just to get the brain working again.

Careers advisers generally prepare candidates thoroughly, and the results are usually fed back during a follow up interview. It's not as fraught as doing an exam, and there's no time restriction, so overall it's quite a valuable and painless exercise.

Another guidance tool is CASCAID-HE. Although the questions differ from the Gradscope form, it has a similar function and also produces an occupations printout. Many people find the format and results easier to understand, but in any case it's a useful starting point.

PLANNED MOVE

MARK ASTON FOLLOWED A
VOCATIONAL COURSE BUT
FOUND HE HAD TO
CONSIDER ALTERNATIVES

After five years at Cardiff University studying town planning, people are often surprised that I ended up working for British Telecom in a debt control section.

At the time I started my degree, town planning was a growth area. Since then, Government cut backs have not only reduced job opportunities drastically but even made it difficult to find placements for the professional training practical.

I only had a vague idea of what I wanted to do. When I approached the university careers service for advice, I learnt that I wasn't the only one with this problem. An excellent careers adviser spent a lot of time with me discussing areas that might be suitable. I was very lucky and managed to get relevant vacation work, which helped me at interviews.

My careers adviser suggested I cast my net widely, although by this stage we'd decided that I should apply mainly for general management, marketing and distribution in large companies or public corporations. What I wanted was a clear career structure and good training schemes. And I applied for competitive jobs—it's good experience.

Doing your homework on employers is very important. I started off by going to the careers library for annual reports of companies; I found equally useful brief career profiles of various types of work and professions. The graduate recruitment brochures tend to be glossy and rather dangerous to rely on alone, but the better daily newspapers were invaluable.

During my second interview with British Telecom I was asked some questions I would never have been able to answer if I had not done this digging. Perhaps it made the difference.

I imagined most employers would view my five years on a vocational degree course with some suspicion, but most employers were surprisingly broad-minded. In fact, I found that my course had given me some very useful business knowledge.

In all, I made about 40 applications and amongst scores of rejections I collected a few second interviews and job offers. British Telecom was one of the companies I applied to 'on spec'. It seemed the only company to fulfil all my criteria. I wouldn't be trapped in a specialised career because of the flexibility of the organisation, the prospects were good and the product was unlikely to become obsolete.

Most graduates overlook the implications of mobility. This is stressed by some employers, though other criteria seemed more important to me. Is the financial incentive worth the disruption to your social life? I expected a fairly high starting salary because of my vocational training, even so it was not a major issue.

At British Telecom I was initially involved in general administration and had staff to supervise. I have since moved on to the personnel division to help in my career development. My future will obviously depend considerably on how the business responds to its return to the private sector. The government now plans to denationalise 50% of the organisation since the British Telecommunications Bill has been passed.

But after 18 months at work, I am confident that my prospects and job satisfaction will be much greater than they would be had I remained in planning.

BRAVE NEW WORLDS OF WORK

YOU DON'T HAVE TO ACCEPT THE EMPLOYMENT STATUS QUO. CAREERS ADVISER HELEN WOOD POINTS OUT THAT THERE ARE WAYS OF SIDESTEPPING TRADITIONAL CAREER PATTERNS

Cheer up, – we all know the spectre of unemployment is hovering. But for final year undergraduates as well as other groups trying to break into the labour market, more and more attention is being paid to alternative areas of employment.

Conventional opportunities have declined though there are some notable exceptions like electronics, data processing and finance. And there are few, if any, signs to herald a dramatic increase in the number of vacancies within the new slimline British industry and commerce, if or when they emerge from the recession. Yet evidence of real growth does exist in such areas as the so-called black economy, the unofficial exchange of skills and resources, and in the small scale entrepreneurial sector, the co-operatives and common ownerships, even in the voluntary and work experience groups.

Peter Till

UNEMPLOYMENT COULD ENCOURAGE JOB SEEKERS TO CHALLENGE THE TRADITIONAL WORK ETHIC AND CREATE A NEW KIND OF FUTURE AT WORK

Naturally many graduates, the majority, will still choose to compete for conventional jobs and be successful. But such jobs only represent one of a range of socially important and valuable types of work. In fact a growing proportion of graduates may prefer or will have to look elsewhere to find ways of earning a living and fulfilling ambitions.

For some students the choice of a less conventional job will be resisted or seen as a second best imposed by force of circumstance. But others will welcome wholeheartedly a chance to break out of the mould of orthodox employment. The usual graduate opportunities have always seemed inappropriate and incompatible to some whose moral and philosophical standpoints led them to pursue alternative careers in ways which they found acceptable and stimulating. Perhaps now is the time to start building on their pioneering efforts and view the current recession and unemployment as something more than an appalling waste of energy and talent. Looked at in a more constructive and exciting way, it could encourage job seekers to examine and challenge conventional ways of living and working. Many of us would prefer to question the traditional work ethic, and create a new kind of future at work.

As the impact of new technology makes itself felt should we honestly expect and would we really want to see a return to traditional full time, full employment, 40 hours a week, 48 weeks a year, for 40 years? What are the alternatives to the Government's short-term palliatives now on offer? The tyranny of the work ethic might be replaced by more satisfying and humane work arrangements which make better use of energy and skills, without loss of productivity.

Utopia-seekers in all generations have often been dismissed quite rightly as escapists, dreamers, and drop-outs. Utopias have rarely been created in remote communes, but maybe it is now realistic to take up the challenge of the recession and modern technology and to alter our attitudes and approach to work radically. All members of society might benefit, not just the few who manage to escape from it.

A POSSIBILITY FOR THOSE WITH IDEAS, RESOURCEFULNESS AND DETERMINATION IS SELF EMPLOYMENT – BUT YOU'LL HAVE TO WORK TWICE AS HARD

Many graduates are already busy and successful in unconventional work, which improves the quality of life for themselves and others. Some of the activities in which they are involved may provide opportunities and models for you to follow.

Self employment is a possibility for those with ideas, resourcefulness and determination. Setting up a business is not the exclusive province of the wealthy with vast amounts of capital to invest in market research, premises, equipment and distribution. Money can be found for the right idea. But you must expect to work twice as hard as you would for any other employer. Although the rewards of being the boss can be yours and you can run things the way you choose, to establish the working conditions you dream of and produce the goods and services you believe are right, you have to accept that the risk and responsibilities involved in running a business won't leave you as you slam the office door at evenings or weekends. Marketable skills and ideas are only part, you have to have an appropriately phlegmatic temperament to cope with the knocks and crises before you start to reap the benefits of being your own boss.

It is obviously crucial for anyone thinking about self-employment to spend time assessing themselves, their ideas, ambitions and talents. If it seems a realistic business plan then practical guidance and advice must be found. Finance is a key area to consider – who will put up the money: the bank, a finance company, the local authority, an EEC development grant? Premises can be another headache – where can you legally (and cheaply) conduct your business? Staffing has to be planned for unless you can manage the show on your own. What do you know about balancing the books, paying tax, and being insured? Once the project is off the ground it needs marketing and selling – does anyone want your product or service, how will you advertise it and who will sell it for you?

Specialist advice can be sought and bought from accountants, solicitors and bank managers, but the Small Firms' Information Service run by the Department of Industry, which has centres throughout the country, is probably the best source of general information. It publishes a range of booklets answering basic and more complex queries, and offers personal advice and counselling on setting up and running any kind of small business. COSIRA (the Council for Small Industries in Rural Areas) offers a similar service to those planning to operate in rural areas. Your nearest Citizens Advice Bureau should be able to tell you of any local schemes for funding or otherwise supporting new business initiatives. Your careers service may also have an information sheet *Starting Your Own Business*.

SUCCESSFUL CO-OPERATIVES ALREADY EXIST WHICH OFFER PEOPLE THE CHANCE TO CONTROL THEIR WORKING AND EVEN DOMESTIC LIVES

Rather than tackling the business world on your own, you may prefer to share your energy and ideas with like-minded others and form a co-operative or common ownership. Successful co-operatives already exist in a variety of forms in manufacturing industry, retailing and services like printing or transport. They provide members with greater control over their working and, in some cases, their domestic lives. They liberate people from hierarchical organisation with its rules and constraints, and emphasise self help.

Yet they are not soft options, for the business needs to be as viable as any other. Members are expected to contribute fully and share responsibility for decision making and management as well as for the work itself. Obviously members have to agree on fundamental issues such as the material rewards for different levels of input to the co-operative. 'From each according to his ability, to each

Our best ideas

Getting good ideas off the ground is what we're all about – and because every problem we tackle offers a new challenge, no two days are ever the same at EASAMS.

Operating independently of hardware manufacturers, we are a leading systems engineering company. Most of our projects are in the defence field, but our interpretation of systems is broad. Computers are used extensively in much of our business, with complex simulations helping us find realistic answers to some of today's – and tomorrow's most involved technical questions.

As a member of one of our small, enthusiastic teams where the atmosphere is young and friendly, your personality counts for a lot, with different disciplines interacting in a most stimulating way.

You'll gain plenty of varied, worthwhile experience early on, and do your own analysis and programming in working out your approach to every new problem. So you'll have the chance to equip yourself with many vital new skills. Our scope is exceptionally wide, and working with us can be extremely rewarding.

Except as convincing proof of raw brainpower, your background is relatively unimportant: **Mathematics, Computer Science, Operational Research, Physics, Electrical, Electronic, Mechanical, Aeronautical, Systems, or Control Engineering** – a degree in any of these would demonstrate the sort of capacity we're looking for, though any **numerate Arts graduate** may be attracted by the challenges of our work.

Although for all practical purposes we're fully autonomous, being part of GEC makes an important difference to personal benefits and future prospects. And we're conveniently situated for some of Surrey's most attractive countryside.

If you'd like further information, contact your Careers Advisor or write to Graeme Leech, Personnel Manager, EASAMS Ltd., Lyon Way, Frimley Road, Camberley, Surrey, GU16 5EX.

are the most down-to-earth!

EASAMS

A GEC-Marconi Electronics Company

see also page 177

according to his needs' could be a starting point.

Sometimes it's difficult to shake off a traditional upbringing and education which approves of competition and the concept of rewards for effort. But, without alienation and bureaucracy, co-operative working does seem to have enormous potential for revitalising enthusiasm and satisfaction in work. If you are interested, members of your local Co-operative Development Group or the Co-operative Development Agency, 20 Albert Embankment, London SE1 will be pleased to supply you with further information and advice. Otherwise consult the *Directory of Radical Co-operation* published by *In the Making*, 44 Albion Road, Sutton, Surrey.

THERE IS NO REASON WHY GRADUATES CAN'T CHOOSE JOB SHARING AS A GOOD WAY OF COMBINING WORK WITH OTHER PERSONAL INTERESTS

Not everyone will be able or willing to get involved in creating new jobs but while unemployment remains high and the number of existing jobs stays low, it seems logical to consider a redistribution of the available work.

Shorter working weeks, prolonged education or training, and early retirement are examples of this, but job sharing is one perhaps more likely to appeal to graduates. Many people have such a variety of personal interests and responsibilities that it seems unfortunate for those in employment to be so work bound that they are unable to find anywhere near enough time for them. On the other hand those out of work lack the resources and, perhaps, the stimulation to turn their so-called leisure to best advantage.

A solution providing income and employment as well as leisure for two people rather than one is attractive. It can be found in various forms of job sharing. Although the idea of dividing one professional job between two people has become increasingly common in the USA, job sharing has only recently started to gain acceptance in the UK. Large employers in the UK – in education, local authorities, the media, banking and the health service, are beginning to acknowledge its merits. Two minds on one job, fewer absences for domestic reasons, more energetic staff, greater continuity of work if one job sharer leaves, flexible

working to cope with busy and slack periods of work, are all good reasons for experimenting with job sharing. It has also helped organisations to give full employment protection and improve promotion prospects which some of the unions have welcomed.

Women in particular are interested in finding satisfying careers on a part time basis where family and domestic commitments would not allow them to work full time. In many cases part time work would have been inappropriate, and possibly exploitative, in terms of salary and career development: very few jobs offered a good package or intrinsic job satisfaction.

Although women have largely paved the way in this area, there is no reason why any graduate, male or female, should not choose job sharing as the most appropriate way of combining work with other personal commitments. Here's your chance to write that book, become self-sufficient in vegetable growing or take up herbalism. For advice on how to approach employers and on local groups campaigning for greater recognition of job sharing, contact New Ways to Work, 347a Upper Street, London N1, 01-226 4026.

Certain jobs ought to be done by society with official recognition and payment, but the fact remains that many areas of social and community need are met only by voluntary and charitable organisations. Some provide day care facilities for the elderly or handicapped, holiday play schemes or environmental conservation and although they will have a few opportunities for paid employment many others offer shorter term involvement in voluntary or semi-voluntary activities which can be worthwhile and enjoyable.

EXPERIENCE OF WORKING FOR VOLUNTARY ORGANISATIONS CAN LEAD TO CAREERS IN COMMUNITY SERVICE AND BE OF VALUE WHEN JOB SEEKING

Voluntary work offers valuable experience before moving to a more conventional job. (Graduates with experience of administration, fund raising or motivating and organising their fellows to help, might find satisfying careers in these charities.) Publications such as *Time Between* by Hobsons Press and the NCVO *Directory of Voluntary Organisations*, or specific organisations such as Community Service Volunteers and more local volunteer centres will provide ideas, encouragement and practical suggestions as to where and how you can get involved.

Graduates are often attracted by the prospect of working overseas or just travelling for a time after leaving higher education. The excitement, the variety, the release from academic and cultural pressures are bound to appeal but the attractions of the graduate are not always so obvious to other countries.

Several agencies operate schemes to send suitably qualified and experienced graduates overseas, usually to the Third World. These schemes are funded by charities, the host countries, the British government and sometimes partly by the volunteers themselves. But it is important to remember who is supposed to benefit from such programmes. Many of the host countries, even the developing countries, now have their own reasonably educated, if inexperienced, unemployed.

Today the requirements from aid-giving countries are for specialists – teachers, doctors, nurses, accountants, engineers. The demand for those without specific skills or experience grows less except where extra pairs of hands are always welcome as on kibbutzim or International Voluntary Service (IVS) work camps. So before approaching organisations like the British Volunteer Programme or Christians Abroad, assess carefully what you have to offer and who might benefit from your skills.

Working overseas will be interesting, but you may need to spend some time training or acquiring relevant skills if your host country is to benefit. Teaching English as a foreign language or nursing could be a good idea.

These are just a few of the alternatives you can seek if conventional job opportunities don't exist or don't appeal. In the Alternative Opportunities section of your Careers Service Library you can find more detail. You may like to meet and talk with people who have tried alternative careers. At the University of York we organise an annual Alternative Opportunities Fair. Others have been held at the Universities of Sussex and Cambridge, and more are planned. So, don't despair if the milk round doesn't produce the job you want; search beyond conventional horizons and you may find alternative ways of fulfilling your ambitions.

POINT•CHECKPOINT•CHECKPOINT•CHECK

Where to start – self employment
● Small Firms Information Service – London
8 Bulstrode Street, London W1. Use telephone directory for local branches
● National Federation of Self Employed & Small Businesses
Head Office – 32 St Anne's Road West, Lytham St Anne's, Lancs FY8 1NY
London – 45 Russell Square, London WC1B 4JF
● The London Enterprise Agency and the London Chamber of Commerce and Industry, both at 69 Cannon Street, London EC4, can usually advise on setting up a small business.
● Local Chamber of Commerce and Citizens Advice Bureaux provide a similar service.
● Scottish Development Agency
Small Business Division
102 Telford Road, Edinburgh EH4 2NP
● Council for Small Industries in Rural Areas (COSIRA)
11 Cowley Street, London SW1

Voluntary work
● National Council for Voluntary Organisations
26 Bedford Square, London WC1B 3HU
● National Council for Voluntary Youth Services
Wellington House, 29 Albion Street, Leicester LE1 6GD
● Community Service Volunteers
237 Pentonville Road, London N1 9NJ
● The Scottish Community Education Council
4 Queensferry Street, Edinburgh EH2 4PA
● British Volunteer Programme
22 Coleman Fields, London N1 7AG
● Christians Abroad
15 Tufton Street, London SW1
● Voluntary Service Overseas
9 Belgrave Square, London SW1X 8PW
● International Voluntary Service
Ceresole House, 53 Regent Road, Leicester LE1 6YL

FREEWHEELING

MORE RESPONSIBILITY FOR CHRIS FRAMPTON MEANT LESS INVOLVEMENT IN THE WORK HE LIKED, SO HE SET UP HIS OWN COMPANY

The members of System 696 have "chosen a peculiar path" says Chris Frampton, "we're working for the improvement of health, and for our own personal autonomy. But the buck stops with us, we take the responsibility."

Chris wanted to use his electronics degree, so he took up a research post at St Bartholomew's Hospital in London and combined it with an MSc degree in medical electronics and physics. By then his job responsibility and involvement had grown, "I certainly found out what medical electronics was all about, working with four technicians on the maintenance of electronic equipment for five hospitals." Requests for specialised equipment meant that Chris would "design and manufacture whatever came in the door". Designing a kidney machine involved five years' research; a speech aid amplifier or a heart beat rate meter took less time.

After seven years, Chris realised promotion "was a case of dead man's shoes". And he started getting too many administrative jobs for his liking. "Fewer and fewer development projects became available unless I went shopping for them," he recalls.

Five years ago Chris and three of his colleagues began to work out the commercial viability of their ideas. Eventually they set up a company to protect and promote their inventions. Most evenings were taken up with development work so by the time Chris and another engineer decided to leave the NHS the company structure was already operational. Two other professional engineers joined the team which runs on a "slice of the cake basis". They may operate from cramped basement premises but, working closely together they produce effective results. "We generate the goals but you need sparks to achieve them. All our efforts go into producing goods not into divisive competition: we're all directors."

System 696 has meant that Chris could return to working as an electronics engineer. "It's the nuts and bolts of engineering that interest me, I want to work with the design and development of medical equipment to solve engineering problems in measurement and control," he says. The company seems to have been fortunate in avoiding capital investment problems normally associated with setting up a small business. Chris and one other registered themselves as a limited company so that "neither was putting their house on the line".

But the company does face promotional problems. No-one has any marketing experience and Chris firmly believes when you start up on your own "you need ready made connections." But "we're coping with recession because we provide an economic way through engineering problems."

Understandably Chris misses the security he had in the NHS. His autonomy depends on gaining customers, "you're only your own boss if you make money."

Chris finds "the lies in business annoy me. A supplier will take four days instead of one which makes us late. But I'm not cynical, I'm learning to ask more searching questions."

Despite the problems, Chris is glad he's running System 696, "I'm not so bored and frustrated as I was at Barts. I'm doing things I want to do, and every week the problem, the solution and the technology are different."

Voluntary Service Overseas

'There's so much scope. You get to know more about your own abilities'.

'Simple little improvements really matter'.

'A different culture, a different approach – it's rewarding and stimulating'.

'You have to stop and think about the way you are doing things'.

These were just some of the answers we got when we asked VSO volunteers what they had gained from the experience overseas.

If you could hear yourself talking like this, read on.

What is VSO?

Voluntary Service Overseas is an independent organisation. It is a charity funded partly by the Government and partly by private donations. Its aim is to help Third World development by providing opportunities for people with a wide range of skills to make a practical and individual contribution.

Why volunteers?

We are looking for people who are prepared to offer their skills where they are most acutely needed; people willing to adopt a life style sensitive to the poverty around them. We believe we offer a new vision of manpower aid from the rich world to the poor. Our volunteers are to be found at middle-level, far from the capital cities, dispersed into smaller towns and poor rural communities.

A few years ago, the typical volunteer would have been a school leaver usefully filling in a year before going to university. Nowadays, he or she will normally be either a graduate or someone with professional/technical qualifications and several years' work experience.

What qualities does a volunteer need?

Our volunteers are eager to adapt their skills to local needs, rather than introduce complex Western methods and technology. They have a commitment to train local successors and phase themselves out, rather than create dependency. They are self-reliant.

What are the terms of service?

In almost every case, the country employing a VSO volunteer pays his or her local wage and provides housing for the two years of service. VSO pays fares and various grants. It is mutual aid, not charity – a fifty-fifty relationship.

Is there any training?

Training is provided for all volunteers before they leave. Courses last from ten days to five weeks.

When and where would I go?

We send volunteers to Africa, Asia, the near and far East, the Pacific and the Caribbean. Most volunteers go overseas in August or September, some in January and a few at other times.

Who can apply?

Anyone over 20, who is in good health and a citizen of the UK, or a Commonwealth citizen domiciled in the UK. Married couples can apply so long as they have relevant skills and no dependent children. Although requests are increasingly for more mature and better qualified volunteers, we can still place graduates without further professional experience or training, provided they are prepared to teach a subject in demand. You should apply as early as possible in your final year.

For further information and application form, write to:

Voluntary Service Overseas
9 Belgrave Square
London SW1X 8PW
Telephone: 01-235 5191

IF AT FIRST YOU DON'T SUCCEED . . .

CAREERS ADVISER HELEN NIXON OUTLINES SOME UNCONVENTIONAL WAYS OF USING YOUR TIME IF JOBS PROVE MORE ELUSIVE THAN YOU EXPECTED

"As You Slide Down The Banister of Life
Slide with Joy and Not Dismay
And I Hope Sincerely for Your Sake
The Splinters Are Facing the Other Way."
W McCorrisken, *Cream of the Crackers*

By the end of your degree course, after many unsuccessful job applications, you may feel that you have already come into contact with a few splinters facing the wrong way. Employer rejection is like any other kind of rejection, by lover, parent or friend; it hurts. Continuous employer rejection can be caused by a number of factors and it might be useful to consider

them and possible remedies as well as the end result – unemployment.

You're bound to ask yourself, "Where have I gone wrong?". If you are being rejected before you ever get to the interview stage it is pretty clear that you are not presenting yourself well enough on paper. It is so easy to underestimate the importance of an application form or curriculum vitae, but the answers you provide help to complete a skeleton on which an interviewer, if you get to that stage, will want to add the meat. So be prepared to enlarge on any of the information in your written applications.

KEEP A COOL HEAD AND TRY TO AVOID DRIFTING INTO APATHY WHILE YOU WAIT FOR THINGS TO HAPPEN

The way you come across at interviews is the next crucial stage in your job quest. If you don't receive an invitation for second interview you may have let yourself down in the first instance by not doing enough homework on the company. Maybe you didn't know enough about the job you were applying for, or even about yourself. Before you graduate, check with your careers service to see if group sessions are being arranged on campus which will help improve your presentation on paper and at interview. Your failure in the early stages of selection should be easier to pinpoint and your careers adviser may be able to help you. If you have already graduated and doubt your ability to sell yourself, short courses (sometimes one-day) are organised by some careers services in conjunction with the Manpower Services Commission (MSC) which could be helpful sessions. They may be advertised as 'Careers Review Courses' and will cover topics like application forms, self-assessment and interviews. You can contact your nearest careers service or MSC office to check if there is a course in your region.

The effect of failure and rejection can be increasingly depressing and it is important that you keep a cool head and try to avoid drifting into apathy while you wait for things to happen. *You* have to take the initiative.

"Success isn't the result of spontaneous combustion. You must set yourself on fire."
Arnold Glasgow.

This maxim is perhaps more important once you leave college and the support of fellow students who are going through the same job-hunting process. Family and friends are usually well meaning but they don't always appreciate your lack of success even in these difficult times because they assume graduates always get jobs.

So what happens now that you are away from your comfortable niche on campus? Having lived off a grant you will be used to cutting corners to conserve cash. And you will have to count the pennies if you are on state benefits. It is unlikely that you will have worked long enough to qualify for unemployment benefit so check out the system to avoid missing out on other money for which you might be eligible. When signing on for the first time it's important to mention that you've been a student. You need a form B1, which will not be given to you automatically. It is essential to complete the form if you want to claim supplementary benefit. You will be interviewed by someone from the DHSS who will then decide whether or not you qualify for benefits. Leaflets which may be of interest are NI12 *Unemployment Benefit* and NP12 *School Leavers & Students. What you pay and what you get.*

DON'T GIVE UP HOPE. IT'S SURPRISING HOW MANY VACANCIES ARE AVAILABLE LATER ON IN THE YEAR

One way to cut costs is to make use of a local library (either public or careers service) where you can call in and scan relevant newspapers and magazines to find out which firms are recruiting. You should aim to do this at least three times a week. Don't give up hope; it's surprising how many vacancies are available quite late on in the year. If you're not near a library but live near some fellow graduates, why not form a consortium to share the cost of newspapers, journals, and magazines to have access to a wider range of opportunities at less cost. Contact either your own careers service or the one nearest your home and arrange to have *Current Vacancies* and the local vacancy list sent to you. You will probably be charged for postage but each service decides its own policy.

Mutual Aid is another useful scheme. Graduates can generally use the information room or have a careers advisory interview at the most convenient careers service. The staff want to help but it is up to you to make the first approach. Because of the pressure of work some services may offer limited facilities, such as access to the information room only, or ask for a letter of introduction from the careers service of your alma mater before you can have an advisory interview.

IT IS ALWAYS BETTER TO TAKE A JOB, SHORT OR LONG TERM, THAN TO STAY AT HOME BECOMING MORE AND MORE DEPRESSED

You'll all have come across the Catch 22 situation where you can't get the job without experience but you can't get the experience until you have a job. In such cases it may be necessary to adjust your sights until you can obtain that essential experience they demand. Similar types of work however, may give you related experience. It is nearly always better to take a job, short or long term, than to stay at home becoming more and more depressed and self-pitying. And it's easier to find work from a position of employment than from the dole queue. At least you learn the discipline of starting and finishing at set times. You'll be mixing with and having to communicate with others who may or may not be your academic equals. There's no need to stop looking for your long-term job while you are in temporary employment and your earnings at least pay postage and stationery bills. Temporary work is still fairly difficult to find but if you shop around and are prepared to tackle anything you should be successful. You could be in for a surprise too. Stop-gap work has been known to fulfil the job satisfaction a graduate has been looking for.

The local Jobcentre or PER office may be able to offer temporary work and though some jobs may be pretty basic labouring or working in hotels, occasionally a government sponsored scheme may be available. Don't forget to try local shops, supermarkets, factories, the local council, hotels and so on, and check if there is an agency dealing with temporary work in your area. Obviously there are books published which deal specifically with short term employment but they tend to concentrate on the summer period. Some of the work may run on into autumn. If you live in a neighbourhood where small ads appear in the newsagent's window, keep your eyes open, there could be something interesting on offer.

Practical hobbies or skills and an eye for business may tempt you to look at self-employment (see p 56) while skills like typing, languages, driving, (with a clean licence!) could be useful. If you don't have these skills it's not a bad idea to use some free time to acquire them.

Many vocational courses are offered at colleges and universities. The best place to find out is the careers office which should have a copy of *Graduate Studies*. This publication is a valuable source of information on a wide range of courses and provides some guidelines on entry requirements and, where applicable, sources of funding from the Research Councils. That thorny problem, funding, is so complex you'll probably need to have a discussion with someone in the careers service. Regulations vary depending on factors like where you live, the level of postgraduate study which interests you, even your class of degree. If money is not available from a central funding body it may be necessary to consider applying for help from trust funds. Useful publications are *The Grants Register*, *The Directory of Grant Making Trusts* and *Educational Charities*. An information sheet which gives advice on further study and funding is produced by AGCAS and should be available from your careers service.

Understandably a company looks for the

best. If you can't convince yourself of your competence how can you expect to convince a potential employer. Keep a sense of humour, whatever you do. If you can find something to laugh at, or about, even if it is only yourself, you may avoid falling quite so far into the depths of despair. Making an effort to keep up your outside interests or to find some will help, otherwise your world will become smaller and smaller and your problems larger. Don't lose your self-respect or you will not be able to psyche yourself up for the all important interview. Those descriptions of the ideal candidate in advertisements could have made you feel that it wasn't worth applying. Possibly you could claim only three out of the four skills specified. Unless the requirement is something very necessary such as a specific degree, it could be worth enquiring, especially if there is a chance to acquire the extra skill on the job. Don't give up trying, or sell yourself short. Personality can be crucial and a hang dog expression won't get you where you want to be.

It would be fatuous to hope that you are reading this article because you have a few minutes to spare rather than that you are unemployed. Just keep on saying to yourself that recessions don't usually last for ever – even if it feels that way!

Good luck in your job search.

POINT·CHECKPOINT·CHECKPOINT·CHECK

Support services
Graduates are supposed to be the least vulnerable group in the employment or unemployment race, according to the Manpower Services Commission (MSC). So the official provision of measures to assist those unfortunate enough not to find something suitable early on is extremely limited.

The Community Programme Scheme (from 1st October 1982) is designed to combine the existing Community Enterprise Programme (CEP) with community benefit work and a scheme for voluntary work activities. Those eligible will be 18 to 24 year olds who have been unemployed for six months or more, and those aged 25 and over who have been unemployed for at least a year. The Government's other effort to beat unemployment is a job splitting scheme, so it's certainly

worth enquiring about the local situation from your Jobcentre or employment office.

University and polytechnic careers services make continued efforts to provide appropriate activities for improving job-seeking skills. Practical workshops and support sessions are run depending on demand; so if nothing has been arranged in your area maybe you could get things started.

Students themselves occasionally organise and run support groups. Many find these a great help just to know they are not alone and there are others in the same situation. The Inner London Education Authority Careers Service has produced a pack of information to help overcome the unemployment blues, and it's worth checking with other services to see what goodies they have come up with.

Honours Graduates

Bend your mind to problem-solving

The evidence of the eye is not always conclusive. It often takes a penetrating intellect to differentiate between reality and the illusion, between fact and fiction. And this is precisely the challenge that faces today's Tax Inspector in assessing the tax liabilities of companies and organisations of all types and sizes.

In order to read between the lines of a company's accounts, and to reach a fair decision, the Tax Inspector must practise, at times, the skills of the lawyer, accountant, detective, businessman, and negotiator. In all, it is a satisfying career in which responsibility comes early; and where independence and extensive contacts with senior managers in industry and commerce feature prominently.

Training is comprehensive and can begin at any one of hundreds of offices throughout Britain. Within a few months, you will be handling your own casework, and after 18 months you will move on to quite complex negotiations. About 3 years into your career you can expect your first management role leading a sizeable staff, and after about 5 years you should be running your own tax district.

Qualifications: Under 32 and a degree with at least second class honours. Final Year Students may apply.

Starting salary: £5,270 – £7,245 according to experience. You should be earning £7,980 after 2 years and £11,370 3 years later.
Within 10 years you should be on a salary scale rising to £18,755. In another 5 years you could be on a scale rising to £20,895 either in a Tax Inspectorate post or in general management in the Civil Service. Salaries higher in London.

There are vacancies all over the country.
To find out more, and for an invitation to visit a Tax Inspector write to Civil Service Commission, Alencon Link, Basingstoke, Hants, RG21 1JB.
Please quote reference: A/320/D27.

see also page 127

Guide to employers

Entries from organisations actively recruiting graduates are arranged alphabetically.

The Sex Discrimination Act makes it unlawful for employers to discriminate on the grounds of sex. We wish to make clear that where the pronoun he (or she) is used in this publication it covers both men and women, and that both men and women are eligible to train and apply for all posts save where there is express provision to the contrary.

When applying to a company it would help them if you would quote DOG as your source.

See also the sections on
Professional Bodies and Industrial Training Boards   377
Opportunities Overseas   387

Abbott Laboratories Limited

Activities
Manufacturing, marketing and developing a range of hospital and pharmaceutical products

Employees
700

Location: UK
South East

Opportunities
Chemists; Pharmacists; Business

Vacancies
2–4

Application address
Personnel Manager, Abbott Laboratories Limited, Queenborough, Sheerness, Kent ME11 5EL

The company is a member of a large international group of pharmaceutical manufacturers with branches throughout the world. Abbott in the United Kingdom is concerned with, in this country and many overseas markets, the development, manufacture, distribution, and sale of fine chemicals and pharmaceuticals and a range of hospital products. The company has enjoyed an impressive rate of growth over the past twenty years which it confidently expects to maintain.

Types of graduate required
Science graduates in *chemistry* or *pharmacy* will find excellent opportunities for a career in development, production and quality control. *Business* graduates will find openings in marketing and administrative departments.

Training
Graduates are normally recruited to fill specific vacancies and are given training designed to develop to the full the talents of the individual according to the need and the particular field covered.

Salaries
Initial salary is competitive and depends upon qualifications and experience. Conditions of employment are very attractive with good prospects for promotion where initiative and enthusiasm are shown.

Location
All the company's activities in the United Kingdom are centred on a modern plant in the Isle of Sheppey on the North Kent coast. Approximately 70 minutes by train from London, Queenborough has good road and rail communications with the Medway and North Kent coast.

Accountancy and Financial Management in the Public Sector

Activities
Accounting and financial management in the public sector

Locations: UK
General

Opportunities
Trainee accountants

Application addresses
See main text

The education and training scheme leading to the professional qualification of Institute of Public Finance Accountant (IPFA), is designed to produce financial managers of the highest quality.

CIPFA members fill a wide range of top and senior posts in financial management and accounting in the public services. This includes financial advice and information, corporate management, financial accounting, budgeting and budgetary control, forward financial planning, project appraisal, management of funds, auditing and cost effectiveness studies.

During their training students receive practical instruction in finance, accounting and auditing in public sector organisations.

Applications
CIPFA operates a regional recruitment scheme for graduate trainees throughout the United Kingdom. The regional recruitment co-ordinator will give advice on possible employment vacancies and arrange initial interviews.

If you hold a degree and are interested, please contact your nearest regional recruitment co-ordinator for full details.

North East *GS Pollard, Director of Finance, West Yorkshire MCC, County Hall, Wakefield WF1 2QN. Tel: 0924 367111*

North West and North Wales *PW Jenkins, County Treasurer, Merseyside*

MCC, PO Box 95, Old Hall Street, Liverpool L69 3EL. Tel: 051-227
5234

Midlands *PR Sabin, Deputy City Treasurer, Birmingham City Council, The
Council House, Victoria Square, Birmingham B1 1BB. Tel: 021-235
2993*

South East (including London) *DJ Hopkins, City Treasurer, Westminster
City Council, PO Box 240, Westminster City Hall, Victoria Street,
London SW1E 6QP. Tel: 01-828 8070*

South Wales and West of England *DG Morgan, County Treasurer, Avon
County Council, PO Box 22, Avon House, The Haymarket, Bristol
BS99 7RT. Tel: 0272 290777.*

AE Group

Activities
Manufacture and distribution of precision
engineering

Employees
24,000

Locations: UK
General

Locations: Overseas
France, Germany, Italy

Opportunities
Production and mechanical engineering;
Production management; R&D; Management
services; Marketing; Distribution

Application address
Mr JF Cliffe, AE Group, Cawston House,
Cawston, Rugby, Warwickshire

AE is a group of highly autonomous companies in the UK and overseas
which manufacture and market a wide range of engine components and
other products. The group's companies supply most types of engineering
customers, but in particular they provide a vital service to the
automotive, transport, marine and aerospace industries.

In keeping with the group's philosophy of decentralisation,
recruitment of graduates is undertaken by the individual companies to
suit their own particular manning programmes. A limited number of
high potential graduates, (mainly engineers) are however, recruited
directly by the group headquarters and provided with group-wide
exposure.

Types of graduate required
The main need is for *mechanical* and *production engineers*, *metallurgists* and
physicists, although vacancies occur from time to time for graduates in
other disciplines.

Salaries
Starting salaries are competitive and our policy is to develop and promote
effective people quickly to positions of seniority.

Locations
The group has establishments throughout the UK, but the main centres
of operations are Scotland, the North East, the Midlands, London and
the South West.

Training
In the case of centrally recruited engineers training will be orientated to
satisfy CEI requirements. We are approved by the Institutions of
Mechanical and Production Engineers and operate their monitored
professional development and training experience schemes. The training
of graduates of other disciplines will be designed to meet individual
requirements with the objective of giving each person responsibility for
real work as soon as possible. Training and development are continued
during the subsequent career in accordance with individuals' needs and
capabilities.

AGB

Activities
Market research, magazine and book
publishing

Employees
1,100+

Locations: UK
London; Home Counties

Opportunities
Client service; Ad hoc consumer market
research; Data processing; Industrial market
research; Journalism; Production management

Vacancies
22

Application address
Personnel Manager, AGB Research plc, AGB
Research Centre, West Gate, Hanger Lane,
Ealing, London W5 1DW

AGB Research Group

AGB Research plc is the largest market research group in Europe and one
of the leading publishers of trade, technical and specialist journals in the
UK. AGB is recognised at home and abroad as a major force in the
information industry, which makes a growing contribution to the
promotion of effective administration and business control in most
developed countries.

Continuous research has formed a major part of the company's
business, and Audits of Great Britain Limited, which carries out this type
of research, is the largest of the group's subsidiaries. Ad hoc surveys are
carried out by Research Surveys of Great Britain Limited, and industrial
market research and consultancy by Industrial Market Research
Limited. The group is also represented in various countries abroad.

Types of graduate required
The group is interested in those who have graudated in virtually *any*
subject. For market research, numeracy is essential but, in practice,
graduates are recruited from a wide range of academic backgrounds.
Important attributes are an inquiring and creative mind, an ability to
solve problems impartially, attention to detail and an ability to
communicate both verbally and in writing.

Training
A formalised training scheme is not offered, but graduates receive a
practical course of training with some off the job training. During the
training process, graduates are guided through areas where it is felt they
will make the greatest contribution and receive the most benefit. Regular
discussions with managers provide the opportunity to discuss training
and career development.

Salaries and prospects
Starting salaries are good and rise rapidly with promotion. They are
assessed in accordance with market rates and reviewed regularly.

Application address
Our graduate brochure gives further information about the group and
details seven areas within the group where graduates are employed. The
brochure, may be obtained on application to the Personnel Manager.

Activities
Design and construction of process plants;
Marketing of industrial gases

Employees
2,300 UK

Locations: UK
General

Locations: Overseas
USA, France, Belgium, Holland, Germany

Opportunities
Engineering; Sales; Marketing; Computer
programming and analysis; Finance; OR

Vacancies
30

Air Products plc

The gases that are produced and marketed by Air Products come, in the
main, from sophisticated air separation and cryogenic plants that turn the
various atmospheric gases into liquid at different temperatures, thus
allowing the production of individual commercially useful gases such as
nitrogen, hydrogen and oxygen.

The design, manufacture and construction of these plants is the job of
the Process System Division – Engineering, working from our
engineering centre at Hersham, Surrey; with our manufacturing centre at
Acrefair, in North Wales, producing air separation plants and
components for customers all over the world. Gases are also supplied to
larger industrial clients, from adjacent production sites.

The Industrial Gas Division is involved with the supply and marketing
of gases in cylinder and bulk liquid form to European industry. A
national network of distribution centres supplies merchant gases to many
major customers, including the electronic, food processing and
petrochemical industries. This division also supplied the UK food

industry with the cyro-quick system, which is vital for maintaining the
freshness of frozen foods.

The Finance and Administration Division is essential for the success
and support of the operating divisions. In this group we have brought
together financial control and analysis, management information
functions, communications and personnel.

New developments
Air Products are involved in new developments such as providing
hydrogen for the space shuttle. We are also closely involved in the
microprocessor industry and in the development of North Sea oil.

Types of graduate required
If your degree is *engineering, science* or *business* oriented, you should
investigate the opportunities available every year at Air Products. We
believe that we offer outstanding graduates an exceptional chance to
prove themselves, and through our career development programme, we
pay great attention to developing your abilities.

Each year we provide a comprehensive vacancy list and a career
development programme brochure.

Career development programme
The career development programme enables you to have assignments in
three different departments during your two-year training scheme. It is
designed to introduce graduates to the broad range of company activities,
its methods of operation, its resources and capabilities, and to provide
them with early responsibility, backed with the support of experienced
professionals. Essential to this is the flexibility for entrants to change
direction, into a different area if they so wish.

We believe that we must spend time and effort in discovering where
your skills lie, and in aiding your development of them. Through this,
you will discover a more satisfying career, and the company will continue
to achieve success.

Direct entrants
For graduates qualified in a relevant subject, such as computing, our
direct entry scheme combines immediate responsibility with additional
training. It is ideal for the entrant who has a clear career path mapped out
already.

Formal training
Formal training, which is available for both sets of graduates, comprises
courses allied to our technology and general management. There will be
opportunities for such specialised training throughout your career at Air
Products. We're also interested in encouraging you to gain professional
qualifications.

Salaries and rewards
Financial rewards are an essential part of the motivation we have already
mentioned. They are geared to attracting and retaining the highest
quality of staff, who will therefore be able to take advantage of the
opportunities for development and promotion within the company.
There are also many other benefits, as you'd expect from such a major
international organisation.

Applications
If you would be interested in applying to Air Products, just write to our
Career Development Co-ordinator at the address given.

Alfa-Laval Company Limited

Activities
Manufacturers of separation, thermal, agricultural and liquid-handling equipment

Employees
700 UK
18,000 worldwide

Locations: UK
London and Wales

Locations: Overseas
Worldwide

Opportunities
Proposals engineering; Project and design engineers

Application address
Personnel Manager, Alfa-Laval Co Ltd, Great West Road, Brentford, Middlesex TW8 9BT

When Swedish inventor Gustaf de Laval designed a new form of milk separator in 1878, he also laid the foundation stone of what is today a worldwide enterprise. An enterprise that still serves the farming industry, but that has also developed in many other directions and into many other industries.

Alfa-Laval is one of the world's foremost manufacturers of separation, thermal and liquid handling equipment: activities and products that find their markets in a wide range of industrial applications. We are world leaders in milking machines, centrifuges, heat exchangers and marine refrigeration systems. Whether as simple units of equipment or as complex automated processes for the agricultural and food handling, chemical, marine, power, pollution control or engineering industries, Alfa-Laval stands for high levels of technical achievement and product quality. It also stands for over 17,800 people employed in 35 countries.

In the UK, we are basically a marketing and contracting organisation, but one that invokes technical and engineering competence and is closely involved in the development of new ideas and the identification of marketing opportunities for new products and product applications. In identity, organisation and achievements, we are a large company, but one that retains the personalised values of people working efficiently in small teams and units.

Types of graduate required
Our main requirement is for *mechanical* and *chemical engineers*. Good communicators who can adapt easily to people or to problem situations and who will bring their special interests and knowledge to bear on the technical involvement of specific industries.

Training
We will provide up to 12 months training. A general induction course is followed by training and experience in specific technical or administration areas. As your career develops, you will be able to undergo further training or technical up-dating to match up with increasing responsibilities. A firm policy of promotion from within at all levels ensures that there will be no shortage of such opportunities for progress.

Amersham International plc

Activities
Development, production and marketing of radioactive materials

Employees
1,500

Locations: UK
South East; Cardiff; Gloucester

Locations: Overseas
United States; France; West Germany; Belgium; Australia; the Netherlands; Japan

Opportunities & places
Science 20/25; Other 5

We are a world leader in the supply of isotopes. The very wide product range is under constant expansion and we also develop particular items to meet customer requests. The three main product areas are radio-isotopes for use in medicine, industry and research. Medical products are used for diagnostic purposes, and are our fastest growing interest. In industry, isotopes are used for non-destructive testing and the elimination of static. In the life sciences, radioactive tracers are used in fundamental and applied research.

Locations
The head office and principal laboratories are in Amersham. There is also a major new site at Cardiff, and smaller units at Harwell and Gloucester. Nearly 85% of our sales are abroad and many of the scientific and marketing staff spend time overseas supporting the marketing of our products.

Types of graduate required
Chemists, biochemists, physicists required with postgraduate qualifications

Application address
Senior Training Adviser, Amersham
International plc, White Lion Road, Amersham,
Buckinghamshire
Tel: 02404 4444

and/or first or upper second class honours degree for R&D work, also with good honours degree for production and quality control.

Metallurgists, *materials scientists* and *electrical/mechanical engineers* required for multi-disciplinary teams to work on R&D of new equipment for development and production of new products.

Chemists, *life scientists* required for marketing and sales liaison work for home and export markets.

Graduates in *science* or *accountancy* required for accountancy training scheme.

Career development
Graduates can progress to technical management in either development or production work or move to marketing, quality control and other service or commercial areas.

The Analysts Schlumberger

THE ANALYSTS
Schlumberger

Activities
Data acquisition and interpretation to the international petroleum industry

Employees
1,200 worldwide

Locations: UK
Aberdeen and London

Locations: Overseas
Norway; West Africa; Nigeria; Egypt; Spain; France; Middle East; South East Asia; Australia; North, Central and South America

Opportunities
Mechanical or petroleum engineers; Geologists

Vacancies
100

Application address
Mr Christie, Personnel Manager, The Analysts Inland Services Inc, 2 Park West Place, London W2 2QZ

The Analysts Schlumberger is a group of oil service companies involved in on-site data acquisition and interpretation. The company was the first to introduce on-line computers on drilling rigs and remain leaders with the introduction of the first multi-purpose MWD (measurement while drilling) instrument package.

Types of graduate required
We require graduates who wish to apply their degrees in *geology*, or *engineering* to a job which offers interest, variety and challenge. Trainees must be capable of developing a sound technical knowledge of the equipment they will use, as they have to maintain and calibrate their own instruments.

Applicants should be self-reliant, have the desire to travel, and must be adaptable to widely varying work locations and conditions. They must have self-motivation and initiative, and must be physically fit.

Training
Our planned training programme gives engineers both theoretical knowledge and practical experience by combining seminars with on-site training. Constant assessment of each engineer's ability and progress up to and beyond total concept unit manager (TCUM) grade ensures that progress is related to individual competence and ability. We offer field engineers an advanced training programme to prepare them for promotion to senior grades and specialisations.

Career prospects
Field engineers can progress to any managerial or staff position in line management or consultancy.

Locations
Our overseas locations cover Europe, West Africa, Nigeria, the Middle East, the Mediterranean, the Americas and South East Asia.

Benefits
We offer high salaries and field bonuses, and our benefits package includes a permanent health scheme, life assurance and a pension scheme.

Arthur Andersen & Co

Activities
Chartered accountancy

Employees
20,000 worldwide

Locations: UK
General

Locations: Overseas
Worldwide

Opportunities & places
Trainee chartered accountants 250

Upper age limit
28

Application address
See main text

An international partnership of chartered accountants with over 140 offices worldwide. Situated on the banks of the Thames in London, and in ten other cities in the British Isles, Arthur Andersen & Co provide a full range of financial services to industry, commerce, and the public sector including small private concerns and large multi-national consortia.

Types of graduate required
Applications are invited from male and female graduates of *all* disciplines.

Training
Great importance is attached to developing the knowledge and skills of the firm's members, and new graduates enter upon a rapid progression towards partnership. Trainees under a three year contract participate each year in courses on principles of accounting and taxation, auditing techniques, the financial community and institutions, computer applications and other technical topics. In addition, they attend a residential tuition centre, either in North Wales or London to prepare for the examinations of the Institute of Chartered Accountants. Training arrangements appropriate to the separate regulations of the respective institutes are made for Irish and Scottish trainees.

Locations
There are vacancies in all our offices in the British Isles with opportunities, at a later stage, to transfer abroad.

Salaries
The salaries we pay our trainees, in both the British and Irish offices, are extremely competitive. Exact details of starting salaries for 1983 can be obtained from your careers officer.

Further information
Further information and application forms can be obtained from:
The Director of Recruiting, Arthur Andersen & Co, 1 Surrey Street, London WC2R 2PS
National Westminster House, 10 Newhall Street, Birmingham, B3 3NP
Bank House, 9 Charlotte Street, Manchester M1 4EU
Royal Exchange Assurance House, 314 St Vincent Street, Glasgow G3 8XD
49 St Stephen's Green, Dublin 2
St Paul's House, Park Square, Leeds LS1 2PJ
Broad Quay House, Broad Quay, Bristol BS1 4DJ
19 St John's Lane, Gloucester GL1 2AT
Virginia House, The Butts, Worcester WR1 3PA
Martins Building, 6 Water Street, Liverpool L2 3UN
44 Charlotte Square, Edinburgh EH2 4HQ

Arthur Andersen & Co Management Consultancy Division

The Management Consultancy Division of Arthur Andersen & Co provides a professional service in designing and installing systems and carrying out studies to produce the information needed by management in directing a broad range of activities. The range of clients is wide and covers manufacturing, banking and finance, retailing, oil and gas, and central and local government.

Activities
Management consultants

Employees
200 UK
3,000 worldwide

Locations: UK & Ireland
London; Dublin

Locations: Overseas
Worldwide

Opportunities & places
Trainee management consultants 35

Upper age limit
28

Application addresses
The Personnel Manager, Management
Consultancy Division, Arthur Andersen & Co,
1 Surrey Street, London WC2R 2PS
or 49, St Stephens Green, Dublin 2

Types of graduate required
Applications are invited from male and female graduates and
postgraduates of *all* disciplines.

Training
Over the first three years trainee consultants receive extensive formal
training as well as gaining experience through assignments. The formal
training is carried out mostly at our centres for professional development
in St Charles, Illinois and Geneva, and provides a thorough grounding in
accounting and business fundamentals, computer programming, systems
installation and design, and financial, manufacturing and marketing
planning and control techniques.

   After this period the consultant will continue to attend specialised
courses throughout his or her career, as well as having the opportunity to
specialise within particular industries. Some travel on overseas
assignments could also be involved.

Locations
There are vacancies in London and Dublin.

Salaries
Salaries are competitive and are reviewed annually. Promotion is based
purely upon merit and the opportunity to become a partner is open to all
who join the firm.

Anglo American Corporation of South Africa Limited

Please see our main entry in the Overseas section.

APV Company Ltd

Activities
Designers and manufacturers of process plant
for food, industrial and petrochemical
applications

Employees
1,600

Locations: UK
South East and Midlands

Locations: Overseas
Worldwide

Opportunities
Mechanical engineering; Electrical engineering;
Computer science; Chemical engineering; Food
technology

Vacancies
6–10

Application address
DJ Golton, Assistant Personnel Manager, APV
Company Ltd, PO Box 4, Manor Royal, Crawley,
Sussex RH10 2QB

The APV Company Limited is part of a vigorous international
organisation comprising over 70 companies which have earned a
worldwide reputation for the development and application of specialised
processing and heat transfer systems and equipment. APV activities are
unusually varied and interesting. They range from the construction of
complete installations for the dairy, brewery, liquid food, fruit juice, soft
drinks, and frozen food industries, to the main contracting of major
projects in chemical and petrochemical engineering, particularly for
distillation and fermentation processes. APV has taken a leading part in
the development of new, continuous processes and is a world leader in
microprocessor controlled process plant. Research, test and laboratory
facilities are extensive, while production is aided by computers and
automated machine tools.

Types of graduate required
Graduates in *mechanical, chemical, electrical* and *electronic engineering, food
technology* and *computer science*. There are also limited openings for
graduates in *chemistry* and *physics*.

Training
Training falls broadly into one of two categories: a period of general
training directed towards a particular area of activity, or planned
experience in a defined task. We ensure that, where appropriate, training
programmes are approved by the relevant engineering institutions.

APV Company Ltd, cont

Opportunities overseas

Much of APV's business is done abroad and the company has been twice honoured by the Queen's Award to Industry. Considerable opportunity for overseas travel occurs for qualified personnel and permanent overseas positions often arise.

Salaries and prospects

Commencing salaries are competitive and determined by age, qualifications and experience. Development of the individual is a main factor governing salary increases and promotion, and the progress is reviewed regularly by a committee of senior executives. The group policy is to promote from within and graduates are encouraged to increase their knowledge of procedures, policy and business in general.

Pensions

Non-contributory life assurance and contributory staff pension schemes are in operation.

Other amenities

Non-contributory sickness pay scheme; holidays 25 days per annum; company restaurant; medical department; hostel and lively athletics and social club in nine acres of playing fields.

Armitage & Norton

Activities
Chartered accountancy

Employees
500

Locations: UK
London; South East; Midlands; North East; North West; Scotland

Opportunities & places
Student accountants 40

Application address
JD Bannister, Armitage & Norton, PO Box A10, Station Street Buildings, Huddersfield HD1 1LZ

A&N is a national firm of chartered accountants with 14 offices in the UK as well as links with Europe and other parts of the world. The firm provides for its clients a full range of professional accountancy services including audit, taxation, management services, investigations, insolvency, secretarial and trust work etc.

Types of graduate required

We are interested in graduates of *all* disciplines to train as chartered accountants.

Training

Students are prepared for the professional examinations by a training programme which includes periods of full time study and linked home study courses with private sector accountancy tutors. In addition, the practical work gives a very broad experience with all types of client. We have a comprehensive programme of in-house residential courses which are linked to practical experience in all of the firm's activities including, for instance, computer auditing and taxation. Our national training partner runs these courses with the objective of ensuring that all staff, from recruits to partners, are familiar with the firm's methods, are kept up to date on technical matters and can use the managerial skills appropriate to their responsibilities.

Prospects

A&N recruits talented and ambitious graduates. On qualification, opportunities for progress within the firm include specialisation in taxation, computer auditing and management consultancy. Managers are normally appointed in their late 20s, partners in their early 30s.

Locations

The firm has offices in London, Huddersfield, Leeds, Bradford, Halifax, Dewsbury, Manchester, Preston, Blackpool, Loughborough, Leicester, Birmingham, Edinburgh and High Wycombe and there are vacancies for graduates at most of these offices.

Salaries

Salaries are competitive with those offered by other firms. Graduate trainees receive annual increases with further increments awarded for examination success. The full cost of tuition fees and associated study leave is met by the firm.

Further information

You can obtain a copy of our brochure from your careers service or by writing to the address given.

The Regular Army

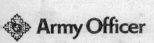

Army Officer

Activities
Operational control and management of men and materials of a defence force

Employees
140,000

Locations
General

Opportunities
Armoured regiments; Artillery; Catering; Engineering; Infantry regiments; Medicine; Pay and accounting; Police; Supply and distribution; Telecommunications; Transport; Veterinary

Vacancies
200

Application addresses
The University Liaison Officer, Ministry of Defence (Army), DAR 1, Lansdowne House, Berkeley Square, London W1X 6AA
WRAC entry, Lansdowne House, Berkeley Square, London W1X 6AA

The Army requires graduates, both men and women, for appointment to commissions in nearly all branches. The Army is a large and complex organisation which is equipped with a steadily increasing quantity of sophisticated equipment in order to make the most economical use of manpower. The control and administration of this organisation requires a very high order of management and technical skills. The Army is thus able to offer a challenging and satisfying career for graduates who have good management capabilities in addition to their graduate discipline.

Types of graduate required

Graduates with degrees in nearly *all* disciplines are required by the fighting arms (armour, artillery and infantry) and such branches as transport, supply, police, pay, education and intelligence. Graduates with degrees in most *engineering* subjects are required for the technical engineering branches. Graduates with appropriate professional qualifications are required for the medical, veterinary, dental and legal services.

Generally applications for all types of commission must be made before the graduate's 25th birthday. However, in certain cases older applicants are acceptable particularly those with professional experience who are applying for technical arms.

Undergraduate cadetships

These five-year cadetships are awarded annually to those qualified to read for *any* degree at a university, polytechnic or college of technology or for *science* or *engineering* degrees at a university or at the Royal Military College of Science, Shrivenham. Successful candidates are commissioned as second lieutenant (on probation) and receive at least £4,390 a year and have their tuition fees paid while at university or Shrivenham. Applications may be made at any time before or after going up to read for a degree.

Undergraduate bursaries

Candidates must have been accepted by or already be at a recognised university, polytechnic or college of technology in the United Kingdom. This scheme is specifically designed for undergraduates who wish to commit themselves initially to the Army for no more than a three-year short service commission. The Army provides financial support of £900 a year during a full (three or four-year) university course to supplement the LEA grant. On achieving his degree he will be granted a commission, on confirmation of which he will be granted an antedate of seniority in recognition of his degree and qualifications.

Training

Graduates will attend a course of about five months at the Royal Military Academy, Sandhurst soon after joining to give them a basic foundation for their career. Thereafter all officers attend various courses throughout their career which will help to fit them for higher posts in the Army.

The Regular Army, cont

Those in most technical branches may also attend postgraduate courses which can lead to professional membership of appropriate institutions.

Prospects

Graduates who are accepted are awarded an immediate commission. They will be given an antedate of seniority which will depend on their qualifications but will enable them to start effectively with the rank of lieutenant with promotion to captain after about three and a half years. For those graduates who intend to make a career in the Army, promotion to the rank of major and above is by selection. Promotion to major is between 32 and 34 years and to lieutenant colonel soon after 37 if outstanding.

Salaries

Graduates will normally start at not less than £7,646 per annum. On promotion to captain pay will be £9,573 with increment after every two years in the ranks. A lieutenant colonel receives about £16,337. In addition various allowances are payable.

Pensions and other amenities

Graduates with short service commissions are eligible for a gratuity at the rate of £1,010 per year of service with a minimum of three years' service up to a maximum of eight years' service. Officers on regular commissions receive a gratuity if they retire after 10 years' service and retired pay together with a terminal grant after 16 years' service. The rate of retired pay will depend on the rank achieved and the length of service, rising to a maximum after 34 years' service. Officers are granted six weeks' leave per year. Accommodation is provided for single officers and in most stations houses are available for married officers, though rent is charged for both single and married accommodation. Assistance is given towards the cost of educating children.

Opportunities overseas

Though the bulk of the Army is based in Germany and the UK, there are a number of small garrisons throughout the world and a variety of appointments both with staffs of other nations and, in the case of technical arms, on projects to assist other countries. There are frequent opportunities in field force units for service overseas.

Types of commission

Short service commissions are available for those who wish to serve between three and eight years. Regular commissions offer employment up to age 55; the length of service generally depending on the officer's wish.

Women's Royal Army Corps: Officer entry

There are opportunities for interesting work in the communications, data processing, transport, catering and welfare and personnel administration, and more specialised work in photographic interpretation, and intelligence duties, education and others. Minimum age for all commission applicants is 18 years 5 months at the start of training, but the upper limit varies according to the type of commission, 25 years for regular commission, 35 years for special regular commission, and no upper limit for short service commission.

Service on a regular commission gives a pensionable career to age 55, with promotion to senior rank and special regular commission gives 16 years' pensionable service from the age 21, and a short service commission is for a minimum period of two years' service, maximum eight years, with a tax free gratuity depending on length of full time service. There is a reserve commitment on this commission.

Qualifications

All cadets must have five O levels, including English language and a maths or science subject, and more academic subjects. For a regular commission, two academic A levels are also required. Graduates are welcome, and their degree may attract a seniority antedate. WRAC applicants are eligible for one year undergraduate bursaries. All candidates must pass the Army Medical and Regular Commissions Board prior to entry for training at the WRAC College, Camberley. Officers may be permitted to resign their commission on marriage.

Officers initially accepted for SRC and SSC commissions may apply to convert to regular or special regular commissions after some service.

Further information

Detailed information is available from the university appointments boards, university officer training corps and also from the addresses given.

Arthur Young McClelland Moores & Co

Activities
Chartered accountancy

Employees
2,250 UK

Locations: UK
General

Locations: Overseas
Worldwide

Opportunities & places
Trainee chartered accountants 250

Application address
Valentine West, Director of Personnel, Arthur Young McClelland Moores & Co, Rolls House, 7 Rolls Buildings, Fetter Lane, London EC4A 1NH

Arthur Young McClelland Moores & Co is a leading firm of chartered accountants and is associated with the worldwide organisation of Arthur Young & Company, which employs 20,000 professional staff and has offices in over 70 countries.

Types of graduate required

The type of discipline is less important than a capacity for logical thought and an ability to communicate clearly. A career in the profession demands high levels of energy, initiative and personal integrity.

Training

In their first year students spend up to 14 weeks in full time training, which greatly eases the transition from an often unrelated degree course to a new discipline and ensures that the students' training begins on the best possible basis. Students are expected to take responsibility and make an effective contribution from an early stage on a variety of auditing and other practical assignments under the guidance of qualified seniors. It is this practical work, with clients ranging from large multinational companies to small one-man firms, which is the most essential part of professional development. Our own training programme is supplemented by external full time courses and study programmes leading to the qualifying examinations of the English and Scottish Institutes of Chartered Accountants. Students can study for the Scottish qualification in some of our English offices as well as in Scotland. Also, students who have already identified an interest in taxation can opt for an emphasis on tax experience during the training contract. During training, students are given the necessary study leave and all training and tuition costs are borne by the firm.

Locations

There will be 250 vacancies for graduates in 1983 in offices in Aberdeen, Birmingham, Bradford, Bristol, Crewe, Dundee, Edinburgh, Glasgow, Leeds, Liverpool, London, Luton, Manchester, Newcastle, Nottingham, Oldham, Perth, Southampton, Taunton and also in Dublin and Jersey.

Salaries

The salary in London in 1982 was £4,900, and slightly less outside

London. For 1983 salaries will be fully competitive and reflect the current market environment.

Prospects

After qualifying, advancement in the firm depends entirely on ability and you could be a manager after three or four years post-qualifying experience and a partner in your early 30s. There are opportunities to transfer into one of our specialist departments or for secondment to other AY offices throughout the world. The experience which you will gain with us and the assistance which we can give through our client contacts would be very useful to you should you subsequently decide to enter commerce or industry.

Further information

Further information and application forms can be obtained from your university careers advisory service or by writing to the address given.

Associated British Foods plc

Activities
Food manufacturing and retailing

Employees
72,400 UK

Locations: UK
General

Opportunities
Engineering; Production; R&D; Retail management

Application addresses
Group Personnel Officer, Associated British Foods plc, Weston Centre, Bowater House, 68 Knightsbridge, London SW1X 7LR
For retail vacancies only: Graduate Recruitment Officer, Fine Fare Group Training Centre, 3 Barnes Wood, Harmer Green Lane, Welwyn, Hertfordshire AL6 0EU

ABF is one of the largest food companies in Europe, widely diversified within the food industry, both at home and overseas. The group comprises many companies which are household names. On the food manufacturing and processing side, Allied Bakeries makes Sunblest, Vitbe, Hibran and specialist breads, much of it made with flour supplied from the milling division. Other companies include Burtons Biscuits whose range includes Wagon Wheels amongst many others; Ryvita the makers of crispbread; and Twinings the blenders of tea and coffee.

On the retailing side we have in the UK, Fine Fare, operating self-service and discount stores, supermarkets and superstores. In Northern Ireland, Stewarts operates the largest chain of supermarkets and lead the way in superstore development. In Eire, Quinnsworth is the largest supermarket chain and Primark operates a successful range of clothing and department stores.

Overseas, ABF has substantial operations in Australasia, where baking and milling interests have extended into other food areas such as poultry and dairy products. In South Africa there is a similarly wide range of food manufacturing activities.

Types of graduate required

We are looking for graduates with initiative and maturity, who have the potential to develop quickly into middle and senior managers. *Food science/technology* degrees would be preferred for the specialist production and research positions and *engineering* graduates will find excellent opportunities for careers in production management, where their skills will be effectively used in a highly automated environment.

Training and career opportunities

Training is tailored to meet individual needs and is designed to give early practical experience and understanding of the company's operations. As we are a decentralised group we can give you real responsibility in an individual company within a matter of months. We would expect you to prove your value early in your career, possibly as an area manager responsible for a group of shops or as a manager controlling part of a factory production process. ABF also has the ability to identify career openings in other companies within the group for those who wish to broaden their experience and further their careers by moving to different functions and environments.

Further information

If you are looking for an exciting, exacting and financially rewarding career in a vital industry please contact the Group Personnel Officer at the address given.

Aurora Holdings plc

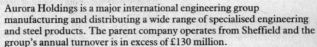

Aurora Holdings is a major international engineering group manufacturing and distributing a wide range of specialised engineering and steel products. The parent company operates from Sheffield and the group's annual turnover is in excess of £130 million.

There are 50 companies and about 4,500 employees managed through the following seven divisions: distribution, engineering, fasteners, forgings and castings, overseas, steels, tools.

Our products find application in the aerospace, nuclear, chemical, foundries, pollution control, special treatment and process industries, to name only the more prominent market sectors.

More than one fifth of Aurora's UK manufactured output is exported. We plan to increase the proportion of our total business conducted overseas and to expand overseas interests.

Training

One graduate is allocated to each division for up to one year's general training prior to first appointment. Any *arts* or *science* degrees will be acceptable especially since intellect is one of the primary considerations. However, the disciplines most relevant to the group's activities include *metallurgy, materials science, mechanical engineering* and *production engineering*.

The objectives of the general training period are:

To provide the graduate with a thorough understanding of the division and its subsidiaries in terms of product range, manufacturing processes, selling methods and financial controls.

To acquaint the graduate with managerial and administrative processes in manufacturing, sales, and finance and to provide an understanding of the methods and skills for problem analysis, decision making and communication.

To enable the graduate to make an informed career choice.

So that the graduate can demonstrate and develop his/her capabilities and make an immediate and worthwhile contribution, general training takes the form of assignments in the division. During this period the graduate is given up to three assignments each of four months' duration, which normally encompass production, sales and marketing, and finance.

Each assignment is at a different company to provide a full understanding of the range of the division's activities. Subjects of assignments vary although examples may include:

Evaluation of a stock control system and analysis of stock movement including recommendations on minimum/maximum stock levels.

Identification of sales opportunities for a product or products by market research.

Each assignment has terms of reference and objectives clearly specified, a target completion date, and on completion is evaluated in terms of content, technique and value.

At the end of general training, the ability and aptitude of the graduate is assessed. The first job placement is jointly agreed and is in a specialist function to establish the graduate's mettle before he/she is given a further programme of external training courses to broaden his/her experience and to develop his/her potential.

Activities
Engineering and special steelmaking

Employees
4,500

Locations: UK
Midlands; North East; North West; Scotland

Opportunities
Production; Sales and marketing; Technical engineering

Vacancies
6

Upper age limit
22

Application address
PWF Wilson, Group Personnel Controller, Aurora Holdings plc, Aurora House, Roman Ridge Road, Wincobank, Sheffield S9 1FZ

Further information
Please apply by completing and sending the standard introduction form of the university careers service to PWF Wilson at the address given.

Babcock International plc

Babcock

Activities
Design, manufacture and site erection of engineering plant and the provision of related services; Major suppliers to the power producing, construction, marine, chemical, steel, mining and automotive industries

Employees
40,000

Locations: UK
General

Locations: Overseas
Worldwide

Opportunities
Chemical, electrical, electronic, mechanical and production engineering; Commissioning; Contracting; Control systems; Design; Metallurgy; Project engineering; Research; Site construction

Upper age limit
25 preferably

Application address
Group Personnel Executive, Babcock International plc, Cleveland House, St James' Square, London SW1Y 4LN

In 1867 two American engineers, Babcock and Wilcox, formed a partnership to patent an original design of boiler. The operation, exclusively in the boiler industry, extended to the United Kingdom in 1891.

In recent years the company has expanded and diversified its products and activities. It has a proud history of endeavour and accomplishment in the vanguard of major engineering development and innovations. The company is jealous of a reputation that has been built up through so many years of service, during which the Babcock nameplate has become established as a hallmark of engineering.

In 1979 the company changed its name to Babcock International, a name more appropriate to its role, size and spheres of activity.

Company structure
The company trades through six operating groups: Babcock Power Limited; Babcock Contractors Limited; Babcock Construction Equipment Limited; Babcock Industrial & Electrical Products Limited; Babcock Overseas Group and Babcock International Inc. Each operating group has a number of subsidiary companies which cater for customers anywhere in the world. Subsidiary and associated companies are located in the UK, the USA, Australia, Belgium, Brazil, Canada, Finland, Holland, India, Italy, Japan, Mexico, New Zealand, Singapore, South Africa, Spain, Sweden, Venezuela, West Germany and Zambia.

Operations
Worldwide activities include the manufacture and provision of: boilers and ancillaries for conventional and nuclear power stations and for industrial and marine applications; pressure vessels and steel fabrications of all types; mechanical construction; steelworks, chemical and processing plant; aerial ropeways for passenger and bulk material transportation; unit and bulk mechanical handling equipment; construction equipment and services; instrumentation and control systems; industrial mixing equipment; desalination, ultra-filtration and pollution control plant; non-ferrous metal casting machines; mining machinery; electrical and electronic equipment; on-line testing and measuring equipment; computer controlled storage and retrieval systems; sortation systems; wire and cable machinery; chain; aerial tow cables; cable controls for motor vehicles; furniture hardware; motor vehicle fittings and trim.

Graduate opportunities
Our long established commitment to the recruitment of graduates has become increasingly important in an era of complex technology. The company's size and diversity offers enormous scope for employment opportunities throughout the entire spectrum of engineering activities. We recruit graduates from a wide variety of disciplines, especially in the *chemical, electronic, electrical, mechanical* and *production engineering* fields. A Babcock employee can expect to be offered a balanced career spanning research, design, development, production, construction, site work, testing and commissioning. There are excellent opportunities to specialise and develop managerial skills in production, contract, project

and general management. For those who gain initial experience in engineering, opportunities occur for transfer to procurement, planning, sales and marketing. There are also career patterns for accountants, systems analysts and computer programmers.

Training and career development

Human as well as capital resources are vital to the operation of a company as large and diverse as Babcock. For many years we have been recognised as operating a well structured postgraduate training scheme which aims to satisfy the recommendations and requirements of the accredited engineering and commercial institutions in addition to providing a balanced overall training. During the first 12 months graduates broaden their engineering experience by working in some of the main areas of the company, including design, production, research and site construction. Dependent upon the graduate's interest and aptitude, training is then arranged to meet the specific needs of the first appointment. Graduate selection and training is designed to produce junior managers at a relatively early age.

Career development constitutes an important part of company philosophy. With the completion of the formal training period, training continues with career development involving job rotation, movement between companies, overseas tours and the opportunity to study for additional qualifications. Selected employees attend management training courses at the recognised colleges and universities.

The company offers excellent career prospects and further career development ensures those with potential are given the opportunity for promotion through management and technical grades to senior appointments. Many graduate entrants now hold top positions including directorships.

Application procedure

Please send a detailed letter of application, stating the type of career in which you are particularly interested, to the Group Personnel Executive at the address given. Brochures on individual Babcock companies are held by your careers advisory service.

John Baker, Sons & Bell

John Baker, Sons & Bell is a progressive firm of chartered accountants with a history stretching over a hundred years, but forward looking and expanding rapidly on a sound professional base.

The firm is situated in the City of London and acts for a wide variety of clients offering a comprehensive professional training in accountancy. It also provides opportunities to specialise in the professional aspects of insurance and both corporate and personal taxation. To the graduate the firm offers a personalised approach both to its staff and to its clients, seeking to attain a high level of standards together with early achievement of professional qualifications.

Types of graduate required

Primarily we place importance upon the individual's personality and integrity and above all his or her determination to succeed.

An ability to communicate and get on with people plus a numerical aptitude are essential as is an enquiring mind, common sense and energy to tackle the academic and office life. For these reasons opportunities exist for graduates of *all* disciplines, preference being given to students with degrees in *accountancy* or allied subjects.

Activities
Chartered accountancy

Employees
60–65

Locations: UK
London and South East

Opportunities & places
Trainee chartered accountants 5/6

Application address
TA Ablett, FCA, John Baker, Sons & Bell, 282 Bishopsgate, London EC2M 4UU

John Baker, Sons & Bell, cont

Training

During the training contract students are employed full time at the firm and operate as part of a pool of staff engaged on audits with in-house training bridging the gap between the theory and practice. Practical work is continuously monitored, and progress reviewed regularly.

Careful integration of the complete range of accounting, auditing and taxation (both personal and corporate) will be given during the training contract. Thorough understanding of all these functions is considered by the firm as essential for the training of the potential chartered accountant.

Students are sent on private sector courses for the Institute's examinations. Payment for these courses is made by the firm and the student's progress is regularly reported to the firm where it is carefully reviewed and discussed with the student by the training manager and principal. The firm gives paid study leave for the professional examinations which is normally ten weeks for the first attempt at each examination.

The in-house courses designed and organised by the firm's training manager occupy approximately 33 days during the students training contract and are designed to supplement and extend the professional studies of the firm's tutors into the day to day work of a practicing accountant.

Salaries

The firm offers salaries which compare generally with those in the profession together with paid tuition fees and study leave. Review of salaries is carried out bi-annually and increases are according to ability and merit. Salaries are also increased on the successful completion of the Institute's examinations.

Locations

The firm is based in the City of London but has its personal taxation department in Thornton Heath, near Croydon. Many of its clients operate throughout the United Kingdom and the students may therefore expect to spend several weeks a year working out of London.

Prospects

Post qualification we offer opportunities to specialise in almost every sphere of a professional accountant's life. We also send qualified staff on Institute, District Society and other courses to further their knowledge and experience. We prefer to promote to the position of managers and partners from within the firm wherever possible and with continued expansion the prospects of such a promotion are good.

Further information

Apply giving details of career to date and examinations passed to TA Ablett.

The Baker Perkins Group of Companies

The Baker Perkins Group of Companies stands foremost in the world as the manufacturer of a wide range of industrial equipment. The group companies design, manufacture and market unit machines and highly automated process plant and equipment for the bakery, biscuit, printing, chemical, paint, rubber, plastic and foundry industries and wrapping and packaging machinery.

Types of graduate required
Mechanical, electrical/electronic or *production engineers* for design, development, production, sales and service. Non-engineering graduates for sales. In both these categories we are also interested in a small number of graduates with fluency in foreign languages.

Training
The company does not stockpile graduates, but recruits to meet identifiable needs in the future. Training programmes for each individual develop capacity to meet long term targets. It is likely to be one or two years before the graduate has acquired the engineering and process experience demanded by the first appointment, but this is determined by the progress of the trainee.

Courses are designed to satisfy the requirements of the appropriate professional institutions, and in certain cases the company awards scholarships to pursue postgraduate and management studies as part of the individual development programme. All graduate trainees are personally sponsored by a director or senior manager and are given the opportunity to become fully acquainted with the work of other factories in the group. Graduates uncertain about immediate targets may be sponsored by Baker Perkins Holdings plc and the first year programme is designed to give a broad based experience of the company to enable them to clarify career objectives.

Locations
In total the group employs 4,500 people in many locations throughout the UK and a further 2,000 in subsidiary and associate companies overseas.

Companies normally recruiting graduates include: Baker Perkins Holdings plc, Peterborough; Baker Perkins Limited, Peterborough and Rose Forgrove Limited at Leeds and Gainsborough.

Salaries and pensions
Graduate starting salaries are competitive, and the graduate who meets demands can expect thereafter rapid progression to reward high performance. We have a contributory pension scheme.

Applications
For details of current vacancies and application procedure consult the Baker Perkins literature at your careers office or write to the address given.

Baker Rooke

Baker Rooke is a medium sized firm of chartered accountants with its largest office based in the Aldwych, in London but with eight other offices in England. Its clients range from public companies to private firms and individuals operating principally in the fields of industry, commerce, the arts and the professions. Clients are also referred to the firm by overseas associates.

Types of graduate required
Accountants come from a very wide selection of disciplines and we hold no preference for any particular degree but we do demand expert use of written and oral English, and evidence of a high level of numeracy.

Training
Formal training for students is dealt with by specialised tutors, and students' progress is monitored by the training partner throughout the contract. Modern auditing and other techniques are employed throughout the firm and these are constantly brought up to date and

Baker Rooke, cont

improved. Training sessions during the contract, commencing with an introductory course on arrival, are arranged. There are also training lectures for all staff, including students, about our methods, practices and systems.

During the course of the contract students have the opportunity of working on auditing and accountancy, and receive training on taxation and trust.

Salaries
Salaries are competitive and reviewed in the light of merit, achievement, exam record and inflation at least annually.

The charges of the tutors preparing candidates for their professional exams are met by us.

Applicants
Please apply before 31 December of your final year if possible.

Prospects
The firm is developing and there are many opportunities for student accountants to progress rapidly through the firm, so that immediately on qualification they become audit seniors and in a relatively short period thereafter can obtain a managerial position, with the eventual goal of partnership. There are no barriers for the right person.

Balfour Beatty Limited

Please refer to the BICC plc entry on page 94.

Bank of Credit and Commerce International SA
Licensed deposit taker

Activities
International banking

Employees 1,400

Locations: UK
London; Midlands; Scotland; North East; North West

Locations: Overseas
Worldwide

Opportunities
Graduate trainee officers in general banking

Vacancies 10 approx

Upper age limit 25

The Bank of Credit and Commerce International was founded in 1972. BCC operates in over 50 countries throughout the world with a particular concentration of branches in the Middle East. In the United Kingdom, it operates an expanding network of over 45 branches from its main UK offices at 100 Leadenhall Street in the City of London.

Types of graduate required
A number of imaginative, high calibre graduates are now required to form the basis of our future management staff in the UK. These may be men or women of *any* discipline provided they have the confidence to accept responsibility within this expanding organisation and the ability to form good relationships at all levels and with all nationalities.

Training and prospects
One year's comprehensive training will be given, both in a branch and in BCCs own academy in London. After confirmation of your appointment to the permanent staff you will consolidate your earlier experience and at this stage should accept more responsibility for the day to day operations of your branch.

Salaries
Starting salaries for graduates are highly competitive with merit based
promotion, and you will be entitled to four weeks annual leave and
membership of the pension scheme.

Further information
More information is available from your careers advisory service and
standard introduction forms should be submitted to the Personnel
Department.

Bank of Scotland

The Bank of Scotland is Scotland's first bank in every sense. It was
founded in 1695 and for more than two and a half centuries it has served
the varied financial needs of its customers, developing and expanding to
meet the increasingly complex requirements of the community.

The head office is located in Edinburgh and chief offices are situated in
London and Glasgow. It has an extensive branch network with over 500
outlets in Scotland, four in London, and one in Birmingham.

Activities
Domestic, international and merchant banking;
investment; Law; Trustee; Registrar; Tax

Employees
3,500

Locations: UK
London; Scotland; West Midlands

Locations: Overseas
USA; Hong Kong

Opportunities
Management training in all areas of the bank's
field of operations

Vacancies
20

Upper age limit
25

Application address
JC Morrison, Staff Manager, Bank of Scotland,
PO Box No 5, The Mound, Edinburgh EH1 1YZ

Our activities
In addition to the traditional banking services provided through its
branch network, the bank offers a comprehensive range of specialist
services for our business and personal customers. For the business
customer, term loan schemes, business advisory services, international
finance, computer payroll services, factoring and leasing. For the private
customer, personal financial services ranging from budget accounts and
loan schemes to tax advice, insurance and investment services.

The bank has played an active role in the development of North Sea oil
from the outset, and now has a rapidly expanding international division
with representative offices in London, New York, Houston,
Los Angeles, Moscow and Hong Kong.

Types of graduate required
We are looking for graduates with enthusiasm and drive of up to age 25
with degrees in *economics*, *mathematics*, *commerce*, *law* and the *arts*.

Training
In the first instance the graduate is assigned to one of the bank's
branches. On the job training is combined with special courses at our
staff training centres, designed to equip the graduate to work effectively
in a supervisory role in the future. The staff training centre maintains
close links with the graduate during this period, after which the
graduate's progress is assessed and he or she then enters the bank's
normal career development system. This provides members of staff of
high potential with the opportunity to broaden their experience during
their early period with the bank. As well as training, the graduate will be
expected to study for the examinations of the Institute of Bankers in
Scotland and to pass the diploma examination of the Institute within two
years of entry to the service. Day release facilities will be available to
assist in studying for these examinations.

Salaries
The salary during training is competitive and thereafter is related to the
salary scale operating in the bank and to the performance of the
individual.

Pensions and other amenities
There is a generous non-contributory pension scheme in operation which

includes provision for widows. There are also facilities for staff house purchase at advantageous rates after a qualifying period.

Holiday entitlement is twenty days plus eight bank holidays throughout the year.

Barclays Bank plc Group

Activities
Banking and financial management

Employees
60,000

Locations: UK
General

Locations: Overseas
Worldwide

Opportunities & places
UK management 45; International management 20; Computer programming and systems analysis 10; Economic intelligence 2; Business research 2/3

Upper age limit
24 usually

Application address
CF Badcock, Manager (Graduate Recruitment and Training), Barclays Bank plc, 54 Lombard Street, London EC3P 3AH

The Barclays Group is an international banking organisation with 5,000 offices in 76 countries. There are opportunities for graduates in each of the group's three divisions which are outlined below.

Barclays Bank UK Management runs the domestic banking business of over 3,000 branches in England and Wales.

Decentralised control has always been a feature of the bank, which has 35 local head offices, each administering the branches in its own area and reporting to the board and general management in London.

Barclays Bank International is now established in most of the world's main financial centres and has a network of over 1,700 branches.

Barclays Bank Trust Company, dealing in investment, taxation and trustee management, has offices throughout England and Wales.

Types of graduate required
Graduates join the management development programme of their choice, either in Barclays UK, or in Barclays International, or in the Trust Company or one of the specialist careers.

Our graduate intake is small, selective and very competitive. Regretfully we have no room for the middle range graduate with middling A levels and an average degree. We seek brains as well as personality.

We look for the best from *any* academic discipline, though some language ability is useful for Barclays International, and the Trust Company prefers degrees in *economics* or *law*.

The specialist careers are mangement services (computer programming and systems analysis), group economics and business research. Candidates for the last two areas should have related degrees.

Training and career development
Our management development programmes are fast and structured. You learn on the job, at bank courses and by study for the Institute of Bankers' examinations. The manager of the programmes monitors and guides your progress continuously.

Barclays UK has totally replanned its programme for 1982 making a very fast course indeed with emphasis on self-help and the quick despatch of professional examinations, and with the possibility of an MBA course after two years. Barclays International makes equal demands on its small graduate intake.

Prospects
We believe that the graduates who join us should have the potential to become managers of large branches, or to occupy comparable management positions in head office or local head offices. Many will go beyond this and occupy very senior positions.

Fringe benefits include a non-contributory pension scheme and excellent sports and social facilities.

This directory is prepared too early for us to indicate the starting salary for graduates in 1983 but up to date information can be obtained from your careers service or direct from us. During training, salaries are revised annually on the basis of performance and potential.

Salaries for specialists are in line with market rates for those skills.

Locations

With branches throughout England and Wales, opportunities may occur anywhere and graduates must be prepared to move around the country at not infrequent intervals to develop their careers. Graduates in Barclays Bank International must contemplate spending the bulk of their careers abroad after an initial training period in London.

Management Services Department is based in Knutsford, Cheshire, Group Economics Department in Poole, Dorset and Business Research Section, in the City of London.

Further information

Selection procedure includes first interviews at universities and head office in January and February, and second interviews at head office in March and April. The booklet, *Barclays Plan for Graduates*, and application forms can be obtained from careers advisory services or direct from us.

Our Trust Company will not be recruiting graduates in 1983.

Barr & Stroud
A member of the Pilkington Group

Barr & Stroud are leaders in the world of optronics, lasers and infra-red thermal imagery. With almost a century of experience, the company has a high reputation in the research, development and engineering of a wide range of precision equipment.

Our products range from laser range-finders and IR thermal imagers, and the application of combinations of these instruments in land and waterborne systems, through thermal scanners for medical use to the applications of lasers for industrial and scientific purposes.

Types of graduate required

We offer many opportunities in development and production to graduates in *mechanical engineering, electronics, physics*. There are also openings for postgraduate students in these disciplines and particularly for those with experience in *applied optics*. As demand increases in this rapidly developing field, there are enormous opportunities for the ambitious graduate.

Training

Our training develops the individual so that he/she can assume the responsibilities of a demanding and satisfying career.

Training programmes are arranged to lead to chartered engineer status with the appropriate professional institutions.

While gaining experience, a graduate would be a member of a multi-disciplinary team of engineers and scientists and would be expected to contribute at a high level to the design and development of instrumentation.

Locations

We employ 2,000 people at our main premises, at Anniesland in Glasgow. The second factory, at Strathleven, is engaged in fibre optics production and crystal growing.

Salaries and benefits

Our salaries are competitive and we operate an excellent pension scheme.

Activities
The development, design and manufacture of optical/electronic instruments

Employees
2,000

Location: UK
Scotland

Opportunities
Development engineers; Electronics and mechanical engineers; Quality assurance engineers; Physicists in R&D for fibre optics thin film coating, laser rangefinding, infra-red thermal imaging, lasers for medical and other scientific purposes

Vacancies
15

Application address
Personnel Manager, Barr & Stroud Limited, Caxton Street, Anniesland, Glasgow

Barr & Stroud, cont

You will have 33 days holiday per annum. There are many work based recreations and clubs, and good sports facilities in the vicinity of the factory.

Beecham Pharmaceuticals

Activities
Research, development, production and marketing of human and veterinary prescription medicines and animal health products

Employees
5,500 UK
11,000 worldwide

Locations: UK
London; South East; Home Counties; Scotland

Opportunities
Research and development: chemical, biological, and biochemical scientists; Production and technical: chemical, biological and biochemical engineers, chemists, biochemists and microbiologists; Marketing and sales

Vacancies
50+

Application address
The Graduate Recruitment Officer (Ref DOG 83), Beecham Pharmaceuticals, Beecham House, Great West Road, Brentford, Middlesex TW8 9BD

Beecham Pharmaceuticals is responsible for all Beecham Group's activities in the area of human and veterinary prescription medicines and animal health products. Like all major pharmaceutical businesses, it operates on an international scale and devotes large and continually increasing resources to research and development. Thirty years ago Beecham did not have an ethical pharmaceutical business and as recently as 15 years ago it was still in its infancy. The rate of growth of Beecham Pharmaceuticals and its commitment to fundamental research is underlined by the continuing expansion of its UK research activities.

Since the launching of the first of the semi-synthetic penicillins, Broxil, in 1959, a worldwide marketing organisation has been created, covering more than a hundred countries with manufacturing facilities in south east England, Scotland, USA, Belgium and Singapore.

Pharmaceutical products now include not only penicillins but also non-antibiotic preparations in the fields of antiviral chemotherapy and the treatment of allergy.

The organisation is committed to extensive research and development, new product innovation and modern techniques of production, administration and marketing.

Research opportunities
For graduates who wish to apply their degree subjects directly, our research laboratories in the Home Counties are interested in men and women with good first degrees, as well as those with postgraduate qualifications. These are *organic chemists, biochemists, biologists, microbiologists, pharmacists, pharmacologists* and *veterinary scientists*. Research is organised on a multidisciplinary project group system. This encourages team work and maximum participation by each member and enables decision making to be delegated to the scientists at the bench. The work requires an innovative mind with an ability to plan and carry out experiments and present facts and findings concisely. Potential products which emerge from the research projects are further developed by scientists in new product development departments, before they are finally handed over to production sites.

Technical and production opportunities
Chemists, chemical and *biochemical engineers* and *biological scientists* are recruited into production, process development and quality assurance departments. In production departments graduates join a support team in one of the chemical or fermentation plants, not only to trouble-shoot, but also to optimise and initiate short and long term plans and process modifications. The process development department is involved in developing new processes for potential and existing products and determining optimal reaction conditions. New graduates are given responsibility for one or two specific projects and generally have two or three technicians working with them. Graduates entering quality assurance will undertake the development of new analytical methods for potential products and assist in the improvement of existing analytical techniques. Within the works engineering department *mechanical engineers*, preferably with some industrial experience on a sandwich

course, assist in particular projects, plant modifications and investigations into maintenance problems across the site.

Marketing and sales

These are crucial areas of our business that can present challenging careers for *arts* or *science* graduates who show real aptitude for self expression as well as numeracy. Our products are not advertised to the public and are, for the most part, only available on doctors' or veterinarians' prescription. This requires a close appreciation of doctors' and patients' needs and an ability to meet exacting communication standards. The graduate is given every opportunity to develop these skills and, as a pre-requisite, will gain a thorough knowledge of the market itself and the clinical background and therapeutic qualities of each product.

Training and career development

Graduates are appointed to fill definite vacancies and will acquire the necessary expertise largely through training and experience in the job. Outside courses are used to supplement internal training schemes; it is part of the company's overall policy to provide thorough training in scientific and technical skills and progression into management where appropriate. Early job rotation and short periods of specific training are also organised, as well as appraisal and counselling of staff to ensure their appropriate development.

Locations

The marketing and administrative departments are based at Brentford, Middlesex, with 14 sales regions throughout the UK.

The technical and production departments are located at Worthing, Sussex; Crawley, Sussex; and Irvine, Ayrshire.

The research departments are at Brockham Park, Surrey; Walton Oaks, Surrey; Harlow, Essex; Great Burgh, Surrey; and Worthing, Sussex.

Salaries

Salaries are competitive and are regularly reviewed, related to individual performance and increasing responsibility. Generous fringe benefits that will apply include a non-contributory pension and life assurance scheme and, with our objectives set towards further development for the future, ambitious graduates will find plenty of scope for promotion, within a stimulating working environment.

Literature and more detailed information are available from your careers service or the Graduate Recruitment Officer, Beecham Pharmaceuticals.

Beecham Products

Activities
Manufacturing, marketing and distribution of consumer goods

Employees
12,500 UK
10,000 overseas

Locations: UK
General

Locations: Overseas
Worldwide

Beecham Products is one of the two subgroups that operate worldwide for Beecham Group Ltd. The head office is at Brentford and there are 35 factories, numerous distribution depots in the United Kingdom, and 40 factories overseas. Beecham Products holds a leading position in the research and development, manufacturing, marketing and distribution of food and drink products, cosmetics, toiletries, advertised proprietary medicines and domestic adhesives. A large number of these are nationally known brands and include Ribena, Lucozade and Horlicks; Corona, Hunts and Quosh; Silvikrin, Macleans and Brylcreem; Phensic, Veno's, Germolene, Beecham Pills and Beecham Powders, and UHU Adhesives.

Selling our consumer products through retail outlets relies on the team

Opportunities

Accountancy; Company secretary; Chemistry;
Computer services; Distribution management;
Engineering: chemical, mechanical, electrical;
Marketing; Market research; Personnel;
Production management; Purchasing; Quality
assurance; Research and development; Sales

Application address

The Graduate Recruitment Manager
(ref DOG 83), Beecham Products, Beecham
House, Great West Road, Brentford, Middlesex
TW8 9BD

work and expertise of those within the various functions of the business,
which are backed by sound financial control.

Types of graduate required

We recruit a limited number of graduates each year. Graduates of *any*
discipline are engaged for accountancy, company secretary, computer
services, distribution, marketing, market research and analysis,
personnel, purchasing and sales. More specialised qualifications are
required for production and quality assurance (*chemists, chemical
engineers, mechanical/electrical engineers, food technologists*); and for
product research and development (*biochemists, biologists, chemists, food
scientists, microbiologists, pharmacists*).

Training

Graduates are appointed to fill immediate vacancies and subsequent
development is through planned individual training programmes, based
on job experience, early job rotation, in company and external courses.

Location

The majority of graduates are initially located at Brentford or the Home
Counties, but occasional vacancies occur elsewhere in the UK.

Salaries and prospects

Salaries are competitive and are regularly reviewed, related to
performance, and there are generous fringe benefits including a non-
contributory pension and life assurance scheme. The continued growth
of this successful business provides opportunities for promotion in all
parts of the organisation.

Further literature

The booklet *Careers for Graduates with Beecham Products* is available at
your university careers advisory service or you can get a copy by writing
to the address given.

Applications

For an application form, please apply to your careers office or direct to
the Graduate Recruitment Manager.

B&B

Activities

Development of advertising campaigns,
plus full agency service

Employees

240

Location: UK

London

Opportunities & places

Account management trainees 6

Upper age limit

23

Application address

M Stepan, Graduate Recruitment,
Benton & Bowles Ltd, 197 Knightsbridge,
London SW7 1RP

Benton & Bowles Limited

Benton & Bowles is a highly successful, international advertising agency
with a staff of over 200, and currently bills £42 million. Totally British
managed, B & B is a subsidiary of Benton & Bowles Inc, one of the
largest agencies in the world. Work within the agency covers the
development of advertising campaigns for press, tv, radio and posters as
well as the provision of comprehensive marketing services, including
merchandising, plus all types of research and product development.
Benton & Bowles' accounts include such successful names as General
Foods, Procter & Gamble, Johnson Wax, Sony, Gillette, Jaguar, Thomas
Cook, and Diners Club.

Types of graduate required

We need graduates irrespective of degree course, who can demonstrate a
high degree of intelligence and business-like approach allied with creative
flair. They would eventually be employed as account managers, liaising
between client and agency.

Training

Every individual receives practical and systematic on the job training, as
well as a more formal training programme.

Location
The agency is in Knightsbridge, but work takes members out all over the country.

Salaries
Trainee salaries are competitive. The rate of increase depends on the individual's performance and is usually fast. For the special talents required, there is a most rewarding future.

Bestobell plc

Activities
An international engineering group

Employees
4,600

Locations: UK
South East; Midlands; North East

Locations: Overseas
Europe; Southern Africa; North America; Australia

Opportunities
Sales; Personnel; Marketing; Manufacturing

Vacancies
4

Application address
Mr PGD Naylor, Group Personnel Manager, Bestobell plc, Bestobell House, 16 Bath Road, Slough, Berks SL1 3SS

Bestobell is an international group whose operations cover the UK, Europe, Australia, South and Central Africa, North America and South East Asia.

Bestobell products serve the needs of many industries in the fields of controls, aviation and energy engineering, mainly in the form of: valves, pipeline fittings, boiler liquid level and process controls, temperature controls, air conditioning controls, acoustic enclosures, industrial seals, aircraft components, etc.

Bestobell is successful in world markets because of the diversity and range of its products, the vigour and professionalism of its marketing, the reliability of its technical service and distribution organisation, and the logic of its corporate policy and long term planning approach. It is a reasonably large organisation which preserves the efficiency of small and medium sized units and offers wide scope to the individual, whose career development could include management experience overseas as well as in our UK locations.

Types of graduate required
We are likely to require graduates for marketing for which a *business studies* or *economics* qualification would be most suitable. Graduates in *engineering* disciplines will also be welcomed to apply for vacancies in their respective fields. In each case, we are looking at the person as well as the qualification, in anticipation of the characteristics and potential that will carry you forward in your career.

Training
The usual programme is for you to be given projects and work assignments which allow you to develop experience in a practical situation in preparation for your first permanent appointment. This work may be augmented by specialised courses or further training in specific subject areas, according to the development of interests and preferences. To say that any business is as good as its people may be a cliche, but it is obviously in the interests of our future as well as yours, that you are given full scope to express yourself and to assume responsibility.

Locations
Even without the extra dimension of our many overseas companies, there are a number of alternatives in the UK at Slough, Rotherham, Blackburn or Glasgow, for the commencement of your career with Bestobell.

Further information
Details of our current vacancies and of the salaries, benefits and other tangible aspects of your appointment may be obtained from the Group Personnel Manager.

BHS (British Home Stores) plc

Activities
Multiple group of variety chain stores

Employees
25,000

Locations: UK
General

Opportunities
Store management; Staff management;
Restaurant management; Food management

Vacancies
60

Upper age limit
25

Application address
JMF Cherrie, Personnel Manager (DOG 83),
British Home Stores plc, Marylebone House,
129–137 Marylebone Road, London NW1 5QD

BHS is one of the fastest growing retailing groups in the UK, with over 100 stores in major cities and towns and a planned programme of modernisation to existing stores and the opening of large new stores. Most stores carry a full range of departments covering fashions, knitwear, household goods, lighting, toiletries and food. Public restaurants in selected stores are another feature of the BHS operation.

Types of graduate required
BHS take some 60 graduates a year from *all* disciplines. No specialised qualifications are required as all necessary training and development will be given. Applicants must possess intelligence, initiative, resourcefulness and be willing to accept responsibility at an early stage. Leadership qualities are essential and should be reflected in school or university activities.

Training and career development
All trainees join the 12 month management training programme. It is largely store based, supplemented by various head office courses and designed to give a comprehensive introduction to store management. On successful completion of training, promotion is to section manager. Development at this stage depends upon individual ability. Within two years you should be equipped to take over an assistant store manager's responsibilities and within another two years be well on the path to full store management and a salary of around £8,000 while still in your twenties. Staff management trainees follow a planned development programme which will lead to an appointment as staff manager within two to three years.

Locations
To take full advantage of promotion opportunities trainees are expected to be totally mobile. The store network covers the whole of the UK, Ireland and St Helier, Jersey and a large distribution centre is located at Atherstone in Warwickshire. Head office administration and buying offices are in London.

Salary
Starting salaries depend on age and qualifications and are discussed at interview. They are reviewed regularly and are based on an individual's progress.

Applications and further information
Either contact your local store or write directly to the address given for an application form and management brochure.

BICC plc

Activities
Design, research, manufacture and contracting
in the transmission and distribution of electrical
energy for power and communications

BICC is the parent company of a group of associated companies with complete facilities for design, research, manufacture and contracting in the transmission of electrical energy for power and communications. The group, which is the largest cable organisation in the world, has manufacturing interests in 16 countries and trading connections in over 100. Balfour Beatty joined the BICC Group in 1969 and, with 17,000 employees is currently one of the largest civil, electrical and mechanical engineering concerns in the UK.

Types of graduate required
Electrical, *mechanical* and *civil engineers*, *physicists*, *metallurgists* and *accountants*, are sought for posts in design, research, development,

Employees
53,000

Locations: UK
London; Wales; Midlands; North East; North West; Scotland

Locations: Overseas
Europe; Near East

Opportunities
Engineering trainees: mechanical, electrical, civil; Metallurgists; Physicists; Chemists; Accountancy trainees; Commercial trainees; Systems analysts; Computer programmers

Vacancies
60

Application address
MJ Ackerley, Education Officer, BICC plc, Organisation and Personnel Development, Group Management Centre, PO Box 1, Prescot, Merseyside L34 5SZ

production, accountancy, sales and installation (home and overseas). Graduates enter BICC by either direct entry, graduate traineeship or special training schemes.

Training

Traineeships for engineers and scientists last up to two years. Accountancy recruits take a theoretical and practical training, before appointment as assistant accountants. Subsequently, under a development scheme, staff work in various fields to broaden their experience and fit them for posts in management. Balfour Beatty provide training in site and design work for civil engineers and a smaller number of electrical and mechanical engineers; training leads to membership of the appropriate engineering institution.

Locations

BICC's manufacturing headquarters are in Merseyside. Other main units are located in the Midlands and the South East. Trainees may be required to work in any part of the UK.

Salaries

Salaries are in line with those of other leading engineering companies.

Binder Hamlyn

Activities
Chartered accountancy

Employees
1,400

Locations: UK
General

Opportunities & places
Student accountants 70

Application address
TB Burton, Binder Hamlyn, 8 St Bride Street, London EC4A 4DA

Binder Hamlyn is a an old established but most progressive firm of chartered accountants providing a wide variety of professional services to clients ranging from household names to small private concerns covering the entire business spectrum.

It is London based with regional offices in the British Isles involving 130 partners and about 1,400 staff. The international firm, Binder Dijker Otte & Co, operates in the majority of the major finance centres in the world.

Many myths surround chartered accountancy. One way to check these out is to read our brochure. In it you will find comments from students who have only completed six months with us, students who have qualified and stayed with us as senior staff in the British Isles or on secondment overseas and students who qualified and have become senior executives filling important appointments in finance and industry.

Qualities

In accountancy, your degree discipline is less important than your general ability. You'll need to like people, because it's people we work with and for. You'll need a reasoning mind, because accountancy is a logical exercise in which systems are far more significant than the figures they contain. You'll need to think about and solve other peoples' problems. You'll need the confidence to find out what you don't know and to act on what you do know. You'll need the ability to write clearly and briefly.

Training

At Binder Hamlyn you train to qualify, to pass the graduate conversion course examinations, PEI and PEII. This involves in-house training and an external programme linking periods of full time tutorial education with a correspondence course of study packs and test papers. The aim is to teach the principles underlying accountancy as well as the detail of what to do next. Your degree may exempt you from certain graduate conversion course papers. Throughout your training the partners and senior qualified staff will be taking a personal interest in your progress.

Binder Hamlyn, cont

Prospects

Our brochure shows the average time spent at each grade: three to four years as a student, one to two as a senior, one to two, as a supervisor and so on. It is common knowledge that the first years have to be regarded as an investment. Initial salaries are good, although not high. It is hard work, but the end result can be personally satisfying and financially rewarding, as our brochure shows. Long term prospects depend on individual ambitions and abilities.

How to apply

You can get our recruitment brochure, which gives you detailed information about chartered accountancy and Binder Hamlyn, through your careers service. Otherwise we would like to hear from you direct.

BIS Software Limited

Activities
Developing and implementing computerised systems for financial institutions

Employees 300

Location: UK London

Locations: Overseas
New York; Toronto; Hong Kong; Luxembourg; Singapore; Bahrain; Sydney; Tokyo

Opportunities & places
Trainee programmers 24

Upper age limit 26

Application address
Personnel Manager, BIS Software Limited, York House, 199 Westminster Bridge Road, London SE1 7UT

BIS Software is a young, fast growing international company. Currently employing over 300 permanent professional staff to develop, install and maintain the company's financial systems in international banks, insurance companies and related institutions in 50 countries. New products under development include telecommunications and micro-computer systems.

Types of graduate required
The company seeks graduates of *all* disciplines with a logical and structured approach to solving problems and an interest in the financial industry.

Training and development
Initial introduction and basic programming training will be followed by assignment to development and implementation projects working with experienced teams of consultants. Personal development and performance are reviewed regularly and continuing general and specialist training is given. Advancement in the managerial, technical and sales career paths available within the company is based on competence, record of achievement and demonstrated potential. Rapid promotion to consultant is available to high fliers. Opportunities to travel and relocate abroad occur regularly.

Salaries
Salaries are very attractive and include a profit sharing bonus at consultant level.

BIS Applied Systems Ltd

Activities
A technically oriented information processing management consultancy

Employees
160

BIS Applied Systems is a technically oriented information processing consultancy. Our work consists of such projects as: computer configuration planning, data base strategy and design projects, real time consultancy, planning and production of DP management, procedural and control systems, introduction to client installations of new techniques like structured programming and design, development of complete systems for clients, machine selection, and office automation.

Types of graduate required
We need graduates of *any* discipline, but preferably one in which

Locations: UK
London; Birmingham; Manchester

Locations: Overseas
Australia; Africa; Middle East; Europe

Opportunities & places
Trainee computer consultants   up to 10

Application address
Michael Hunt, Personnel Manager, BIS Applied
Systems Limited, York House, 199 Westminster
Bridge Road, London SE1 7UT

computing is involved, to train as consultants. Approximately one year's computer experience is required outside of academic degree work, and the ability to communicate well verbally and in writing is necessary. This experience may arise from computing work in sandwich course practical assignments or vacation jobs and work prior to the course.

Prospects and career development

Training is via the comprehensive series of courses which we give on a public basis and by working with other experienced consultants on projects. Career prospects are exceptional. Progress to project manager status within the project development activity is possible, with increasing involvement in other areas of consultancy as experience grows. The major benefit to new graduates is the opportunity to be trained early in such techniques as structured programming and project management and the association with people of great experience. The atmosphere in the company is informal, friendly and very professional.

Location

Offices are in London, Birmingham and Manchester. Graduates will commence employment in our London office.

Boase Massimi Pollitt

Activities
Advertising

Employees
150

Location: UK
London

Opportunities
Account planners and managers

Application address
David Cowan, BMP, 12 Bishops Bridge Road,
London W2 6AA

Boase Massimi Pollitt is a young and informal advertising agency with a 1981 turnover of £35 million, mostly on tv. The agency was started only 14 years ago, and has a staff of 150. Among our leading brands are: Smash, Southern Comfort, Quaker Sugar Puffs, Courage Best Bitter, Prize, Toyota, Prestel, Tjaereborg, Fisher Price Toys, Channel Four.

   We lack the usual hierarchies; our structure is based around small teams of creative staff, planners and account managers.

   We offer traineeships in account planning and account management. Although the two jobs are different, both jobs have equal career opportunities and senior positions in the company are filled by people coming up through either discipline. The initial placing of a trainee for account planning or account management depends on the applicants' interest and our judgement of suitability.

Types of graduate required

The academic speciality is largely irrelevant. For account planning graduates who are numerate and who have studied *natural sciences* or degree subjects which have involved *analytical* or *statistical* disciplines are of interest to us. However, this academic background is not essential. Both account planners and account managers will enjoy being busy, taking on new problems and working in an uncertain discipline. We are looking for self starters who will quickly develop the ability to work without close supervision.

Training

By doing the job, initially with a lot of guidance and help.

Salary

The salary opportunities are very good and in the medium term are considerably in advance of what is offered by most major manufacturing companies.

Applications

Send your cv with a covering letter to David Cowan.

BOC Limited

Activities
Industrial, rare and medical gases, engineering, welding, medical equipment, distribution, computer services, and cryogenics

Employees
42,000 worldwide

Locations: UK
General

Locations: Overseas
Worldwide

Opportunities
Engineering; Manufacturing; Computing/systems; Accountancy

Vacancies
20

Application address
Staff Development and Recruitment, BOC Limited, PO Box 39, Great West House, Great West Road, Brentford, Middlesex TW8 9DQ
Tel: 01-560 5166

The BOC Group is a multi-million pound international corporation. The basis of the group's operations in the UK is the production and distribution of industrial, medical and rare gases, supported by major activities in the welding, cryogenics, medical equipment, distribution and vacuum technology industries. To support these businesses BOC Limited has its own information systems department which uses the latest data processing technology.

As a capital intensive engineering business the company relies on an annual intake of a limited number of high quality graduates with analytical, creative and communication skills who will provide the leaders of the future.

Types of graduate required
We require *mechanical, chemical, electrical* and *production engineers* entering by direct appointment positions in design, development, manufacturing, installation and commissioning.

Arts, science, social science, engineering or *business studies* graduates may enter careers in computers and systems. These are indications of the areas in which graduates are appointed, but are by no means fixed. Please check current vacancies at your appointments board before applying to us.

Training and development
BOC sees graduate recruitment as the source of future senior management. As such the graduates development and performance is monitored and a formal appraisal conducted annually. Training both on and off the job is designed to meet the experience and performance standards required, and attempts to give a breadth of exposure during early career.

Those whose performance in early years in the UK proves their long term potential may be attracted to BOC Group's increasing number of overseas secondments and placements, particularly in the gas business.

Salaries and conditions
Starting salaries and progression is very competitive. Benefits are continuously under review.

Boehringer Corporation (London) Limited

Activities
Marketing of biochemicals, diagnostics and laboratory equipment

Employees 100

Locations: UK General

Opportunities & places
Sales representatives 4

Application address
The Sales Manager, BCL, Bell Lane, Lewes, East Sussex BN7 1LG

BCL is a subsidiary of Boehringer Mannheim, a large research orientated diagnostic and biochemical manufacturer. Our progession in the UK market since our founding in 1965 has been such that we are now one of the leading diagnostic companies in the UK.

Opportunities for graduates
Graduates are needed to promote our products to laboratories and research establishments as technical sales representatives. Willingness to travel, and the drive and determination to make a career in a competitive commercial environment are essential pre-requisites of the job. In return a competitive remuneration package, reviewable annually, is offered together with a company car. For further information please contact the Sales Manager at the address given.

The Boots Company plc

Activities
Manufacturing, retailing and marketing of pharmaceuticals, toiletries and fine chemicals

Employees
65,000 UK

Locations: UK
Nottingham and London

Opportunities
Buying; Marketing; Finance; Management services (computer programming); Personnel; Production; Quality control; Research and development; Engineering; Warehousing and distribution; Consumer products development

Vacancies
60

Application address
The Graduate Recruitment Officer, The Boots Company plc, Head Office, Nottingham NG2 3AA

Although Boots is best known for its retail business, behind our public face on the high streets of Britain there is a great deal more than most people realise. We are a major manufacturing organisation backed by research and development with the marketing expertise to make a significant contribution to UK and international trade. Over 14,500 people are employed in the research, manufacture, marketing and distribution of a very wide range of goods including pharmaceuticals, cosmetics, fine chemicals and domestic household products. A multi-million pound investment programme ensures the continued growth of the business and provides a secure base for the future both in the UK and our overseas operations.

The head offices of the company are in Nottingham, where the main factories, warehouses, laboratories and research facilities are also located.

Types of graduate required
Graduates are taken from *all* disciplines: *arts* or *science* for retail marketing, distribution, finance, marketing and marketing research, personnel, and management services; *chemists, pharmacists, biochemists* and *chemical engineers* for pharmaceutical and chemical production; *chemists, pharmacists, biochemists,* and *biologists* for research and development; *chemists* and *pharmacists* for quality control, *chemists, pharmacists* and *biochemists* for consumer products development; *chemical, mechanical* and *electrical engineers* for engineering.

Training
Graduates are appointed to clearly defined posts providing practical training, backed by an introductory course giving graduates a broad outline of the company. During the first two years graduates also participate in short intensive training courses in business techniques and methods.

Location
The majority of vacancies for graduates occur in Nottingham with a few vacancies each year in our merchandise buying offices in London.

Salaries
Initial salary is fixed according to a special graduate scale which is reviewed annually. Subsequent salary will depend on individual progress.

Further literature
Additional information is obtainable from university careers advisory services or on request from the address given.

Applications
Graduate recruitment is organised separately for the industrial and for the retail activities of the company.

During the first two months of 1983 representatives of the company will visit many universities to meet graduates and students in their final year. If you wish to have an interview at this time you should contact your careers advisory service, or write (quoting the reference DOG 83) to the Graduate Recruitment Officer.

The Bowater Organisation
Bowater Building Products and Bowater Freight Services Ltd

Activities
International freight services and building products

Employees
19,875 UK

Locations: UK
General

Locations: Overseas
Europe

Opportunities
Marketing; Sales; Accountancy; Personnel

Application address
Mr TP Kenny, Personnel Director, Bowater Building Products or Bowater Freight Services Ltd, 84 Upper Richmond Road, London SW15 2ST

Bowater is an international, diversified organisation, British in origin and control. Founded in the City of London 100 years ago as a firm of paper merchants, the company has diversified into different areas such as building products and transport.

Due to the policy of the group to move to a management structure based on products and markets rather than on geographic groupings, the Continental interests in building products and freight services have been integrated with those in Great Britain.

Bowater Building Products Limited has recently been formed to incorporate the joinery manufacture and plastic window companies in Britain, France and Germany. In 1981 Bowater Freight Services Limited was formed, incorporating all the companies involved in the forwarding and distribution of raw materials and manufactured goods throughout north west Europe.

Control and management of companies within Bowater Building Products and Bowater Freight Services, though finally resposing in London, is decentralised. There is a very large measure of autonomy for each main trading area and for groups and units within those areas.

Types of graduate required
The number of UK graduate vacancies in Bowater Building Products and Bowater Freight Services is limited and competition is keen. There are, however, opportunities for promotion within these groups or in general management and in specialist areas. There are occasionally opportunities for promotion to posts overseas for those who have proved themselves in this country. Vacancies exist in these expanding groups in marketing, sales, accountancy and personnel.

CT Bowring & Co Ltd

Bowring

Activities
Insurance broking at Lloyd's

Employees
3,000

Locations: UK
General

Opportunities
Trainee Lloyd's insurance broker

Prominent among our activities is insurance broking at Lloyd's of London. In 1980 when the group was bought by Marsh & McLennan Companies, Inc of New York we became a part of the largest insurance broking group in the world.

We operate through three major subsidiary companies. CT Bowring & Co (Insurance) Ltd which is subdivided into General, Energy & Liability and Aviation Divisions; CT Bowring Reinsurance Ltd subdivided into North American, International and Winchester Bowring Divisons; Bowring (UK) Ltd, which has responsibility for UK clients (excepting aviation and marine business).

Some 2,000 staff are in the City of London. A further 1,000 are employed in the 15 or so companies within Bowring (UK) which operate from major industrial and commercial centres outside London.

Opportunities for graduates
Insurance is a service industry and is dependant especially on the skills and personal qualities of those it employs. It is a demanding environment, but for the individualist, for the person with a flair for negotiation and especially the ability to get on well with people, it offers a career full of opportunity. Training on the job is augmented by internal and external courses in insurance and reinsurance. After the initial learning period, promotion opportunities can develop rapidly.

Vacancies in 1983 will be few and will be notified to careers services when they occur.

Bradford & Bingley Building Society

Activities
Providing a wide range of savings, investment and mortgage facilities

Employees
1,600

Locations: UK
General

Opportunities
Management trainee

Upper age limit
28

Application address
Staff Department, Bradford & Bingley Building Society, PO Box 2, Main Street, Bingley, West Yorkshire BD16 2LW

The Bradford & Bingley is one of the country's largest and fastest growing building societies, with over 1,600 employees and a network of nearly 200 branches covering the whole country. Head office is in Bingley, West Yorkshire.

Management trainee scheme

Opportunities for graduates to join the management trainee scheme occur on an ongoing basis, as existing management trainees are promoted. The scheme is intended primarily to develop the society's future branch managers and training and career progression to management status is therefore through the branch network.

A branch career offers the potential for promotion up to senior executive level. However, occasional opportunities do exist for transfer to head office managerial and specialist appointments, for those with successful branch careers. In addition a small number of management trainees are offered secondments in head office as part of their training.

All management trainees are expected to study for professional examinations as a condition of entry to the scheme and in addition they must be prepared and able to relocate geographically in order to take advantage of the career progression planned for them.

Work in the society's branch environment requires the ability to deal competently and confidently with customers and professional connections in what has become a very competitive market. Promotion to a supervisory appointment occurs after approximately 18 months and management trainees joining straight from university, can expect to reach a management appointment in their late 20s.

Applications

Applications are welcome at any time from graduates with good class honours degrees (in *any* discipline), provided the applicant will be able to start work within a short period.

Apply, in your own handwriting, and include a good photograph (which will be returned), to the Staff Department.

Brebner, Allen & Trapp

Activities
Chartered accountancy

Employees
120

Locations: UK
London and South East

Opportunities & places
Student accountants 10

Application address
Staff Partners, Brebner, Allen & Trapp, 107–111 Baker Street, London W1M 2BH

Brebner Allen & Trapp was founded in central London in 1934. By organic growth, acquisition and merger it has become a firm of 14 partners and 120 staff. It has offices in Baker Street, London; Tunbridge Wells, Kent; Aylesbury, Bucks; Fleet, Hants; Plymouth, Devon and Hove, Sussex.

Much of the firm's achievements has been based on the close professional relationships established for each client whose work is under the supervision and control of one or more partners. Specialist partners who control the taxation, audit and trust departments, support the general partners in the fulfilment of their professional responsibilties. The firm's computer installation serves both its own accounting and financial requirements and those of many of its clients.

Clients

The range of clients is well spread in the UK and there are extensive audit responsibilities for clients with interests in the USA and Europe. In addition to a number of publicly quoted companies, the firm acts for many substantial private companies and personal interests in all type of industry, commerce and professional practice.

Brebner, Allen & Trapp, cont

Staff

Staff salaries, regularly reviewed are competitive, based on market rates and rise rapidly according to ability and performance.

The firm's fully staffed training centre in North London provides trainee students with comprehensive training and in-house courses and has developed a course of structured programmes providing continuing professional education courses for qualified staff.

Prospects

Brebner, Allen & Trapp and associated firms provide a challenging and rewarding career to all levels of staff from postgraduate trainees to the newly qualified in both specialist and general professional fields. Prospects for managership and local partnership are particularly good in the out of London offices.

Brewer & Co

Activities
Audit, accountancy and taxation services for companies and individuals

Employees 60

Locations: UK London and South East

Opportunities & places
Trainee chartered accountants 5

Application address
HAT, 16 Red Lion Square, London WC1R 4QH

We are a medium sized firm with offices in London, Guildford and Cranleigh, Surrey. We provide a personal and individual service for our clients who range from public companies to private individuals.

Training

We are members of a group training scheme known as HAT Training Syndicate (see entry under HAT). This provides a comprehensive training programme covering both practice techniques and the professional exams, the course fees for which are paid for by the firm.

Brian Ingram Associates

Activities
Trainee chartered accountant recruitment for 7 medium sized firms

Location: UK
London

Opportunities & places
Student accountants 110–120 for September also 7 for January intake

Application address
John Morgan, Brian Ingram Associates, 26 Spencer Drive, London N2 0QX
Tel: 01-458 9188

Brian Ingram Associates recruits trainee chartered accountants on behalf of seven medium sized chartered accountancy firms in central London. This is the fourth year of this service, which is available free to students. We co-ordinate interviews and recruitment at universities and in London, and a successful first interview should lead to second interviews with several firms. The firms we represent are Safferys, Pridie Brewster, Russell Limebeer, Kingston Smith, Wood King, Harold Everett Wreford and Jeffreys Henry Rudolph & Marks. Each have about 12–16 partners and 110–160 staff, with clients ranging from small family businesses to large public companies.

Training and experience

Each firm has training arrangements which combine in-house and external courses usually at ATC or FT. Training includes practical experience of taxation and accountancy as well as the auditing of large companies; partners take a personal interest.

Types of graduate required

Applications are invited from graduates of *all* disciplines. Personal qualities are highly valued and numeracy is useful.

Further information

See our brochure and video cassette at your careers service and apply to John Morgan with the university standard introductory form.

British Aerospace – Dynamics Group

Activities
Design and manufacture of guided weapons
systems, space satellites, infra-red and laser
systems plus other high technology systems

Employees
17,000

Locations: UK
South East; South West; North West

Opportunities
Engineers: electronic, electrical, mechanical,
control, production, aeronautical; Physicists;
Mathematicians; Computer scientists; Business
studies; Economists; Materials scientists

Application address
Group Graduate Recruitment Officer, British
Aerospace – Dynamics Group, Site A,
Six Hills Way, Stevenage, Herts

The group combines the total resources and experience of companies that
have established themselves as leaders in the fields of guided missile
design, space engineering and associated high technology projects for
over a quarter of a century. These companies now form a partnership that
is unsurpassed in its technical capability and its resolve to maintain its
lead in the future.

Each year we need to recruit newly qualified engineers and scientists to
provide a sound, structured organisation with which to meet the
increasing challenge of modern technology.

Our projects are complex and varied, ranging from guided missile
systems to plastics technology, from communications and scientific
satellites to oceanographic equipment, from infra-red and laser
technology to automatic test equipment.

The Dynamics Group has an order book which reflects confidence in
its ability to meet the demands of it's customers both nationally and
internationally.

Locations
The group has design, development and production facilities in
Hertfordshire (two factories at Stevenage and one in Hatfield), Bristol
and near Bolton, Lancashire.

Entry and training
Most vacancies that occur are for direct entry graduates. After a short
induction period a programme is established which will include any
specialist training or courses considered necessary and thus provide a
logical and progressive development of experience.

The work
The sort of work upon which you will be engaged will be relevant to your
studies, your interests and ambitions but equally it is governed by our
needs and ability to determine, through mutual discussion, how best the
group can utilise your particular skills. The choice is wide: research and
development, production, management services, quality assurance or
other specialist activities.

If you are an electronics engineer you may join a team working on the
development of guidance and control systems of a guided missile or
designing circuits and sensors for a satellite. The mathematician may be
concerned with theoretical design and assessment studies or developing
mathematical models of complete systems; or be concerned with
computer systems design, programming or scientific engineering data
processing.

The opportunities are similar for the aeronautical and mechanical
engineer, computer scientist, physicist and other required disciplines.

Types of graduate required
We are looking for graduates in *electronic, electrical, control, mechanical*
and *aeronautical engineering, physics, mathematics* and *computer science*.
There are also a few vacancies for *materials scientists* and people with
commercial and production qualifications. If you are of any *scientific*
discipline but feel that your background may be of interest to us please
make enquiries direct to the address in the margin.

Graduates interested in approaching British Aerospace – Aircraft
Group should apply to the Graduate Recruitment Officer, British
Aerospace – Aircraft Group, Hatfield – Chester Division, Hatfield,
Hertfordshire.

Salaries
Our starting salaries are continuously under review and are based on

British Aerospace – Dynamics Group, cont

qualifications and experience. (The average for 1982 graduates was over £6,000 per annum.)

Applications
The group will be visiting many universities and polytechnics in the spring term and you should make arrangements to meet us through your careers and advisory service. Should we not be visiting your particular university we would welcome direct application and you should write to the address given in the margin.

British Airports

Activities
Ownership and management of airports

Employees
7,200

Locations: UK
South East and Scotland

Opportunities
Electrical, electronic, mechanical and civil engineering; Commercial development and management; Airport planning

Vacancies
Up to 10

Upper age limit
25

Application address
The Graduate Recruitment Officer, Personnel, Head Office, British Airports, Gatwick Airport, West Sussex RH6 0HZ

British Airports own and manage seven major UK airports: Heathrow (the world's busiest international airport), Gatwick, (the fastest growing airport in Europe), Stansted, Glasgow, Edinburgh, Prestwick and Aberdeen.

We are a successful and profitable publicly owned organisation with a brief to maintain and develop the airport facilities needed for both the present and the future and also to operate our airports on a commercial basis.

What types of graduate are we looking for?
Primarily engineering graduates; as the increasing sophistication of airport facilities demands specific skills in *electrical, electronic, mechanical* and *civil engineering*.

The engineering department is responsible for the design and construction of our multi-million pound development programme which includes establishing Terminal 4 at Heathrow, and the expansion of Gatwick and Stansted airports. In addition, the department undertakes a significant amount of maintenance and upgrading on existing airport facilities.

From day one you will be assigned to a challenging role on one of our current projects and you will also follow a planned programme designed to give a broad understanding of our engineering work. We will also provide the training needed to comply with the requirements of the appropriate professional institution and give you every encouragement to achieve the status of chartered engineer.

In addition, we may also recruit a select number of graduates to train for general management positions. Your degree discipline is less important than your personal characteristics. It is essential that you are numerate, and decisive with the ability to sell your ideas to staff at all levels.

The next step
If you would like to know more about British Airports please either contact your careers advisor or write to us directly. Please note, however, that our closing date for all applications is 31 January 1983.

British Airways

British airways

British Airways, the national airline of Great Britain, operates a fleet of some 200 aircraft and carries over 16 million passengers annually, plus a quarter of a million tonnes of freight and mail on international and domestic networks.

The airline's 42,000 employees earn in excess of £1,500 million pa, half

Activities
Civil air transport

Employees
42,000

Location: UK
London

Opportunities
Management and computer trainees

Application addresses
BATS: British Airways Trainee Scheme, PO Box
10, Heathrow Airport, Hounslow TW6 2JA
BACTS: British Airways Computer Trainee
Scheme, PO Box 10, Heathrow Airport,
Hounslow TW6 2JA

of which comes from overseas. Graduate and graduate level entrants are
needed to meet future demands throughout the airline. British Airways is
a complex and highly sophisticated organisation made up of a number of
operating divisions and service departments. The four main divisions are
commercial, flight operations, operations and engineering. Service
departments include legal, finance, public relations, personnel, planning
and management services.

Training
British Airways is offering two training schemes: the British Airways
trainee scheme for administrative and managerial careers, and the British
Airways computer trainee scheme for a specialist training in computer
programming.

The British Airways trainee scheme
The objective of this scheme is to recruit and train an appropriate
number of high calibre graduates and graduate level entrants to help meet
forecast future needs for senior airline management throughout British
Airways. Vacancies could be throughout a wide range of areas, and
entrants will be given a comprehensive induction to British Airways in
preparation for appointment in their chosen job area.

Types of graduate required
The scheme is open to all graduates including mature graduates and
graduate level entrants. Degrees could be in *any* discipline for the
majority of posts, although some specialisms may be required, eg
catering. Applications are also welcome from short service commissioned
officers participating in the industrial career scheme.

Applications
Actual areas where vacancies are likely to occur have not yet been
identified, but further information will be available in the new year.
Candidates from universities and colleges should check the details nearer
the date with their careers advisory service; other candidates should write
direct to the address given.

The British Airways computer trainee scheme
The British Airways computer trainee scheme provides opportunities to
graduates, offering them a nine-month course leading to interesting and
progressive career openings.

As the computer network is vital to its worldwide operation, British
Airways has installed one of the biggest installations outside the USA.

Computers are used in almost every aspect of airline operations from
reservations and engineering to timetable production and accounting.

The most up to date system development techniques are used
including real-time processing, data-base methods, word processing and
structured programming.

The formal training lasts nine months and involves an initial
programming course followed by on the job training within one of our
project teams. During the second phase a tutor is assigned to provide
personal guidance and assistance.

Types of graduate required
British Airways will welcome applications from graduates or holders of
equivalent qualifications of *any* discipline who will be leaving full time
education next summer or who have already had postgraduate
experience. Applicants should have a genuine interest in computing and
should be able to communicate effectively both verbally and in writing.

Applications
The closing date for receipt of applications is 31 January 1983.

British Airways, cont
Candidates from universities and colleges should check the details with their careers advisory service; other candidates should write direct to the address given.

British Gas Corporation

BRITISH GAS

Activities
Distribution and marketing of gas and gas appliances

Employees
106,000

Locations: UK
General

Opportunities
Engineering; Computer; R&D; Finance; Marketing and sales; Management services; Purchasing; Personnel; Secretariat

Application addresses
See main text

British Gas is making an important contribution to the life of the community by helping to meet Britain's vital energy needs. Within the space of 10 years, the British gas industry has been transformed from a traditional coal based industry, via oil gasification and liquefied natural gas imports, into an industry committed to indigenous natural gas. Sophisticated techniques from many disciplines have been introduced to meet the challenge of a new technology.

Functional organisation

Through our 12 regions, we service and supply over 15½ million customers. The regions deal with the day to day affairs which directly affect the customer, such as the sales of gas and appliances, servicing and local gas distribution. Headquarters is more concerned with national matters, research and development and bulk transmission of gas through high pressure pipelines.

Extensive training facilities exist as part of a continuing career development programme. This training may be on the job supplemented by formal courses, or through secondment to gain experience in other related areas of work. It is our policy to provide opportunities for employees, in appropriate cases, to take courses of further education related to their work and personal development within British Gas and every encouragement is given to obtaining professional qualifications. Education and training is normally discussed at employment interviews. Promotion is from within wherever possible, vacant and new posts are advertised throughout British Gas before appearing in the press.

Applications

To find out more about us and our current vacancies please contact your careers advisory service. Each British Gas region is responsible for its own recruitment, selection and training. Applications should be made directly to the Graduate Recruiter, Personnel Department of the region or regions in which you would prefer to work. Only applicants interested in headquarters (including research and development) vacancies should send applications to the British Gas HQ.

Application forms can be obtained from your careers advisory service or from our regional offices. Alternatively, in cases of difficulty, standard introduction forms may be used.

Scottish Gas, *Granton House, 4 Marine Drive, Edinburgh EH5 1YB*
Northern Gas, *PO Box 1GB, Newcastle upon Tyne NE99 1GB*
North West Gas, *Welman House, Altrincham WA15 8AE*
NEGAS, *New York Road, Leeds LS2 7PE*
EMGAS, *PO Box 145, De Montfort Street, Leicester LE1 9DB*
West Midlands Gas, *Wharf Lane, Solihull B91 2JP*
Wales Gas, *Snelling House, Bute Terrace, Cardiff CF1 2UF*
Eastern Gas, *Star House, Mutton Lane, Potters Bar, Herts EN6 2PD*
North Thames Gas, *North Thames House, London Road, Staines, Middlesex TW18 8AE*
SEGAS, *Katharine Street, Croydon CR9 1JU*
Southern Gas, *80 St Mary's Road, Southampton SO9 5AT*
South West Gas, *Riverside, Temple Street, Keynsham, Bristol BS18 1EQ*

British Gas HQ, *Management Training and Development Department,
59 Bryanston Street, Marble Arch, London W1A 2AZ.*

British Linen Bank Limited

Activities
Merchant banking

Employees
110

The British Linen Bank which is the largest merchant bank in Scotland,
is the merchant banking arm of the Bank of Scotland group.

The bank does not normally recruit direct from university preferring
to utilise those graduates who have initially joined the Bank of Scotland
and gained a good grounding in domestic banking.

See under Bank of Scotland for graduate entry.

The British National Oil Corporation

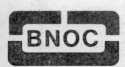

Activities
Exploration, production and trading of oil and oil
related products

Employees
2,500+

Locations: UK
London and Scotland

Opportunities
Engineering; Petroleum engineering; Drilling;
Exploration; Computing

Vacancies
50 approx

Upper age limit
29–30

Application address
The Graduate Recruitment Co-ordinator, The
British National Oil Corporation, 150 St Vincent
St, Glasgow G2 5LJ

The British National Oil Corporation was established in 1976 to
safeguard the nation's interest in the development of Britain's oil
resources. The corporation is engaged in a programme of exploration,
development and production operations and petroleum trading both at
home and overseas. From an initial staff of five people there are now over
2,500 employees of whom nearly 50% are graduates or professionally
qualified.

The Government has recently announced its intention to introduce
private sector capital into the exploration, development and production
activities of the corporation. When legislation, introduced into
Parliament at the end of 1981, has been passed, the Government intends
that these activities will be carried on under the name of a new private
sector company, to be called BRITOIL. The trading activities will
continue to be carried out by the 100% Government owned corporation.

Exploration
This is a rapidly expanding area of the corporation's development, both
alone and in partnership with other companies. BNOC is now the leading
explorer in the United Kingdom Continental Shelf (UKCS).

The exploration division employs a large number of geologists and
geophysicists as well as those trained in computers and librarianship.

Development and production
In 1976, BNOC took over the development of the Thistle oil field. The
complex development necessary to make this field productive has rapidly
expanded the corporation's experience and skills. In 1979 the corporation
took over the operatorship of the Beatrice oil field, which came on stream
in late 1981, as well as an integrated terminal system at Nigg Bay. In mid
1980 the decision was announced to proceed with the development plans
for the Clyde Field discovered in 1978.

Petroleum trading
BNOC began crude oil sales in 1978. It is the major UK oil trader with
access to about two-thirds of the two million barrels produced each day
from the UKCS. The corporation trades in gas from the Viking field and
has begun bulk product operating in liquid petroleum gas and fuel oil.

Types of graduate required
Exploration: *Geology, geophysics, physics with geology.*
Petroleum engineering: *Petroleum engineering, mining, chemical, civil or
mechanical engineering, physics, maths* and *geology.*
Engineering: *Civil, mechanical, electrical, electronic* and *chemical
engineering, naval architecture* and *maths.*

GRADUATES

British Nuclear Fuels Limited is the energy provider to the nuclear industry. The task of meeting international needs for nuclear fuel is a challenge to the professionals we employ in process development, instrument and plant design, manufacturing control, administration and commercial management. The continuous development of our process and administration techniques provides a stimulating environment for our graduate entrants together with genuine room for growth and career development.

With our expansion programme well underway we require more qualified people.

Each of our 5 locations has its own speciality and although a graduate may join any site the opportunity exists to move around within the Company. Scope for career development is a common factor throughout.

RISLEY

Risley near Warrington in Cheshire is the location of the Headquarters of British Nuclear Fuels Limited.

This is our Design and Administration H.Q. where mechanical, chemical and electrical/instrument engineers chemists, mathematicians and metallurgists evolve the conceptual designs for Company plant and equipment.

The Administration function is directly concerned with the business of organising and running the Company as a commercial enterprise.

SELLAFIELD

The site of our major expansion programme, Sellafield Works in Cumbria provides a comprehensive fuel reprocessing facility to both U.K. and overseas customers. The site also operates a 200 MW nuclear power station.

A major new chemical reprocessing plant is being built, incorporating the latest developments in remote process control systems, computer based analytical devices and sophisticated switching and operating systems.

WHERE DO YOU FIT IN AT BNFL?

We have career openings for graduates in Chemical, Mechanical and Electrical Engineering, for Physicists, Chemists, Metallurgists and Mathematicians. We also have one or two vacancies for graduates of other disciplines.

Starting salaries in excess of £6,000 will be offered to the right candidates. We provide excellent further training and encourage all our graduates to obtain professional status. Individually tailored training programmes are provided which will enable graduates to satisfy the corporate membership requirements of their appropriate institution.

If you want to make the most of your future in the security of a Company which is a world leader in a rapidly developing technology, why not write to Mrs. Karen Walkden Graduate Recruitment Section, British Nuclear Fuels Limited, Risley, Warrington, Cheshire WA3 6AS.

SPRINGFIELDS

Our Springfields Works, near Preston, is the fuel manufacturing site of British Nuclear Fuels.

The range of products includes intermediate chemicals like Uranium Hexafloride and Uranium Dioxide and finished fuel elements for reactors in the UK and Overseas.

The processes include relatively heavy chemical processes, metallurgical and ceramic processes, component manufacturing and light engineering assembly.

CHAPELCROSS

Commissioned in 1959, this location near the Solway Firth is the site of Scotland's first nuclear power station. It comprises 4 Magnox reactors and employs graduates on plant operations, development, maintenance, technical and safety studies, production programming and health physics.

commissioning and development. Areas of development include instrumentation and control, electrical drive mechanisms and engineering physics.

Construction is underway of a large centrifuge plant with work phased over a 3 year period at a cost of about £150 million.

CAPENHURST

This is our uranium enrichment plant near Chester where engineers are employed in centrifuge manufacture,

BNFL

For an infinitely brighter future

The British National Oil Corporation, cont

Drilling: *Mechanical, mining, civil, petroleum* and other *engineeering* based services.
Computer services: *Computing, physics, mathematics, business studies, physical sciences, engineering science.*

Graduate training schemes
Schemes are available for: all engineering disciplines including petroleum engineering (for petroleum and non-petroleum engineering graduates), geology, geophysics and computing leading to membership of appropriate professional institutes.

Starting salaries are determined in January of each year. Other benefits include a relocation package available to graduates and membership of BUPA.

The number of vacancies varies; a detailed list is available from university careers advisory services.

UK operations
The management functions and services are in Glasgow (head office); the operational shorebase for offshore activities is in Aberdeen; relations with Government and crude oil trading is in London.

Overseas operations
The overseas operations are expanding and further active exploration has taken place during 1982. This involvement includes among other things consultancy and advisory services as well as staff exchange schemes.

Selection procedure
Pre-visits to universities take place in October to December each year. Early in 1983 we will be visiting universities and colleges for a first interview. Final interviews will take place at the Glasgow headquarters or Aberdeen offices. For further information and a graduate brochure please contact the Graduate Recruitment Co-ordinator at the address given.

British Nuclear Fuels Limited

Activities
Provides a complete nuclear fuel service for reactor operators throughout the world

Employees
16,000 +

Locations: UK
North West; Scotland

Opportunities
Mechanical engineers; Chemical engineers; Chemists; Physicists; Metallurgists and electrical/instrument engineers; Occasionally vacancies in administrative fields

Vacancies
50

Application address
Karen Walkden, Graduate Recruitment Officer, (grad/83/DOG), British Nuclear Fuels Limited, (Freepost), Risley, Warrington, Cheshire WA3 1BR
Tel: 0925 35953

BNFL, a Government owned company, provides and recycles all the fuel for Britain's nuclear power programme. Already possibly the biggest single producer of nuclear fuels in the world. BNFL has an expanding export business and with energy sources of all kinds at a premium, has embarked on a heavy capital investment programme to meet the growth in demand.

An introduction
BNFL has been manufacturing and reprocessing nuclear fuels for over a quarter of a century.

Our ever increasing export market and our substantial contribution to the UK electricity generating boards has necessitated an extensive programme of plant modifications and expansion throughout the company. In excess of £3,500 million will be invested over the next 10 years.

Our activities
We employ over 16,000 people in the provision and sale of nuclear fuel services, which include the conversion and enrichment of uranium based fuels and the reprocessing of irradiated or spent nuclear fuel.

Our needs
We require ambitious, self-motivated graduates with first and second

class honour degrees to take on substantial roles within the company.

We need: *mechanical engineers, chemical engineers, electrical/instrument engineers, physicists, chemists, mathematicians, metallurgists,* and occasionally *arts* graduates.

A place to work

The company is organised on a divisional basis and is spread throughout the North West on five sites, each requiring specialists to deal with its particular process. The company does not restrict people to any one site; graduates are encouraged to move from one site to another, building up both experience and versatility within the industry.

Our head office

The head office is directly concerned with the business of organising and running the company as a commercial enterprise. As well as policy making, design, planning, finance, marketing and sales, other areas covered include procurement, accounting and audit, personnel management, and other specialist management services.

Our fuel division

Fuel manufacture is centred at our Springfields Works, near Preston, where metal or oxide fuel elements are produced from natural ore, from enriched material or from material recycled and enriched after previous use. Intermediate products such as uranium oxide and uranium hexafluoride are also supplied for export.

Our enrichment division

Uranium is enriched at our Capenhurst Works, near Chester, by the latest gas centrifuge plant which is being further developed and extended. The process is employed to enrich either natural uranium, or uranium which has been recycled after use as reactor fuel. Development and manufacture of centrifuge machines is also an important activity.

Our reprocessing division

The reprocessing of used nuclear fuel is carried out at Sellafield on the Cumbrian coast. The purpose is first to separate for our future use in fast reactors the plutonium which is created during irradiation, second to recover uranium for recycling, and third to ensure that the safe storage or disposal of the waste. An extensive technical development and support programme is aimed at the continuing improvement of processes.

We provide excellent further training and encourage all our graduates to obtain professional status. Individually tailored training programmes are provided to enable engineers to satisfy the corporate membership requirements of their professional institutions.

Our salaries are excellent: the promotion opportunities superb. We are able to offer an opportunity to be part of the brightest future currently available in engineering, scientific development and technological innovations anywhere in the UK today.

Applications

For an application form, please telephone Graduate Recruitment on Warrington (0925) 35953 or send a postcard stating the subject of your degree to the address given.

Activities
Rail and sea passenger transport, freight distribution, ancillary services and business

Employees
230,000

Locations: UK
General

Locations: Overseas
Worldwide

Opportunities
Computing; Engineering; Estate management; Finance and accountancy; Operations; Personnel; Marketing; Research and development; Operational research

Vacancies
150

Upper age limit
28 normally

Application address
Apply to your careers service except unemployed graduates who should apply direct to: Management Recruitment Officer, British Railways Board, Rail House, PO Box 100, Euston Square, London NW1 2DZ

British Rail

British Rail is an industrial organisation of separate businesses– passenger, parcels, freight, engineering, shipping, hotels, catering and property – interdependent one upon the other and using the common resources of manpower, finance, land and equipment. They employ about 230,000 persons at a variety of locations throughout the whole country.

Types of graduate required and training

Graduates in *any* discipline to train for management posts in the operations, marketing, personnel, and finance departments; graduate *engineers* for civil, mechanical, electrical and electronic, and signal and telecommunications engineering departments, to train for membership of the appropriate professional engineering institution. Graduates in *estate management* or other suitable subjects to train for management positions with the British Rail Property Board. Graduates in *mathematics, statistics, science, technology* or *economics* associated with mathematics or statistics, for direct entry into the the operational research division. Graduates in *engineering, science,* and *technology* for direct entry to the research and development division. Graduates of *mathematics, statistics* or *computer science* for appointments as computer programmers.

In the operations field graduates are given a broad training in railway operating, commercial and financial work with a view towards an initial appointment following training at the area management level.

In the personnel and marketing fields training is given of a specialist nature following a broad introduction to the day to day running of the railway.

Graduates entering the financial training scheme attend sandwich courses to prepare for membership of a professional accountancy body.

Salaries and prospects

Salaries during training are within the range £5,200–£6,700 a year. Salaries for direct appointments range from £6,000–£7,500 a year. according to qualifications and experience. Salaries are reviewed annually and it is possible that the figures quoted may not represent the salaries payable when those selected in 1983 take up their appointments.

Further information

British Rail have contact officers in most universities and colleges. These are senior managers, invariably former graduate trainees, who will advise you on graduate opportunities with British Rail. Your careers advisor will give details of his/her name and address or other specialist advisers.

British Rail operates a vigorous programme of career development and men and women of real ability can look forward to a rewarding and satisfying career.

The British Ship Research Association

Activities
Research and development in ship design and shipbuilding methods

The British Ship Research Association (BSRA) is the co-operative research organisation for the United Kingdom shipbuilding industry. Although not part of British Shipbuilders the two organisations work closely together on a programme of research and development. In addition, the association undertakes contracts for other sponsors, including the Government, and carries out a growing amount of consultancy work on a commercial basis.

Employees
250

Location: UK
North East

Opportunities & places
Research officers 6 approx

Application address
Miss C Fish, Personnel Assistant, British Ship Research Association, Wallsend Research Station, Wallsend, Tyne and Wear NE28 6UY Tel: 0632 625242

The British Ship Research Association, cont

Types of graduate required
We look for graduates from a number of disciplines including *naval architecture* and *marine engineering, computer scientists, mathematicians,* and *engineering*. Occasionally there are vacancies for *physicists, metallurgists* and specific *engineering* disciplines, such as *electronic engineers*.

Training and career development
Graduates are recruited to a specific project team and are, therefore, expected to make a real contribution at an early stage in their career. A naval architect may join a project researching into the problem of noise and vibration on board ship. A computer scientist could be involved in a project in a number of areas ranging from computer aided design to the automisation of ship control systems.

BSRA supports and encourages its staff to take further degrees and courses as it is essential for a research association that individuals keep up with developments in their own and related fields.

New graduates are recruited as research officers. Promotion through the grades depends on the individual's own performance and aspirations and the contribution he or she makes to each project they work on.

Salaries
We offer a competitive salary which will be reviewed in two ways each year, once on an across the board basis and once in a merit way as a result of your own performance. In addition we offer the full range of benefits you would expect from a forward thinking employer including five weeks holiday, free lunch facilities, and sports and social clubs.

Further information
If you want further information which includes notes on the type of work we do, or you want to apply to join us please contact Miss Cathy Fish at the address given.

Activities
Warshipbuilding; Merchant shipbuilding; Marine engineering; Ship repair; General engineering; Offshore engineering

Employees
67,000

Locations: UK
General

Opportunities
Ship design; Marine, electrical, mechanical engineering; Production engineering; Production management; Commercial management

Application address
Chief Training Officer, British Shipbuilders, Benton House, 136 Sandyford Road, Newcastle upon Tyne NE2 1QE

British Shipbuilders

Shipbuilding is a major industry and a constant flow of new ships are being designed and built in our yards by methods ranging from adaptions of traditional craft skills to the application of many aspects of modern engineering and marine technology.

British Shipbuilders is a state corporation with a central responsibility for the majority of shipbuilding and marine engine building activities in the UK. Many famous shipyards with historic associations and worldwide reputations are now part of this lively shipbuilding enterprise which is looking to the future. Some of the more historic traditions and attitudes may have to be broken in the process, but the future is bound to provide the excitement of both competition and challenge. Above all, the future depends, as it always has, on the energies, skills and commitment of a wide range of people.

Types of graduate required
There are opportunities for graduates in *marine, mechanical, electrical, offshore* and *production engineering, naval architecture, nautical studies, computer sciences, physics, mathematics, accountancy, law, economics* and *business studies* to build their careers in British shipbuilding.

Training scheme
Before and since nationalisation, several of British Shipbuilders' subsidiary companies operated graduate training schemes to meet their own requirements. Our intention is to take the best of such practices and

use them as a basis for the corporation's scheme. This allows the industry to build on its experience of graduate training and develop a scheme to suit the needs of graduates, the individual subsidiaries and the corporation as a whole.

In general, graduates are recruited for a traineeship which satisfies the requirements of the relevant professional institution. In the case of engineers the basic training requirements for chartered status are satisfied as a minimum condition. The training programmes are organised such that the trainees have the opportunity to gain experience in different parts of the industry and give them an insight into the range of careers available.

It is expected that during the latter part of their training, the graduates will begin to specialise in a particular area which matches both their own aspirations and the needs of the corporation. On completion of the training period, an offer of a suitable and mutually acceptable first appointment should be made.

Salary
Salaries and other terms of employment are competitive with those of other major employers.

The British Standards Institution
Quality Assurance Division

BSI is the national standards making body for the UK and represents this country in the international standards world. Apart from its major task of producing the standards on which industry depends, BSI operates a number of quality assurance services, including product testing, inspection, certification and assessment.

The BSI test house, based in Hemel Hempstead, is known and respected throughout the world for its experience, accuracy and independence. In 14 modern laboratories a wide range of products are tested to national and international standards, and regulations, as well as to client's own specifications. Although well established, the test house is still expanding and has become associated with areas of advanced technology.

Types of graduate required
BSI offers excellent career opportunities to graduates in *physics*, *telecommunications*, *electrical*, *electronic* and *mechanical engineering*. Initial tasks include conducting tests and writing reports but with increasing emphasis on special projects and development work. The sheer variety of work undertaken by the test house provides the necessary scope for graduates to progress in their chosen field.

Prospects
Graduates usually join BSI as technicians or assistant test engineers but promotion comes rapidly for the right people. The test house is growing fast and so the opportunities to advance are excellent.

Further information
To find out more about the BSI test house, or specific vacancies, please write to the Personnel Officer at the address given.

Activities
The testing and assessment of electrical and mechanical products and equipment

Employees
400

Location: UK
South East

Opportunities
Engineering: electrical, electronic, electromedical, physical, telecommunications

Application address
The Personnel Section, British Standards Institution, Maylands Avenue, Hemel Hempstead, Herts HP2 4SQ

In British Steel ....

. . . we have the challenges and opportunities of a major industry and maybe more than our share of problems.

If you feel that you can respond positively to problems and have the intelligence, persistence and determination to succeed, then choosing to work with BSC could be the right career step for you.

We regularly have vacancies in:—

Engineering

Sales and Marketing

Management Services

Production Control

Supplies and Transport

Research

Quality Control

Personnel

Production

Finance

 **British Steel Corporation**

British Steel Corporation

The corporation operates in a tough environment. The international market is severely competitive. Nevertheless BSC manufacturing performance is improving. We are moving ahead firmly and your opportunity is to help run a corporation which is potentially among the most efficient steel producers in the world.

Graduate opportunities

Most graduates join us in areas where there are large scale operations and a diverse range of activities. Graduate entrants can therefore make progress without having to hop around the country; although every opening is publicised throughout the corporation so that you can move locations if you wish.

The objective of graduate training is to get you into a productive job quickly. It will take account of any industrial experience you may have had, for example as a sandwich student, and it will be the first step into a career which could take you far beyond your current plans.

This is an organisation with real problems which needs brains to solve them. Graduates are regarded as the management of the future. Our training and development is designed to make the most of the individual not to standardise. We welcome movement between different functions. The experience is so often profitable to the individual and the corporation.

Application addresses

Applications may be sent to any of the addresses given below. If no suitable vacancies exist at the selected location your application will be referred to other parts of the corporation for further consideration unless you indicate that you do not wish this to be done.

British Steel Corporation, Head Office, 12 Addiscombe Road, Croydon CR9 3JH
British Steel Corporation, Ravenscraig Works, Motherwell, Lanarkshire ML1 1SW
British Steel Corporation, Steel House, Redcar, Cleveland TS10 5QW
British Steel Corporation, Scunthorpe Works, Frodingham House, PO Box 1, Scunthorpe, South Humberside DN16 1BP
BSC Special Steels, PO Box 29, Sheffield Road, Rotherham S60 1DQ
BSC Strip Products Group, Headquarters, Llanwern Works, Newport, Gwent NPT 0XN
BSC Tubes Division, Divisional Training Office, Corby Works, Northants NN17 1UA

British Sugar plc

The company's 13 factories process the UK sugar beet crop and produce half of Britain's sugar. Production capacity has been expanded. The retail brand is Silver Spoon.

The development of process techniques and investment in modern plant and controls is specially attractive to those graduates whose interests lie in this field. As the beet crop is processed during the months September to January, a part of the year is devoted to major maintenance and reconstruction work. All but the more specialised installations are undertaken by corporation factory staff, and opportunities arise for graduates to follow through the construction, installation, commissioning and operation of much of the new plant installed.

Locations: UK
Yorkshire; Midlands; East Midlands

Opportunities & places
Shift superintendent 2–3

Upper age limit
30

Application address
Staff Development Manager, British Sugar plc,
PO Box 26, Oundle Road, Peterborough
PE2 9QU

British Sugar plc, cont

Types of graduate required
Chemical engineers, mechanical and *electrical engineers* are recruited.
Personality and qualities of leadership are important.

Training
A training period of two to three years covering all aspects of the
manufacturing process, maintenance work and experience of technical
headquarters departments and commercial departments.

Locations
Nine factories in the eastern counties, one in the Midlands, one in
Yorkshire, two in the West Country, headquarters at Peterborough.

Salaries
A competitive salary is paid to graduates with no previous industrial
experience, with annual increment during the training period (subject to
legislation). Management staff salaries are reviewed annually, and
progression depends on merit. Membership of the contributory staff
superannuation scheme is a condition of employment.

Prospects
Promotion through line management to senior management and technical
appointments is dependent on merit. Senior appointments where
possible are filled from within the company.

Britoil

Please see under British National Oil Corporation.

John Brown Engineers & Constructors Limited

Activities
International engineering contractors to the
oil/gas, chemical, petrochemical and process
based industries

Employees
2,000

Locations: UK
London and South West

Locations: Overseas
Worldwide

Opportunities
Chemical, mechanical, electrical,
instrumentation engineers

Vacancies
15

In the field of engineering contracting, John Brown Engineers &
Constructors Limited, a British company within the John Brown Group,
are heavily committed to an expanding programme of work on a wide
range of major oil/gas, chemical, petrochemical and other process
projects on a worldwide scale.

With offices in London, Portsmouth and St Albans, we provide a
complete capability from initial feasibility studies through design,
engineering, construction, commissioning and project management
covering: oil gas production processing and transportation; polymers and
plastics; synthetic fibres petrochemicals; agrochemicals; fine chemicals;
inorganic chemicals; detergents; food industry and mineral processing.

Types of graduate required
The nature of our work involves many disciplines and we can, therefore,
provide graduates with exceptional scope to gain valuable experience in
all aspects of our specialist contracting activities. Our present needs are
for graduates with a degree in one of the following *engineering* disciplines:
chemical, mechanical, electrical, and *instrumentation/control.*

Training
Our two year training courses, covering either design or site activities,
will involve you in actual work situations as an integral member of a
project team. You will be given increasing responsibility to enable you to

gain the necessary level of experience and expertise for admission to the
appropriate professional institution.

Prospects

Provided you are able to demonstrate the necessary potential you will be
given every opportunity to develop your career as far as your ability will
take you and if you have the level of skills we are looking for, the
opportunities of promotion into project management are excellent.

Brown & Root (UK) Limited

Brown & Root (UK) Limited is a subsidiary of Brown & Root Inc, of
Houston, USA, one of the world's largest engineering and construction
companies. The company is concerned with engineering and operational
activities throughout Great Britain, Europe and Africa providing clients
with a complete service in engineering design, construction, installation
and project management. Our UK services are principally concerned
with the design, fabrication, installation, commissioning and project
management of both offshore oil and gas platforms and their associated
facilities, and of petrochemical plants throughout Europe and Africa.

Brown & Root (UK) Limited has been concerned with more than 80
platforms installed in the North Sea and is currently working with several
major oil companies on further offshore projects; the company is now
involved in petrochemical plant activities throughout Europe and Africa.

Types of graduate required

There is a continuing requirement for graduates with degrees in *civil/
structural, mechanical, electrical, instrument, naval architectural, chemical/
process* and *materials engineering* who believe that they would both benefit
from and contribute to the offshore industry. Graduates with relevant
degrees are required for materials management, data processing and
administrative training schemes.

Training

The challenge and consequent responsibilities in the marine industry are
considerable and graduates who join Brown & Root are given systematic
and thorough training. Graduates are enrolled on a two-year training
programme which is designed to correspond with the requirements of the
professional institutions. Engineering graduates are encouraged to
pursue chartered engineer status. Starting each September, graduates
gain experience in company systems and procedures in both on and
offshore departments throughout the United Kingdom and the North
Sea operating area. Graduates will not be in a teaching environment but
will further their experience in a practical and productive way and with
rapidly increasing responsibility.

Among the principal locations to which engineering graduates will be
assigned are London: head office (client liaison, offshore technology
studies, sales and contracts work), London: engineering design offices;
Highlands Fabricators Ltd, Scotland (fabrication yard); Aberdeen
(engineering design, client liaison and sales and contracts duties); Great
Yarmouth (fabrication yard); Norway (project offices) and North Sea
platforms and North Sea barge and survey ship duties. There may also be
opportunities to work from our locations in Abu Dhabi, Bahrain and
Rotterdam.

Varied and testing projects extending outside the North Sea area to
include Africa and the Middle and Far East continue to be the keystone
on which Brown & Root bases its graduate training schemes.

Brown & Root (UK) Limited, cont

Further information
If, therefore, your interests are in our field of engineering and you believe
that you could make a contribution to our operations, we would like to
hear from you. Write to us for a company application form or complete a
standard introduction form available from your careers service. Address
your letter to the Graduate Training Officer.

Brush Electrical Machines Ltd

Activities
Manufacture of electrical equipment

Employees
2,400

Location: UK
Loughborough, Leicestershire

Opportunities
Design; Development; Production; Sales
engineering; Accountancy; Management

Application address
The Education and Training Officer, Brush
Electrical Machines Ltd, Falcon Works,
Loughborough, Leics LE11 1HJ

The name of Brush has been associated with power generation and
electrical drives since before the turn of the century. Today, as one of the
major subsidiaries of Hawker Siddeley Group we have maintained and
developed our international reputation for design and performance
standards. Brush diesel and turbine driven generators are produced for
world markets and combine traditional concepts of engineering
workmanship with the ever increasing sophistication of modern power
and generation technology.

Types of graduate required
Graduates in *electrical, electronic, mechanical* or *production engineering* may
be offered training courses which will equip them for specific tasks in
design, development, production or sales engineering. There may also be
opportunities for *computer science* graduates to develop their careers in our
systems departments.

Training
We have established traditions of comprehensive graduate training which
are all approved by the major engineering institutions and are designed to
build on the trainee's qualifications and abilities with a view both to
taking up a specific appointment and to shaping the pattern of his future
career. Movement between various levels of the organisation is a flexible
and continuous process and regular assessments of performance will help
you, and the company, to maximise your career potential and to assume
responsibility.

Further information
For further information and details of our salaries, benefits, extensive
sports and social club amenities, write to the address given.

Burmah Oil plc

Activities
Oil and gas exploration and production;
Lubricants and fuels; Retailing and distribution;
Shipping; Speciality chemicals

Employees
27,000

Locations: UK
General

Locations: Overseas
Worldwide

The Burmah Group is an oil based industrial enterprise consisting of over
200 companies, whose products and services are sold in most countries of
the world. There are five core businesses organised as substantial
free-standing divisions, which are described below.

Exploration and production
The Burmah Oil Company is the longest established British oil company,
having been continuously involved in exploration for and the production
of oil and gas since 1886.
    The group is involved in the UK offshore, Gabon, Sudan, Italy,
Tunisia and the USA. It has specialist teams in the fields of geology,
geophysics, petroleum engineering and drilling engineering.

Lubricants and fuels
Burmah-Castrol is the world's largest specialist lubricants marketing
organisation. The product range includes automotive, industrial, marine,

pplication address
he Recruitment Officer, Burmah Oil Trading
'd, Burmah House, Pipers Way, Swindon, Wilts
N3 1RE

aviation and agricultural lubricants; metal-working fluids; medicinal and technical white oils; plastics and rubber process oils; NDT fluids; brake fluids and anti-freeze.

There are networks for distributing gasoline and other fuels in the UK under the Burmah, Major and Apex brands, and also in Europe.

Burmah-Castrol has subsidiaries or agents in over 30 countries throughout the world; it accounts for a substantial part of the group's turnover and profit, and has about 8,000 employees.

Retailing and distribution

Halfords Ltd is the leading retail company in the UK specialising in car parts, cycles and accessories through a network of 365 shops. Cycles are supplied by Halmanco, manufacturing for Halfords, and by Leonard Newman, which imports and distributes cycles and accessories.

Maccess wholesales auto accessories at eight cash and carry warehouses. The expertise which has been built up in this area has lead to the establishment of a new company, Stax, with a similar operation in the home improvement market.

Shipping

Burmah's shipping activities consist of firstly the transportation of liquid natural gas (LNG) from Indonesia to Japan in eight vessels chartered by US subsidiaries of Burmah and secondly the operation of a crude oil tanker fleet (11 vessels, two million tons, owned and chartered) and a Bahamas based crude oil trans-shipment terminal.

Speciality chemicals

Burmah's expertise in speciality chemicals was identified in 1981 as a promising platform for future business growth. Group companies were already active in the fields of cable saturants and Solignum wood preservatives, (Dussek Campbell); and jointing, waterproofing and adhesive materials, (Expandite).

Significant expansion of the division is envisaged in the coming years.

Investment division

This division manages, on a decentralised basis, the group's other interests, which represent above average investment opportunities.

Burmah Engineering Services Ltd undertakes telecommunications projects, chemical process engineering, contracts management, and food technology projects.

Flexibox Ltd manufactures and markets a unique range of flexible power transmission couplings, and mechanical seals capable of solving almost any problem in shaft sealing.

Kerry Ultrasonics specialises in the development and marketing of high intensity ultrasonic equipment for cleaning, welding and plastics assembly.

Rawlplug manufactures and distributes internationally its famous range of specialised fixings.

Opportunities and vacancies

Graduates are recruited into openings within individual operating companies or head office; these may vary from year to year and may number approximately 25 in total.

Details of vacancies are publicised by individual group companies but for general information about the Burmah Group please contact the Recruitment Officer at the address given.

Leo Burnett Limited

Activities
Advertising agency

Employees
250

Location: UK
London

Locations: Overseas
Worldwide

Opportunities & places
Trainee account manager 4/5

Application address
Head of Client Service, Leo Burnett Ltd,
48 St Martin's Lane, London WC2N 4EJ

It's an ironic fact that the all too easy public image of life in an advertising agency is propagated by the very media which depend on advertising for their survival. Biting the hand that feeds? Looking the gift horse in the mouth? Perhaps. More likely, a failure to understand the genuine role which advertising plays in the marketing of goods and services, in the quest for a newsy, sensational story.

Not convinced? Ask yourself this question, then: 'How do advertising agencies survive in an economic climate of rampant inflation and tightening belts?'

The answer is simple. By relying on qualities which for some reason, the media never tell you about. Marketing expertise, professionalism, creative thinking at every level, common sense and long hard work.

Far from offering you wealth and social disgrace beyond your wildest dreams, a career in advertising offers you a unique opportunity to be part of a dynamic, competitive and stimulating industry, which makes an important contribution to the success of every major company in the country (indeed most of the companies whose ads are in this book).

Why Leo Burnett?

If you are genuinely interested in working in advertising, the choice of your first agency is critical. For, in the early years of your career, the personal qualities you bring to the industry will be developed and augmented by the professional skills and disciplines you will need throughout it.

At Leo Burnett, the training and development of staff at every level is given the highest priority, and a unique and highly successful graduate recruitment and training scheme has been in operation for over a decade. With the result that the great majority of graduates who have completed the course in the last five years are still with us today.

As the London office of the world's fourth largest advertising agency network with an estimated 1981 turnover of £50 million, Leo Burnett has a wide spectrum of clients (28 in all) covering a multitude of markets. Austin Morris, Beecham, Bulmers, Cadbury, Kelloggs, Philip Morris, Scottish & Newcastle Breweries, and Times Newspapers are some of the better known names but each client receives our full marketing and advertising service. From the early stages of new product development, through marketing strategy, consumer research, launch advertising recommendations, media planning and creative work to maintaining brand growth in subsequent campaigns.

We've laid out in more detail the functions of the agency departments and described the complex and varied job of the account manager in a booklet entitled *A career in advertising* which you will find at your university appointments office. (You'll probably find it's worth a look if you're thinking about jobs in marketing as well).

Whatever your degree discipline, if you're interested in a career in advertising, we'd like to hear from you. Because, however you see your long term career plans, we believe that no other agency offers a more thorough, professional, varied and enjoyable grounding in the principles and practices of advertising.

Applications and further information

For further details contact your university appointments office, or write to the address given.

Buzzacott & Co

Activities
Chartered accountancy

Employees
120

Location: UK
London

Opportunities & places
Trainee chartered accountants 10

Application address
ATBC Simpson, Buzzacott & Co, Salisbury
Square House, Salisbury Square, London
EC4Y 8HR

Located in the City, our size may be described as less than mammoth but comfortably beyond the small category. We serve clients both large and small, in industry, commerce, finance, property, merchanting, retailing, the professions, education and health. Our tax clients are even more varied. We are associated with firms in other parts of the world.

Types of graduate required

We require graduates of high calibre and resourcefulness. Whilst basic numeracy is necessary, the subject of your degree is less important, but we do look for a logical approach, mental flexibility and leadership qualities. Minimum academic requirements are expectation of a second class degree, one A grade or two B grade A levels and B grade O level mathematics.

Training and career development

Our training is a programme of theoretical studies and practical experience. In preparation for the professional examinations, students are enrolled at the firm's expense on linked courses with professional tutors. Paid study leave is given for these courses. In addition we have in-house courses to develop your knowledge of the firm's systems and prepare you for greater responsibility as you progress.

We can offer variety and intellectual rigour. The allocation of practical work to graduate students is tailored to ensure that you obtain wide experience and are not faced with long and somewhat pedestrian audits which sometimes happens in the large firms. Nevertheless we apply sophisticated techniques, the firm has its own computer, our training is thorough and ensures that your responsibility is increased so that towards the end of your training you can expect to be acting in a senior capacity regarding the affairs of larger clients. Your progress is closely monitored by both the firm's training staff and tutors.

Prospects

We like students to remain with the firm for at least a year after qualification. Some of our partners and managers were students with the firm so if you have the right qualities there are clearly opportunities for promotion.

Salaries

These are competitive within market rates and increase as you gain experience and responsibility, and pass examinations. All salaries are reviewed annually.

Pensions, benefits and amenities

We offer the following: the government pension scheme plus a top up arrangement for long serving staff; four weeks annual holiday; luncheon vouchers; good sports and medical facilities and various social activities.

Further information

If you would like to be interviewed please send a university standard introduction form or write to ATBC Simpson.

Activities
Manufacture of low-density polyethylene and
flexible packaging material

Employees
3,000

Locations: UK
London; South East; Midlands; North East;
North West; Scotland

Opportunities
Production and technical; Sales and personnel
(occasionally)

Vacancies
4 project vacancies, some direct entry
vacancies

Application addresses
See main text

BXL Plastics Limited

BXL Plastics Limited, a wholly owned subsidiary of BP Chemicals Ltd,
is a leading manufacturer of polyethylene resins and compounds and a
major producer of plastics products for the packaging,
telecommunications, medical, sport and leisure, and printing industries.

The company has six divisions, each with its own marketing,
production, technical and support facilities and employs 3,000 people at
its 10 locations.

Types of graduate required

BXL Plastics Ltd employs many graduates, primarily from *scientific* and
technical disciplines such as *mechanical* and *chemical engineering*, *materials
technology* and *production engineering*. The opportunities for these
graduates are generally in production, technical and commercial
functions of the company. *Business studies* and *arts* graduates are
employed, but in rather smaller numbers than scientists and
technologists. When recruiting graduates, the company concentrates on
the personal qualities of the individual rather than on the class of the
degree, or the university attended. Entry is via the centrally organised
project scheme or by direct entry into an operating division.

The first method has been developed to suit the needs of the newly
qualified graduate, particularly when he or she is not entirely decided on
the most appropriate career path to follow. The scheme is open to all
graduates but obviously most of the posts are for technologists of the
disciplines mentioned above. Applicants for this method of entry should
write to the Staff Personnel Manager in London.

Application addresses

Direct entry candidates should apply to the appropriate division:

*Polyethylene Division, Inchyra Road, Grangemouth, Stirlingshire
FK3 9XG*. Products: Polyethylene resins, compounds, and colour
masterbatches.

*Cascelloid Division, Abbey Meadow, Abbey Park Rd, Leicester
LE4 5EA*. Products: Plastics bottles, tubes and closures.

*Flexible Packaging Division, Huddersfield Road, Darton, Barnsley,
Yorkshire S75 5NA*. Products: Polyethylene film and converted products
such as sacks, carrier bags and layflat tubing.

ERP Division, 675 Mitcham Road, Croydon, Surrey CR9 3AL.
Products: Foamed crosslinked polyethylene and EVA materials for
protective packaging, bouyancy, energy absorption, sealing, medical
applications, etc.

*Synthetic Paper Division, Stephenson Road, Clacton-on-Sea, Essex
CO15 4NS*. Products: Polyart – Europe's leading synthetic paper.

Scintillex Division, 34 Purewell, Christchurch, Dorset BH23 1ER.
Products: High frequency welding of PVC sheet, mainly for display
packaging.

Head Office, Buchanan House, 3 St James's Square, London SW1Y 4JS
for project scheme entrants only.

Cadbury Schweppes

It has often been said that figures can be used to prove almost anything.
Some figures, however, are open to only one interpretation, and none
more so than those for Cadbury Schweppes' turnover and profit over the
last few years. Turnover for 1979 was £1,006m, and profit before tax was
£48.2m; 1980 turnover was £1,119m and profit before tax £61.3m;
turnover for 1981 was £1,271m and profit before tax was £80.6m.

Activities
Confectionery, food, drink and household
chemical manufacture

Employees
23,000 UK
13,000 overseas

Locations: UK
General

Locations: Overseas
Worldwide

Opportunities
Engineering; R&D; Production; Personnel;
Buying; Marketing; Export marketing; Marketing
research; Market analysis; Sales; Distribution;
Finance; Computer services; Operational
research; Office systems

Application address
The Group Recruitment Manager, A29 Cadbury
Schweppes Limited, Bournville, Birmingham
B30 2LU
Tel: 021-458 7343

It does not take an accountant to perceive the strong underlying trend towards increased profitability. The figure for 1981 is particularly impressive in view of the influences of a current worldwide recession and the very competitive markets in which we operate.

Figures of this magnitude are only achieved through sound investment in both people and technology, flexibility, commercial acumen and a forward looking attitude.

Cadbury Schweppes is a very large, very efficient and highly progressive organisation; one which any graduate would do well to consider as a potential outlet for his or her particular skills.

So it should come as no surprise that we seek correspondingly exceptional qualities in our graduate recruits, of whom there are about 70 each year.

Training
Each graduate undergoes an individually structured training programme supplemented by management courses. Specific responsibilities are allocated early, with a first management role within two years for those who match our expectations.

Most of these are trained and subsequently work in Birmingham, London, Liverpool or Bristol, although some are directed to our other sites throughout Britain.

Salaries and benefits
Our salaries are competitive and the benefits package includes a contributory pension scheme and medical services. The larger factories offer a full range of sporting and social facilities. We are able to provide assistance in finding accommodation.

Further information
Your university appointments service will normally have copies of our graduate booklet, vacancy list and application forms. If you experience difficulty in obtaining these please write to us direct.

Summary
For those graduates with enthusiasm, imagination and the ability to meet the challenge of a demanding job, Cadbury Schweppes can offer an exciting and satisfying future.

CAP Group Limited

Activities
Contractor in information systems

Employees
800+

Locations: UK
London; South East; North West

Opportunities
Trainee programmers; Trainee consultants

Application address
Graduate Recruitment Officer, CAP Group
Limited, 20–26 Lambs Conduit Street, London
WC1N 3LF
Tel: 01-404 0911

CAP is a British owned company founded in 1962 with an established reputation as a leading contractor in information systems. Our clients come from industry, finance, commerce and government. Our business is to help clients with the creation and maintenance of working computer systems through the skills of our staff. The group structure reflects our broad client base and we have specialist business units at our three UK locations serving these market sections. The CAP group is over 800 strong and over 90% of our staff are graduates. The average age of our employees is 27.

Types of graduate required
Although most of our vacancies are open to graduates of *any* discipline we are happy to receive applications from those students who would positively wish to use their degree background; either by using a science background in a more technical area such as industrial applications or a commerce or business training in a commercial or financial environment.

For vacancies in CAP Scientific, our specialist scientific consultancy, we can only consider applicants with an *applied science* degree such as *maths, stats, OR, electronic* or *control engineering* or *computer science*.

A CLOSE KNIT FRIENDLY FIRM
YOU CAN FIND OUT MORE
ABOUT US ON
THE OPPOSITE PAGE

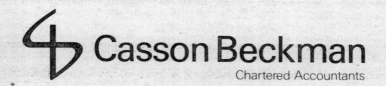

Casson Beckman

Chartered Accountants

CAP Group Limited, cont

Training

All graduate trainees will undergo an intensive six-week training course. The emphasis of this initial training is on practical work, and help and guidance is provided by experienced programmers.

Prospects

Performance is assessed at the completion of every project and also at regular fixed intervals. Most graduates gain their first promotion after about six months. Subsequent promotions are based on individual merit and technical competence, and junior staff have the opportunity to discuss their career progress with their staff manager every six months.

As our staff gain experience we expect them to take on more responsibility, either by tackling more complicated programming tasks, supervising junior staff, liaising with clients or by becoming more involved with program and system design.

Locations

Our largest operating centre is in London, where there are commercial, financial and industrial branches, as well as our Scientific company. Industrial and commercial systems work is also undertaken at our Manchester and Reading offices. Graduate entrants will initially be based at one of the above locations but, as some of our work is performed on client premises, staff should be prepared to travel on a daily basis or live away from home to meet project needs.

Further information

Your careers service should have copies of our graduate recruitment brochure, which gives comprehensive information about CAP and details of our 1983 vacancies. Applications should be made initially to our London address on either our form or the standard introduction form.

Casson Beckman

The partnership is situated in the West End of London and has a staff of approximately 150. It is founded on the concept of creative forward thinking and planning and great emphasis is placed by the firm on taxation and commercial advice.

A comprehensive manual provides the basis for developing the highest standards, and guides the approach to auditing and accountancy assignments. Emphasis is laid on the importance of management information and the carrying out of system based audits which helps provide suggestions for advising clients on how to maximise their profits and increase efficiency.

The firm succeeds only if staff enjoy job satisfaction to the fullest extent. To this end, the firm attempts to offer the following to all members: variety of work; training; good working conditions and facilities; an informal atmosphere whereby ideas are exchanged at any time; job responsibility and promotion commensurate with ability and performance; a competitive reward with regular reviews.

Types of graduate required

The firm is interested in those who have graduated in virtually *any* subject, but special consideration is given to those with approved degrees. The essential requirements are ability to mix with people, and analyse and communicate ideas, and a determination to advance.

Activities
Accounting, auditing, taxation, investigations, commercial advice

Employees
150

Location: UK
London

Opportunities & places
Student accountants 12–15

Application address
Robert Goodwin, Staff Partner, Casson Beckman, 27-29 Queen Anne Street, London W1M 0DA

Applications
Our brochure gives further information about the firm, training facilities and other conditions of employment. This brochure, and other details, may be obtained from the staff partner.

CASE Computer and Systems Engineering plc

Activities
Data and office communications systems suppliers

Employees
550

Location: UK
South East

Opportunities
Engineers; Programmers; Trainee systems specialists; Systems test and commissioning engineers

Vacancies
10

Application address
Eileen Murphy, Personnel Manager, CASE plc, Holywell Industrial Estate, Caxton Way, Watford, Herts WD1 8XH

CASE is a British company servicing industry through design and production of data and office communications equipment. Since its formation in 1970 CASE has become a leading company in its field. CASE products including modems, multiplexers, concentrators and automatic message switching systems, are designed to make major economies to communications networks and to simplify their operation and maintenance. A recent addition to our product range is the CASE word processing system. CASE has a friendly informal working atmosphere. Employee benefits include a bonus scheme linked to output and a profit sharing scheme. Some 550 people are at present employed by the company.

Types of graduate required
In 1983 we hope to engage approximately 10 new graduates to work in our production, systems support and product development divisions. The disciplines we require are *electronic engineering, computer science*, or a relevant combination of these.

Training and career development
New graduates are allocated to specific projects and in addition receive in-company training on CASE products. The company is committed to a policy offering parallel promotional prospects along both technical and man-management routes.

Locations
The company moves in August 1982 to new large premises in Watford, Hertfordshire and this is where new graduates will be based. There are excellent road and rail links to London, the North and the West. We do also have sales and service offices throughout Great Britain.

Applications
These should arrive not later than 31 January 1983 and be addressed to Eileen Murphy, Personnel Manager.

Ciba-Geigy Plastics and Additives Company

CIBA—GEIGY

Activities
Manufacture and marketing of specialist chemical products

Employees
2,800

Locations: UK
East Anglia; North West; Scotland

Ciba-Geigy is an international research based chemical manufacturing enterprise with its headquarters in Switzerland. Ciba-Geigy Plastics and Additives Company, part of the UK group, manufactures a wide range of specialist chemicals for use in paints, printing inks, plastics, textiles and man made fibres, lubricants and hydraulic fluids, corrosion inhibitors, resins and adhesives. Ciba-Geigy is associated throughout the world with technical expertise and high standards of manufacture. Research and development programmes take a substantial part of our investment expenditure.

Location: Overseas
Switzerland

Opportunities & places
Research chemists 2; Chemical engineers 2;
Mechanical engineer 1

Application address
Graduate Recruitment Officer, Ciba-Geigy
Plastics and Additives Company, 30
Buckingham Gate, London SW1E 6LH

Types of graduate required

Graduates with honours degrees or PhDs in *organic chemistry* or *chemical engineering* are recruited for research, product and process development, process and quality control, applications development and technical service. There are also openings for *chemical, mechanical, electrical* and *instrument engineers* to undertake work on project design or maintenance engineering. Occasionally openings may occur for direct entry into sales, marketing, management services or production, but normally such posts are filled by graduates who have already gained experience in the areas previously mentioned.

Training and career development

Graduate entrants constitute the main source of supply for senior management jobs in the company. Initially, training is aimed at developing professional expertise in the chosen job area, however a graduate can expect to be given specific opportunities for management training when career preferences are clearer. We encourage job rotation into areas such as sales, marketing or production. Such moves are accompanied by specific training and support programmes to develop management or other specialist skills.

Locations

Ciba-Geigy Plastics and Additives Company has three major UK divisions. These are: Pigments Division based in Paisley, Renfrewshire; Industrial Chemicals Division which is at Trafford Park, Manchester and Plastics Division, Duxford, Cambridgeshire.

Applications

If you are interested in learning more about opportunities in the company, please write to the Graduate Recruitment Officer at the address given.

Civil Service

Activities
National government

Employees
500,000+

Locations: UK
General

Opportunities & places
Various

Application address
Careers Advisory Services, or Mr G Smith,
Civil Service Commission, Alencon Link,
Basingstoke, Hampshire RG21 1JB

The Civil Service offers worthwhile careers to graduates in all disciplines, whether or not they wish to specialise in their degree subjects. The work is varied, interesting and demanding, a reflection of the wide span of government activity and its increasing complexity. It is carried out by a large number of departments ranging from small central ones chiefly concerned with broad policy issues to very big ones which combine policy work and executive functions calling for regional and local organisations which operate nationwide. Write for the booklet *Civil Service Careers 1982 – Degree Level.*

Opportunities for graduates in any subject

Graduates in *any* subject are recruited into the following occupations: administration trainees, who are groomed with a view to filling the top policy formulation positions; executive officers, who are responsible for the day-to-day work of departments, and provide most of future management; management trainees for the Department of Employment; inspectors of taxes for Inland Revenue; assistant governors for prison service; a few posts in the Diplomatic Service, and trainee auditors.

Social science and related subject opportunities

Graduates in *social science* and related subjects are recruited as social survey officers in community research. *Psychologists* work on a range of projects. *Economists* and *statisticians* are employed by many departments, including centrally by the Treasury and the Central Statistical Office.

Science and engineering opportunities
Scientists are recruited to work in research and development, to provide scientific services and advice to the public, government and departments. They also undertake scientific and technical administration. For further information see the entry under Scientific Civil Service.

Civil, mechanical, electrical and *electronic engineers* are concerned with design, construction, production, quality assurance, maintenance, and research and development.

Environmental studies opportunities
Architects are responsible for all aspects of their profession from design and supervision of construction to development work. *Surveyors* are employed in all the recognised divisions of surveying including agriculture, building, estate management (rural and urban), land, mineral, quantity and valuation.

Agriculturalists and *related disciplines* are employed by the Agriculture Service and the Science Service of the Agricultural Development and Advisory Service. There are opportunities for *agriculturalists, horticulturists, scientists, chemists* and *biologists. Veterinarians* are recruited for field work and laboratory research.

Other degree opportunities
Linguists are employed in transcription, translation and foreign document research. Graduates in *mathematics* or a similar subject train as actuaries. Specialists with some years' experience are required as lawyers, accountants, inspectors of schools and medical officers. Graduates with appropriate degrees are recruited into the national museums, galleries, hydrography, map research and to work as librarians.

Training
The amount and type of training given to graduates varies widely according to their work and their needs and it often affords the opportunity to gain further necessary qualifications. Formal training is organised by individual departments, the Civil Service College and other organisations.

Locations
Specialist posts are often available in various parts of the country. Posts most closely concerned with government policy are located in London, Edinburgh and Cardiff.

Salaries
Up-to-date information about current levels is available from the Civil Service Commission.

C & J Clark Limited

Activities
Manufacturers, retailers, wholesalers and exporters of shoes and related commodities throughout the world

Employees
24,000

Locations: UK
General

Clarks of Street, Somerset are renowned as one of the largest and most successful shoe manufacturers and retailers in the world. We are very much a family business, and one of the very few private companies in the UK still managed by the direct descendants of the men who founded it 150 years ago. We have considerable experience of successfully developing senior managers from those who joined us straight from university.

Policy of the company
Is to operate in all spheres of the shoe trade, both in the UK and throughout the world.

In the United Kingdom the company holds the major share of the

Opportunities
Production and retail management

Application address
The Director of Management Development,
C & J Clark Limited, Street, Somerset
BA16 0YA

manufacturer branded business with the Clarks and K brands. There are 18 factories manufacturing some 25 million pairs of shoes per annum in the UK.

In retailing the company sells through more than 800 shops in the high street, trading under such names as Peter Lord, K and Ravel.

It also manufactures components, basic materials, chemicals, machinery and tools for the shoemaking industry in general. It has a substantial engineering subsidiary.

Overseas, the company controls large shoe manufacturing concerns in the USA, Eire and Australia and also manufacturers under the Clarks brand in New Zealand and South Africa. It has retail chains in the USA, Canada, France, Holland and Australia.

Turnover in 1981 was nearly £500 million.

The people we are looking for

Our policy is to develop professional managers from graduates of *any* faculty who are eager to venture outside their previous experience and training, quick to grasp the essentials of specialities other than their own, and yet painstaking and persistent enough to master each responsibility they assume. We want men and women who are prepared to devote their early years and effort to the task of doing things, to managing people and costs. They must be willing to work in a factory or manage a shop and to demonstrate persistence, technical knowledge and supervisory ability in junior roles they were not primarily selected to fill.

This is essential because there is no substitute for successful experience of managing. And responsibility can only be given slowly at first as trainees earn the acceptance of their colleagues. Every graduate must recognise that the initial challenge of industry is not to their intelligence but their ability to earn acceptance. That requires a great deal of patience, persistence and determination. Graduates who drop out seldom fail because they are not good enough. They leave because the goal of senior responsibility is not sufficiently attractive to compensate for the difficulties and frustrations of the first few years. The company recognises the difficulty; it exists in any company.

We have streamlined training to a minumum. We take risks in giving greater responsibility at the earliest possible moment. Those who persist average £16,500 pa by age 35.

The company is particularly interested in *engineers, mathematicians* and *scientists* who want general management rather than a narrow functional career and *arts* graduates (particularly *linguists*) who are numerate. *Any* faculty will do. It is the person who matters.

The actions you should take

Talk over the prospect of joining us with someone in your careers advisory service or write giving details about yourself and asking for a booklet about careers with us to the Director of Management Development at the address given.

Clark Pixley

We are one of the 20 or so firms of accountants which have offices in most areas of the UK and associates all over the world. Whilst we are big enough to number among our clients institutions with assets of over £1 thousand million, we are also small enough to prepare the accounts and tax returns of a one-man business. Clark Pixley can offer a student the widest possible range of professional experience and a mixture of career opportunities sufficiently rich and varied to satisfy most ambitions.

Although we are nowhere near being the biggest firm, we have over

Activities
Chartered accountancy

Employees
550

Locations: UK
General

Locations: Overseas
76 countries through associations – principally North America, Europe and Australasia

Opportunities & places
Trainee chartered accountants 50

Application address
Graduate Recruitment Partner, Clark Pixley, 6 Eldon Street, London EC2M 7LU
Tel: 01-377 9166

200 staff in our London office, plus 22 partners. There are 12 associated offices elsewhere in the UK plus about 180 other offices of our own or our associates overseas. We are probably the only firm of our UK size which has such a well developed international operation.

For atmosphere we feel we are informal, friendly and personal, partly because of our size (for example, all our clients have a partner to deal with directly, and this attitude carries through to working relationships inside), and partly because we like it that way. So although we expect a good standard of academic achievement from our prospective students, degree subject is less important than a capacity for logical thought, the ability to communicate clearly, enthusiasm and a sense of humour.

Training and career development
Obviously, it is in our interests as well as yours that you should pass the Institute examinations at first attempt and we'll give you all the help you need in preparation for these. Like most other firms we engage a firm of professional tutors but, in addition, we monitor your progress very closely through in-house exams based on home study and provide any additional tuition you may need from within our own training department. Your first five weeks, three of which are residential, are spent on training courses designed to give a basic grounding in bookkeeping and the firm's approach to auditing. In-house courses continue both during and after training to keep you up to date with current developments and our firm's methods, and we will sponsor you on external courses wherever we feel them to be beneficial.

Practical experience is gained principally in audit groups, but there are also opportunities to transfer for periods of secondment to both the taxation and small business departments within the firm.

Prospects
Once you've qualified, as you might expect, the demands of our profession are such that progress is always entirely dependent upon merit. If you stay, opportunities exist for transfer to one of our specialist departments or for secondment to our overseas offices, and partners are invariably admitted from within the firm, usually by their early 30s. If you decide not to stay within the profession, your qualifications will always stand you in good stead in industry or commerce.

Further information
Clark Pixley will be visiting a number of universities during the autumn and spring terms. You should check details of dates and obtain a copy of our graduate recruitment brochure from their careers advisory service. Alternatively, you can write to the London office.

Cleanaway

Activities
Waste management, transportation and waste disposal

Employees
1,000

Locations: UK
General

Cleanaway Limited is a joint venture partnership between Guest Keen and Nettlefolds Limited and Brambles Industries Limited of Australia, employing approximately 1,000 people. The company is involved in waste treatment and disposal services for industry and local authorities, including the operation of major landfill sites and facilities for the disposal of industrial wastes by incineration and chemical treatment. The company arranges for the transportation of waste in its own vehicles and has a fleet of tugs and barges to carry London's refuse.

Types of graduate required
There is likely to be a graduate intake every year. The company is specifically interested in people reading *business studies, chemical*

Opportunities
Management: site, transportation; Engineeering: chemical, civil; Administration

Application address
Personnel Manager, Cleanaway Limited, Claydons Lane, Rayleigh, Essex SS6 7UW

engineering, chemistry, civil engineering and *economics* who wish to pursue a commercial career. First year projects on transportation, landfill disposal, chemical treatment and incineration will lead to opportunities to assume depot and site management responsibilities in transportation depots and on landfill sites.

Locations
Graduates must be prepared to travel within the UK (driving licence preferred) and could be based anywhere in the country.

Applications
Contact the Personnel Manager, at the address given, for an application form.

Clerical Medical & General Life Assurance Society

Clerical Medical was founded over 150 years ago and is now recognised as one of Britain's leading life offices with assets exceeding £800 million and with over 40 branches throughout the United Kingdom. As a mutual office we have no shareholders; our with-profits policyholders benefit from the profits made and we have paid bonuses continuously despite two world wars since 1832. In spite of our financial growth, our staff numbers remain relatively small. We are a company large enough to offer scope for progression and development yet small enough, with only 1,100 employed, to maintain a personal atmosphere. As a graduate joining us, you can pursue a rewarding career without the anonymity of a vast organisation.

Activities
Life assurance and pensions business

Employees
1,100

Locations: UK
London; Bristol

Opportunities & places
Actuarial work 4; Accountancy 4

Application address
Deputy Secretary (Personnel), Clerical Medical & General Life Assurance Society, Narrow Plain, Bristol BS2 0JH

UK operations
Our principal office is situated in London's St James's Square, where some 150 staff deal with such aspects of our business as investment, marketing and legal, together with the main actuarial function.

Our business administration departments are in Bristol where our head office of 600 staff includes areas dealing with life assurance and pensions contracts, our chief accounting and computer areas, and other management services.

Types of graduate required
While we expect a good honours degree from each graduate recruit, we also look for such qualities as initiative, adaptability and self-motivation.

Our main requirement is for graduates who intend to train and qualify for membership of the Institute of Actuaries, for which a degree in *maths, statistics, actuarial science* or *economics* is particularly suitable. We also welcome graduates of *any* discipline for accountancy training and qualification.

In both professions the course of study is demanding and a high degree of determination is necessary if you are to be successful.

Training
Training is a continuing process up to and beyond the point at which you qualify. Study for qualification goes hand in hand with planned practical experience, supported by a range of internal courses covering the principles of insurance through to the development of supervisory skills.

There are vacancies for actuarial students both in London and Bristol. As a student, and later as a qualified actuary, you may be asked to transfer from one of these locations to the other as your training and the needs of the office dictate. As an accountancy student you are likely to be Bristol based throughout your training, and on qualification.

We offer you practical encouragement in your professional studies, with a day time release scheme. Financial assistance is given in the form of interest free tuition loans and lump sum payments on passing examinations. Salaries are adjusted on qualification. Throughout training, an experienced member of our staff is appointed to oversee your progress.

Career development

The demands on the actuary and accountant in influencing our levels of income and expenditure are particularly high in a difficult economy.

In recruiting graduates into these areas of business, our main aim is to strengthen our future management resources. We are therefore looking for people with potential who, with experience and professional qualification, will make an important contribution to our continued success.

Salaries

Our starting salaries, which are reviewed annually, are competitive with other major employers. Annual salary progress is performance linked in relation to a job evaluated system.

Amenities

We offer a range of employee benefits which includes a first class life and pensions scheme, flexible working hours, luncheon vouchers, a highly active sports and social club, and, after a qualifying period, a staff house purchase loan scheme. Staff in Bristol have the use of the subsidised staff restaurant.

Applications

Our initial selection, which will be completed by 21 December each year, is made on the basis of your letter and cv, so please write fully to the Deputy Secretary (Personnel) at the address given.

Clydesdale Bank plc

Activities
Complete range of banking services

Employees
6,000

Location: UK
Scotland

Opportunities
Branch banking and various specialised departments

Vacancies
10

Upper age limit
24

Application address
Staff Manager, Clydesdale Bank plc,
150 Buchanan Street, Glasgow G1 2HL

The Clydesdale Bank has branches throughout Scotland, is also represented in London and the north east of England and provides comprehensive banking facilities for industry, commerce and the private individual. The bank's progressive outlook and expanding business offers excellent opportunities for the graduate to gain early advancement to managerial status.

Types of graduate required

We are looking for graduates with a suitable university degree and who possess the necessary personal qualifications of integrity, ambition, enthusiasm and initiative. Successful applicants must be prepared to serve in any part of the United Kingdom.

Training

We operate an accelerated training programme which lasts for four years and covers all aspects of general banking. Regular assessments are made to provide an appraisal of career progress.

The professional qualification of the Institute of Bankers in Scotland is essential and day release facilities are available to enable you to study for these examinations.

Salaries, pensions and amenities

The starting salary is competitive and during training regular increments are received. The bank operates a non-contributory pension scheme as well as a house purchase scheme at favourable terms. In addition various sporting facilities are available for the benefit of the staff.

Coles Cranes Limited

Activities
Design, manufacture and worldwide marketing of mobile cranes

Employees 2,400

Application address
The Group Training Manager, Coles Cranes Limited, Crown Works, Pallion, Sunderland, Tyne and Wear SR4 6TT

In 1983 we shall be seeking graduate *engineers* who wish to pursue a career through to management via design, production or technical service, and also graduates from other disciplines for finance, production control and purchasing.

Full information on the specific opportunities available plus case histories on recent graduate recruits will be found in your careers service reference library.

Computer Machinery Company (CMC) Limited

Activities
Design, manufacture, marketing, installing and maintenance of minicomputer systems

Employees
00

Locations: UK
General

Locations: Overseas
Worldwide

Opportunities & places
Programmers 10; Systems analysts 3; Hardware and software design staff 4; Customer service engineers 3; Technical support staff 3

Application address
Manpower Development Manager, CMC Ltd, Maylands House, Hemel Hempstead, Herts HP2 4RL
Tel: 0442 61266

Computer Machinery Company (established in 1969) manufacturers at Hemel Hempstead, Herts, the Reality minicomputer business information system and the Sovereign distributed data processing system which, together with its key to disc predecessors, are used by over 1,200 UK customers and in 31 countries worldwide where high speed data entry, data communications, transaction processing and user programming are required. In the UK besides a manufacturing plant, CMC has a product development group, a customer training centre and a network of branch sales and support offices plus engineering service centres.

Types of graduate required
Opportunities exist for graduates in *any* discipline but CMC would particularly like to hear from those with qualifications in *computer science, maths* or *electronics*.

In any year there may be vacancies in the branch offices for technical support personnel whose major functions are to assist salesmen in the technical selling, presentation and demonstration of our products and to give advice and guidance to our customers in the planning and implementation of our systems. Vacancies may also exist within customer service centres for engineers to install and maintain our minicomputer systems and within the product development division to work on the design and creation of new hardware and software products.

Training
Appropriate training is given to all employees according to their needs. Customer service, product development and technical support personnel all receive intensive product education and the latter group will also be trained for pre-sales activities including communication, technical reporting, presenting and demonstrating.

Locations
Product development and manufacturing divisions are located at Hemel Hempstead. Sales/support offices and engineering service centres are located in many principal cities throughout the UK.

Salaries and prospects
Your starting salary will be competitive with other companies in the

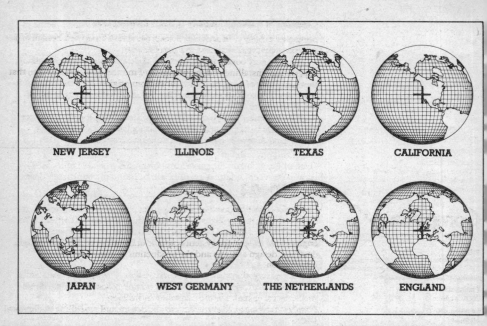

| NEW JERSEY | ILLINOIS | TEXAS | CALIFORNIA |
| JAPAN | WEST GERMANY | THE NETHERLANDS | ENGLAND |

WORLDWIDE DESIGNS ON COMPUTER AIDED ENGINEERING

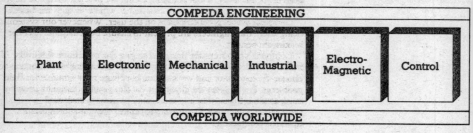

COMPEDA ENGINEERING

| Plant | Electronic | Mechanical | Industrial | Electro-Magnetic | Control |

COMPEDA WORLDWIDE

Compeda ✓
Integrated Systems for Engineering

Head office: Compeda House, Walkern Road, Stevenage, Hertfordshire SG1 3QP, England
Telephone: Stevenage (0438) 56123 Telex: 826308
Branch offices: Paramus, NJ; Chicago; Houston; Menlo Park, CA; Tokyo; Munich; Zoetermeer

computer industry. In addition certain personnel based in a branch office or service centre are entitled to a company car.

The company covers the whole field of design, manufacture, selling, supporting, installing and maintenance of minicomputer systems so that there is plenty of opportunity to move from original job employment to other fields or to progress up the chosen ladder within a professional career structure.

CMC provides the opportunity for successful employees to become very quickly an important part of a growing successful supplier of distributed data base and data entry computer systems.

Compeda Limited

Integrated Systems for Engineering

Activities
Marketing and support of high technology (CAD/CAM) software systems having a wide range of engineering applications

Employees
200 worldwide

Location: UK
South East

Locations: Overseas
USA; Germany; Japan; Netherlands

Opportunities
Software development; Applications engineering; Field engineering; Productivity support; Computer programming

Application address
The Personnel Manager, Compeda Limited, Compeda House, Walkern Road, Stevenage, Herts

Compeda markets, develops and supports computer aided engineering software, high technology systems that meet the needs of engineers both now and in the future. Compeda uses the term computer aided engineering to describe systems capable of handling conceptual design, drafting, design analysis and the production of manufacturing information.

Compeda products are based on the results of research carried out in UK universities, research centres and private industry. Today, these products are installed in the following industries:

Plant engineering an example here is the design and modelling of chemical plant.

Mechanical engineering examples include computer aided drafting, stress analysis, surface modelling and control systems design.

Electro-magnetic engineering examples include designs involving magnetics or electrostatic fields.

Industrial engineering examples include work study, man and work place interaction and production planning.

Electronic engineering an example here is the design of integrated electronic circuits.

Compeda's services

Compeda CAE systems and support services enable companies to shorten the time taken to develop and manufacture new products, and obtain greater productivity, while reducing costs. We provide complete support services within easy reach of our customers, wherever they are based.

Compeda places great emphasis on the user. Whenever our systems are being used, our engineers are present to ensure our customers get the maximum benefit.

Compeda's products are designed to give the maximum flexibility. The hardware independence of all Compeda's products enables engineers to choose the computer and workstation hardware most suitable for their problems. It also gives the flexibility for this product usage to grow by using extended hardware as the number of users or technical requirements increase. Compeda guarantees that data formats are upwards compatible.

Types of graduate required

Compeda will grow rapidly throughout the early 1980s and the company will be looking for high calibre, practically minded graduates in *mechanical, electronic, electrical, plant* and *industrial engineering, computer sciences* and *mathematics*.

Training and career development

Whatever your discipline you will receive full and comprehensive

Compeda Limited, cont

training when you join Compeda and you will work in one of the following areas: software development, applications engineering, field engineering, productivity support, computer programming.

Compeda provides full and comprehensive training and aims to develop the careers of it's young graduate staff by giving them positions of responsibility as soon as possible after the completion of training and field experience.

The company's structure is such that we can offer considerable promotion flexibility, your career path can be in a technical specialisation, in management or perhaps a combination.

Locations
In addition to its headquarters in Stevenage, UK, Compeda has a network of offices in the USA, Continental Europe and Japan. Each office is staffed by local management backed by technical support teams and applications engineers. There is plenty of scope for travel and for working in a variety of locations.

Benefits and applications
Compeda pays highly competitive salaries, offers realistic benefits and there is a comprehensive relocation package where applicable. To obtain our application form and company information please contact the Personnel Manager at the address given.

Come and join tomorrow's technology – today.

Computer Technology Limited

CTL are the main operating subsidiary of the Information Technology Group of companies, an organisation which since its inception has worked at the very forefront of emergent computer technology.

Our activities cover the design, manufacture, marketing and complete support of a range of sophisticated computer systems used in business, technical, government and medical applications.

Our expanding applied systems division which incorporates extensive in house systems software capabilities, currently represents the main source of opportunities for high calibre *computer science* and *electrical/electronic engineering* graduates.

Prospects
A progressive working environment combined with a distinctive management philosophy has helped enhance an effective and rapidly expanding research based manufacturing and systems design resource, providing excellent opportunities for career advancement and personal development.

Applications
Our initial selection is made on the basis of the information you provide. You may apply by sending a detailed cv or standard introduction form to David Drake, at the address given.

Computer Technology Limited

Activities
Design, manufacture, marketing, sales and complete support of a range of computer systems

Employees
400

Location: UK
Hemel Hempstead, Herts

Opportunities
Hardware and software production; Design and development; Sales; Marketing

Application address
David Drake, Computer Technology Limited, Eaton Road, Hemel Hempstead, Herts

The Conoco Group in the UK

Conoco is one of the world's leading energy companies and part of Du Pont, a unique natural resources/high technology enterprise ranking among the 10 largest industrial corporations in the world.

The UK is Conoco's most intensive investment area outside the United States and comprises Conoco (UK) Limited, Conoco Limited and Continental Oil Company Limited.

We are an energetic, innovative and fast moving organisation and can offer graduates the opportunity to become part of one of the most successful and progressive groups within the energy industry.

Salaries and benefits

Starting salaries for new graduates are competitive and subsequent salary progression is dependent upon performance. There is a non-contributory pension plan, four weeks holiday per year, personal accident cover and other benefits normally associated with a major company.

Applications and further information

If you want to apply to us please find out from your careers office whether we are visiting your university or college. If not, write to the appropriate address as shown in the main text.

Conoco (UK) Limited

Activities
Exploration for, and production of, oil and gas

Employees
850

Locations: UK
London, Midlands and Scotland

Occupations
Engineering: chemical, mechanical, electrical, petroleum; Administration: business/management, accounting; Exploration: geologists, geophysicists

Application address
Engineers: Engineering Development Coordinator
Business admin: Administrative Training Coordinator
Exploration: Personnel Officer (Exploration)
Conoco (UK) Limited, Park House, 116 Park Street, London W1Y 4NN

Conoco (UK) Limited is a leader in the exploration for, and development of, UK oil and natural gas resources. Through its discoveries the company is making an important contribution to Britain's energy requirements. Conoco holds interests in five oil fields north east of the Shetlands and one gas field off the Lincolnshire coast.

We are operators on behalf of our partners for the Murchison and Hutton fields from our offices in Aberdeen, and for the Viking gas field from our Mablethorpe Gas Terminal. Murchison came into production in 1980 and the development of the Hutton field is now advancing using the revolutionary Tension Leg Platform for the first time. The field is due on stream in 1984.

Currently Conoco is involved in the search for new reserves both in the North Sea and onshore in southern England.

Types of graduate required

Engineering: A variety of *engineering* disciplines including *petroleum*, *mechanical*, *electrical* and *civil*, fit well into the company's need for engineers at all our operating locations and our London head office.

Administration: *Business* graduates are needed for our administrative services department in London, Aberdeen and Mablethorpe which support the operating departments in the management of their budgets, cost control and cash requirement forecasting. Preference is given to those who have had industrial training experience with Conoco.

Exploration: Graduates and postgraduates in *geology* and *geophysics* are required to work in our exploration department which is actively engaged in North Sea and onshore exploratory programmes.

Training

Engineering, administration and exploration each have their own graduate training programmes. Generally, introductory training lasts six months. Engineers and business graduates, after an initial induction in London, have training assignments at the company's major UK locations involving work related projects. Exploration graduates' initial training is in London with periods spent at well sites and onshore seismic surveys.

Conoco (UK) Limited, cont

After orientation in the USA graduates complete a six-month interpretation project. In-company and outside training courses are used to strengthen the new graduates' knowledge of the industry.

Conoco Limited (Humber Refinery)

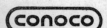

Activities
Manufacture of petroleum and petrochemical products

Employees
650

Location: UK
North East

Opportunities
Chemical engineers; Mechanical engineers

Application address
Mr JH Chappell, Personnel Officer, Conoco Limited (Humber Refinery), South Killingholme, Grimsby, Humberside DN40 3DW

Conoco Limited's Humber Refinery was commissioned during 1969/70 and a subsequent £45 million expansion has increased its initial capacity by nearly 30%. Expansion is continuing, thereby maintaining the refinery's position as one of the most complex and sophisticated refining facilities in the UK. The refinery is ideally situated to process North Sea oil and distribute its products to the company's UK and Western European markets. These products include Jet petrol, gas oil, kerosene, diesel fuel, liquefied petroleum gas, benzene, and electrode grade petroleum coke.

Types of graduate required
Good honours graduates (male and female), in *chemical* and *mechanical engineering* are required to work in the process engineering division of our technical services department and the design services section of our project and engineering department.
   Chemical engineers They provide chemical engineering advice on a wide range of technological matters. This could involve trouble shooting to resolve operating problems, or studies on the plant to increase throughput, improve yields and/or quality, or reduce operating costs.
   Mechanical engineers They are involved in a wide range of engineering trouble shooting, management of projects, and the design of equipment (such as pressure vessels, heat exchangers, piping and mechanical handling equipment). The work also includes studies of mechanical, operational, and maintenance problems.

Training
After initial introductory period, training is mainly on the job and, where necessary as experience develops, may be supplemented by more formal courses, both in-company and external. These appointments are ideal opportunities to familiarise oneself with modern plant and equipment and develop the practical expertise to become professional engineers.

Conoco Limited (Marketing)

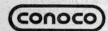

Activities
Marketing and distribution of fuel and heating oils and liquefied petroleum gases

Employees
1,500

Location: UK
London

Opportunities
Marketing; Administration; Engineering

Application address
Personnel Manager, Conoco Limited (Marketing Division), Conoco House, 230 Blackfriars Road, London SE1 8NR

Conoco Limited (Marketing) employs 1,500 people throughout the UK. It is primarily concerned with the marketing and distribution of automotive fuels, heating oils and liquefied petroleum gases. Jet is the principal retail brand name and the company holds a 5% share of Britain's retail petrol market through its 1,000 service stations. It markets home heating oils, industrial fuels and LPG under the Conoco brand name.
   The company operates 11 storage depots and distributes products to them from its refinery by sea, rail and pipeline. It has a fleet of 250 road tankers operating from these depots and 8 other associated locations.

Types of graduate required
There is a periodic need for graduates with *business studies* degrees in the marketing and administration divisions and for *engineers* in its operations division.

Training

Training is on the job, supported by in-house and external specialist courses.

Continental Oil Company Limited

Activities
Service company

Employees
350

Location: UK
London

Opportunities
Data processing; Employee relations

Application address
Continental Oil Company Ltd, 105 Wigmore Street, London W1H 0EL

This company provides a variety of service functions (legal, tax, employee relations etc) and acts as overall co-ordinator of Conoco's UK activities. It also contains a large computer centre in London and operates the company's marine fleet.

Types of graduate required

The company has an annual programme of recruitment, aimed primarily at graduates in *computer science* for employment in the London data centre. Occasionally there are openings for graduates in other disciplines, mainly in *business* courses, for the employee relations division.

Training

Training is provided for all graduates to ensure a thorough orientation into the company and is mainly on the job but supplemented by company and outside specialist courses according to individual needs.

Consolidated Gold Fields plc

There are opportunities in South Africa for newly qualified graduates in *mining engineering* and *mineral processing*.

For further information please see our entry in the Overseas section.

Co-operative Insurance Society Limited

Activities
Insurance

Employees
11,000

Location: UK
North West

Opportunities
Actuaries

Application address
MC Bennett, Co-operative Insurance Society Limited, Miller Street, Manchester M60 0AL

The CIS is one of the largest insurance offices in the country. It has eleven million life assurance policies in force and a large volume of motor, fire and accident business. The total funds are over £1,300 million and it has a staff of around 11,000 employees and full time agents.

Types of graduate required and training

Graduates are required as actuarial students. A sound mathematical background is important, as is a high level of numeracy. In addition to *mathematicians* and those reading allied subjects the CIS may be prepared to consider other graduates with the qualifications necessary to join the Institute or Faculty of Actuaries.

The CIS requires actuaries for work in the financial management of both its life and non-life insurance business, and there are opportunities for actuaries in the investment of the funds.

Actuarial students are allowed time for study in office hours, and they receive practical training through working directly with qualified actuaries.

Salaries

Initial salaries are competitive within the insurance industry. Salaries increase annually during training, with special increases for each examination subject passed.

Prospects for promotion are good for those who are able to make a useful contribution and undertake responsibility. Most actuarial staff are likely to be promoted to junior executive positions fairly soon after completing the examinations. As a guide, the salary scales for junior executive positions rose to a maximum of around £14,000 as at January 1982.

Further information
A booklet giving more details of an actuarial career with the CIS is available from university careers offices or from the address given.

Coopers & Lybrand

In 1979 Coopers & Lybrand celebrated 125 years of growth, a growth that has been particularly strong since the last war, and has been largely self-generated. Our clients encompass all walks of life, commercial and government, nationalised and privately owned, large, medium and small, located both in the UK and throughout the world. Our emphasis has always been on professionalism, integrity and the practical advice to clients in a friendly environment.

Opportunities for graduates
We are offering some 250 training contracts for graduates this year in our 28 UK offices. We retain a well known firm of professional tutors to prepare you for the examinations and our examination pass rates are good. You will have the chance to experience different specialisations such as tax or insolvency work during your training. Your audit work will be varied and your audit group will average about 25 people. Our group system helps the student to make the transition from an academic environment to the business world successfully and happily. It also enables us to monitor closely your individual career development. On completing your training, you will have every opportunity to travel overseas; we are represented in 94 countries and we have over 400 staff seconded overseas at any one time. Promotion within the firm is rapid and we recognise and reward individual talent.

Your training
Your training is the responsibility of a number of people, those in our training department, our financial tutors and the qualified members of your small audit group. In addition to the training for membership of the Institute of Chartered Accountants in England and Wales (or, in Scottish offices, for the Institute of Chartered Accountants in Scotland), we will give you in your first few weeks an introductory training course covering the firm's approach to auditing and to practical accountancy. This will give you the knowledge, and confidence, to meet your first client. The courses that you will attend subsequently will continue this practical theme by covering, for example, computer auditing, taxation and reporting to client's management. Training will continue throughout your career with us. The training at all our UK offices, both in London and elsewhere, will be the same. In addition, where possible, we limit overtime to a minimum to ensure that you have time to study for your examinations. You will be given four weeks holiday.

After qualification
When you have passed your examinations you can develop your career with us in many ways either in the UK or abroad. You may wish to remain in the general practice side of our business. You may, however, wish to get experience in a specialist area such as corporate tax or personal services, computer auditing or liquidations. When you have a sufficiently wide experience, you may join our management consultancy department. We are especially conscious of the need to ensure that your

Coopers & Lybrand

Activities
Chartered accountancy, including audit tax, general financial advice and other services

Employees
3,000 UK, Northern Ireland and Channel Islands with over 25,000 worldwide

Locations: UK
General

Locations: Overseas
Worldwide

Opportunities & places
Trainee chartered accountants 250

Application address
National Student Manager, Coopers & Lybrand, Abacus House, Gutter Lane, London EC2V 8AH

training prepares you as a manager for business life whether you stay in the profession or decide to pursue a financial career outside it.

Further information
You can get a copy of our graduate booklet and an application form from your careers advisory service, or by writing to the National Student Manager at the address given.

If you wish to be considered for an interview when we visit your university or polytechnic during the milk round, please contact your careers department. If you wish to apply earlier, please inform your careers department or send your application direct to the National Student Manager.

Coopers & Lybrand Associates Limited

The UK firm of Coopers & Lybrand Associates Limited forms part of the international firm of Coopers & Lybrand which provides public accounting and management consulting services throughout the world. Of the staff of over 22,000 some 1,100 specialise in management consultancy.

As one of the largest British management consulting firms Coopers & Lybrand Associates has a multi-discipline staff of over 200 consultants including specialists in data processing, management accounting, production management, marketing, organisation and personnel, operations research and economic studies. Consulting clients include both large and small industrial and commercial firms and a wide range of Government and other public sector organisations. A significant part of our work is carried out overseas.

Types of graduate required
We are looking primarily for *computer science* and *numerate* graduates but are prepared to consider other degree students. Graduates join our London based computer and communications group, which is responsible for the design, programming and implementation of computer systems, and for giving technical advice on the use of hardware and software and for general EDP consultancy work.

Starting as a programming member of a project team, staff rapidly gain experience of many computers, languages and applications. The technical knowledge gained on assignments is supplemented by courses which are geared to expand your EDP business and consulting skills. Staff are given progressively increased responsibility and develop rapidly in accordance with their own abilities and talents from programming through project leadership to systems analysis and design and consultancy work. Promotion can be gained to the highest levels in the group and you may develop to more general EDP consultancy work such as strategic planning, organisation studies and effectiveness reviews.

Benefits
Coopers & Lybrand Associates Limited offers graduates a challenging career with the stimulus provided by a variety of assignments and clients and by colleagues who are intellectually demanding. Experience is gained rapidly, progression is through ability and there are opportunities for worldwide travel.

Further information
For further information see your careers adviser who will have our booklet *A career in data processing* or write direct to Octavia Jennings.

Coopers &Lybrand associates

Activities
Management consultancy

Employees
200

Location: UK
London

Locations: Overseas
Europe; Africa; Middle East; Far East; West Indies

Opportunities
Programming initially, followed by systems design and eventually consultancy

Vacancies
10

Upper age limit
26

Application address
Octavia Jennings, Coopers & Lybrand Associates Limited, Shelley House, Noble Street, London EC2V 7DQ

Cossor Electronics Limited

Activities
Design and manufacture of advanced electronic equipment and systems

Employees
2,000

Location: UK
South East

Opportunities
Electronic systems engineer; Hardware and software development; Quality engineering; Test gear design; Service engineer; Production engineer

Vacancies
20

Application address
Mr D King, Manager, Manpower Resources, Cossor Electronics Limited, The Pinnacles, Harlow, Essex CM19 5BB

Cossor Electronics Limited is a designer and manufacturer of high technology electronic products. The rapid innovations centred around the growth in microelectronics are bringing about revolutionary changes. Cossor is in the forefront of that revolution.

The company's product range includes: ground radar equipment and systems; IFF (identification friend or foe) and SSR (secondary surveillance radar); instrument landing and airborne navigation equipment; telecommunications and computer visual display terminal systems. Equipment is sold to armed forces, civil authorities and commercial concerns throughout the world. For example, among the current developments are: ADSEL, a selectively addressed SSR system for the Civil Aviation Authority; the first fully electronic military teleprinter which will be standard equipment for the British Forces in the 1980's; the new IFF 3500 which has been developed for the UK fit of the Tornado multi-role combat aircraft; and NIS, the new NATO identification system.

Cossor is a British company, part of the AC Cossor Group which is in turn owned by the multi-billion dollar Raytheon company. Each company benefits from the resources and skills of the group. Cossor are currently working closely in the computer programming field with Data Logic Limited and exploring the exciting new area of fibre-optics with Sterling Cables Limited, both sister companies in the British group.

Types of graduate required
Cossor Electronics has embarked on an ambitious expansion programme which will more than double its present turnover to £57 million within five years and will increase the number employed to 2,500. This means that there are opportunities for graduates (including mature students) in all spheres of operation: systems, design, hardware, software, quality, production engineering, manufacture, sales, service, finance and management services. Graduates in *electronic engineering, computer science* and *production engineering* are particularly required.

Training
Cossor Electronics offers a flexible career development programme, with training programmes that include internal and external courses and full on the job instruction.

The company believes in providing competitive salaries and terms of employment. Rapid business expansion and a policy of promotion from within the company mean excellent promotional opportunities are assured for enthusiastic graduates able to make an early contribution to our business.

Richard Costain plc

Activities
Construction of major civil engineering contracts throughout the world

Employees
15,000

Locations: UK
General

Richard Costain plc is engaged in a worldwide programme of ambitious civil engineering projects; a programme encompassing all aspects of civil engineering construction including marine works, dams, tunnels, airports and major road and bridge contracts.

Much of this work involves the application of ever increasing knowhow and methods of modern technology and therefore calls for trained and experienced managers and specialists who can contribute to the future progress and expansion of a forward looking group.

Types of graduate required
Our requirement is for graduates with a *civil engineering* degree.

Locations: Overseas
Worldwide
Opportunities
Civil engineers
Application address
Education and Training Officer, Richard Costain
plc, 111 Westminster Bridge Road, London SE1

Training and prospects

A three year training programme allows those with the above qualification to gain the necessary experience, both on-site and in an office, to give their career a confident foundation as well as preparing them for their professional MICE qualification. The acquisition of further specialised experience and understanding of modern technical developments and methods is regarded as a continuous process and even at later stages of their career, civil engineers will attend training courses designed to extend or update their knowledge. Career progress within the group, which implies the assumption of greater management or specialist responsibility, rests entirely on achievements and the evidence of ability.

Location

For the first two years, employment will almost certainly be in a UK location. After that, there may be opportunities for service on short term overseas contracts.

Courage Limited

Please see under Imperial Brewing and Leisure Ltd.

Crown Life

Activities
Sale and administration of life, pensions and group insurance products

Employees
460

Location: UK
Woking, Surrey

Opportunities
Actuarial trainees

Application address
Alan Clarke, Personnel Manager, Crown Life Group of Companies, Crown Life House, Woking, Surrey GU21 1XW

The Crown Life Group of Companies is a subsidiary of the Crown Life Insurance Company of Canada, one of the largest life offices in North America. Crown Life has been operating in the UK since 1934, but in 1978 activities in this country were brought under the control of a separate UK corporate organisation. The companies in the UK group are the Crown Life Assurance Company and Crown Life Pensions, which together form one of the fastest growing life offices in the UK, Crown Life Management Services and Crown Computer Services. The latter was launched in 1981 to exploit Crown Life's expertise in the design of computer programs for the insurance industry. To further this profitable expansion Crown Life is committed to entry into Europe in 1984.

Disciplines and related jobs

There are opportunities for highly self-motivated graduates in numerate subjects such as *mathematics*, *statistics* and *physics* who would like to study to become actuaries.

Training

Examination fees, study expenses, plus two half-days study leave a week are given for the Institute of Actuaries qualification. There is as much personal advice and tuition from our own qualified staff as you require, and being a medium sized company we are able to offer you the chance to work in all the different areas of the actuarial function.

Career development

Your own capacity and willingness to assume responsibility will obviously have a direct bearing on your development, but there are few ceilings.

Salaries and conditions

Starting salaries for actuarial students will not be less than £5,750 and fringe benefits include free life assurance, subsidised mortgage facilities on completion of a service requirement and interest free season ticket

Our future is in your hands

Crosfield Electronics recognises that technology plays an ever increasing role in our lives. We have rewarding careers for graduates to be responsible for the design, manufacture and management of multi-discipline high technology equipment for the graphic arts industry. This involves the use of digital electronics, micro/mini-computers, lasers and complex optical systems.

So to secure yourself a better future, please telephone or write to:

Personnel Department,
Crosfield Electronics Limited,
766 Holloway Road, London N19 3JG.
Telephone: 01-272 7766.

A De La Rue Company

Crosfield Electronics

Success in exporting Advanced Technology

Crown Life, cont

loans. There is also a subsidised staff cafeteria and an active sports and social club.

Applications procedure
If you feel you have the motivation and commitment necessary for this type of work, send brief details of your academic achievement and outside interests to Alan Clarke at the address given.

Crosfield Electronics Limited

Crosfield Electronics
Success in exporting
Advanced Technology

Activities
Development, manufacture and worldwide marketing of advanced electronics equipment for the printing and graphic arts industry.

Employees
1,200 worldwide

Locations: UK
London and Midlands

Locations: Overseas
All EEC countries; South America; Far East

Opportunities
Developing analogue and digital electronics, precision optics and laser technology

Application address
Personnel Department, Crosfield Electronics Limited, 766 Holloway Road, London N19 3JG

Crossfield Electronics Limited, a member of the highly successful De La Rue Group, is one of Britain's most exciting electronics companies. Right at the forefront of technology, the company designs, manufactures and supplies sophisticated equipment to the graphics industry internationally and is a leader in the graphic arts and printing control business, its most important products being printing press controls and electronic colour scanners.

The organisation, which employs some 1,200 personnel worldwide, has its headquarters in London and its manufacturing operation in Peterborough and has a multi-million pound turnover. There are sales and service companies in the USA, Germany, France, Italy, Switzerland, South Africa, Brazil and Austria (serving Eastern Europe) and agents representing the company in most other countries. Approximately 80% of Crosfield products are exported, with a substantial proportion going to the USA and Japan, no mean feat for a British electronics organisation. Furthermore, Crosfield's enviable reputation for technological and export achievement has earned no less then six Queens Awards to Industry.

Prospects for young graduates entering the company are excellent; the rate of expansion and heavy investment in research and development allows *engineering science* graduates to gain early responsibility as members of small multi-discipline project teams developing micro and mini-computers, lasers, digital electronics and precision optics. The company operates modern management techniques and has excellent conditions of employment, including four weeks annual holiday, rising to over five weeks in accordance with service, a contributory pension scheme, flexible working hours, annual profit sharing bonus scheme, and a whole range of other benefits normally associated with a progressive employer.

C & S Antennas

Activities
Development, manufacture and installation of antennas for broadcasting and telecommunications

Employees
90

CSA is the largest specialist UK manufacturer of antennas. Its products and services are used by broadcasting and telecommunications services all over the world. The company is a member of a British group with diverse engineering interests.

Antenna development provides a variety of challenging practical and theoretical work for creative engineers. In the environment of a small technically alert company you will find that your skills and interests will be encouraged and you will see your own ideas put quickly into practice. We have good technical facilities and make wide use of computer methods in our design work.

Our products, some of which are entirely unique and are at the forefront of antenna technology, span the whole RF spectrum from LF to

Location: UK
South East

Opportunities
Antenna development engineers

Application address
BS Collins, The Technical Director, C&S Antennas Ltd, Knight Road, Strood, Rochester, Kent ME2 2AX

SHF. They range from complex high power transmitting systems to high directivity multi-beam receiving antennas.

We need more engineering skills in development, product support and on-site commissioning work both in the UK and abroad.

Types of graduate required
The basic qualification sought is an *electrical/electronic engineering* or *physics* degree. We look for applicants who are well motivated and will rise to the challenge of working in a small team.

Prospects
CSA is a vigorous expanding company. As the company grows, larger and more complex projects are undertaken, providing engineering staff with growing experience and increasing responsibility. There are also opportunities for engineers to move into marketing or general management. Most engineers have opportunities to travel and work abroad for short periods.

Training
As well as providing on the job training we encourage all our engineers to widen their experience by attending conferences and seminars and writing papers and articles. We encourage engineers to obtain corporate membership of the professional institutions.

Salaries and other benefits
Salaries are competitive and are reviewed annually. Other benefits include good pensions, disability and life insurance schemes. Our location is in the Medway towns with pleasant countryside and good sailing water nearby.

Applications
If you would like to know more about a career with CSA, please write to BS Collins at the address given.

Cubie Wood & Co Ltd

Activities
Actuarial advice to clients

Employees
75

Locations: UK
Croydon, Surrey and general

Locations: Overseas
Associated companies in Ireland, Australia, New Zealand, South Africa, Germany, USA

Vacancies
6 approx

Application address
Phil Bainbridge, Personnel Manager, Cubie Wood & Co Ltd, Norfolk House, Wellesley Road, Croydon, Surrey CR9 3EB

Cubie Wood is an expanding and dynamic organisation offering the advice of its actuaries to a broad range of clients. Most of our work relates to UK pension schemes, although involvement in international assignments is expanding. We offer considerable scope for personal development, which is appropriately rewarded. Cubie Wood is a subsidiary of Noble Lowndes & Partners Ltd who are part of the Hill Samuel Group.

Types of graduate required
We require *maths* or *statistics* graduates who wish to study with the Institute or Faculty of Actuaries; they must be analytical and logical and be able to communicate effectively.

Training
Graduate recruits are immediately involved in the work of a small team with a principle actuary, responsible for their professional development. In-house training is mainly informal, though use is made of external courses offered by professional bodies. Trainees are also encouraged to participate in training schemes operated by Noble Lowndes & Partners and Hill Samuel. Graduates' study leave, examination and tuition fees are paid.

Salaries and benefits
Our 1983 salaries and benefits package will be competitive to attract the
high calibre graduates we need.

Cummins Engine Company Limited

Innovation in the then new field of diesel engines established Cummins in
1919, gained them front page headlines in 1930 with the first public
demonstration of a diesel car – 'Indianapolis to New York on $1.38 of
fuel' – and made them America's major source of truck and marine
diesels in World War II.

Today Cummins is the largest independent producer of diesel engines
in the world and is committed not only to building engines that meet
tough performance standards but also to the development and welfare of
its employees.

UK company
The operations in the UK are largely autonomous and comprise
manufacturing facilities at Darlington (with a satellite plant at Peterlee),
Shotts and Daventry plus office facilities for central staff functions at
Darlington and New Malden. Holset Limited, based at Huddersfield and
manufacturing turbochargers, is a wholly owned subsidiary. Some 6,000
personnel are now employed throughout the UK organisation.

Darlington operation
The Darlington plant is responsible for the manufacture of the V6 and V8
range of diesel engines for a growing number of truck, marine and
construction equipment applications.

Additionally, located at Darlington are a number of central functions
providing technical, financial and purchasing support to all UK
locations.

Opportunities for graduates
We are seeking to recruit male or female graduates for all the major
functions. An *engineering* degree is a prerequisite for the technical
functions of manufacturing and engineering, but graduates of *any*
discipline will be considered for functions such as finance, purchasing,
personnel and management, and commercial services.

Training
We operate a flexible training scheme with the emphasis on the
attainment of professional qualifications. During your training period
you will generally be located at Darlington, and will gain exposure to a
broad spectrum of the company's activities. You will be assigned
carefully selected projects and given opportunities for problem solving of
sufficient diversity to enable you to attain a sound understanding of the
role of your chosen function within the organisation as a whole. The
range of selected projects can cover a wide variety of activities: anything
from preparing future graduate recruitment literature for a graduate in
personnel to the investigation of engine warranty problems for a graduate
in engineering.

During your period as a graduate trainee regular review meetings will
be held to assess the effectiveness of your training programme. You will
be counselled and guided as to possible career paths. Training thereafter
will be based on individual needs and the requirements of the chosen
career path.

The future
The company's policy is always to promote from within wherever
possible. For the graduate this means that every entrant is watched

Activities
Manufacture of the world's leading high speed
diesel engine

Employees
6000

Locations: UK
London and North East

Opportunities
See main text

Application address
Josie Pottinger, Personnel Manager, Cummins
Engine Company Limited, Yarm Road,
Darlington, County Durham DL1 4PW
Tel: 0325 60606

Cummins Engine Company Limited, cont

carefully and given the kind of experience which will make the most of their abilities. We know that the graduates of today may well provide the company's leaders in future years, either within the UK or other areas of the world wide organisation.

Cummins benefits

We can offer a very competitive salary and all the benefits associated with a large progressive organisation. All staff participate in a contributory pension scheme, free life assurance and have 25 days holiday each complete year with the company.

If you are interested in getting to know more about us, further details should be available from your university careers office.

If you need any additional information please address your questions to Josie Pottinger, Personnel Manager, at the address given.

Daresbury Laboratory
Science and Engineering Research Council

Activities
Scientific research; Engineering; Computing; Electronics

Employees
555

Location: UK
North West

Opportunities
Applied physics; Mechanical/electrical engineering; Computer programming; User support; Electronics design and development; Experimental physics

Vacancies
15 maximum

Upper age limit
27 preferably

Application address
Mr KV Ahmed, Personnel Officer, Daresbury Laboratory, Science and Engineering Research Council, Daresbury, Nr Warrington WA4 4AD

Daresbury Laboratory, an establishment of the Science and Engineering Research Council situated in the north Cheshire countryside is looking for graduates in science, computing and engineering.

The laboratory has two major projects:

The Synchrotron Radiation Source: the world's first high energy (2 GeV) electron storage ring specifically designed to provide a large number of synchrotron radiation beams.

The Nuclear Structure Facility: the world's largest tandem electrostatic accelerator which will be used to accelerate ions for use for research into the nucleus of the atom.

Types of graduate required

Scientists are required for the new facilities described above. *Computing* graduates are needed for the laboratory's very advanced computer system based on a Cray 1 and an AS 7,000 with GEC 4070's, PDP-11's and Interdatas. There are *engineering* vacancies for engineering support in mechanical, electrical and electronic engineering.

Training will be given in all areas of work but it is expected that you will be contributing fully to the work of the laboratory in a very short time and that you will have specific tasks to carry out.

Salaries and benefits

Salaries are under review. At present the scales are scientific officer £5,176–£6,964 and graduate engineer £6,557–£8,697.

There is a non-contributory superannuation scheme, a generous leave allowance and a flexible working hours scheme.

Applications

If you are interested in being involved in work at the frontiers of science and engineering which will also provide good opportunities for career development and advancement, write for an application form to Kamal Ahmed at the address given.

Data Logic Limited

A Raytheon Company

Activities
consultancy, software, systems supply, terminal systems, data communications products, word processors, microprocessor systems, field service

Employees
60

Locations: UK
London; West London; Midlands; North West

Opportunities
systems analysts and programmers; Digital engineers

Vacancies
5

Application address
Personnel Manager, Data Logic Limited,
20 Ruislip Road East, Greenford, Middlesex
B6 9BH

Data Logic is a unique systems company, with services ranging from consultancy to the supply of computer and data communications products. Software and hardware skills are equally represented, reflecting the balance between hardware and software in contemporary computer systems. The field service force is larger than that in any comparable systems company, providing the necessary degree of nationwide support to the systems the company supplies.

As a subsidiary of Raytheon, one of the world's leading high technology companies, Data Logic offers the advantages of a relatively small company coupled with the security of very large organisations.

Data Logic operates at the forefront of computing, applying the very latest hardware and techniques to practical commercial problems. We cover the range from mainframes to the smallest computers. We are leaders in the use of microprocessors for applications that not so long ago required far larger machines. Several projects involve dispersed networks of ten or more minicomputers.

The exceptional scope of work is important to our staff. We can match their individual experience to their projects. Equally, we can ensure that each project adds to their experience. As computing itself develops, so do they. In short, people at Data Logic have some of the most satisfying work you can find. And the extra satisfaction of learning as they do it.

Types of graduate required
Applications are welcomed from men and women following a single or joint honours course in *computing/computer science*. Students following a course in *business* or business related studies are also invited to apply. Relevant industrial experience would be an advantage.

Career development
Ultimately, graduates may progress to: technical specialisation, project management or general management. All are equally rewarded and recognised. A rigorous career counselling system is aimed at identifying each individual's personal abilities and preferences, then steering each member of staff along the best career path for them.

Prospects
Data Logic's growth has been, and will continue to be, governed by the rate at which our staff can assume responsibility and develop their technical skills. Promotion is primarily a matter of the individual's skills and his or her motivation. Data Logic tries to provide the framework within which personal ambitions, whether high or modest, have the best possible chance of being realised.

Application address
Applications should be made initially to our office in West London. The standard introduction form is quite acceptable. As many universities as possible are visited each year for on the spot interviews.

Davy McKee Limited

a Davy Corporation company

Activities
Design, engineering and project management
of plant and equipment for the iron and
steelmaking, minerals processing, metallurgical
extraction and related industries

Employees
1,000

Location: UK
North East

Locations: Overseas
Worldwide

Opportunities
Mechanical engineering; Electrical engineering;
Process engineering; Chemical engineering

Vacancies
15–20

Application address
Recruitment Officer, Davy McKee Limited,
Ashmore House, Stockton on Tees, Cleveland
TS18 3LT

The name of Davy McKee is associated with many of the world's largest
developments in a wide variety of process industries. The company is a
world leader in engineering and contracting and has the capacity to
design, engineer and supply multi-million pound turnkey projects from
design stage through to commissioning.

Activities

The company is part of Davy Corporation, a multinational engineering
and contracting group serving the world's petrochemical, plastics,
synthetic fibres, minerals, iron and steel, non-ferrous metals, gas and
other process industries. Davy McKee Limited has grown steadily in the
last few years and currently has over 1,000 employees, many of whom are
highly qualified and experienced professional engineers, technologists,
and members of management. The specialised skills of these staff are
widely used on the overall design, engineering, planning and
management of major projects. The company is based in Stockton on
Tees, but a large part of its work is overseas, and staff may travel
extensively or be seconded to sites in many parts of the world.

Opportunities

The principal opportunities are for graduates in the following disciplines:
*mechanical engineering, chemical engineering, electrical engineering,
metallurgy, instrumentation* and *control, minerals processing, fuels science.*

There may also be opportunities for a few graduates in non-
engineering disciplines such as *economics* or *law* to train in the
commercial, legal, financial or administrative areas. The training is,
however, broadly based and graduates trained initially as mechanical,
electrical or process engineers may in time move into sales, contracts or
site management.

Training

The training programme covers approximately 18 months, and is
designed to give graduates a thorough grounding in most aspects of
engineering contracting.

The programme is tailored to meet the particular needs or wishes of the
individual trainee. Emphasis is placed on involvement in the work of the
department to which the graduate is assigned, and trainees are expected
to make a positive contribution from an early stage. There are
opportunities to gain experience on sites in the UK and overseas.

Further information

Further information can be found in the company's booklet *Careers for
Graduates in Engineering* which is available at your university or college
careers centre. This booklet contains up to date details on current
activities, recruitment requirements, starting salaries, etc.

If you are interested in a career in an exciting and expanding
environment please complete the standard university introduction form
available from your appointments officer, or write for an application form
to the Recruitment Officer.

Davy McKee (London) Limited

Davy Corporation company

1979

Activities
Design, procurement, construction and project management of chemical process plant

Employees
700

Location: UK
London

Locations: Overseas
Worldwide

Opportunities
Process design; Design engineering; Procurement

Application address
Personnel Manager, Recruitment, Davy McKee (London) Limited, 250 Euston Road, London NW1 2PG

Davy McKee (London) Limited is a major British engineering and construction company offering clients throughout the world a complete start to finish capability from master planning and process and engineering design, to the construction and commissioning of a complete complex. We are involved in projects for the oil and gas, chemical and petrochemical industries, both onshore and offshore.

We are part of Davy McKee, the British group of engineering companies which covers a wider span of technology than any other comparable group in the world. Davy McKee has its main engineering contracting centres in the UK, USA and West Germany. There are fully equipped engineering companies in a further nine countries, and offices, associates and representatives in an additional 13 countries.

Types of graduate required
We recruit *chemical* and *mechanical engineers* annually for our engineering departments. Non-engineering graduates interested in a career in procurement should also apply.

Training and career progression
Engineering graduates will join either our process engineering or design engineering departments where they will spend up to two years on a training programme. During this time they gain on the job experience of the broad spectrum of a contractor's work with site and other practical experience away from head office, as required. The training is geared to the requirements of the professional institutions and normally leads to a first appointment in one of the process or design engineering groups. Subsequent careers can continue in these departments up to senior management or technical level, or after in-depth design experience graduates can pursue careers in project engineering and management, proposals, sales, business development or site management.

Non-engineering or engineering graduates who have decided to specialise in procurement will, after training and subsequent experience, be making decisions which affect the success of multi-million pound projects. The procurement department plays a vital role in supplying a vast range of equipment, from miles of pipelines to compressors worth over £10 million each. Procurement management arranges these supplies from worldwide sources and ensures they reach remote sites in the right order and at the right time.

Salaries and conditions
Initial salaries are in line with those offered by London based engineering companies generally. Earnings of trained personnel in this highly competitive and demanding industry are appreciably higher than those paid in general engineering or manufacturing. Pension, holiday and other benefits are excellent.

Further information
Men and women interested in one of the most satisfying careers in engineering should apply to the Personnel Manager, Recruitment.

Dearborn Chemicals Limited

Activities
Complete water treatment service to industry

Employees
270

Locations: UK
General

Locations: Overseas
Italy; Greece

Opportunities & places
Junior consultants 5 approx

Upper age limit
25

Application address
Recruitment Manager, Dearborn Chemicals Limited, Widnes, Cheshire WA8 8TZ

Dearborn, part of the WR Grace Corporation (USA), offers a comprehensive water and fuel treatment service to industry; aimed at preventing the costly effects of scale, corrosion and other fouling deposits on heated metal surfaces.

Dearborn's work falls into two broad catagories: preventative treatment and problem solving; firstly anticipating client's problems and providing the necessary solution, and secondly rectifying problems in existing plant.

Training

Dearborn employs a field force of nearly 100 trained sales consultants backed by research and testing facilities. We wish to recruit graduates or equivalent, in *chemistry* or *chemical engineering* who can use our comprehensive training and sales induction programme to build a great sales career in field consultancy. Your success will largely depend on your commercial acumen and technical awareness therefore no previous experience in water treatment is necessary.

Successful completion of training leads to appointment as sales consultant, usually in about 12 months. Most Dearborn management appointments are made from within the company therefore career advancement opportunities are excellent.

Benefits

An attractive remuneration package comprises a competitive basic salary, a profit sharing scheme, lunch allowance and a fully maintained company car.

Dearden Farrow

Activities
Chartered accountancy

Employees
400 London

Locations: UK
London; South East; South West; North West; Scotland

Opportunities & places
Trainee chartered accountants 30

Application address
George Bunney, Dearden Farrow, 1 Serjeants Inn, Fleet Street, London EC4Y 1JD

Dearden Farrow was formed in April 1977 by an amalgamation of three firms of chartered accountants. In our London office we have 44 partners and a staff of 400, and this low ratio results in a much more personal relationship between partners, staff and clients than is normal in a firm of our size. We also have offices or associated offices in other UK cities and associations with many local firms abroad.

Our clients range from substantial public companies to the smallest businesses operating in the fields of industry, finance and the professions. Thus we offer our student accountants a first class background to their careers as chartered accountants.

During the three years of your contract you will be a member of one of our audit groups, each of which is a self contained unit of about 20 people under the control of a manager. This gives the advantages of working in a small unit and as each group has a wide range of clients you will also get extensive experience. Your progress will be constantly supervised by your manager who will give you the responsibility that you are capable of taking.

Training

We send all students to one of the leading accountancy tutors to assist in preparation for the examinations and we have an in-house training department who are responsible for training in the more practical aspects of accountancy.

Further information

For a copy of our booklet or for any further information please contact George Bunney, Staff Partner at the given address.

Deloitte Haskins & Sells

Activities
Chartered accountancy and financial services

Employees
3,500 UK
20,000 worldwide

Locations: UK
General

Locations: Overseas
Worldwide

Opportunities & places
Trainee chartered accountants 350

Upper age limit
28

Application address
Philip Johnson, Deloitte Haskins & Sells,
25 Bread Street, PO Box 142, London
EC4V 4AJ

Deloitte Haskins & Sells is a leading international firm of chartered accountants which has offices throughout the United Kingdom and in all five continents, providing a comprehensive range of professional accountancy services. Its clients include many leading industrial, commercial and financial organisations throughout the world as well as many medium and small sized companies and partnerships.

Deloittes' staff receive excellent training and experience in all the major accounting areas, including financial and management accounting, auditing, taxation, EDP and investigations. There are many opportunities for rewarding careers in the firm, both in the UK and overseas, either in general practice work, or in specialist departments. For those who choose not to make their careers with the firm, the training given will fit them for senior positions in other organisations, including many of the firm's clients.

Types of graduate required
Graduates of *all* disciplines are recruited: almost half the vacancies each year are in the London office. Most graduates commence in the autumn, but there is a small intake of about 20 in the London office each spring. The firm also has a small number of vacancies in management consultancy and taxation each year. Candidates are considered at the time of the main intake selection procedure or in the early stages of a training contract for transfer on qualification. This is considered to be one of the earliest available routes into consultancy work and tax.

Training
The firm attaches considerable importance to the regular and progressive training of graduates, to equip them to carry out practical work and to pass examinations. So that graduates can take on considerable responsibility in as short a time as possible and at the same time acquire a good grounding in modern auditing and accounting techniques, much emphasis is placed on the extensive practical training programme which is conducted by senior members of the firm's practice staff, working under the general guidance of one of the firm's four regional training centres which are located in different parts of the UK. During their first three years with the firm, graduates will attend six practical training courses totalling some eight weeks and regular training continues after qualifying. These courses are based to a large extent on case studies and group discussions and ensure that graduates are fully capable of carrying out smaller audits by themselves after one year and can then progressively take on more complicated work. Examination tuition is provided at the firm's expense, by professional tutors who give comprehensive tutorial courses combining home study with periods of full time instruction during study leave. An integrated tutorial programme provides for technical guidance through regular day release.

Further information
Representatives from the firm visit many of the universities each year. After each visit, selected applicants for the London office are invited to one of the recruitment seminars which are held in London between November and March and selected applicants for other offices are invited to a further interview at the office of their choice. Applicants should check the dates of the visits and should apply for an interview through their careers advisory service or directly to the address given. If no university visit is planned or if the date of the visit presents difficulties for you it may be possible to arrange an earlier interview by writing directly to Philip Johnson.

Department of Industry
Science Group Staff

Activities
Scientific research and development

Employees
1,700

Locations: UK
Scotland; London; South East

Opportunities
Chemistry; Computer science; Engineering;
Mathematics; Physics

Vacancies
40

Upper age limit
27–32 according to grade

Application address
See main text

The Department of Industry Science Group offers challenging opportunities for graduates to join programmes which aim to foster the application of technology within the country's manufacturing industries. The Department's activities are carried out at the following establishments:

The National Physical Laboratory Teddington TW11 0LW. This laboratory is chiefly responsible for establishing, maintaining and disseminating national standards of measurement of physical quantities and with research into methods of measurement, engineering properties of materials and computer usage.

The National Engineering Laboratory East Kilbride G75 0QU. This laboratory conducts research and development over a wide range of engineering problems including numerical control of machine tools, hydrostatic pumps, robotics and many other items of economic importance to engineering industry.

The National Maritime Institute Feltham TW14 0LQ. Although largely concerned with ship hydrodynamics, handling and propulsion, the Institute is increasingly occupied with studies of stresses associated with offshore structures. A government decision has been taken to convert the institute into an independent research laboratory. The operative date for this to take effect is (at the time of going to press) 1st October 1982.

The Laboratory of the Government Chemist London SE1 9NQ. This laboratory carries out chemical analysis for Government departments. Its interests include food chemistry, alcohol, agricultural materials, radiochemistry and forensic science, to name but a few. Research into methods of analysis is also undertaken and the laboratory possess a wide range of modern equipment to assist in this task.

The Warren Spring Laboratory Stevenage SG1 2BX. This is a multi-disciplinary research eatablishment. Research includes physical and chemical methods of mineral concentration, the treatment of domestic and industrial waste and the measurement and abatement of pollution.

Types of graduate required
Graduates with qualifications in *mathematics, physics, chemistry, electrical, mechanical* and *chemical engineering* are required. The number recruited each year is not high and personal qualities as well as academic achievements are of considerable importance.

Salaries and prospects
Candidates may be offered a starting salary above the minimum of the published scales according to their qualifications and experience.

Promotion is on merit by annual review. Those who later wish to move from research and engage in the wider policy activities of the Department, as technological generalists, will be encouraged to develop the necessary qualities. Scientific careers can progress to very senior levels where considerable management responsibilities are involved. For the high quality research scientist the alternative individual merit promotion scheme offers appointments to similar senior levels whilst the officer's specialist studies continue. Enquiries to the individual laboratories should be addressed to the Director (Ref DOG 83).

Robert M Douglas Holdings plc

Activities
Civil engineering and building construction

Employees
3,000

Locations: UK
General

Opportunities
Civil engineers; Builders; Quantity surveyors

Vacancies
20 approx

Application address
KJ Hayzelden, BA, MIPM, Group Training
Manager, Robert M Douglas Holdings plc,
395 George Road, Erdington, Birmingham
B23 7RZ

Robert M Douglas Holdings Limited, the holding company of a group operating in civil engineering and building construction, was founded in 1930.

The principal subsidiary company, RM Douglas Construction Limited undertakes a variety of projects in all parts of the British Isles and has successfully completed many schemes for government departments, public authorities and industrial organisations.

In 1959 British Lift Slab Limited was formed as the sole licensee in the United Kingdom of the lift slab method of multi-storey building construction. In addition, this company is the United Kingdom licensee for the siemcrete system of sliding formwork (Slipform).

Full details of the Douglas Group may be found in our publication *Opportunities for Graduates*.

Types of graduate required

The Douglas Group offers opportunities in the United Kingdom to graduates in *civil* and *construction engineering* and *building* as engineers on construction sites, and later at headquarters in connection with design, planning and administration. Opportunities also arise for *mechanical engineers* interested in the operation and maintenance of contractors' plant and transport.

Opportunities occur each year for graduate *quantity surveyors* at our various area offices. Graduates are expected to take early responsibility and receive the majority of their training on-site.

Training

Graduates are encouraged to achieve early professional status and opportunities are given to obtain practical and theoretical experience in the construction industry.

Salaries

Initial salaries and allowances are dependent on qualifications and annual increments are based on merit. On completion of training there are opportunities for promotion in all branches of the group's operations, including contract management, design, estimating etc.

Dow Corning Limited

Activities
Manufacture and marketing of silicones

Employees
500 UK

Location: UK
Barry, South Wales

Locations: Overseas
Worldwide

Opportunities
Research and development; Process control
and instrumentation; Engineering; Technical
sales

Vacancies
10 approx

We are a wholly owned subsidiary of an American company, Dow Corning Corporation. Formed in 1942 to produce the first commercial silicone materials, we have developed as world technology leaders in the field of organo-silicones, with further major contributions to silicon and solid lubricant technology.

Company structure

A highly capital intensive and profitable company, we are divided globally into five areas and a mature business matrix organisation co-ordinates profit plans across line functions and areas. Our 1980 worldwide employment levels of 5,500 (with 1,000 in Europe and 500 in the UK) ensure small company-style personal contact with large company rewards and opportunities. Sales in 1981 exceeded $721 million and profits after tax exceeded $75 million. Over half of our sales were achieved outside the USA.

SET YOUR CAREER IN MOTION

Are you looking for a scheme to take you up to chartered engineer status? Dunlop's four year training and career development scheme satisfies the requirements of the Institutions of Mechanical, Electrical and Production Engineers, and will give the foundation on which to build your professional career.

During the first two years you will learn basic workshop skills, and design appreciation by completing on-the-job projects and assignments. In the following years you will use this knowledge and experience to gain your first permanent appointment and professional competency.

The discipline is tough, calling for considerable dedication and application. Once successfully completed, it opens the door to a satisfying career in engineering and can lead to multifunctional experience in manufacturing, marketing and sales, and general management.

Previous experience gained in manufacturing industry as a technician engineer or as part of a sandwich degree course is likely to accelerate the process to early responsibility and chartered status.

Dunlop is a leading worldwide organization manufacturing and marketing a wide range of industrial and consumer products, ranging from tyres to conveyor systems and from off-shore oil products to liferafts. We need engineers on every factory site, particularly in automotive, aviation and tyre engineering.

If our scheme appeals to you and you think you match up to our requirements, further details are available from: Manager, Graduate Careers, Dunlop Limited, Dunlop House, Ryder Street, London SW1Y 6PX.

UK operations

In our capital expansion plan for the next five years in Europe, is included a $300 million development already underway in Barry, South Wales.

Overseas operations

Our global operations are divided into five areas: USA, Europe (including East Bloc, Middle East and Africa), Pacific, Canada and Latin America.

Disciplines and related jobs

To help us build and operate our Barry plant we will need graduates of all *engineering* disciplines. To fine tune our technology and products to meet European market needs, we need more *chemists* and *chemical engineers*. Our five year plan includes more basic research and doctoral candidates will be welcome. Technical sales opportunities will also occur. Anticipated recruitment is in the region of 10 new or recent graduates a year for the UK, with occasional recruitment for other Dow Corning locations in Europe.

Training detail

Graduates will be given jobs in their specific fields and will become familiar with the company's products, technologies and processes. During the early years of employment, movement across functions or product groups is the norm. Formal training, both internal and external, will be provided for technical development, managerial skills and languages.

Career development

A well established career development structure offering opportunities in the professional and/or managerial field.

Salaries and amenities

We have a competitive salary scale, and our amenities include a subsidised canteen.

Applications and further information

Brochures are available at university careers offices. Interested candidates should apply in writing to the Industrial Relations Manager at the address given.

Application address
Industrial Relations Manager, Dow Corning Limited, Barry, S Glamorgan, South Wales CF6 7YL

Dunlop

From its beginnings with tyres, Dunlop's interests now encompass a vast range of manufactured goods, from aircraft brakes to sports goods and from vehicle suspension systems to off-shore oil products.

While tyres still form more than 50% of turnover and create the majority of opportunities within Dunlop, particularly in activities overseas, there are graduate opportunities throughout the range of the company's activities.

Opportunities

The ability to work independently and manage others is as important as the discipline of your degree. While initially progress is via functional specialisation either through professional training schemes or direct appointment, multi-functional career development is the route to success in general management.

Engineering

Engineers are recruited from *mechanical, electrical, electronic* and

Activities
Manufacturers of automotive, engineering, industrial and consumer products, and sports goods

Employees
27,000 UK

Locations: UK
Wales; Midlands; North East; North West

Dunlop, cont

Opportunities
Engineering; Finance; Information services;
Manufacturing management; Marketing and
sales; Personnel; Research; Technical

Vacancies
40–50

Application address
Manager, Graduate Careers, Dunlop Limited,
Ryder Street, London SW1Y 6PX

production engineering graduates, who have the capability of initiating a
project as well as following it through to completion. Four years of
training and professional development start with registration as a student
engineer with the appropriate engineering Institution on a monitored
scheme covering basic elements of machine tool skills, design and
development of product and plant by on the job management of
resources.

You learn by doing and working alongside experienced qualified
engineers to satisfy the requirements for chartered status. Previous
industrial experience as a technician engineer or as part of a sandwich
degree course could accelerate the process to early responsibility and
becoming a chartered engineer.

Science function
Chosen from *chemists, physicists, metallurgists, mathematicians* and
materials scientists: technologists of the future innovate, and develop and
adapt products, materials and manufacturing processes to satisfy
tomorrow's markets.

Production management
Production managers are recruited from *physical* and *applied science*
graduates with organisational and management abilities. Managers start
as shift supervisors and foremen, gaining experience in productivity
services; process and production planning can lead to senior management
in the manufacturing function.

Accountancy
Accountants are recruited from graduates in *accountancy, economics* and
business subjects. The three-year training scheme, which leads to ICMA
or ACCA examinations, concentrates on practical experience and gives
early responsibility; a first appointment can be made after two years.

Marketing
Trainees are recruited from *economics, business* and *science* graduates with
enthusiasm and a commitment to selling. A European language is also an
advantage. Assignments in product divisions give a thorough knowledge
of processes and products.

Personnel
Recruits should be all-rounders, preferably *numerate* and *science* based
with the ability to communicate and have an understanding of the other
functions in the manufacturing environment including industrial and
human relations, training and career development.

Information processing
Information processing requires graduates in *numerate* disciplines,
preferably in *computer science* or *engineering*, to work in data processing
with all types of systems appropriate to commercial, production,
marketing and technological applications.

Career development
Dunlop can offer you variety and the opportunity to develop multi-
functionally: its organisation ensures that motivation and ability are
rewarded, by recognising early achievement and success.

Further information
See your career or appointments service for information and a graduate
application form.

Activities
Aircraft, mining, industrial, hydraulic and
electronics equipment

Employees
15,000

Locations: UK
South West; Midlands; Wales; London

Opportunities
Design; Performance; Development; Stress;
Sales; Production and electronics engineering;
R&D; Computing; Administration

Vacancies
16

Upper age limit
25

Application addresses
Training Manager, Dowty Group Services
Limited, Arle Court, Cheltenham, Glos
Personnel Manager, Dowty UEL Limited
Marlow Place, Station Road, Marlow, Bucks
SL7 1NB
Training Executive, Dowty Boulton Paul Limited,
Pendeford Lane, Wolverhampton, Staffs

Dowty Group Limited

The Dowty Group consists of over 45 engineering companies designing
and manufacturing a wide range of electronic hydraulic and mechanical
equipment, radio frequency beacons, sonar devices and communications
systems for the aircraft, mining, marine, railway, automobile, earth
moving and agricultural industries; as well as rubber seals mouldings for
industry generally, and engine controls for the aircraft, automobile and
marine industries.

Types of graduate required
Graduates in *mechanical, production, aeronautical, electronics engineering*
and *computer science* are required both for training and for direct
appointments. The group can also accept a very limited number of
economics and *arts* graduates.

Training
A considerable range of training and expertise is offered throughout the
group. Graduates enter a two year apprenticeship, which includes a
period at training centres and subsequently in other departments.
Graduates under training normally study for further professional
qualifications and a programme is arranged to suit the particular needs of
each individual.

The group usually has openings for young men and women in design,
performance, development, stress, sales, production and electronics
engineering, R&D, computers and administrative departments. The
training manager will be pleased to discuss details with individual
applicants.

Location
The majority of the group's companies are located in and around the
Gloucestershire, Midlands, Wales and London areas. Although the
group has factories and offices in other countries, opportunities to work
abroad are limited.

Salaries
Salaries are highly competitive and reviewed annually, backed up with
the benefits associated with a large and successful organisation.
Promotion prospects are good throughout the group.

Activities
Personal insurances

Employees
300

Locations: UK
General

Opportunities
Sales; Underwriting and claims

Endsleigh Insurance Services

Since Endsleigh's formation in 1965, one of our principal personnel
policies has been the recruitment of young and ambitious people.
Flexible, committed people, with the ability and confidence to initiate
and realise their own thoughts and ideas. People determined to make real
progress as soon as possible.

There are two main career avenues open to graduates and each is likely
to appeal to a different type of candidate.

Insurance technician
The company provides a comprehensive training programme, the initial
part of which normally lasts around two years, geared to providing the
necessary technical knowledge and skills to fit the graduate for a career in
either our underwriting or claims department. Technicians enjoy an
unusual degree of personal autonomy plus a wide range of commercial
activities.

Normal progression would usually be initially to the role of senior

Application address
Alan Merry, Personnel Services Manager,
Endsleigh Insurance Services Limited,
Endsleigh House, Cheltenham Spa, Glos
GL50 3NR
Tel: 0242 36151

Endsleigh Insurance Services, cont

technician, with responsibility for the supervision and training of junior staff, as part of a comprehensive management development programme.

Sales division

The largest number of opportunities this year will be in the sales division, on our 15 month training programme leading to the position of insurance advisor. An advisor has an individual sales area to cover and is normally based on a university college or town. During the second stage of training, usually under the personal supervision of a senior advisor or area manager, the advisor will be visiting clients regularly at home to discuss the wider aspects of the insurance and financial planning needs. This implies a highly flexible approach to working hours and regular evening work. During this period, the trainee will be expected to show his or her capacity to reach and maintain monthly sales targets and at the same time ensuring that Endsleigh's name is synonymous with very best in client service and sound insurance advice.

After two years with us, our best trainees would expect to participate in our management development programme leading to appointment as senior advisor with specific responsibility for junior staff and a wider sector of commercial activities.

Location during training

Insurance technicians are based throughout their career at our Cheltenham head office. This year the company will be able to offer trainees within the sales division positions at the following locations: central London, Bristol, Cardiff, Birmingham, Liverpool, Manchester, Leeds, Newcastle, Edinburgh and East Midlands.

Salaries and benefits

Graduates can expect an attractive starting salary, which will be reviewed after six months. Trainee advisers are provided with a company car, upon completion of the initial training period, roughly nine months after joining. All staff, aged over 21, are members of a comprehensive and free pension, life assurance and permanent health insurance scheme.

Applications

Applications may be made, preferably on the company's own application form, either through your careers service or direct to the address given.

Equity & Law Life Assurance Society plc

Equity & Law was established in 1844 and is today a leading company in the demanding and competitive life assurance and pensions industry.

Types of graduate required

Graduates in *mathematics* or related subjects are required to train as actuaries. Graduates of *any* discipline are required to train in administration. Such applicants should also be numerate and be prepared to study for the examinations of the Chartered Insurance Institute.

Graduates of *any* discipline who are seeking careers in data processing are required. Successful applicants receive immediate training in programming techniques and are given commercial experience in order that they can become effective systems analysts.

Graduates of *any* discipline who are seeking careers in sales are required. Successful applicants are expected to work on their own

Equity & Law

Activities
Life assurance, annuities and pensions business

Employees
1,550

Locations: UK
General

Locations: Overseas
Holland and West Germany

Opportunities
Actuarial; Administration; Data processing;
Sales

Upper age limit
24

Application address
Graduate Recruitment Manager, Staff
(Research & Development) Department, Equity
& Law Life Assurance Society plc, Amersham
Road, High Wycombe, Bucks HP13 5AL

initiative and integrate into a highly professional sales team, and they must be able to communicate effectively with financial experts.

Training and career development

Our comprehensive training and development programme will prepare you for a managerial, senior supervisory or technical position. Training within the branches or departments in which you are employed continues throughout your career and is supplemented by a variety of in-company training courses. Our policy of promotion from within ensures that recruits have real career prospects.

Locations

Our head offices are in High Wycombe and Coventry, with our investment department being based in London, and we have over 40 branches throughout the UK. Actuarial and administration trainees are recruited mainly at High Wycombe but vacancies also occur at Coventry. Opportunities also arise for actuarial trainees in the investment department in London. Data processing trainees are employed at High Wycombe and sales trainees are recruited at branches.

Salaries and benefits

Salaries for graduates are competitive and are reviewed regularly. Additional increases are given for success in professional examinations. A comprehensive range of fringe benefits includes: non-contributory pension scheme, subsidised house purchase loan scheme, annual cash bonus scheme, generous holidays, free lunches and flexible working hours and sports and social facilities at head office, incentive scheme and private use of company car for sales staff.

Activities
Chartered accountancy

Employees
2,800 plus 200 partners in UK
20,000 worldwide

Locations: UK
General

Locations: Overseas
Worldwide (71 countries)

Opportunities & places
Student accountants 280 approx

Upper age limit
26

Application address
Neil Tee, Student Recruitment & Development,
Ernst & Whinney, Becket House, Lambeth
Palace Road, London SE1 7EU

Ernst & Whinney

As one of the world's leading firms of chartered accountants we are looking for over 280 graduates to join us in 1983. Over half our intake will start at our London office but there are 22 other offices in the UK with vacancies for graduates. Those who join us will have the opportunity of training in a expanding and innovative firm marked by its friendly atmosphere and modern thinking.

We welcome applications from graduates and undergraduates of all degree disciplines. We normally only consider applicants with a good degree and A level background (at least three C grades), who have a pleasant personality and a record of interest in financial affairs.

Distinguishing features

We appreciate that many applicants have the dilemma of distinguishing the differences between accountancy firms who will have many characteristics in common. We consider the following to be important features of Ernst & Whinney:

● overall range and financial strength of our clients which we consider to be unrivalled amongst the major accountancy firms.

● our working atmosphere where our staff work to the highest technical and professional standards, but demonstrate their effectiveness at the clients in a pleasant and efficient way.

● a concern within every office that the individual is given the best possible facilities to develop.

The following two features of the London office typify the efforts we make: if requested, we arrange for up to six weeks subsidised accommodation in the City at the time of starting the training contract; all trainees are appointed to one of our audit groups which are large

Ernst & Whinney, cont

enough to give you a wide range of practical experience at different clients, but small enough to ensure you soon get to know your colleagues.

Training and developments

If you join, your first few weeks are spent learning the elements of bookkeeping and auditing techniques. These introduce graduates of all disciplines to auditing, an area which will occupy a substantial part of the three year training contract. You would normally work on about 30 assignments for a wide range of clients during this period, and rapidly get the chance to take charge of smaller jobs. Meanwhile, study for professional exams is helped by the provision of the best possible independent professional tutors. Tuition and exam fees are paid for and you receive paid study leave.

The tuition package includes provision for trainees to take mock exams in-house. These therefore provide better practice and greater realism in results. Where appropriate, results are followed by informal seminars or individual sessions using our own young staff as personal tutors.

The tuition is supplemented by comprehensive in-house training and professional development covering the practical aspects of immediate relevance to your day to day work. Training continues throughout your career. The firm's training courses are run on a seminar basis for groups of 25 to encourage full participation and involvement by those attending.

Promotion comes quickly and your performance is formally reviewed by managers and partners every six months along with your training and study record. Help is provided wherever necessary. Informal reviews can be more frequent.

Learning about an audit

Most of you will know that an audit is an independent examination of the accounts of an organisation. What the job actually involves is less well known unless you have worked for a firm of accountants during vacations. To audit effectively with Ernst & Whinney you must understand the clients' business as well as their accounting systems and how their transactions are recorded. As a trainee you carry out various sophisticated tests to check that all transactions like purchases, sales, payments etc are recorded accurately in the books of account. Our clients' systems are evaluated to established whether they can be relied upon to generate accounts that give a true and fair view of the state of affairs of the business. Our analytical methods can identify high and low periods of trading activity perhaps due to seasonal factors or economic causes. This can allow you to predict cash flow problems and help the business to be managed more effectively. This practical experience will give you the detailed understanding of how a business works and from the start of your career you will be able to contribute to the advice being given to our clients.

Simulated audit courses

For those who wish to learn more about auditing we run simulated audit courses at universities. Details are sent regularly to careers services.

Variety of opportunities

The clients whom we audit vary from the largest multinationals and household names to small family businesses and sole traders. In addition to auditing we provide many specialist services including taxation, insolvency, computer audit, investigations and management consultancy. These are supported by technical and professional development departments, which specialise in developing accountancy standards and accountancy staff respectively. All these options are open to you after qualification, as is the chance to gain experience overseas through our major integrated worldwide organisation. Alternatively, having provided a successful professional service to commerce and industry a number of our people move into this area, often joining client companies. Opportunities for development in our progressive and expanding organisation are numerous and most partners are in their early 30s when appointed.

Applications

Applications (using the firm's own form) should be made to the office of your choice. Regional offices often fill their limited numbers of vacancies quickly. Early application is therefore advisable. Brochures with details of the firm's offices are available from careers services or from the London office. We would also draw your attention to the booklet *Facts About Chartered Accountancy* which is also available from the same sources.

Esso Group of Companies

Our business is the exploration, production, marine transportation, refining, distribution, and marketing of petroleum and petro-chemical products, and we employ 9,000 people. There is also a research centre.

Products dealt with by Esso Petroleum cover the range obtainable from crude oil and include liquefiable gases, petrol, turbo-jet fuel, diesel and gas oils, lubricating oils, fuel oil, and bitumen. The manufacture and marketing of petro-chemical products is handled by Esso Chemical Limited.

Types of graduate required

In all cases the personal qualities of graduates and their future management potential would be the prime factors in selection.

Esso Petroleum

The three main operational sides of Esso Petroleum are refining, transportation and marketing. Jointly their activities demand graduate staff as follows: *chemical engineers*, *mechanical engineers*, *control engineers* and occasionally *chemists*, *electrical engineers* and *economists*. Graduates in *any* discipline are eligible for positions in personnel and commercial computer programming. There are also occasionally openings for *mathematicians* or *statisticians* in one or more of the head office departments and for trainee accountants. At the research centre much of the work is of an inter-disciplinary nature and is suited to graduates (with or without postgraduate experience) in *chemistry* (particularly *organic* and *analytical*), *chemical engineering*, *mechanical engineering*, and *fuel technology*. There are also vacancies for *geologists* and *geophysicists*, at postgraduate level only, in the exploration division and for engineers in the production division.

Esso Chemical

There are vacancies for *chemical* and *mechanical engineers* and *chemists* in manufacturing and research and for all disciplines in marketing.

Training

All graduates are given responsibility straight away except for those entering marketing and computing for which departments there is a training programme of four and two months respectively. Training is also provided at a later stage by means of both internal and external courses.

Locations

Graduates engaged by head office departments will work in London. Principal marketing offices are located in major towns and sales

Activities
Exploration, production, marine transportation, refining, distribution and marketing of petro-chemical and petroleum products

Employees
9,000

Locations: UK
London; South East; Wales

Opportunities
Chemical engineering (process); Petroleum engineering; Mechanical engineering (process); Exploration; Computer programming; Marketing (sales and distribution); Operational research; Research and development; Trainee accountancy; Logistics planning; Personnel

Vacancies
30 approx

Application address
Head of Recruitment (C223),
Esso Petroleum Co Ltd, Victoria Street,
London SW1 E5 JW

personnel can therefore be based in any part of the UK. The Esso refineries are located at Fawley near Southampton and at Milford Haven, Dyfed, Wales. The research centre is at Abingdon in Oxfordshire. The transportation department is located at Fawley. The Esso Chemical head office is located in Southampton. The companies do not recruit graduates specifically for posts overseas.

Career development and prospects
Each graduate's career is carefully planned and it is not unusual to have had three different major assignments before the age of 30. An annual appraisal ensures that career development and job performance are both carefully monitored.

Further information
A brochure containing more detailed information both about the companies and about the vacancies themselves can be obtained from your careers adviser.

Eurotherm International

EUROTHERM

Activities
Manufacture of electronic equipment for industry

Employees
1,900

Location: UK
Worthing

Locations: Overseas
Italy; Germany; France; Japan; Hong Kong; Switzerland; USA; Holland

Opportunities
Engineering: electronic, electrical and mechanical; Computing; Production; Marketing and sales

Vacancies
15–25

Application address
Dr GF Turnbull, Technical Director, Eurotherm International, 8 High Street, Worthing, West Sussex

Eurotherm International is a vigorous young group of companies involved in the manufacture of advanced products principally for control and monitoring of industrial processes. It was formed in 1965 when its four founders set up a company making a new type of temperature controller. Their initial aim was for the company to become a world leader in this market area, which aim was realised some ten years later when sales topped £5 million with exports accounting for 70% of this figure: this resulted in a Queens Award for Exports. High growth rate has continued ever since. There are now five companies in the group Eurotherm Limited, Chessell Limited, Turnbull Control Systems, Shackleton System Drives, and Energy Technology and Control.

Types of graduate required
Within the group we need graduates with honours degrees in *engineering*, both *electrical* and *light mechanical, electronics, physics* and *computer science* for research and development posts. Each company has its own research and development teams centred on the next generation of products. The range of activities is extremely varied and microprocessors are used extensively; strong emphasis here is placed on good computer resources such as cross assemblers and powerful simulation tools such as Pascal. New graduates are encouraged to develop overall skills in hardware and software engineering. Opportunities are also available in engineering; this includes production back-up, product enhancement, automatic testing and application engineering. The latter involves significant customer contact and can lead to appointments in the sales area.

There is also a need for graduates with degrees in *production engineering* to develop sophisticated manufacturing techniques and for *business studies* graduates to work in the area of marketing.

Location
Worthing is the largest town in West Sussex and enjoys a favoured position on the mild South Coast. A fine modern sports centre caters for the majority of pursuits. In addition there are an abundance of sailing clubs and the South Downs provide many opportunities for walking and hang-gliding.

Career development
Training is mostly through working on a project in contact with

experienced engineers, and access to good facilities such as powerful computers. Since companies in the group are small and flexible, people move from one area to another and from one company to another. Success depends solely on the level of personal achievement.

Exploration Logging

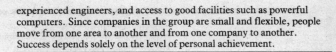

Exlog is a subsidiary of Baker International, and provides worldwide geological and engineering services in oil, gas and geothermal exploration and production. The Exlog group of companies has kept pace with the considerable expansion in petroleum exploration and our geologists and engineers now staff over 240 logging units, both onshore and offshore around the world.

Types of graduate required
We expect a good honours degree in *geology*, *geological* and *petroleum engineering*, *earth* and *environmental science*, *geochemistry* or a *combined degree* incorporating one of these. Useful subsidiary subjects are physics, chemistry, computer science and mathematics.

However the demanding nature of the job and its varying locations, (assignments in the past year varied from the Arctic Circle in Norway to the Seychelles, Australia, Syria, Tanzania, Argentina and many other countries) will require applicants to be adaptable, healthy and capable of communicating clearly. We also offer careers in electronic and electrical engineering to anyone with the relevant degree or industrial equivalent.

Training
This entails a two week oil field familiarisation school followed by a four month period of practical training at the wellsite leading to an assignment with a field crew anywhere in the world. Advanced training schools are held throughout the geologist's career and financial awards can be given to some of those who wish to take further degrees.

Salaries and prospects
Our salaries are competitive, with bonuses for time spent working at the rigsite and extra responsibilities. Prospects are excellent leading to opportunities in consultancy and management.

Benefits
These include travel expenses to and from and within the UK, a contributory pension scheme, free life assurance, medical and dental cover outside the UK.

Applications
Application to Martin Ellins at the address given.

Fairey Hydraulics Limited

Fairey Hydraulics Limited is an expanding company, and a wholly owned subsidiary of Fairey Holdings Ltd.

Fairey Hydraulics employs some 560 people at its Heston site, close to London airport, and at Claverham, between Bristol and Weston super Mare, where the design, manufacturing and product support facilities are located and where the company conducts research and development programmes. A number of Fairey Hydraulics equipments are also in production in Europe, part of several collaborative projects to which the company is a major supplier. These include the Panavia Tornado multi-role combat aircraft and the BAC-Breguet Jaguar.

Activities
Provides geological engineering service to the international petroleum and geothermal industries

Employees
1,200

Opportunities
Geology; Petroleum engineering; Geochemistry

Application address
Martin Ellins, Educational Systems Engineer, Exploration Logging (Services) Limited, PO Box 46, Windsor, Berkshire

Activities
Research, design and manufacture of electro-hydraulic power flying controls

Employees
560

Locations: UK
Middlesex and Avon

Opportunities
Stress engineers; Development engineers;
Production engineers; Design engineers

Vacancies
5

Upper age limit
25

Application address
EH Brown, Personnel Manager, Fairey
Hydraulics Limited, Cranford Lane, Heston,
Hounslow, Middlesex
Tel: 01-759 2666

Fairey Hydraulics Limited, cont

Types of graduate required
Graduates in *mechanical, electronic, aeronautical* or *production engineering*
or *engineering science* are required both for training and direct
appointment.

Training
Graduates will enter the company for one year's training leading to a
departmental appointment as appropriate. Outside courses are arranged
throughout an individual's career especially at times of promotion. Staff
are encouraged to study for appropriate professional examinations.

Locations
Fairey Heston site, Middlesex, and Claverham in the county of Avon.

Salaries
The starting salary will be circa £6,100 and is subject to annual review.
We have all the normal benefits that one would expect from a major
company.

Prospects
Promotion is entirely on merit. Opportunities are increasing with the
expansion of the company.

Further information
Initial enquiries to the Personnel Manager.

Activities
Department and fashion stores retailing

Employees
2,500

Locations: UK
South East; Midlands; North East

Opportunities
Trainee buyer

Application addresses
Staff Manager, Fenwick Limited,
Northumberland Street,
Newcastle upon Tyne
Staff Manager, Fenwick Limited, Brent Cross
Shopping Centre, London NW4 3FN

Fenwick Limited

Fenwick Limited is an independent company, founded in 1882, with
stores in Newcastle, Bond Street W1, Brent Cross, Leicester, Oxford
and Windsor. The group employs nearly 2,500 staff. The company has
an envied success record resulting from a reputation for quality and the
best in today's fashion and household goods, and a very personal style of
management and commercial skill in merchandising. Each store
generally operates as an autonomous unit with its own managing director,
senior management and responsibility for buying merchandise. Fenwick
buyers also have responsibility for sales, and this policy ensures that they
enjoy an interesting career with total merchandising responsibility.

Newcastle, Brent Cross and Leicester are departmental stores, whilst
Bond Street, Oxford and Windsor are fashion stores. The departmental
stores, the traditional Fenwick store being Newcastle, offer a wide range
of fashion accessories, household goods, furniture, furnishings and food.

Types of graduate required
Excellent career opportunities are open to both male and female
graduates of *any* discipline who have the ability to succeed in retailing
and have the personality that can adapt to both buying and selling.
Promotion normally is from within, at a young age, and responsibility is
given according to ability.

Training
The initial six to nine months is spent on obtaining a thorough grounding
in retailing, with the emphasis on selling under the guidance of a
merchandise manager. After this initial period the trainee should be
ready for an under-buyer post and promotion to buyer could follow after
demonstration of their flair and ability to manage.

Further information

Please write to the Staff Manager at either of the two stores depending on your preferred locality.

Ferranti plc

Activities
General electrical and electronic engineering

Employees
18,000

Locations: UK
North West; South East; Scotland; South Wales

Opportunities
Research; Development and design engineering; Test, quality and commissioning engineering; Production engineering and service support; Programming; Systems analysis; Sales and marketing; Technical authorship

Vacancies
150

Application addresses
PW Ashton, Company Training Manager, Ferranti plc, Bridge House, Park Road, Gatley, Cheadle, Cheshire SK8 4H2
J Mercer, University Liason Officer, Ferranti plc, Ferry Road, Edinburgh EH5 2XS

Ferranti plc is a company whose activities have an emphasis on technical innovation, notably in the field of electronic engineering and particularly in micro-electronics, computers and aviation electronics. Among its 18,000 employees are about 1,500 qualified scientists and technologists. The company has laboratories and manufacturing facilities in the Manchester area, Edinburgh and Dundee, Bracknell (Berks) and subsidiary companies in the USA, West Germany, Belgium, Brazil and Australia. Its interests in high technology engineering include computers for on-line applications in process control, information and communication systems, air traffic control systems and in tactical control and action data automation systems for naval vessels; microprocessors, semiconductors, integrated circuit and microwave devices; airborne radar, inertial navigation and other avionics equipment; electronic display components and systems; lasers; instrumentation and precision components.

Types of graduate required

Electronic engineers and *physicists* for Manchester, Bracknell, Edinburgh and Dundee, chiefly for research and development, particularly in computers, semiconductor devices, radar and navigational aids, information, communication and display systems. *Mathematicians* chiefly for programming and systems analysis in Manchester, Bracknell, Cwmbran (South Wales) and Edinburgh. Occasional vacancies for *mechanical engineers* in Manchester, Bracknell and Edinburgh.

Training

Scientist and engineers may join research groups for direct employment without formal training. Early opportunity for technical challenge and supervision by well qualified and experienced group leaders provide the right basis for continuous personal development and the right atmosphere for technical innovation. Use is made where necessary of internal and external courses. Engineers with electrical and mechanical interests may receive formalised training on the basis of individual and institutional requirements.

Prospects

The company in general promotes from within on the basis of individual achievement.

Salaries

Salaries are entirely competitive and are administered as part of a comprehensive grading scheme which provides for annual review and increment. The company has good pension and life assurance arrangements with provisions for dependants and the facility of medical insurance.

Finnie Ross Allfields

Activities
Chartered accountancy

Employees
220 professional staff

Application addresses
See display ad

We are a 30 partner firm of chartered accountants with seven UK offices and a founder member of Kreston International, an association of leading medium sized accountancy firms throughout the world.

The philosophy of the practice is to provide clients with a personal service which extends beyond the pure compliance areas of audit and tax and is geared to all round financial advice. The development of strong client relationships is therefore essential at all staff levels within the practice. Staff are able to identify closely with client development and have the opportunity of dealing with a wide range of client problems.

For further information regarding student training contract vacancies see our display entry in the index section.

Activities
Manufacturing printing inks and related products for the printing, packaging and metal decorating industries and colourants for the plastics industry

Employees
550 approx

Locations: UK
Scotland; North East; North West; Midlands; South West; South East

Opportunities
Process manufacturing; Industrial chemistry; Product development; Quality control

Application address
The Personnel & Training Officer, Fishburn Printing Ink Company Limited, 94 St Albans Road, Watford, Herts WD2 4BU

Fishburn Printing Ink Co Ltd

Fishburn Printing Ink Company Limited started trading in Watford in 1929, encouraged by the requirements of the new and expanding waxed wrappings industry and flourishing local printing and paper making industries. The company became successful, eventually requiring an additional North West manufacturing unit and several branches to service its customers countrywide. In 1964 Fishburns became the British subsidiary of Interchemical Corporation, now Inmont Corporation of America which represents the world's largest group of ink/automotive paint manufacturers. (Inmont are part of the major multinational United Technologies group.) This connection maximises Fishburn's resources and, in real terms, means investment in long term development.

Employing about 550 staff, our current UK turnover is approximately £18 million. We have established a reputation as suppliers of top quality printing inks and associated products for publishing, packaging and metal decorating, and more recently of colourants for plastics. Our products are readily marketed amongst keen competition; product research and development continuously responds to new challenges from the industries we serve. A high level of technical service reinforces our commitment to our customers and their continued business.

Training and career development
In the process manufacturing area a high level of technical expertise is provided by our technical staff. This expertise is a pre-requisite for the many specialist areas in our company where career opportunities will arise. The business area also provides a wide range of management, sales and other opportunities for employees.

Locations
Our head office is at Watford together with a large manufacturing site and development facility. We have a second large factory in Liverpool, and branches at Orpington, Bristol, Hinckley, Leeds and Cumbernauld. Each location is responsible for product preparation and distribution, client servicing and area market development.

Salaries and benefits
Salaries are competitive and additionally are supplemented by a productivity bonus. We provide 22 days holiday each year and have an excellent contributory pension scheme.

Further information
Vacancies are advertised in national, local, trade press and *Current Vacancies*. Only specific applications to advertised posts can be considered.

Flopetrol International SA

For further information please see our entry in the Overseas section.

Ford Motor Company Limited

Activities
Motor manufacturer

Employees
66,000

Locations: UK
General

Opportunities
Product engineering; Plant engineering;
Manufacturing engineering; Supply; Finance;
Industrial relations; Sales and marketing;
Production supervision; Computer systems;
Quality control; Computer aided engineering

Vacancies
100 approx

Application address
The Manager, College Recruitment and
Training, 1/178, Ford Motor Company Limited,
Eagle Way, Warley, Brentwood, Essex
CM13 3BW

Ford is Britain's most successful motor manufacturer. We have continued to make profits throughout the current recession, and for five successive years, 1977–81 we have been market leaders in Britain in all three sectors of the vehicle market: cars, commercial vehicles, and tractors. We have ambitious plans for the future, too.

How is it done? First of all, we find out what our customers want and then ensure that they get it. Second, we control costs effectively. This means that we can sell vehicles at prices which ensure both that our customers are satisfied and that we make a profit. Third, by consistent investment in new plant and new products. And finally, by developing good managers.

This is where you come in. We always need talented, ambitious young graduates to train for the exacting role of managing a fast changing business. One point is worth emphasising – you should not assume that because we are an engineering company we need only engineering graduates. This is our specification:

Graduates with *vocational* degrees are needed for: design engineering, manufacturing and plant engineering, quality control, customer service, computer systems, and computer aided engineering.

Graduates of *any* discipline are employed in: sales and marketing, finance, industrial relations, supply, and production management.

Full details about training and salaries, and descriptions of the areas which employ graduates will be found in our 1983 brochure, which is available from your careers service or from the Manager, College Recruitment and Training, at the address given.

Foseco Minsep Group

Activities
Worldwide manufacturing and marketing of products and services for the metallurgical, engineering, construction and mining industries

Employees
13,000 worldwide

Foseco Minsep is a UK controlled worldwide manufacturing and marketing group of companies. Our business is materials technology: the manufacture and supply of specialist products and technical services principally to the metallurgical, engineering, construction and mining industries throughout the world. We also have a number of specialist trading interests. Our products range from chemical additives to abrasives and diamond drilling products. They are aimed at raising productivity and product quality, often achieving energy and raw materials savings and improved working conditions for our customers.

We are determined to continue to grow as we have done rapidly in the past, by extending our product range and our operations throughout the world. We can offer a career of challenge and excitement for graduates with initiative, flexibility and determination to succeed in a competitive changing environment.

Locations: UK
Home Counties; Midlands; West Country

Locations: Overseas
Worldwide, over 30 countries

Opportunities
Product development, central research and development laboratories or manufacturing services, leading to marketing or production management

Vacancies
10–20

Application address
Mrs Paula Rayer-Dyson, Group Personnel Administrator, Foseco Minsep International Ltd, 36 Queen Anne's Gate, London SW1H 9AR
Tel: 01-222 7030

Foseco Minsep Group, cont

Openings for graduates

We recruit 10–20 new graduates in the UK each year, mainly from the technical and scientific disciplines, with special emphasis on *chemists, chemical* and *mechanical engineers, materials scientists* and *metallurgists*. Apart from formal education achievement, we are particularly interested in what each graduate can bring to the group, for example in terms of motivation, personality and proven achievement in other fields of activity.

Graduates are always placed in real jobs after a very brief induction and the majority start in research and product development, though a few go straight into technical marketing or production. Initial postings will be normally in the Midlands or in the Home Counties.

Subsequent career

Progress and rewards depend on the graduate's ability and contribution to the group. Our organisation is flexible and highly commercially orientated. There are no set career or formal training paths. Our emphasis is on the provisions of a succession of challenging tasks of progressive responsibility according to the graduate's aptitude and inclination. Such progress can be in central group management and development companies, usually with significant travel, or in operating companies in the UK or overseas. Movements between these two broad paths are common as are transfers between functions, and between the different sectors of the group's trading activities.

Our aim is to provide, through our graduate recruitment, a succession of senior managers and technical specialists throughout the group, and graduates can reach positions of very major responsibility by their early 30s or before. Many have.

Further information

For further information please contact your careers advisory centre or write direct to Mrs Paula Rayer-Dyson at the address given.

Four Square
A division of Mars Ltd

Four Square, part of the Mars Group of Companies, specialises in the manufacture and provision of high quality food and beverage vending services to industry and commerce throughout the UK. It is the largest as well as the leading vending operator in this field.

Types of graduate required

Most graduate openings in Four Square lead to management positions, mainly in sales or in managing the staff who provide services to our clients, although there are also opportunities in technical, production, engineering and personnel. Applications are invited from graduates in any related discipline; communication and managerial abilities are especially valued.

Training

Our training programme is designed to cater for each individual's particular needs, and gives a complete knowledge of the company's activities as well as equipping you with the specialist knowledge you will require. Trainees assume responsibility early, and should achieve a full management position within 18 to 24 months.

Locations

The majority of Four Square personnel are field based, and vacancies

Activities
High quality beverage and food vending services to industry and commerce

Employees
1,000

Locations: UK
General

Opportunities
Sales; Operations; Catering; Technical; Production; Engineering; Personnel

Upper age limit
25

Application address
Management Development Manager, Four Square, Ajax Avenue, Slough, Berks SL1 4DE

could arise anywhere in the UK, so there is a requirement for mobility in your early career.

Salaries and benefits
Salaries are highly competitive, and are directly related to ability; on promotion to management, salaries are in the range £10,000–£16,000. A non-contributory pension, life assurance, and sick pay scheme is provided, with 22 days' holiday a year.

Fraser Keen

Activities
Chartered accountancy

Employees
80

Location: UK
London

Opportunities & places
Student accountants 9

Application address
Mr Henry L Fisher, Staff Partner, Fraser Keen, 4 London Wall Buildings, London EC2M 5NT

Fraser Keen is a well established medium sized firm with 17 partners in London, mainly engaged in providing a wide variety of clients with accounting, audit, taxation and many other services. We consider ourselves well placed to enable trainees to combine their examination syllabus studies with broad and varied practical experience in a milieu which respects their sense of personal identity.

Types of graduate required
We accept graduates in *any* discipline, having regard to personal qualities and academic levels, but an approved degree is an advantage.

Training
We provide through a leading firm of tutors a professional examination tuition course involving periods of full time instruction as well as home study. We also provide a planned programme of in-house training. Practical experience is mainly gained in audit teams working at clients' premises.

We believe that for trainees who have common sense (preferably not untinged with a sense of humour) and can work hard, think straight, express themselves clearly and get on with people, a practice of our size and type has much to offer by way of experience to be gained through progressively interesting and responsible work in an atmosphere in which personal contact is developed with both principals and clients.

Locations
Our main office is in the City of London. Most of our clients are in London and the Home Counties, but a number of audits are carried out in other parts of the UK.

Salaries
Salary rates are regularly reviewed and kept in line with those of the profession generally, giving increments twice yearly and on passing examinations, and additionally recognising exceptional performance.

Prospects
There are good opportunities for trainees when they have qualified to stay on in positions offering greater responsibility and wider experience.

Fraser Williams

Fraser Williams
computer consultants

Activities
Computer consultancy and professional services

Fraser Williams has been established since 1969 as a computer consultancy, offering advisory, systems and programming services, based on a wide variety of hardware. Clients vary in size and are widely spread over government, local government, computer manufacturers, commerce and industry, both in the UK and abroad.

Types of graduate required
Positions are available for graduates of high potential. A degree in

Employees
320

Locations: UK
General

Opportunities & places
Trainee analyst/programmers 25

Application address
Graduate Personnel Officer at any of the
locations listed in the main text

computer science or a related subject is usually an advantage, but
opportunities also exist for graduates of *any* discipline who have a
significant practical experience of computing. In addition, the London
office will consider graduates in *accountancy* or *business studies* who can
demonstrate an aptitude for computing.

Training and career development
We have found that the graduate with some computing background
develops more quickly by early involvement with actual projects.
Accordingly graduates are employed almost immediately on assignments,
working on programming tasks under the direction of experienced
consultants. Career progression in a growing company should be rapid,
and should be through programming and systems analysis with eventual
promotion into consultancy or management. Regular appraisals assist
staff in determining the career path to which they are most suited.

Locations
All our offices recruit graduates but, since most of our work is performed
on client premises, a certain amount of travel can be expected.
*Fraser Williams Group Ltd, Port of Liverpool Building, Pier Head,
   Liverpool L3 1BY. Tel: 051-227 3371 and at: Queens Chambers, Tower
   Lane, Bristol BS1 2JN. Tel: 0272 214641*
*Fraser Williams (London) Ltd, Landseer House, 19 Charing Cross Road,
   London WC2H 0ES. Tel: 01-930 4041*
*Fraser Williams (Hertfordshire) Ltd, 3A Canberra House 17–19 London
   Road, St Albans Herts. Tel: 0727 34301*
*Fraser Williams (Midlands) Ltd, Monaco House, Bristol Street, Birmingham
   B5 7AS. Tel: 021-622 6234*
*Fraser Williams (Northern) Ltd, St James House, Vicar Lane, Sheffield
   S1 2EX. Tel: 0742 28538 and at: Enterprise House, 12 St Paul's Street,
   Leeds LS1 2LE. Tel: 0532 448927*
*Fraser Williams (Manchester) Ltd, Warwickgate House, Warwick Road,
   Manchester M16 0QQ. Tel: 061-872 8428*
*Fraser Williams (Scotland) Ltd, Stock Exchange Building, St Georges
   Place, Glasgow G2 1QY. Tel: 041-226 3864.*

French Kier Construction Limited

Activities
Civil engineering and building contracting

Employees
4,000

Locations: UK
General

Locations: Overseas
Asia; Africa; Middle East; Latin America;
Australasia

Opportunities & places
Civil engineering, building and quantity
surveying 20; Computer programmers/systems
analysts 5

Application address
The Company Personnel Manager, French Kier
Construction Limited, Tempsford Hall, Sandy,
Bedfordshire SG19 2BD

French Kier Construction Limited is a major civil engineering and
building contractor in the United Kingdom. Our construction interests
cover the whole range of contracting, particularly within the specialised
field of reinforced concrete, marine projects and tunnelling.
   Work currently being undertaken includes marine pipelines, jetties,
tunnelling, sewage, roadworks, tidal barriers, dockyards, factories,
public buildings, office blocks and housing.

Types of graduate required
Entry is highly competitive and we seek mainly graduates with a good
class honours degree in *civil engineering, building, quantity surveying* and
computing science. Additionally, we look for those individuals who have
taken full advantage of school and university life and who possess a high
degree of drive and initiative.

Training
Civil engineering, building and quantity surveying graduates are initially
appointed to site positions to give them some practical experience. We
encourage graduates to attain membership of the Institution of Civil
Engineers, the Chartered Institute of Building or the Institute of

Quantity Surveyors. For civil engineers, design training is either at our head office or in a consultant's office. Selected graduates are trained under an ICE agreement.

Computer science graduates will work within our head office data processing department and will receive experience and training on our comprehensive range of systems, hardware and software.

Training in professional, technical and managerial techniques is arranged to meet personal needs and progress.

Locations
Contracts are located generally throughout Britain and mobility is essential if full advantage of opportunities is to be taken.

Opportunities overseas
There are openings for transfers overseas within the group, including the Caribbean, Africa, the Middle East and the Far East, but prior experience on UK contracts is normally required, and selection is determined by suitability and length of service.

Salaries and benefits
As we seek to attract only the best graduates, our salary scale is highly competitive, supplemented by allowances for overtime and subsistence, when appropriate. The figure will be determined near the time of the appointment. Fringe benefits are excellent, including 26 working days holiday per annum, pension and life assurance schemes.

Prospects
Progress is almost entirely within an individual's control. Merit is recognised and earns early promotion.

Friends' Provident Life Office

The origins of Friends' Provident Life Office date back as far as 1832. Since that time the Office has developed and expanded its sphere of operations until today it ranks as one of Britain's leading specialist life offices, and its activities extend to a number of overseas countries. All the main classes of long term insurance business are transacted, including life, pensions and permanent health insurance. The Office is an enthusiastic user of advanced computer techniques and is operating the most advanced real-time system in the insurance industry. Even our competitors pay tribute to it. We are now engaged in extensive development to further exploit computer technology.

Activities
Life assurance, pensions and permanent health insurance

Employees
1,250

Opportunities
Actuarial trainees; Sales and marketing trainees; Administrative trainees for pensions department; Trainees for computer services department

Vacancies
20–25

Upper age limit
25

Application address
K Browell, MIPM, DMS, Personnel & Administration Services, Friends' Provident Life Office, Pixham End, Dorking, Surrey RH4 1QA
Tel: 0306 885055

Types of graduate required
The majority of vacancies are open to graduates who expect a good honours degree in *any* subject, provided they are equipped with initiative, determination and sound judgement. Graduates are regularly recruited for training in the technical fields of pensions administration and documentation, data processing, legal work, sales and marketing, and actuarial work. For actuarial work a degree in *maths*, *stats*, *economics* or *actuarial science* is normally required, although candidates from other disciplines will be considered if they have obtained a good A level background in mathematics.

Training and career development
Training is planned to meet the needs of the particular appointment. The attainment of professional qualifications will normally be expected and day release facilities are granted for approved examinations. All appointments offer excellent prospects of promotion to senior positions which are filled as a matter of policy from within the organisation.

Friends' Provident Life Office, cont

Locations

The principal office is at Dorking and there are branches in many of the main cities and towns throughout the UK. The Stock Exchange department is based in London.

Salaries

Salaries are at least as good as those offered by comparable firms with higher salaries for exceptionally well qualified applicants. Salaries are reviewed annually. Additional benefits include an annual bonus, pension scheme, staff house purchase scheme, flexible working hours, etc.

Further information

Please refer to our companion brochures *Computing with Friends* and *Careers for Graduates* and list of current vacancies which are available at all university and selected polytechnic careers offices. If you require personal copies of the recruitment material please write giving background details and areas of interest to K Browell address aside.

Fryer Whitehill & Co

Activities
Chartered accountancy

Employees
250

Locations: UK
London; Home Counties and South East; Bristol and South West; East Midlands and East Anglia

Opportunities & places
Trainee accountants 24

Upper age limit
30

Application addresses
See main text

Fryer Whitehill is a medium sized firm of accountants based in London, Birmingham, Reading and Cheltenham. We are represented throughout the United Kingdom by associated firms in 20 other towns and cities. Similar arrangements exist with associated firms in America, Europe, Australia and the Far East.

Graduates join in August and spend their first 10 days on an in-house training course. Thereafter student accountants are assigned to individual audit teams, tackling varied assignments, ranging from public companies through family companies to professional partnerships. The principal services offered by the firm, apart from auditing, are the preparation of accounts, forecasts, management information, taxation computations, financial planning and computer consultancy. It is expected that students will be exposed to some if not all of these other areas during their training contract.

Types of graduate required

Invitations are extended to graduates from *all* disciplines. Preference is given to honours graduates. However, the ability to communicate lucidly is considered to be a necessary prerequisite. We are particularly looking for young men and women with energy and a genuine enthusiasm for accountancy.

Training

Training falls into three categories. Firstly, academic tuition is undertaken by one of the most successful firms of professional accountancy tutors under the firm's overall supervision and at its expense. The programme consists of introductory, mid-term, and extensive pre-examination revision courses. The second element is provided by our own training department who give tuition in our own systems and methods of working. In the first year with the firm, students can expect 12 days in-house training in addition to the eight weeks of study leave and tuition for examination purposes. On the job training is the most important element. It involves being part of a team, working with and learning from experienced seniors, managers and partners. It comprises a varied work pattern and offers the opportunity to find out how many different organisations order their affairs. The main business of the trainee accountant consists of meeting people, finding out about their problems and offering constructive advice.

Location
We are looking for 12 graduates in London, five each in Reading and Cheltenham and two in Birmingham.

Salaries
Salaries are increased twice yearly and are set according to practical and examination success. Cost of living increments are awarded at regular salary reviews. The firm also meets the cost of the academic tuition courses amounting to approximately £600.

Prospects
Opportunities for promotion after qualification from junior manager to manager and to partner are open to students who have trained with the firm and who are able to demonstrate technical competence coupled with a degree of personal motivation and the ability to get on with people.

Further information
London *JHF Gemmell, 24/30 Holborn, London EC1N 2PX*
Reading *PJ Pearce, 37 Minster Street, Reading, Berkshire RG1 2RY*
Cheltenham *JJ May, Carrick House, Lypiatt Road, Cheltenham GL50 2QJ*
Birmingham *KD Bartlett, Daimler House, Paradise Circus, Birmingham B1 2BY*

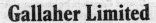

Gallaher Limited

Gallaher Limited has an established place in the UK tobacco market with cigarette brands Benson and Hedges, Silk Cut, Senior Service, Kensitas and Park Drive; Hamlet and Manikin cigars, and Condor and Old Holborn tobaccos.

Activities
Manufacturers of tobacco products

Employees
8,500

Locations: UK
General

Opportunities
General management trainee; Sales

Vacancies
Up to 6

Upper age limit
25

Application address
Mrs DEJ Bowles, Recruitment Manager, Gallaher Limited, 65 Kingsway, London WC2B 6TG

Types of graduate required
Graduates from *any* discipline are offered challenging and rewarding careers either in general commercial management or in sales. Drive, enthusiasm, numeracy and the desire to succeed are all essential for successful candidates.

Most specialised vacancies are notified separately to careers advisory services.

Training
Those who have decided on a sales career are entered directly into the national field sales force and proceed through the standard stages of a sales representative's progression. Practical training precedes each stage.

Graduates with wider aspirations and who have not been able to decide on their early career path are attached to the principal line departments of production, sales, marketing and distribution over a period of 16 to 18 months. They spend approximately four months in each learning largely through project work and on the job experience. Depending on results and preference, they then concentrate on development through one of those departments.

Location
Full mobility within the UK is required.

Prospects
Outstanding success in the first two or three years can earn promotion to first line management.

Applications
Please write to the address given.

Gardline Surveys

Activities
Hydrographic and marine geophysical offshore surveying

Employees
200

Locations: UK
East Anglia; Aberdeen

Locations: Overseas
Houston; Kuala Lumpur; Singapore

Opportunities
Electronic engineers; Surveyors; Geophysicists; Computing

Application address
Gardline Surveys, Admiralty Road, Great Yarmouth, Norfolk NR30 3NG

Gardline Surveys is one of Britain's major hydrographic and geophysical survey companies. The company provides ships, equipment and personnel for all aspects of offshore surveying primarily for oil companies and government institutions.

The company employs approximately 200 people and has operational bases in Great Yarmouth, Aberdeen, Houston, Kuala Lumpur and Singapore.

Graduates required
Primarily graduates in *electronic engineering, surveying, geology, geophysics* and *computing*.

Training
A comprehensive training course including initial induction, equipment familiarisation and in-house training seminars in geophysical equipment, computer/navigation systems are provided.

Salary
A competitive basic salary is paid together with generous offshore allowances.

Applications
Applications should be made to the Manager at the given address.

The General Electric Company, plc

GEC

Activities
Largest British owned manufacturer of electrical and electronic products

Employees
200,000

Locations: UK
General

Locations: Overseas
Worldwide

Opportunities
Electrical, electronic, mechanical and production engineers; Physicists; Materials scientists/chemists; Computer scientists; Mathematicians

Vacancies
1,400

Application address
See main text

GEC is the largest British owned electrical and electronic manufacturer supplying products and services ranging from the largest complete power station down to the smallest device in the microelectronic field, with an international recognition as one of the world's leading electrical companies.

GEC has nearly 200,000 employees throughout the world, with 155,000 in the UK, of whom 13,000 are employed as scientists and technologists. Although GEC is a large organisation, its continuing business success is due mainly to the practice of decentralisation, which encourages each operating company to run its own business in the most efficient way to meet the needs of its markets. The numerical size of operating companies varies from a considerable number with less than 200 employees to three companies with over 5,000. This selection of operating companies provides an excellent choice for the new graduate to join a company best suited to his or her aspirations in making a starting point in an industrial career; also to feel that they will be recognised as individuals and not lost in some mammoth organisation.

The operating companies maintain leading positions in their technical and commercial achievements in competitive home and worldwide markets. The major groups of companies have substantial design and development facilities and where appropriate conduct their own product research.

Types of graduate required
The company activities can be divided broadly into the following major groups:

Power engineering dealing with generation, transmission and distribution equipment, gas turbines and nuclear reactor equipment.

In this group the main vacancies are for graduates in *electrical, mechanical* and *production engineering* in GEC Gas Turbines Ltd, GEC

The General Electric Company plc, cont

Turbine Generators Ltd, Ruston Gas Turbines Ltd, GEC Switchgear Ltd and GEC Energy Systems Ltd.

Industrial dealing with diesels, traction, machines, lifts, fans and furnaces. In this group the main vacancies are for graduates in *electrical*, *mechanical* and *production engineering* in GEC Diesels Ltd, GEC Traction Ltd and GEC Machines Ltd.

Electronics and automation is one of the largest groups, dealing with a range of comprehensive and advanced electronic products and services, computer systems, scientific measuring equipment; and a range of sophisticated automation systems. This group of companies offers the largest number of appointments to graduates and postgraduates in *electrical* and *electronic engineering*, *mechanical* and *production engineering*, *physicists*, *computer scientists*, *mathematicians*, *materials scientists* interested in research, design, development manufacture and application of electronics with world famous companies such as: Marconi Avionics Ltd, Marconi Communication Systems Ltd, Marconic Radar Systems Ltd, Marconi Space & Defence Systems Ltd, Marconi Electronic Devices Ltd, Marconi International Marine Company Ltd, Marconi Instruments Ltd, Easams Ltd, GEC Computers Ltd, GEC Transportation Projects Ltd, GEC Traffic Automation Ltd, GEC-General Signal Ltd and AB Dick Ltd.

In automation activities the main vacancies are for *electrical* and *electronic engineering* and *mechanical engineering* graduates for GEC Electrical Projects Limited; GEC Industrial Controls Ltd and GEC Mechanical Handling Ltd.

Telecommunications is another of the largest groups, GEC Telecommunications Ltd mainly based at Coventry, offering a range of choice and appointments to *electrical* and *electronic engineering*, *production engineering*, *physics* and *computer science* graduates in design, development, application, manufacturing and installation in complete telecommunication systems, public telephone exchanges, transmission systems, private telephone systems and telephone instruments.

Components This group of companies covers a range of products extending from weighing and counting machines, and meter pumps, to special valves, cables and wire. The main *electronic engineering*, *physics*, *materials science* graduate vacancies are in the GEC Avery Group, English Electric Valve Co Ltd, GEC Measurements Ltd and Londex Ltd.

Consumer products dealing with television, domestic appliances, lamps and lighting.

There are a limited number of vacancies for *electrical* and *electronic engineering*, *physcists*, *materials scientists* graduates in Redring Electric Ltd, Hotpoint Ltd and Cannon Industries Ltd.

In addition GEC Midlands Computer Services Ltd offers commercial and technical data processing services and time sharing services.

The Power Engineering Research Laboratories and the GEC Research Laboratories, consisting of the Hirst Research Centre and the Marconi Research Centre have vacancies for *electrical* and *electronic engineering*, *mechanical engineering*, *physics* and *materials science* graduates and postgraduates in a number of specialist fields of advanced technology.

Training and career development

Graduates may be recruited as trainees for up to 12 to 18 months planned training programmes to suit individual needs, designed to encourage an early decision to be made on the choice of first staff appointments, with the last part of training directed towards this objective. Alternatively many graduates are recruited to direct entry appointments so that after a short induction training they can make immediate use of their skills. In all cases there is the opportunity for study or experience to satisfy the requirements of the professional institutions.

There is a policy of promotion from within, which, coupled with varied products and constantly changing market requirements, provides excellent opportunities for graduates to progress, either within their own organisation or by transfer from one company to another. In addition many graduates will have the opportunity of obtaining overseas experience, either on short term visits or by longer term attachments to one of the overseas companies.

The company has its own staff training colleges which provide a range of short term courses for junior, middle and senior management, and encouragement is given to all capable of developing their career from planned experience and acceptance of greater responsibilities. In addition to the career development plans provided by each operating company for its own staff, the GEC fellowship scheme enables suitable members of the staff to select postgraduate study or experience of their own choice which will be to the mutual benefit of themselves and their operating company.

Further information
More detailed information on the individual companies, products, location of works and number of graduate vacancies with preferred degree subjects is supplied to appointments or careers advisory offices in all colleges, polytechnics and universities in the UK.

Applications can be made, preferably on the company's own form direct to:

University Liaison Officer, GEC Power Engineering Ltd, Trafford Park, Manchester M17 1PR

University Liaison Officer, GEC Telecommunications Ltd, Telephone Works, PO Box 53, Coventry CV3 1HJ

University Liaison Officer, GEC–Marconi Electronics Ltd, Marconi House, New Street, Chelmsford CM1 1RL

The Administration Manager, GEC Hirst Research Centre, East Lane, Wembley HA9 7PP

or if you are uncertain which company to select, or if you wish to be considered by more than one operating company, please forward the form to:

GEC University Liaison, PO Box 79, Wembley, Middlesex HA9 7PP.

General Motors Limited

Activities
Manufacture and marketing of automobile components

Employees
5,000

Application address
Mr K Tothill, Senior Personnel Officer, PO Box 242, Delaware Drive, Tongwell, Milton Keynes MK15 8HA

General Motors Limited employ a total of some 5,000 people involved with all aspects of the manufacture and distribution of automobile components, replacements and accessories, and with the building and distribution of diesel engines and their conversion for industrial and marine applications. In other words, General Motors Limited is a spectrum of achievements and activities largely, but not exclusively, linked to the automobile industry.

Types of graduate required
It is doubtful that we will be recruiting any graduates during 1983. If we do, the need will probably be in the area of *engineering*, (particularly *electrical/electronic*).

Salaries and benefits
An attractive starting salary, reviewed annually, is offered together with the range of benefits expected from a major employer.

Geophysical Service International
A group of Texas Instruments

Activities
Geophysical data collection, processing and interpretation

Employees
1,600 Europe, Africa and Middle East

Locations: UK
London and South East

Locations: Overseas
Worldwide

Opportunities
Data processing and field seismologists; Instrument and systems engineers; Computer maintenance engineers; Software development; Surveyors

Vacancies
125

Application address
Personnel Dept, Geophysical Service International, A Group of Texas Instruments Ltd, Manton Lane, Bedford MK41 7PA

GSI is an exploration company engaged in the worldwide search for oil. Our work as contractors and consultants includes collection processing and interpretation of land and marine seismic data for oil companies. GSI, founded in 1930, was a leader in introducing seismic digital recording techniques in 1964 and is currently one of the forerunners in three-dimensional seismic data collection and processing.

Land and marine data collection crews operate worldwide and the data is processed in centres in 14 different countries. From Bedford, we control operations in Europe, Africa and the Middle East.

Types of graduate required
Geophysics, physics, maths and *geology* graduates are recruited as seismologists. Geologists must have a maths/physics background. Seismologists would start in either one of our UK data processing centres or in our geophysical support group in Dhahran, Saudi Arabia. After training they could transfer to one of our overseas processing centres or to a land or marine data collection crew.

Electronic engineering graduates are recruited to train as instrument and systems engineers on our land and marine data collection crews, or computer maintenance engineers in our processing centres.

Physics and *maths* graduates are recruited to join our software development group in Bedford.

Graduates in *surveying* join as land surveyors or possibly as support staff in our marine navigation group.

Training
The seismic industry is one of progressive technical improvement and, therefore, at GSI we believe in continual training throughout one's career. The following methods are used:

On the job training by experienced personnel.

Specialised courses such as our Dallas run schools for data processing seismologists, instrument engineers and marine systems engineers.

Videotape training programmes. Most of our crews have video machines and a good stock of tapes on various subjects.

Prospects
Starting salaries are competitive with those paid by other companies within the industry. Promotion is based entirely on merit and with the industry expanding at its current rate, opportunities for career advancement are excellent.

Geoservices

Activities
Geological and petroleum engineering; production services on drilling rigs

Employees
1,000

Location: UK
Scotland

Locations: Overseas
Worldwide

We are an international service company which provides oil companies with total geological and engineering control throughout drilling operations, and with production services as well. The oil industry is constantly expanding to meet world petroleum requirements, and it is our company's aim to give a highly efficient service to our clients all over the world with a team of thorough and skilled geologists and engineers and the most up to date equipment.

A career with Geoservices offers you varied work, scope for initiative and responsibility as well as a great deal of travelling.

Our work
Our geologists and engineers work from a mobile laboratory equipped with machinery and testing instruments, which is located on the drilling

Opportunities
Well logging engineers; Well-site geologists;
Petroleum engineers; Wireline and well testing
engineers

Vacancies
50

Application addresses
Recruitment Officer, Geoservices, 7 Rue
Newton, Z I du Coudray, 93.150 Le Blanc,
Mesnil, France.

site. The job entails carrying out geological surveillance including the
collection, study and analysis of cutting samples and cores from the
different strata in which the well is drilled. Instruments are used to detect
gas and oil shows and eventual hydrocarbon bearing formations, to
record mud and drilling parameters and to integrate the relevance of
these factors to drilling operation. The information gained by analysis of
instrument readings and sample analysis enables the geologist to draw a
complete description or log of the operation for the client and to act as an
adviser to the drillers. The Geoservices geologists and engineers are also
responsible for the maintenance and repair of the equipment.

Training and prospects
A graduate joining Geoservices attends a training course and then
receives additional on-site training under the supervision of our
experienced geologists and engineers. After he has got sufficient
experience, if he can show very good professional ability, he can then be
trained to become a total drilling control engineer, well-site geologist or
petroleum engineer, positions which carry a great deal of responsibility.
Opportunities in consultancy and management are also possible.

Types of graduate required
We are seeking young graduates in *geology* or related geological fields, we
also consider holders of BSc or HNC/HND in *electricity, electronic* or
mechanical engineering; some knowledge of computer science will be
appreciated. Applicants must be in good health, preferably single and
available to work anywhere.

Salary and benefits
Our salaries are competitive and vary according to the region, working
conditions and responsibilities. All travelling expensives are paid as well
as a living allowance on-site when accommodation is not provided free.
We also offer a free life insurance and a contributory medical and pension
scheme.

Further information
Please send a complete resume and explain your motivation to seek this
post. Candidates selected will be invited for a day's introduction to the
company.

Gestetner

Activities
The manufacture and sales of reprographic
equipment, stencil and offset duplicators,
copiers, supplies and accessories

Employees
16,000

Locations: UK
General

Locations: Overseas
Worldwide

Opportunities
Electrical and mechanical development and
production engineering; Management and
financial accounting; Computer programming
and commercial export work; Commercial and
sales

Gestetner, an international organisation with annual sales of over £300
million, is a world leader in the manufacture and sales of reprographic
equipment, stencil and offset duplicators, copiers, the velo-bind process
for binding documents, together with their supplies and accessories.

The Tottenham based head office and manufacturing plant occupies an
area of about one million square feet in North London. Its paper mill at
Kilbagie, Scotland, is one of the best equipped installations of its kind in
the country. The British sales organisation, a wholly owned Gestetner
subsidiary, with its head office at Euston Road, London, and sales and
services centres at more than forty points around the UK, is responsible
for retailing Gestetner products in Britain.

Gestetner subsidiaries overseas, together with a group of approved
agents, operate more than 1,300 sales and service centres in 130 countries
around the world. Through them the company annually exports more
than 80% of production.

The world's thirst for knowledge and the ever increasing demands for a
faster and less expensive means of communication have provided the

Vacancies
12 approx

Application addresses
The Staff Personnel Officer, Gestetner
Manufacturing Limited, Fawley Road, London
N17 9LT
For sales opportunities only: The Personnel
Manager, Gestetner Duplicators Limited,
Gestetner House, 210 Euston Road, London
NW1 2DA

Gestetner, cont

reprographic industry with a challenge. It is to meet this challenge that we annually recruit new graduates.

Types of graduate required
The number of vacancies varies from year to year as we recruit graduates for specific positions in particular departments.

For graduates in *engineering*, vacancies exist in both the electrical and mechanical development departments and in the production engineering division.

Opportunities exist within the computer department for male and female graduates to be trained as programmers and systems analysts. Providing graduates can show a highly developed faculty of logical analysis, specific disciplines are not considered necessary.

Graduates in *physics* and *chemistry* are required to work in our research laboratory which deals with all research and development aspects concerned with copying and duplicating.

The commercial department, which acts as an interface between the manufacturing units and worldwide sales organisations, provides an opportunity for business studies graduates. Knowledge of a foreign language plus a statistical bias would be advantageous.

For *accounting* or *business studies* graduates, the company offers the opportunity to become a fully qualified ACMA or ACCA.

Sales: graduates of *any* discipline are invited to join an already highly successful and professional sales team. Working within the British sales organisation you will receive a thorough training which will enable you to take full advantage of the excellent career opportunities which we are able to offer.

Training
Graduate engineers are expected to undertake a training programme which not only leads to a full appreciation of the total engineering function of the company but also a wider understanding of the business: this programme has been designed to help each individual reach chartered engineer status in the shortest time possible.

For graduates entering the computer department, intensive basic training is given over the first six months, which includes the use of our in-house audio visual training system as well as external courses.

In the commercial and scientific areas of the company, job training is carried out within the department, usually under the guidance of senior colleagues. This is backed up by the provision of external courses and seminars to meet the requirements of the individual.

In management and financial accounting, provision is made to obtain the appropriate professional qualification by day or block release backed up by relevant work experience.

Location
The Gestetner head office is adjacent to the Tottenham Hale station on the Victoria underground and Liverpool Street–Cambridge line of British Rail. It can be reached from central London in less then 20 minutes.

Salaries
Starting salaries are fully competitive and reviewed regularly, increments being awarded upon merit and ability.

Prospects
The policy is to promote from within and you will find that we offer excellent opportunities within the company provided you have demonstrated the right qualities.

Getty Oil (Britain) Limited

Activities
Exploration and production of petroleum and allied products

Employees 98

Location: UK London

Locations: Overseas
Bergen, Norway and Madrid, Spain

Opportunities
Petroleum engineers; Geologists; Geophysicists; Accountants; Computer staff

Application address
JJ Forty, Personnel Executive, Getty Oil (Britain) Limited, 1 Butler Place, London SW1H 0PS

Getty Oil (Britain) is a wholly owned subsidiary of the Getty Oil Company of California, USA. Getty is partner in the Occidental North Sea Consortium covering Piper and Claymore and with Unionoil the Heather field. We have exploration offices in Bergen in Norway, and a current operatorship off the east coast of Spain. There are further operating prospects offshore Denmark, Norway and Southern Africa.

Types of graduate required
We require *engineering* and *science* based graduates with at least three years experience, as well as graduates in *geology*, *geophysics* or related sciences with at least three years experience. Getty offer sponsorships from time to time to universities for scholarships to MSc students (one year) in relevant subjects.

Training and career development
Getty (London) is expanding rapidly and offers excellent career prospects to graduates with the ability and stamina to undertake a wide variety of projects. There is a policy of promotion from within. Opportunities for overseas postings form part of career development.

Government Communications Headquarters

Activities
Communications and communications security research and development

Location: UK
South West

Occupations
Government communications trainee (administrative/specialist); Electronic engineers; Electronics scientists; Executive officers; Maths/computer scientists

Vacancies
60 approx

Upper age limit
GCT: 28; EE: 26; ES: 30; EO: 45; MCS: 30

Application address
Graduate Appointments Officer, Room A/1108, GCHQ, Oakley, Priors Road, Cheltenham, Gloucestershire GL52 5AJ
Tel: 0242-21491 ext 2099
Closing date for the Civil Service Commission open competition entry Jan/Feb

GCHQ is a department of the Foreign and Commonwealth Office concerned with many aspects of communications and communications techniques, including communications security and the development of communications equipment.

The department has an unusually varied range of work, and can offer uniquely challenging problems to graduates in both scientific and non-scientific disciplines.

Types of graduate required
Scientists and *engineers* for research and development work on electronic equipment; *mathematicians*, *statisticians* and *computer scientists* for work on communications problems and in the computer division; and graduates from *all* disciplines for work which is not purely scientific in character, ranging from administration to specialised research.

The prime requisites in all fields are an inquiring mind, flexibility, some aptitude for research, and penetration coupled with breadth of vision. Apply as early as possible during final year of studies.

Training
Training is by a combination of on the job instruction and formal courses, according to the particular area of work. For Government Communications trainees there is a period of planned postings in order to provide them with the broad experience necessary for success in the higher grades.

Location
GCHQ is situated at Cheltenham, Gloucestershire, in the exceptionally attractive setting of the Cotswolds. Many graduate recruits have the opportunity for visits or tours of duty abroad.

With 16 separate departments as diverse as Finance, Education, Recreation and the Arts, Public Health Engineering, the GLC can offer careers of tremendous scope, variety and challenge in Administration.

At County Hall, Administration is a career in itself – leading up to the most senior positions; there are no barriers to moving between departments, or between broad areas of work to widen your experience on the way there! **In short, it's a career you won't grow out of.**

Graduate trainees are posted direct to Project Administration, Financial or Personnel Management, work with GLC Members, Management Services or Education. Full induction and on-the-job training is provided, supplemented by courses in personnel and management skills and background to the Council.

After your first year there are opportunities to study for further professional qualifications, such as the Institute of Personnel Management Examination or Diploma in Management Studies. Specialist training will then be available throughout your career.

Applications for Administrative positions are invited from graduates and final year undergraduates of all disciplines. Appointment is by competitive interview.

There are also a number of professional and specialist trainee schemes open to graduates. These are in: Accounting & Finance, Archives, Civil Engineering, Estate Management, Librarianship, Planning, Scientific Work, Strategic Planning & Statistics and Work Study.

The GLC is an equal opportunities employer.

Further details of graduate careers are contained in the booklet 'Careers for Graduates with the GLC/ILEA' obtainable from Manpower Services Department, Room 334A, County Hall, London SE1 7PB. Telephone: 01-633 8986.

Get it together under one roof...

GLC

Working for London

Salaries and prospects

Salaries are generally those current throughout the Civil Service; certain departmental grades are on closely comparable scales. The career structure is designed to give a full range of opportunities to each recruit.

The Greater London Council

GLC
Working for London

Activities
One of the country's largest local government bodies

Employees
6,000

Location: UK
London

Opportunities
Project administration; Financial management; Personnel management; Management services; Education; Work with GLC members

Vacancies
0

Application address
Central Recruitment Division, MP/PS1/DOG, Room 334A, Greater London Council, The County Hall, London SE1 7PB

The GLC came into being in 1965 and today provides vital services for over eight million people living and working within the 610 square miles it administers.

Activities centre around County Hall, where the elected members, working through a number of committees and the ILEA, set policy for the management of Greater London. Advice to the council is provided by 16 specialist departments who are also responsible for implementing council decisions and running its services.

The council's services include town planning, industrial development, traffic management, firefighting and prevention, refuse disposal, flood prevention, environmental control, preservation of historic buildings, South Bank, management and development of parks and open spaces.

Types of graduate required

Within the GLC, administration is regarded as a career in itself, offering tremendous scope, variety and challenge for graduates in *any* discipline, in departments as diverse as finance, education, recreation and the arts, and public health engineering.

Opportunities fall in the following areas:

Project administration Working alongside professional staff in project teams implementing, monitoring and revising policies. Some sections focus on interpretation of existing rules and legislation, dealing with building regulations, buildings work contracts and traffic orders.

Financial management Within the finance department, and in most other departments, covering full financial management services: from budget preparation to audit; providing financial support and advice to senior management and members on special projects, financial control and major contracts, with involvement in contract management and claims investigation.

Personnel management Personnel work is carried out centrally by manpower services and locally within each department. Work is concerned with IR, recruitment, career development and training, staff management, and co-ordination of staffing policy.

Work with GLC members Within the director general's department, in the secretariats of council committees; involved in policy formulation and in daily contact with members and officers, attending meetings, preparing reports, correspondence, case studies and other often highly confidential paperwork.

Management services Within manpower services and individual management services branches of other departments; offering a complete management consultancy service.

Education The ILEA's administrative functions are mainly carried out by the education officer's department. Administrators work throughout the education service at County Hall, divisional offices, colleges of further and higher education and divisions of the careers service.

Specialist trainee schemes are also open to graduates. These are in accounting and finance, archives, civil engineering, estate management, London Fire Brigade, librarianship, planning, scientific work, strategic planning and statistics.

The Greater London Council, cont

Training and career development

Graduates receive full induction and on the job training, supplemented by courses in public administration and staff management.

After the first year, opportunities are given to study for additional professional qualifications. Specialist training is available on an ongoing basis.

Careers in administration can lead to the most senior positions. There are no barriers to moving between departments, or broad areas of work.

Graduates join at administrative officer A level and are promoted to grade B when considered ready to assume full administrative responsibilities. Good prospects exist for further promotion.

Salaries

Salaries are age related and rise annually on an incremental scale. Details of current levels are available on application.

Amenities

A wide variety of clubs and societies exist for the benefit of staff, covering sport, hobbies, general interest, music and drama etc. The council also runs subsidised canteen facilities.

Further information

Further details are contained in the booklet *Careers for Graduates with the GLC/ILEA* obtainable from the address given.

Applications should be received by the end of March, but later applications may be considered.

Candidates are advised to meet members of the manpower services department during their visits to universities early in the year.

The GLC is an equal opportunities employer.

Guardian Royal Exchange Assurance plc

Activities
Insurance of all classes and ancilliary financial business

Employees
7,500 UK
15,000 worldwide

Locations: UK
General

Opportunities
General professional trainees; Investment trainees; Actuarial trainees

Vacancies
30 approx

Application address
Mr MK Paisley, Personnel Officer, Guardian Royal Exchange Assurance plc, Royal Exchange, London EC3V 3LS

Guardian Royal Exchange is one of the largest and most progressive groups in insurance, long standing in tradition, yet forward thinking in outlook. Royal Exchange was founded by Royal Charter in 1720. Guardian dates from 1821. The two amalgamated in 1969 and now head an international group of some 180 companies, with gross assets of £3,899 million and an annual premium income of £1,094 million. They transact every class of insurance and financial business through a network of branches and agencies throughout the UK and overseas. In the last two and a half centuries, the member companies have played a leading role in the establishment of London as the accepted centre of international insurance; and today their worldwide activities make a vital contribution to Britain's invisible exports and balance of payments.

Types of graduate required

We offer a progressive career to selected graduates (preferably with at least second class honours) who possess personality, initiative, ambition and the ability to advance rapidly to early administrative and managerial responsibility. In the wide scope of our business there is a need for graduates in various disciplines, particularly in *arts, economics, commerce* and *law*. We are also interested in graduates in *mathematics* and *statistics* as actuarial trainees in London, Lytham St Annes and Edinburgh.

Advancement to senior appointment is intended for each accepted candidate who proves his/her potential. Consequently recruitment must be strictly limited in order to conform to the planned development of the future management of the company.

Training
Organised training in the various fields of insurance (fire, life, accident and motor) is considered to be of major importance. Our professional training scheme has been designed, therefore to provide comprehensive and concentrated training in all classes of business transacted. The course follows a carefully prepared programme a copy of which is handed to each graduate on joining our service. It involves planned periodic moves through all departments to gain wide practical experience under the guidance of a tutor. This is supplemented by attendance at various residential courses at our own training centre at Ipswich, where we use the most modern equipment and methods.

Trainees will also be expected to study for the diploma examinations of the Chartered Insurance Institute (or other appropriate professional bodies) and day release facilities are provided. Tuition and examination fees are reimbursed, and success is recognised by financial reward.

Location
Opportunities are available at our head offices in London, Ipswich, Lytham St Annes and Edinburgh and at branch offices in many large towns in the United Kingdom. Willingness to move, on request, to any of these locations will be essential.

Salaries
Starting salaries which compare most favourably with those of similar employers are dependent upon the class of degree and are progressive with ready recognition of merit and performance. Generous staff benefits are also provided, including a non-contributory pension and life assurance scheme, luncheon facilities, assistance with house purchase in approved cases, and sports and social facilities.

Guest Keen and Nettlefolds plc

Activities
Steel processing, production of components for engineering industry; Manufacture of capital goods; Distribution

Employees
78,000

Locations: UK
Mainly Midlands, Yorkshire, North Wales

Opportunities & places
Engineers 15; Finance 2; Management services 2; Metallurgy 5; Commercial 5

Application address
Appointments Officer, Management Resources, Guest Keen and Nettlefolds plc, Group Head Office, Smethwick, Warley, West Midlands B66 2RZ

The Guest Keen and Nettlefolds group of companies is one of the largest industrial and engineering groups in the United Kingdom. It employs around 78,000 people all over the world, and has an annual sales turnover of £1,855 million. Its activities range from the processing of steel to large scale production of components for the engineering industry and the design and manufacture of capital goods for many industries. Activity in distribution and in industrial services is increasing.

The group comprises over 100 operating companies in the United Kingdom, organised on a divisional basis; they retain a fair amount of independence and autonomy of control of day to day operations. They also have the benefit of a number of group services designed to provide expert guidance in such aspects as economic appraisal and data processing. Comprehensive financial control systems are operated throughout the group. There is a well established group technological centre covering all fields of technological development. Group companies are located mainly in the Midlands, Yorkshire and North Wales.

Types of graduate required
Many vacancies are more suited to those with technically oriented degrees, although there are some vacancies suited to non-technical graduates.

Training and career development
Pre-selection will be operated on a group basis. Recruitment will then be carried out by individual companies for substantive appointments.

Training will be provided by the employing company in association with group management resources, as appropriate. Such training will last for three to eighteen months according to individual requirements. Engineering and other graduates are encouraged to undertake the necessary training to qualify for membership of professional institutions.

Salaries
Details of salaries will be published as soon as possible in 1983.

Further information
Those wishing to be considered for any vacancies should contact their university careers advisory services who will be able to supply up to date information on such vacancies and on methods of application.

Appointments for preliminary interviews will be available only to those who complete and return the group's application forms and who specify the vacancies in which they are interested.

Habitat

Activities
Multiple store retailing

Employees
1,300

Locations: UK
General

Opportunities
Commercial and management

Vacancies
20

Upper age limit
26

Application address
Lesley Myland, Management Training Officer, Habitat Designs Limited, Hithercroft Road, Wallingford, Oxon OX10 9EU
Tel: 0491 35000

In 1964, the first Habitat store opened in London. It offered home furnishings that were attractive, functional and gave value for money. It was a huge success, and we now have stores throughout the UK, as well as on the continent and, under the Conran name, in the USA.

Our prize winning designs are only a part of the reason for our success. We are an innovative and professional business organisation, and as such depend heavily on first class management.

Selection
Graduates of *all* disciplines may apply; commitment to management of people as a career, together with ambition to succeed at high level, is essential. Candidates should be aged between 21 and 26 years, fit and totally mobile. Previous retail experience gained while undertaking vacation work is desirable.

Training
If you meet our requirements, we will train you quickly and systematically to acquire the special skills needed for successful management. The intensive ten-month training programme consists of practical involvement in all areas of store management, backed up by formal courses on the more theoretical aspects. Projects that you undertake are designed to provide you with skills and knowledge for your future use, so all have a practical application within Habitat.

The performance of each trainee is monitored closely, giving you the necessary guidance and encouragement to take up your first managerial appointment and to help you succeed in our business.

Career progression
Floor manager is the first step on the managerial ladder; you will spend three months out of the ten, as an acting floor manager before being confirmed in this role. This is an integral part of your training, giving you an opportunity to put into practice the skills you have acquired although still under the supervision of the training department. Responsible to the store manager for everything concerned with your department, priorities will be staff training, appraisal and development, sales, merchandising, cost control and administration.

We are a company committed to developing and promoting people from within and after your first full floor manager appointment, there will be every opportunity to progress quickly to move to senior management positions, initially assistant and store manager posts.

The pace of your promotion will depend very much on personal ambition and achievement; however, you should expect to reach store manager level in four to five years.

Salaries
Highly competitive salaries are coupled with valuable benefits including staff discount and the chance to own shares in the company.

Hacker Young

Activities
Chartered accountancy

Employees
170

Location: UK
London

Opportunities & places
Trainee chartered accountants 15

Application address
The Staff Partner, Hacker Young, St Alphage House, Fore Street, London EC2Y 5DH

Hacker Young is a medium sized firm of chartered accountants based in the City of London. We provide professional services to a large number of clients who are engaged in a wide variety of industrial, commercial and professional activities. The scope of our work includes auditing, accountancy, taxation, investigations and insolvency.

Types of graduate required
We are especially interested in graduates in *accounting, economics, business studies* or *mathematics*, but also welcome enquiries from graduates in other disciplines.

Training
As our high professional standards depend entirely upon the calibre, experience and training of all members of staff, great care is taken to ensure that new graduates are fully trained and developed so that they can shoulder an increasing amount of responsibility during their training.

Graduates will enter into a three-year training contract which combines practical work and formal tuition.

Trainees attend in-house courses to assist them with their practical professional duties and prepare for their professional examinations with the help of a leading accountancy tutorial organisation. Course fees for the professional examinations I and II are paid by the firm.

Prospects
As a newly qualified accountant upon the successful completion of your examinations and training contract, you will be able to choose from a wide variety of career opportunities. Some of our students make their permanent careers with Hacker Young whilst others opt to join other organisations or types of enterprises in industry, commerce or the profession.

Salaries
These are competitive with the highest professional standards.

Haines Watts

Activities
Accountancy

Employees
250

Locations: UK
South East; Midlands; North West

The Haines Watts Group has offices in Slough, High Wycombe, Reading, Basingstoke, Aldershot, Oxford, Nottingham, Manchester, Sheffield, Bradford, and Birmingham. It is anticipated that further offices will be opened in the Thames Valley and the Midlands.

Our client range covers small and medium sized private sector businesses in both industry and commerce.

Types of graduate required
Consideration will be given to graduates in most disciplines particularly related degrees. We also consider that the ability to get on well with

Opportunities & places
Trainee chartered accountants 25

Upper age limit
26

Application address
Haines Watts Associates, Sterling House, High Street, Lane End, High Wycombe, Bucks HP14 3JF

colleagues and clients, to communicate and to use initiative are of equal importance.

Training

We readily accept the importance of training our students and keep our overall training policy and the progress of individual trainees under constant review.

For the professional examinations we encourage the use of leading firms of accountancy tutors and make a substantial contribution to the cost of the course.

Our in-house training package has been developed to give the trainee a practical approach to this work. On-job training is given by working in our various productive departments which will give experience in accounts preparation, auditing of small and medium size limited companies, taxation, both corporate and personal and company secretarial work. Every effort is made to ensure that practical experience is gained at a time when the subject is being studied for examination purposes.

Prospects

Following qualification our trainees are encouraged to remain with us, undergoing an intensive programme of further training to prepare for partnership after two years of qualification. Our rapid growth provides outstanding opportunities for partnership at an early age with unusually high levels of income.

Salaries

Good starting salaries are paid followed by six-monthly reviews.

Hambros Bank Limited

Hambros Bank is one of the largest of the merchant banks and a leading acceptance house. Activities cover all types of lending, foreign exchange dealing, financial services to industry, investment management and new issues. The bank has extensive and long established connections with Europe, especially Scandinavia. Much of the bank's work is computerised and the systems used are constantly updated. There is a total staff of 900.

Types of graduate required

Graduates in *any* subject may be suitable, with a preference for *economics* and the *law*. Numeracy is an advantage.

Activities
Banking; Foreign exchange dealing; Financial services to industry; Fund management

Employees
900

Locations: UK
London and South East

Opportunities
Banking executives; Credit analysts; Executives in corporate finance; Fund managers; International banking and issues; Investment analysts; Unit trust accounting

Vacancies
4–6

Application address
Head of Personnel, Hambros Bank Limited, 41 Bishopsgate, London EC2

Training

Graduates enter on one year's probation during which time they are given the opportunity to learn the systems and methods of the bank. There are lectures on all aspects of the bank's work and its organisation. After the probationary period graduates will be given further training and experience in various departments of the bank. All entrants are required to study and sit for the certificate in banking for graduates, which is obtainable within a year.

Location

The head office is located at 41 Bishopsgate, London EC2 and there are offices in Pall Mall and at Brentwood and Shenfield in Essex. There are excellent club and sports facilities at Shenfield.

Salaries

Starting salaries will be agreed by interview. The salary scale compares favourably with other banks. After the probationary period there is an annual staff appraisal and salary review. Payment and progress is based on performance.

Prospects
The small number of graduates entering each year is designed to provide good prospects of promotion and a varied and interesting career.

Pensions and other amenities
There is a non-contributory pension scheme with retirement ages of 60 for men and 55 for women, and a staff luncheon club and first class sports and social facilities. There are four weeks holiday per annum.

HAT Accountancy Training Syndicate

Activities
Chartered accountancy

Employees
20–25 approx per firm

Locations: UK
London and South East

Vacancies
2 approx per firm

Application address
HAT, 16 Red Lion Square, London WC1R 4QH

HAT was formed in 1975 by six practices of chartered accountants in the central London area to provide a comprehensive training service for its member firms. Since 1975 the HAT Syndicate has grown to include 14 small to medium sized practices of chartered accountants based in the Holborn and City areas with a combined total of some 450 professional staff (200 students, 100 partners, 150 other staff). The training services offered to member firms include:
● provision of in-house practice work courses for students totalling approximately five weeks over their training contract (including two residential weeks at a university);
● a scheme of studies for the professional examinations with a leading firm of tutors in the private sector;
● the provision of a standard audit and accountancy procedures manual;
● an annual programme of CPE courses for partners, qualified and senior staff covering areas of practice work relevant to member firms;
● screening interviews at the major English universities during the annual milkround;
● regular student reviews in the practice offices.

The advantage of training in our syndicate is that training resources normally found only in the larger firms are available to the student, but without the loss of the close working relationship between principal and student which many larger firms cannot provide. The range and number of clients on which the student will work will also be greater in a smaller firm, and more senior levels of responsibility are reached earlier.

The student's training includes a scheme of studies for the professional examinations of the Institute of Chartered Accountants in England and Wales, centred on a reputable firm of tutors. Students are given paid leave for their first attempt at each of the examinations they are required to sit; the tuition fees for these first attempts are also paid for by the firms.

A list of the firms participating in the scheme is given in the HAT brochure available from university careers departments, or on request from HAT.

Types of graduate required
Students of *any* discipline expecting to obtain at least a second class degree are considered by the member firms. Applications should be sent to HAT who will forward suitable candidates' details to member firms. Application forms are contained in the HAT brochure. (Standard introduction forms may also be used.)

Hawker Siddeley Dynamics Engineering Limited

Activities
Design, manufacturing and marketing of control and monitoring equipment for industrial, mining and prime mover applications

Employees
800

Locations: UK
Hertfordshire and Lancashire

Opportunities
System engineers; Software designers; Electronics design and development engineers; Microprocessor equipment designers

Application address
Personnel Department (Graduate Recruitment), Hawker Siddeley Dynamics Engineering Limited, Bridge Road East, Welwyn Garden City, Hertfordshire AL7 1LR

We are an advanced technology company supplying specialised equipment and software for the control and supervision of machinery, plant and processes and complete systems for electron beam welding. The principal characteristic of our products is that they perform a complex, vital function with greater realiability, often in a hostile environment.

HSDE is a member of the Hawker Siddeley Group which comprises over 150 companies working in electrical and mechanical engineering and employing about 55,000 people throughout the world.

Locations

The headquarters of the company are in Hertfordshire, about 20 miles north of London. Here are the research, design and development facilities which employs approximately 400 people. The main production factory is at Farnworth, near Bolton, in Lancashire, where there are a further 400 people. The work of the company is divided between four product divisions.

Engine and machinery controls division

The division produces digital control systems to provide optimum dynamic performance and health monitoring for gas turbines under varying load – particularly in industrial installations and helicopters; programmable controllers for industry; and vehicle transmission control systems. This division is advanced in the use of microprocessors and is supported by extensive analogue and digital facilities for simulation and computation. At any time these may be found working on a very diverse range of problems in support of any of the product divisions.

Marine systems division

This division manufactures propulsion control systems for gas turbine powered naval ships, providing remote control of engines, gearing and propellers. Work is in hand for many nations around the world and new developments cover digital and distributed systems linked by data highway.

Mining and industrial division

Remote control and monitoring equipment are produced which make mining operations safer and more efficient by enabling the electrical machinery in a mine and the environmental conditions to be controlled from a central station. We also produce specialised control systems for industrial production machinery. Data transmission techniques and mini and micro computers are used extensively.

This division also supplies complete systems for an exciting new welding technology that is making possible assemblies that could not have been considered previously and is advancing the design and manufacture of many products, notably aero engines, motor car gearboxes, steam turbines and marine diesels. New products are also being developed in the field of ion implantation.

Software services division

This new division was established at the beginning of 1980 to provide a wide range of mini and micro computer services to customers in the UK and overseas. The division designs, implements, markets and supports software packages as well as providing consultancy training and associated services.

Opportunities

The strength of HSDE lies in its engineering capability coupled with manufacturing centres skilled in the economic production of high quality equipment and backed by dedicated product support services.

Engineers in HSDE are the designers of the equipment supplied by the company and must have a full understanding of its various applications. The nature of the work can give plenty of opportunity for travel to those who want it.

Types of graduate required

We require graduates with degrees in *electronics, electrical engineering, physics* (with an *electronics* bias), *mathematics* (with a *computing* bias) and *computer science*.

Where the graduate fits

Graduates who join the company benefit in the ability to gain experience over a diverse field. Experienced engineers provide backing during the formative years and encouragement is given to continue training both internally and externally.

We prefer the graduate to have concentrated on electronic engineering. Any specialisation on control subjects would be a benefit.

How to apply

If our business interests you please write for further information to the address given.

Haymarket Publishing Group

Activities
Publishing

Employees
630

Location: UK
London

Opportunities
Selling; Journalism

Application address
The Recruitment and Training Manager,
Haymarket Publishing Limited,
76 Dean Street, London W1A 1BU

We are a vigorous and expanding publishing organisation employing 630 people and publishing over 30 titles. These include Management Today, Campaign, Autosport, What Hi-fi?, General Practitioner, What Camera Weekly and Marketing.

Types of graduate required

The company recruits trainees, graduates and non-graduates, throughout the year for advertisement sales positions. Previous sales experience is not important, but essential qualities are a positive interest in business, an ability to think quickly and argue clearly, and an approach to work which is lively and energetic.

Graduates are also considered for trainee journalist vacancies.

Training

Graduates joining the company as sales people are given an initial training course. Thereafter all sales staff go through intensive and continuous training programmes in order to develop a thoroughly professional approach to sales.

An editorial training scheme is run for journalists.

Salaries and prospects

In their first year of employment, sales executives can earn in the region of £5,500 including commission.

Starting salaries for editorial trainees are in accordance with the terms of the NUJ agreement.

We pursue a policy of promotion from within solely on the basis of proven ability and initiative.

Help the Aged

Activities
Campaign for the rights of the elderly, fund raising

Employees
300–400

Locations: UK
General

Opportunities
Organisation; Campaigning; Fund raising

Vacancies
20

Upper age limit
30

Application address
Recruitment Officer, Personnel Department, Help the Aged, 146 Queen Victoria Street, London EC4V 4BX

The youth division is responsible for a programme of education and fundraising events in schools throughout the UK. Graduates join Help the Aged as trainee youth organisers to work with a team of 80 throughout the country. Based at home, organisers work in 100–150 schools, annually, talking to and motivating large groups of children, organising sponsored events, and presenting illustrated talks based on material provided by the education department.

Types of graduate required
Candidates, of *any* discipline, should be self motivated, with developed organisational and communication skills, confident in their ability to motivate others.

Training
Intensive residential course initially, followed by participative field training with experienced organisers. Appointment to own area generally within six to nine months. Starting dates are August/September.

Salary
A progressive salary is paid linked to a bonus scheme. A car or car allowance is provided (clean driving licence essential). Promotion is based entirely on achievement and performance.

Hickson & Welch Ltd

Activities
Manufacturers of organic chemicals for the dyestuff, pigment, pharmaceutical, agricultural chemicals, textile paper and board, soap and detergent, industrial chemicals industries

Employees
1,000

Location: UK
North East

Opportunities
Plant managers; Research chemists; Engineers

Application address
Mr CR Turner, Personnel Manager, Hickson & Welch Ltd, Ings Lane, Castleford, West Yorkshire WF10 2JT

Hickson & Welch Ltd is the largest UK manufacturer of intermediates based upon benzene, toluene and xylene which are used extensively in the textile, paper, rubber, leather and agricultural industries. Unit operations include nitration (both batch and continuous), sulphonation, halogenation and oxidation. A recently completed multi-million pound investment has produced a range of aromatic amines by hydrogenation, placing the company amongst the UK leaders as manufacturers of these important products.

The company was formed in 1915 to manufacture TNT for munitions, and went on to establish a firm reputation as a manufacturer of dyestuff intermediates. During the Second World War a unit for the production of insecticides was set up, this soon became the largest in the UK.

Whilst the bulk of the chemicals are intermediates destined for further processing, finished products are made. These include the Photine range of fluorescent whitening agents for textiles and paper, agricultural chemicals and the Lanette brand of waxes for use in pharmaceutical industries.

Graduate opportunities and training
The company employs 1,000 people of whom about 100 are graduates, Graduates possessing higher degrees in *chemistry* and *chemical engineering* are recruited for posts in the research, development and production departments. The company follows the policy of providing its own management succession and to meet this aim suitable training is provided by our own training department or outside centres of education.

Holset Engineering Co Ltd

Activities
Precision engineers, automotive, industrial and marine applications

Employees
1,500

Location: UK
North East

Opportunities
Project engineers; Development engineers; Design engineers; Production engineers; Application engineers; Research and development; Personnel; Production control; Data processing; Electronic engineers

Vacancies
7

Upper age limit
29

Application address
Graduate Recruitment Officer, Holset Engineering Co Ltd, PO Box A9, Turnbridge, Huddersfield, West Yorkshire HD1 6RD

Holset Engineering Co Ltd, a subsidiary company of Cummins UK Ltd, is a world leader in the technology and production of turbochargers to the automotive industry. The company is closely involved with major engine builders pursuing an expanding development programme directed at uprating engine power while reducing environmental pollutants such as noise and emission. Holset is Europe's largest maker of torsional vibration dampers, both viscous and rubber, for automotive and marine applications, and is a major manufacturer of fan drives, flexible couplings and rubber components.

Over 60% of total production is exported to worldwide markets.

Types of graduate required
Our main requirement is for *engineers* and *scientists* who can support our continued technical progress and contribute skills and energies in areas of development, manufacturing, technical sales, data processing and administration. In many cases the precise nature of your qualification is less important than the personal qualities that lie behind it. We invest in people no less than in facilities, new methods and equipment.

Training
We adapt the training to meet the graduate's needs, related to the requirements of future positions. A training period is programmed to provide sufficient opportunity to gain experience in the relevant technical and associated departments.

Facilities and locations
Investment in new methods, research and manufacturing facilities has been high with a result that the company has some of the most modern and well equipped premises in the area.

The two factories, at Huddersfield and Halifax, are situated in West Yorkshire which abounds in reasonably priced housing, pleasant countryside and excellent civic, social and educational facilities. All this being enhanced by the business and recreational mobility provided by an easily accessible motorway.

Salaries
Salaries are competitive, with planned progression to first appointment and beyond. Our continued expansion will provide many opportunities; if you feel that you are suited to a company that can offer you plenty of scope in your career, then please write for further details to the Graduate Recruitment Officer.

Horizon Exploration Limited

Activities
Geophysical contractors; acquisition, processing and interpretation of seismic data

Employees
500+

Horizon Exploration Limited, formed in late 1973, is a British owned company located some 25 miles from London at Swanley, Kent. Owned, in partnership, by major English mineral companies, Horizon is the only wholly British geophysical company to offer its clients the complete spectrum of seismic activities.

Horizon Exploration currently operates deep sea seismic survey vessels and a number of land crews in the field whilst, at head office in Kent, a computer centre and comprehensive interpretation department is in continuous operation all year round.

Types of graduate required
Graduates are required for field work as well as office based duties: in some cases experience gained at sea or on our land crews can greatly assist

HUGHES
MICROELECTRONICS

Technology and the future go hand in hand, but at Hughes we realise that a third and probably the most important component is often overlooked. It is, of course, the human element. People are the key to successfully using the technology that we have at our fingertips. The designers, engineers, accountants marketing and sales experts who all play vital roles in Hughes Microelectronics, keeping us at the forefront of the high technology race.

If you're graduating this year, you'll be looking for a company who can offer you commitment, job satisfaction and, above all, career prospects. Read our reference entry. You'll find we employ more than just future technology.

A Future Technology Employer

HUGHES

HUGHES MICROELECTRONICS LTD

in fulfilling technical tasks in the office. There are openings for loners just as much as for the more gregarious type of individual.

Training and career development
It is not expected that new graduates will have gained much expertise in seismic activities when starting work with the company, so considerable emphasis is placed upon on the job training during the initial stage of employment. External courses, when relevant, are also used to build up individual skills and knowledge.

Prospects
As a young and vigorous organisation, Horizon Exploration offers the motivated graduate considerable scope for career and salary development. The company has great potential in both domestic and international markets and our continued growth ensures excellent promotion prospects for employees demonstrating the desired levels of leadership and technical ability. The company has a graded job structure with annually reviewed maximum/minimum salaries attached to each grade. Details of salaries, terms and conditions of employment and all other matters relating to being a member of the Horizon team are given at selection interviews. All candidates are required to complete the company application form, obtainable from head office, Swanley, and to pass a medical examination before any formal offer of employment can be confirmed.

Locations: UK
Head office: Kent
Field crew: general

Locations: Overseas
Field crew: worldwide

Opportunities
Field crew: Physicists; Geophysicists; Geologists; Electronic engineers
Data processing: Physicists; Geophysicists; Geologists; Mathematicians

Application address
Personnel Department, Horizon Exploration Limited, Horizon House, Azalea Drive, Swanley, Kent BR8 8JR

Hughes Microelectronics Ltd

Hughes Microelectronics Ltd (HML) is a long established company, now a wholly owned subsidiary of the Hughes Aircraft Company of California.

The parent company is involved in research, design and manufacture of advanced products such as semiconductor devices, integrated circuits, weapons systems, avionics and communications satellites.

Our product development and growth rate is closely linked with the graduates who join us each year. We pay close attention to the high standards we set in our graduate selection process, ensuring that both they and Hughes take maximum benefit from the opportunities we offer.

This applies to each new graduate who joins us, in product design and development, production process and quality control, or technical sales and marketing.

Activities
Design, development and manufacture of commercial, military and aerospace microelectronic components and assemblies

Employees
450

Location: UK
Glenrothes, Scotland

Location: Overseas
USA

Opportunities
Product design and development; Production process and quality control; Technical sales and marketing

Application address
The Personnel Manager, Hughes Microelectronics Ltd, Queensway Industrial Estate, Glenrothes, Fife KY7 5PY

Types of graduate required
We offer opportunities in the complete range of activities involved in the operation of a state-of-the-art advanced electronics company producing hybrid and MOS integrated circuits, including all related support activities.

We require graduates in *physics, electronics, computer science, metallurgy, production engineering, quality engineering, manufacturing sciences, business studies* and *accountancy*.

Training
Our training schemes are adjusted to each graduate's requirements, tailored specifically to suit any chosen specialisation, either commercial or technical. Where possible we try to provide training in advanced technology to MSc level, where an individual has the capacity to expand with the specialisation. We also encourage graduate level general workshop practice (EP 1).

Hughes Microelectronics Ltd, cont

This system is fully geared to recognise individual achievement and offers first class opportunities for early promotion. Together with our highly competitive salary range and company benefits, we believe that our offer to graduates has a balanced approach that is essential for mutual development. We appreciate that people are the catalyst in high technology.

Further information
If Hughes Microelectronics is the type of organisation which can offer you the maximum benefit from your degree, then write to us. Tell us about yourself, your career plans and what is important to you. We'll tell you about us and how you could fit in at Hughes.

Hughes Allen Payne Stone

Activities
Chartered accountants in public practice

Employees
140

Locations: UK
Greater London; South East; East Anglia

Opportunities & places
Trainee chartered accountants 10/12

Application address
HK Lewis, Hughes Allen Payne Stone, Greenwood House, 4/7 Salisbury Court, London EC4Y 8BT

Hughes Allen Payne Stone is a medium sized firm of chartered accountants which can be traced back to the 1890s. At present there are 15 partners of whom seven are situated in London. The style of client ranges from public companies, large private companies and downwards to individuals. However, it has always stressed the importance of a friendly working environment and its wide range of clients enables all members of staff to gain a great deal of experience.

Types of graduate required
We accept *all* disciplines as we place great reliance on the staff's ability to communicate in the English language. It cannot be stressed too highly that the skills of communication and common sense are of paramount importance when dealing with clients who have widely different problems.

Training
All staff are offered a formal in-house training programme under the auspices of Holborn Accountancy Tuition Limited who also control all professional examinations which are paid for by the firm. (See the entry under HAT).

Prospects
Salaries are attractive and increase with examination success and the students' readiness to assume greater responsibility. Great importance is placed upon the students' attitude towards the profession and they are encouraged to take as much responsibility as they can manage at an early opportunity. There are excellent prospects for promotion and opportunities for partnership within the firm.

Hymans, Robertson & Co

Activities
Consulting actuaries and computing services

Employees
30

Locations: UK
London and scotland

Opportunities
Actuarial assistants; Computer assistants

Upper age limit
23

We are an expanding firm of consulting actuaries, based in London and Glasgow. Our clients are mainly life offices, pension funds and friendly societies. Our subsidiary company, City of London Computer Services Limited, gives direct advice to clients mainly in the insurance and pensions administration fields, as well as assisting the partnership.

Types of graduate required
Actuarial training is demanding and we look for students who have a good honours degree in *mathematics, statistics, computer science,* or *economics.* A good grade in mathematics A level is also required.

Application address
SH Bell, Hymans, Robertson & Co, 35 New
Bridge Street, London EC4V 6BJ

A similar background will also be an advantage to applicants for the
computer assistant posts.

As consultants, we are looking for applicants who would be able to
create a good impression with our clients, both in writing and at
meetings.

Training
Actuarial assistants will be expected to study for fellowship of the
Institute or Faculty of Actuaries, and to make good progress in their
examinations. Students will receive a variety of work covering most
aspects of the examination syllabus. Generous daytime study leave is
given to enable students to supplement their preparation for the
examinations.

Salaries and prospects
Starting salaries will be in line with other graduate opportunities in
central London. Other benefits include an annual bonus and season
ticket loans.

Progress will depend on the student's aptitude and his examination
results. Partners are appointed from within the firm, usually within two
years of qualification. The company has many overseas clients, mainly in
Africa, and there will be opportunities for qualified actuaries to travel
abroad.

Further information
Our brochure is available through your careers office.

IBM United Kingdom Limited

We are part of an international organisation with research and
development laboratories in eight countries, manufacturing plants in 15
and sales and engineering service establishments in over 100.

Activities
Design, manufacture, marketing and
maintenance of computers, computer services,
office products and word processing systems

Employees
14,750

Locations: UK
General

Opportunities
Systems engineering (marketing support);
Programming; Development; Manufacturing;
Finance

Vacancies
50–100

Application address
The Graduate Recruitment Department, IBM
United Kingdom Limited, PO Box 41, North
Harbour, Portsmouth, Hampshire PO6 3AU

Types of graduate required
Except for strictly technical posts, in eg hardware development or
manufacturing, degree background is of less concern to us than the
abilities and personal qualities of applicants. For all jobs concerned with
computers and their applications, numeracy and logical reasoning ability
are essential but it is just as important that candidates are
communicative, lively, resilient, and have a certain presence. Over a
quarter of our employees in this country have degrees or equivalent
professional qualifications.

In any year we may have vacancies for systems engineers (who give
marketing support to our sales representatives and technical support and
guidance to our customers), systems and applications programmers,
hardware and software development engineers and programmers,
engineers for our manufacturing plants, finance department specialists,
and for people to fill other one-off vacancies. We are unable to forecast
our needs for the year with any accuracy before January when we send
preliminary vacancies statements to careers services. We always receive
far too many applications for programming vacancies and too few for
those in systems engineering.

Training
New recruits are always appointed to particular jobs, and appropriate
initial training is given to every employee according to his or her needs.
Training continues as necessary throughout a career.

Locations
Laboratories: Hursley, near Winchester; manufacturing plants: Havant

and Greenock; branch offices, London and principal cities. IBM's head office is located at North Harbour, Portsmouth.

Salaries and prospects

We aim to ensure that our salaries compare favourably with those paid for similar work in other leading companies. For successful men and women there are very good promotion opportunities within professional career structures, and management appointments are invariably made from within the company.

Applications and further information

We use a pre-selection system; we visit certain careers services in the spring term and invite selected students from other places to interviews in the Easter vacation.

The Graduate in IBM, our application forms, and preliminary vacancy estimates will be available in January from your careers service or from the graduate recruitment department.

Ilford Limited

ILFORD

Activities
Manufacture of photographic products

Employees
1,500

Locations: UK
Mobberley, Cheshire and London

Locations: Overseas
France; Switzerland

Opportunities
Scientists; Engineers;

Application address
The Personnel Manager, Ilford Limited, Town Lane, Mobberley, Knutsford, Cheshire

Vacancies for graduates and postgraduates are anticipated as part of Ilford Limited's restructuring programme in which its Mobberley, Cheshire site will by 1984 become the company's single UK manufacturing unit employing circa 1,500 people.

The photographic industry is highly competitive and to meet the challenge ahead the company has streamlined its organisation and rationalised its product range. The marketing effort is geared to expansion by increasing the company's share of existing markets, by finding new outlets for the company's range of photographic products and by the continuous invention and development of products to meet users' needs; investment in research and development will continue to be substantial.

Those joining us can expect to find a lively environment in which innovation and personal initiative are both encouraged and rewarded.

Ilford Limited is a member of the Ciba-Geigy Group of companies in the United Kingdom which is part of the international research based chemical company Ciba-Geigy Limited of Basle, Switzerland. Ciba-Geigy's world sales are over £3,000 million, and it manufactures and markets dyestuffs, pharmaceuticals, agrochemicals, plastics and additives, household and garden products, processing equipment and photographic products. Ilford Limited in the UK is the main manufacturing centre of the worldwide Ilford photographic group, which includes Ciba-Geigy Photochemie AG at Fribourg in Switzerland and Ilford SA at Lyon in France.

The Ilford group manufactures specialised black and white camera films and paper and the range of Cibachrome colour products, plus equipment and photographic chemicals to support these materials. These products are marketed for professional and industrial photographers as well as for the serious amateur. The group also produces scientific plates and nuclear emulsions.

Types of graduate required

The invention, development, manufacture and marketing of technically complex photographic products require a high level of teamwork; we are therefore concerned to recruit not only graduates of high ability but also people who enjoy participating in multi-disciplined projects and who are interested in the achievement of commercial objectives.

Research and development: *Physical, inorganic and organic chemists; physicists; polymer* and *materials scientists*. For some posts previous research experience is considered to be essential.

Engineering: *Applied physicists* and *mechanical engineers*.

Occasional opportunities: Finance, marketing, technical service, production technical, and management services. A broad range of degree disciplines is acceptable but applicants will be expected to have good all round intellectual abilities and sound interpersonal skills.

Training and career development

Comprehensive induction training is given to all new recruits. Science and engineering graduates are trained in photographic science and aspects of the company's technology during their first few months. Those joining departments by direct entry are given individual training programmes. Individual development is reviewed regularly as career interests and abilities become apparent; personal growth is recognised either through upgradings or by promotion to discrete jobs. Considerable emphasis is placed on staff development since it is the company's policy to promote from within whenever possible and to cultivate those who have the ability and desire to pursue careers in functional or general management. There are occasional opportunities for transfer within the UK to other Ciba-Geigy companies or abroad within the Ilford Group or Ciba-Geigy worldwide.

Salaries and benefits

Starting salaries will definitely be competitive; it is the company's policy to reward performance and individual contribution and this therefore determines your rate of progress. Salaries are reviewed annually in November with annual performance reviews in January. Job size is kept under regular review against the company's job evaluation system.

Assistance for graduates to relocate to Cheshire will be given where necessary.

Amenities

The Mobberley site has a subsidised canteen and an expanding social club; the site is set in some of Cheshire's finest countryside yet is within easy reach of surrounding towns, the city of Manchester and the M6 motorway. Housing to suit a variety of needs is within 20–30 minutes travelling time from the site.

Applications

If you would like to explore the possibility of a career with Ilford Limited please consult your university appointments service or write to the Personnel Manager at the address given from whom additional information may also be obtained.

Imperial Brewing and Leisure Limited

Activities
Production, packaging, wholesaling and retail of beer, wine, spirits for hotels, catering and retailing

Employees
30,000

Locations: UK
London; South East; Bristol and South West; North East

Imperial Brewing and Leisure Limited is the management company for the brewing and leisure division of the Imperial Group Limited. We are a broadly based manufacturing and service retailing business providing quality products and services for different areas of the leisure market.

Our business embraces the production, packaging and wholesaling of beers, wines and spirits in the United Kingdom. As retailers, our public houses, hotels, restaurants, motorway service stations and retail off-licences and tobacconists serve the many differing requirements of our customers.

Opportunities
Production; Marketing; Personnel; Management services

Application address
Recruitment and Training Officer, Imperial Brewing and Leisure Limited, Anchor Terrace, Southwark Bridge, London SE1 9HS

Courage – the beer business

Managed by Courage Limited, one of the leading UK breweries, we own over 5,300 public houses, with breweries at Reading, Tadcaster, Bristol, Plymouth and Newark, together with a national network of secondary distribution depots and packaging plants. Among the leading brands produced by the company are Director's Bitter, Courage Best Bitter, John Smith's Yorkshire Bitter and Hofmeister lager. The company's trading activities are managed through four regional operating companies and a specialist Take Home Trade Company which sells to groceries and off-licence outlets.

Saccone & Speed – wines and spirits and retail shops

Saccone & Speed Limited is the main operating company responsible for the division's wines, spirits and retailing interests. It is also responsible for export and the duty free trade. It has the following units:

Saccone & Speed Wholesale Limited is responsible for production, distribution and wholesaling in England and in Scotland.

Saccone & Speed Retail Limited is responsible for wines and spirits sales through Arthur Cooper, Roberts off-licences and the retail tobacconist chain of Finlay and The House of Bewlay.

Saccone & Speed International Limited is responsible for the export of beer, wines and spirits, and the diplomatic trade.

Hotels and catering

Imperial Hotels and Catering Limited co-ordinates all the activities of the hotel and catering group. The companies in the group are: Anchor Hotels & Taverns Limited who operate a chain of 37 individually styled hotels; Chaucer Inns and Falstaff Taverns, which with over 30 retail outlets are specialist public houses designed to meet the identified catering needs of the locality in which they are based; Happy Eater Limited is the roadside restaurant chain catering for the family with 24 outlets on major A-roads and Motoross Limited which operates five motorway service areas providing refreshments and service facilities for the travelling public.

Types of graduate required

The company's fundamental approach is to recruit individuals with skills and potential for specifically identified positions within particular functions eg production, marketing, personnel, and management services. A period of basic training of approximately six months duration including on the job training, backed up by away from the job training, should constitute the formal training period.

At the end of this time, they will be expected to reach a standard which will enable them to take up junior permanent posts which will have an element of managerial responsibility but which will offer further development and job experience in the context of actual responsibilities which each of the posts carries. Further career progression will depend on the indvidual's performance, and available job opportunities.

IMPERIAL LIFE

Activities
Life assurance and pensions business

Employees
900 UK

Location: UK
Guildford, Surrey

Opportunities & places
Actuarial students 2–3

Application address
Miss Eileen Wood, Personnel Manager, The Imperial Life Assurance Company of Canada, Imperial Life House, London Road, Guildford, Surrey GU1 1TA

Imperial Life Assurance Company of Canada
A member of the Laurentian Group of Companies

Imperial Life was established by Canadian Act of Parliament in 1896 and now has worldwide assets in excess of £500 million. Business was first transacted in Great Britain in 1931 and today the GB operation is developing increasingly as an independent life office, with a wide range of traditional and unit-linked life assurance, group and health products now being actively marketed through over 30 branches.

Imperial Life is a professional company. This shows in our products, our training, our modern techniques and continued success. To ensure that we have the human resources to meet the needs of the future in our fast developing organisation, we are seeking additional actuarial trainees at our UK headquarters in Guildford.

Types of graduate required
We require graduates in *mathematics*, *statistics* or *economics* to study to become qualified actuaries. In addition to a good degree, we are looking for those who possess ambition, determination and leadership qualities.

Career development and training
Actuarial students progress through many different areas of the actuarial function, whilst studying for the Institute of Actuaries examinations in order to furnish their career with a broad base. Experience will be gained in pensions, valuations, product development, computing and varied actuarial investigations.

Every encouragement is given for study with day release facilities, financial assistance for tuition and examination fees, and salary increases with each examination success.

Prospects
The commitment to future expansion ensures good prospects for those who are willing to accept responsibility and have the determination to succeed.

Location
Actuarial students are employed at our attractive modern offices within easy reach of Guildford town centre.

Salaries and benefits
Starting salaries will be competitive with those of other major employers. Increases to the basic salary are made for passing, or gaining exemptions from, the actuarial examinations. Salaries are reviewed annually. The company offers excellent working conditions and fringe benefits including flexible working hours, excellent pension scheme, attractive house mortgage scheme and subsidised staff restaurant.

Further information
If you would like to discuss a career with us please write giving full details to the Personnel Manager, at the address given.

Industrial & Commercial Finance Corporation Limited

Activities
Finance and financial services for smaller companies

Employees
270

Locations: UK
England, Scotland and Wales

Opportunities & places
Investment controllers 6

Application address
JW Burnett, Personnel Manager, ICFC Limited, 91 Waterloo Road, London SE1 8XP

'If you've got the guts, we've got the money'

This is one of the lines we use in our marketing effort to make entrepreneurs aware of ICFC as a source of venture capital. It equally applies to the graduates we recruit who deal with the entrepreneurs.

To be a successful investment controller at ICFC you will need to have much in common with the entrepreneurs and small businessmen you serve. Not least, the qualities of courage and commitment.

The controller's job is to market ICFC's services; to evaluate the overall business proposition for which financial backing is sought; and to negotiate terms acceptable to the businessman and us. High responsibility but often offering a high degree of personal satisfaction.

We're now looking for six graduates to train as investment controllers in 1983. To be one of them, you're likely to have exceptional analytical skills, a strong commercial orientation and well-developed communicative ability. And, of course, the guts.

Although it would be helpful if you have studied for a relevant degree such as *business studies* or *accountancy*, we are willing to hear from graduates of *any* discipline who feel they have what we are looking for.

Try and convince us in writing, to me, Julian Burnett, Personnel Manager at the address given.

The Institution of Electrical Engineers

Activities
Professional organisation of electrical engineers; services include information and publications

Employees
450

Locations: UK
London and South East

Opportunities
Editorial staff; Information and library staff; Data processing and administration staff

Application address
Personnel Department, Institution of Electrical Engineers, Station House, Nightingale Road, Hitchin, Hertfordshire SG5 1RJ

The Institution of Electrical Engineers is a qualifying body for the professional electrical engineer. Programmes of meetings and conferences are organised in the fields of electronics, power, computing and control, management and design, and science, education and technology for 64,000 members in this country. The Institution is also well known internationally for its activities in publishing and the provision of technical information services.

Types of graduate required
There are opportunities for *electrical* and *electronics engineers* and *physicists* in publishing and INSPEC (the information services department of the Institution), and for graduates from other disciplines for administrative posts involving committee work and contact with the membership.

Training and career development
Graduates are recruited to specific posts which have a well defined training content. There is a staff appraisal scheme and a policy of promoting from within where suitable candidates exist.

Locations
The secretariat and most departments involved with members' interests are located in Savoy Place, London. Publishing and INSPEC together with finance, professional services and the personnel department are based in Stevenage and Hitchin in Hertfordshire. The total number of staff is 450.

Salaries and benefits
Salares are competitive and benefits include generous leave entitlements,

sickness pay and subsidised catering. There is an excellent pension and life assurance scheme.

Applications
Application forms are available from the address given.

Instron Ltd

Activities
Specialists in the design, manufacture and marketing of machines and systems for testing materials, components and structures

Employees
400

Location: UK
Home Counties

Opportunities
Engineering: electrical, electronic, mechanical; Materials science; Control engineering; Marketing; Programming; Production

Vacancies
10

Upper age limit
23

Application address
The Personnel Manager, Instron Ltd, Coronation Road, High Wycombe, Buckinghamshire HP12 3SY

As an organisation we offer excellent career opportunities to engineering and science graduates. A career path followed with Instron provides the interest and involvement of a prosperous growing company, the excitement of a high technology market leader, excellent conditions of employment and, not least, very good salaries and fringe benefits.

The company's machine division specialises in the most modern materials testing machines and systems designed to meet the requirements of this technological age. Their products are used in educational, industrial and research laboratories throughout the world. Among the many materials being tested are metals, plastics, textiles, rubber, wood, paper, ceramics and foodstuffs.

The Instron Structural Testing Division designs and manufactures a range of systems for testing components and structures. These can range from a simple single actuator system to a multi-actuator rig with full computer control. The division also produces electro-dynamic shakers which are used for a variety of vibration testing applications including production burn-in systems where they are combined with environmental chambers designed and built by Instron's newest subsidiary, Instron Environmental Limited.

Founded in High Wycombe in 1960, Instron Limited's growth has been steady and continuous with exports accounting for 85% of the company's turnover. The company has established sales and service organisations and demonstration centres throughout Europe, and has resident technical sales staff in many other countries.

What do we mean to your career?
Obviously, in such a fast expanding and forward thinking organisation, career prospects for the talented are many.

The fast moving nature of our industry and our worldwide involvement create a stimulating and rewarding environment in any divisions of our organisation.

NEI International Combustion Ltd

Activities
Design, manufacture, erection and commissioning of steam generation plant and process plant

Employees 3,000

Location: UK Midlands

Opportunities
Design engineers; Contract engineers; Site engineers

Now part of the giant Northern Engineering Industries group which combines the resources of some of the country's foremost mechanical and electrical engineering companies, International Combustion has, over a period of more than fifty years built up an enviable reputation for the quality of its products and services in the field of steam generation, process engineering, and allied activities.

Types of graduate required
Mechanical, production, chemical, and *electrical/electronic* engineers, who are able to demonstrate a positive interest in our field of work are required.

Training
Training is normally of two years duration to satisfy individual needs and CEI requirements, embracing manufacturing and design appreciation and objective training allied to envisaged first appointment. The training

Vacancies 10

Upper age limit 25

Application address
CM Barnes, Training Superintendent, NEI International Combustion Limited, Sinfin Lane, Derby DE2 9GJ

period may however be reduced dependent upon previous relevant training or experience.

Salaries
Trainees' first and second year training rates of pay are competitive and are reviewed annually.

Prospects
Post-appointment promotion is dependent upon demonstrated ability. It is the policy of the company to promote from within.

International Computers Limited

Activities
Development, manufacture and support of information processing systems

Employees
23,000

Locations: UK
General

Locations: Overseas
Worldwide

Opportunities
Programming: applications, systems; Engineering: computer production, computer development; Sales support; Personnel; Management accounting; Business systems analysis; Technical authorship; Lecturing

Vacancies
300 approx

Application address
Graduate Recruitment Manager, International Computers Limited, ICL House, Putney, London SW15 1SW

ICL is British owned and Europe's leading computer manufacturer successfully marketing a range of information processing systems in over 80 countries worldwide.

We design, develop and market systems to virtually every sector of industry and commerce, as well as to governments, universities and research establishments.

The convergence of telecommunications and information processing systems technologies together with the rapidly growing importance of the office automation and personal computer markets have presented ICL with new marketing opportunities on an international scale. In order to exploit fully such opportunities ICL is collaborating in development and marketing with other leading high technology companies in Europe, Japan, and North America. As a result we need graduates of high intellectual calibre with the motivation and breadth of vision to help us apply high technology to a wide range of problems in an international context.

Types of graduate required
Computer science, mathematics, physics, electronic/electrical engineering and other numerate *science* graduates are required for a wide range of jobs covering the development, production and support of sophisticated computer hardware and software.

Any discipline will be considered for vacancies in applications programming, sales support, technical writing and lecturing, where interpersonal skills plus a logical mind are more important than the particular degree studied.

For opportunities in personnel, management accounting and business systems analysis, a *business studies* or *social science* degree would be an advatange.

Training and prospects
Graduate entrants follow comprehensive training programmes inter-leaving formal courses with practical experience. Performance and progress is regularly reviewed in a frank exchange between graduate and manager as part of the company's effective manpower development scheme.

In your first two years you would gain an overall grasp of the computer industry and accumulate the experience and expertise you need to take advantage of the many career opportunities that arise in both management and technical fields.

Locations
Graduate entrants are mostly employed in one of our main UK locations in Scotland, Midlands or the South East. However sales support trainees could work in almost any major city.

Further information
Ask your careers advisory service for our recruitment brochure or write
to the Graduate Recruitment Manager at the application address given.

ITT – IDEC

IDEC

Activities
Development activities in the field of business
communications

Employees
400

Location: UK
Stevenage, Herts

Opportunities
High technology software and hardware
development

Application address
IDEC, Graduate Recruitment Coordinator, Six
Hills House, London Road, Stevenage, Herts

IDEC is a leading centre for development activities in the field of
business communications. Based in Stevenage, Herts, our staff of 400
professional programmers and engineers are engaged full time on
extending the use of computers in voice and data communications by the
application of advanced technology.

IDEC's history
We are a relatively new division of ITT in Europe, established as a
separate unit to maximise ITT's potential as a market leader in voice/data
communications by creating a unique design and development house
with a considerable emphasis on software. The centre's activities are
international, offering opportunities for working in Europe and North
America.

Current activities
Our current activities are based on microprocessing techniques using
both high level and assembler programming languages. We are
developing a range of microprocessor controlled next generation
automated business systems equipment and a new range of switching
systems which will be used with data communication networks. ITT
already has a worldwide reputation as a leader in these fields and these
developments are a continuation of our commitment as we move towards
implementing such concepts as electronic mail and the office of the
future.

Working with IDEC
IDEC is an expanding centre and therefore has a very large investment in
training. Graduates follow a short but intensive training course and then
are assigned to development projects on which they will gain first hand
experience. From this stage progress is really up to the individual. We
will make every attempt to assist and advise graduates on training and
development matters, but the factors which really count are ability and
motivation.

Types of graduate required
Hardware: To graduates with a degree in hardware biased *computer
sciences, electrical* or *electronic engineering* we offer a challenging
opportunity for you to join our team of engineers who are responsible for
IDEC's specialised hardware developments.
    Software: Opportunities exist for graduates in *computer sciences,
sciences,* or *engineering* who have a programming knowledge to develop
their careers in high technology software development.

Promotion prospects and remuneration
Our salaries, of course, reflect the individual's capability but these are
generally in the upper quartile of the market. These salaries are reviewed
on a regular basis; twice in the first year of employment for graduates.
    It is our policy to promote from within and to develop staff into senior
positions as soon as it is apparent that they are ready to take on additional
responsibilities.

Benefits
We offer 25 days annual holiday, flexi-time, a subsidised restaurant, very
pleasant working conditions, membership of our contributory pension

scheme and discounts on ITT company products (stereo systems, televisions, radios etc).

Further information
We will be visiting a number of universities and polytechnics personally, and will be represented at others by our parent company, Standard Telephones and Cables Limited.

If the prospect of working for IDEC appeals to you then please contact your careers office and make an appointment to see us so that we can discuss the opportunities offered at greater length.

Your careers office should have a copy of IDEC's 1983 recruitment booklet.

Johannesburg Consolidated Investment Company Limited

Please see our entry in the Overseas section.

The Johnson Matthey Group

Activities
Precious metal refining and fabrication; Manufacture of catalyst systems; Specialist chemical and engineering production; Colours pigments and transfers manufacture; Banking and commodity dealing

Employees
5,500 UK
3,500 overseas subsidiary companies

Locations: UK
London; South East; Midlands

Opportunities
Research and development; Chemical and refining production; Mechanical fabrication; Sales and marketing; Accountancy; Management services; Market research

Vacancies
35–40

Application address
Group Staff Manager, Johnson Matthey Group, 100 High Street, Southgate, London N14 6ET

The Johnson Matthey Group is a major international company and an acknowledged world leader in the fields of precious metal technology and advanced non-ferrous chemical and engineering production.

The group has consistently placed major emphasis on research and development activities, with continuing investment plans to implement the resulting ideas. This has enabled the group to extend product ranges and improve international competitiveness and market position. Product ranges are currently being expanded to include specialised organic chemicals.

Successful developments which have now gone into full scale production include flux coated brazing rods and Thermafilm – a device which can be used to monitor the oxygen content of a premature baby's blood. Continued work on catalytic systems for reducing exhaust emissions from motor cars has led to the development of a lead-tolerant catalyst. Major areas of current research include advanced high temperature materials for the aerospace and glass industries, new materials for the electronics industry, improved metal joining systems and novel metal processing technology.

Types of graduate required
Johnson Matthey's policy has always been to promote from existing staff, wherever possible, and the prerequisite of this policy is an intake of good honours graduates who have the potential and personal attributes to fulfil increasingly responsible appointments.

Graduates from *technical* and *scientific* disciplines are recruited into research, development, production and sales/marketing functions. The principal disciplines employed are *chemistry, metallurgy, materials science, physics* and *chemical, mechanical* and *production engineering*. However, there are also a few openings in the sales and marketing/market research field for graduates with fluency in *modern languages* who have a good science basis (usually to A level standard).

To support its diverse activities the group seeks to recruit a small number of graduates from relevant disciplines into its group wide training scheme for accountants.

In addition, a number of graduates from relevant disciplines (*business studies, maths, statistics* and *computing*) will be recruited into management services functions at the group headquarters.

Locations
The group's headquarters and central service functions are based in North London and long term research is undertaken at the research centre, near Reading. The principal chemical and engineering activities are located at a number of sites throughout the Home Counties while colours and transfers are produced in North Staffordshire.

Training
Appointments are by direct entry to all departments. The experience gained on the job is supplemented by training schemes designed to improve existing knowledge and introduce concepts required in more senior positions. Individual training may also involve secondments to related functions, but, in all areas, graduates are expected to make an early personal contribution. Graduates will also be encouraged to qualify for membership of their professional institutions.

Salaries and career progression
The group maintains a competitive position in respect of initial and subsequent salaries. Progression, both in terms of salary and position, is dependent on ability and performance, each factor being reviewed regularly.

Applications and further information
Further information about careers in the Johnson Matthey Group is available from your careers service, who will also know if representatives from the group will be visiting your university.

Any applications or requests for information should be sent to the address given.

Joint Technical Language Service

The Joint Technical Language Service (JTLS) is a small unit administered by the Foreign and Commonwealth Office that provides foreign language support for other government departments. The JTLS is based at Cheltenham, a pleasant west country town, where it shares buildings and support services (including recruiting) with the Government Communications Headquarters.

Types of graduate required
You should be interested in the practical application of your linguistic skills and be prepared to have these further developed in the technical language field. There are opportunities to gain experience in the use of computers in support of language work but you are not likely to be involved in programme writing. You should have a real interest in languages since you might be asked to learn another language, probably one of the more rare and difficult type. Our language requirements vary from year to year but as a general guide we have had vacancies in recent years for Russian, Greek, Polish, Arabic, Persian and Turkish linguists and for linguists able to offer two of Portuguese, Spanish or Italian.

Activities
Foreign language support for departments of Her Majesty's Government

Location: UK
South West

Opportunities
Assistant linguist specialists

Vacancies
20 approx

Application address
Graduate Appointments Officer, Joint Language Service, Room A/1108, Oakley, Priors Road, Cheltenham, Gloucestershire GL52 5AJ
Tel: 0242 21491 ext 2099
Civil Service Commission open competition applications by early January

MW KELLOGG LIMITED

Your Degree	Your Training	Your Eventual Specialisation

SCIENCE/ TECHNICAL GRADUATES

24 months' Rotational Job Experience Programme

1st year	2nd year
PROCESS SYSTEMS AND GENERAL FACILITIES	VARIOUS OTHER DIVISIONS

CHEMICAL ENGINEER MECHANICAL ENGINEER

24 months' Production and Analytical work + experience in ELECTRICAL, MACHINERY, PROCESS, SYSTEMS and COMMISSIONING DIVISIONS

INSTRUMENT ENGINEER

24 months spent between CONCRETE, STEEL and ARCHITECTURAL SECTIONS + SITE ASSIGNMENTS

CIVIL ENGINEER

24 months' Rotational Programme gaining experience in CPA TECHNIQUES, PERT NETWORK ANALYSIS, REGRESSION ANALYSIS, COST TREND PREDICTIONS, STATISTICAL ANALYSIS and RISK MANAGEMENT

PROJECT SERVICES SPECIALIST (Scheduling, Estimating, Cost Engineering & Control, Man–Hour Control)

SCIENCE/ TECHNICAL OR ARTS GRADUATES

18–24 months' Programme gaining direct experience in the PROCUREMENT DEPARTMENT

PROCUREMENT SPECIALIST

Kalamazoo Business Systems

Kalamazoo of Northfield is one of the largest sales organisations in the world, specialising in computerised and manual business systems. It is a British company with overseas distributors selling in more than 55 countries.

The company has a unique profit sharing scheme for its 2,000 employees on whose behalf a Trust now holds 50% of the company's issued capital. Many facilities are also available to employees eg pensions, sickness fund, free life assurance and sporting facilities.

Opportunities
Graduates are recruited as micro electronics engineers, micro electronics technicians, and into computer programming, systems research/analysis and development, production management and sales.

For details please write to the Personnel Department at the address given.

MW Kellogg Limited

We are a worldwide organisation with some 80 years of outstanding achievement already behind us. Through technical innovation, uncompromising commitment, and of course plenty of hard work, we have established ourselves as pre-eminent consultants and contractors to the oil, gas and chemical industries.

The course of the twentieth century has clearly defined this sphere of activity as of paramount importance, technically as much as economically. It is the sharp end of process engineering, where all new developments are first tried and tested, and we're extremely proud of our well earned reputation as pioneers.

The broad spectrum of our activities ranges from process and offsites design, through equipment and systems design, project engineering, project management, procurement, construction and commissioning of new plant, to plant management and plant maintenance.

Ours is an extremely specialised business, and naturally we're keen to encourage specialist talent to join us, both now and in the future. Our training programmes are highly regarded, and contribute practically and theoretically towards full professional status. Emphasis is on learning by doing through a planned progression of experience in the relevant company operations.

Please see our diagram on the opposite page.

Further information
For further information and an application form please write to or telephone the Graduate Recruitment Officer at the address given.

Kennedy & Donkin

Kennedy & Donkin is one of Britain's leading firms of consulting engineers and was established in 1889. From its foundation it has specialised in the study and development of electricity supply networks and the engineering of projects for power generation, transmission and distribution. In recent years the firm has been increasingly involved in assisting developing countries with the expansion of their electricity resources. Today more than 80% of the firm's effort is directed overseas.

Employees
850

Locations: UK
South East; North West; Northern Ireland

Locations: Overseas
Middle East; Hong Kong; Africa; South America; Europe

Opportunities
Electrical engineers; Environmental services engineers; Mechanical engineers; Control and automation engineers

Vacancies
7

Application address
Personnel Officer, Kennedy & Donkin, Premier House, Woking, Surrey GU21 1DG

The firm is a British partnership and is free from any manufacturing interest. Its independence is internationally recognised by clients and world finance organisations supplying capital to developing countries.

In addition to work in the field of electricity supply the firm is also engaged in projects of an environmental nature. This includes civil works, mechanical and electrical services for all types of public and commercial buildings, district heating schemes and rapid transit systems. An independent quality assurance and expediting service operates for the purpose of visiting manufacturers works and ensuring the maintenance of the required standards of quality and performance and the achievement of planned delivery dates.

Work entrusted to the firm has many facets and is seldom routine. Activities include the study and appraisal of proposed engineering schemes, design and specification of projects and equipment, assessment and recommendation of tenders, contract negotiations and detailed supervision of engineering, construction and commissioning.

Types of graduate required
The firm offers graduates a high degree of involvement and responsibility. We require graduates who display genuine enthusiasm for engineering, willingness to adapt to varying circumstances and the ability to apply academic learning to practical problems.

Electrical, mechanical and *environmental engineering* graduates are employed and preference is given to those with an honours degree. Graduates with no previous practical experience or those who have completed a recognised apprenticeship are equally welcome.

Training
Graduate engineers are given every encouragement to obtain membership of an appropriate professional engineering institution and to obtain the necessary design, site and industrial experience under training schemes approved by the major institutions. Where appropriate, graduates are sent on short courses in specialised subjects to increase their technical knowledge. If necessary, manufacturing experience is provided with appropriate manufacturing organisations in the United Kingdom and occasionally overseas.

Prospects
The firm offers excellent long term prospects for promotion.

Locations
Graduates may be employed at the firm's head office in Woking, Surrey, or in the generation department, Manchester.

Overseas
On completion of training there are excellent opportunities for positions involving residence overseas or making short visits to overseas locations. Normally training is completed in UK but those who require site experience may be required to spend a training period overseas. Overseas locations are worldwide.

Salaries
Initial salaries are competitive and consideration will be given for previous relevant experience. Salaries are reviewed annually taking into account merit and changes in the cost of living.

Kidsons

Kidsons

ctivities
hartered accountants

mployees
00

ocations: UK
2 offices in UK

pportunities & places
rainee chartered accountants 40

pplication address
rian Stapleton, MSc, FCA, Kidsons, Columbia
ouse, 69 Aldwych, London WC2B 4DY

Kidsons is a medium sized firm of chartered accountants, with 32 offices in the UK. The offices range in size from small and beautiful (ten partners and staff) to largish without being impersonal (250 partners and staff).

Our clients

We service a wide range of clients which include a small number of quoted companies. The majority of our clients are private companies which range from small to incredibly big. We also service a sizeable minority of non-corporate small to medium sized businesses and professional firms. If you join us, you will therefore be exposed to a wide range of clients and you will find that dealing with the senior accountant of a large organisation, whilst out on audit, is a quite different process to advising the owner of the local garden centre on basic financial controls.

Work experience

We recognise the importance of providing, within your three year training contract, well supervised and progressive work experience in the three core areas of accounting, auditing and taxation.

Training

Although most of your valid training is carried out on the job, we do run national training courses which get you away from your local office for seven weeks of your contract and which, incidentally, we believe are quite good.

Education for examinations

You are, of course, aware that our professional body sets you the occasional examination during your three years. It is perhaps no surprise to you to learn that we like you to pass your examinations first time. Failure is a costly business, for you and for us. We therefore try to aid this process by selecting tutors for you and paying course and examination fees, and for your essential text books – but only for the first attempt! We are looking for people who realise that a demanding and ongoing course of studies is essential in order to be successful.

Your qualities

If we could set out a checklist, we would! However, we do know that our past successful students have come from many academic disciplines and contain a wide range of backgrounds and personalities: the common factor they have being highly motivated to become expert and professional people. We offer a very personal service to clients and so we rate an ability to communicate as highly as evidence of numeracy. The examinations are tough, so if you have worked hard for your third or have not bothered to work enough to turn your two-two into a first, then please try something less demanding.

Nuts and bolts

Salary, work conditions, holidays and other important details will be provided, if you are selected, at interview in whichever office you apply for: London pays better than Norwich, of course, reflecting the difference in the cost of living. But if initial salary is the most important factor in your decision then accountancy is probably the wrong career for you!

Still interested?

Please get hold of our brochure from your careers office, complete the application form and send it to me, Brian Stapleton.

Knight Frank & Rutley

Knight Frank & Rutley combines professional expertise with the ability to spot and develop new opportunities and negotiate at levels which can involve many millions of pounds. Some 75% of the firm's activities are related to commercial property negotiations including office blocks, shopping centres, hotels, industrial estates and development sites.

Types of graduate required
We are looking for graduates from *any* discipline who want a career where they can develop and use initiative and skills in negotiating and professional work, while maintaining the standards which have made us highly respected.

Training
Within the profession, Knight Frank & Rutley have an excellent reputation for ensuring that all trainees complete the test of professional competence of the Royal Institution of Chartered Surveyors. Training is planned so that all trainees receive the range of experience they need to satisfy the requirements of the institution and to discover for themselves in which area they want to specialise.

Graduate trainees without a degree in estate management will study for the graduate entry scheme preliminary and final examinations in general practice through private study. Study leave is given and we pay for all tuition costs and examination fees. Once they have qualified, graduate trainees have equal opportunities for advancement whether or not their first degree was in estate management.

Activities
International real estate consultants

Employees
250

Locations: UK
London and Scotland

Locations: Overseas
Worldwide

Opportunities & places
Commercial property 6; Building surveyor 1; Land agency 2

Upper age limit
35

Application address
AJ Shelley, Knight Frank & Rutley, 20 Hanover Square, London W1R 0AH

Knill Padgham & Grande

We are a firm of chartered accountants founded in 1887. Currently there are eight partners and some 40 staff. The practice operates from London SW1 and has branches in Saffron Waldon, Essex and Godalming, Surrey. Our aim is always to provide a first class and individually tailored professional service to all our clients.

Each partner looks after a number of clients and it is an object of the firm to maintain a close personal contact with each client and with his affairs. There are specialised departments dealing with audit, personal tax, trust, company registration, accountancy, bookkeeping and payroll and all work processed by these departments is reviewed by a partner or his senior personal assistant.

Training
Great care is taken in the engagement and training of all our staff but in particular we place great emphasis on the education and training of students who wish to qualify into the profession. We are members of a consortium for training purposes and thus employ qualified training officers and operate a full range of in-house courses and study supervision from the consortium training premises. In addition, students who enter a contract of training with one of our partners are entered by us to suitable study courses for which we pay the fees, and are monitored throughout their training, not only through the six-monthly formal review of office and study but through the personal concern and interest of each partner for his own students.

Further information
Further information and applications should be made to J Henman at the address given.

Activities
Chartered accountants in general practice covering all aspects of the profession

Employees
45

Locations: UK
London and South East

Opportunities & places
Trainee accountants 5

Application address
J Henman, FCA, Knill Padgham & Grande, 17 Waterloo Place, Pall Mall, London SW1 4AR

Kyle Stewart Group

tivities
uilding, civil engineering, heating and
ntilating and engineering services
ntracting, design and build

mployees
200

cations: UK
uth East and Midlands

pportunities
uilding; Civil Engineering; Environmental
gineering

cancies
0

pper age limit
,

pplication address
oup Training Manager, Kyle Stewart Group,
ound Floor, Merit House, Colindale, London
W9 5AG

Kyle Stewart is a building contracting group which lays considerable emphasis on the design and build philosophy in construction. The major company within the group is Kyle Stewart Contractors which has its own fast expanding design and build group situated in London. Additionally, there are a number of subsidiary companies in the engineering services field, covering heating and ventilating and a soil testing and site investigation laboratory.

Types of graduate required
In 1983 there will be a number of vacancies for graduates in *building, civil engineering* and *environmental engineering*.

Training
For civil and environmental engineers, the training programme will cover all aspects necessary for obtaining the respective professional qualifications. Building graduates receive a two year programme of training in preparation for assuming managerial responsibilities. The policy for management training requires that, there is sufficient department flexibility to enable each programme to meet both the individual's aspirations and the company's needs. Each graduate will undertake specific responsibilities within different departments throughout training.

Prospects
The group pursues an active policy of promotion from within, and graduates are expected quickly to assume key positions in specialist departments or in general construction management.

Further information
This can be obtained about the group's activities from the Group Training Manager, alternatively you should apply direct enclosing a standard introduction form.

Laser-Scan Laboratories Limited

Laser-Scan

ctivities
anufacture of displays, plotters, and digitisers;
ecial purpose hardware and software
evelopment

mployees
5

ocation: UK
ast Anglia

pportunities
evelopment staff, hardware and software

pplication address
ersonnel Officer, Laser-Scan Laboratories
mited, Cambridge Science Park, Milton Road,
ambridge CB4 4BH

Laser-Scan Laboratories Ltd was formed in 1969 to exploit a development that arose from a higher energy physics research project at the Cavendish Laboratory, Cambridge. Since then, it has developed a range of standard products using the same basic technology, which have applications in high energy physics, automated cartography, and the general graphics field. The company has installed equipment worldwide, and has established a base in the three major national cartographic organisations in the UK. Growth continues both in the sale of standard products and in the contract development area.

Types of graduate required
Computer scientists are required to work in small teams within a small department of high quality. A lot of customer contact is involved, and this may involve significant travel. Most projects are in the digitising and graphics fields, and typically involve use of microprocessors as well as large minicomputers.

Development engineers are recruited to work on contract design and new product development in the fields of optics, electronics, servo systems and microprocessors. Projects involve the full range of development activities from conceptual design to production engineering.

Salaries and benefits
Salary levels are competitively related to current market rates and these

are reviewed twice per annum. We can offer attractive working conditions, generous holiday allowance, and a non-contributory sickness and life assurance scheme.

Training and career development
This is guided by a detailed annual appraisal and graduates have opportunities to make substantial contributions to projects in a wide range of product areas. Training is given both internally and in outside organisations where appropriate.

Lever Brothers Ltd

Activities
Manufacture and sale of soaps and detergents

Application address
Management Development Manager,
Lever House, 3 St James's Road,
Kingston upon Thames KT1 2BA

As well as providing placements for a significant proportion of Unilever's UCMDS trainees, Lever Brothers each year recruits a limited number of *chemists* and *chemical engineers* to join its development department, situated in the North West. For details, see our booklet, or write direct to the Management Development Manager at the address alongside.

Lex Service Group plc

Activities
Service industries

Employees
9,500

Locations: UK
General

Opportunities & places
Management trainees 15

Application address
Management Development Manager, Lex
Service Group plc, 17 Great Cumberland Place,
London W1H 8AD

Lex Service Group is engaged in a range of service and distribution industries in the UK and the USA. We are the sole UK importer of Volvo cars, the largest fork truck hire company in Europe and are leaders in the express parcels industry. Additionally, we have significant involvements in the distribution, hire and servicing of cars and commercial vehicles throughout the UK being substantial Leyland and Rolls Royce distributors. Expansion over the past three years into the United States has brought the group into the areas of electronic components and motor vehicle parts distribution.

The company's turnover exceeds £500 million and employs 9,500 people.

Types of graduate required
All disciplines. The subjects studied in your degree course are less important than the personal qualities and potential skills needed to make a successful manager in a profit conscious environment. Exceptional ability, a mature outlook and a real desire to succeed in industry are the qualities we need.

Training and prospects
Training in relevant skills and knowledge will continue throughout your career and at all times is tailored to meet individual needs. You will be recruited into your preferred business activity with a specific and responsible first job in mind. A period of six months induction training will prepare you thoroughly for this critical first job.

Career progression in a growth company such as Lex can be rapid, entirely dependent upon your job performance and potential. Your first management appointment should come within two years and a general management appointment, in complete control of one of our units, is achievable by your late twenties. We regard our graduate intake as a key part of our overall management development activity and our intent has been rewarded by a number of success stories over the past years. We should like to add your name to our record of success.

Locations
The company's interests are nationwide, but we have particular concentrations in the South East, the North West and the South West.

Salary
Starting salaries are competitive and increases will fully match the rapid progress we expect graduates to make in the company.

For further details apply to the Management Development Manager or obtain an application form and further details on the group from your careers office.

FJC Lilley plc

Activities
Industrial building and civil engineering

Employees
5,400

Locations: UK
General

Locations: Overseas
Middle East; Far East; USA

Opportunities
Civil engineering; Marine engineering

Application address
The Manager, Group Employee Relations, FJC Lilley plc, 331 Charles Street, Glasgow G21 2QY

FJC Lilley Limited are a vigorous and progressive group of companies with an excellent growth record. The group incorporates subsidiary companies strategically placed throughout the United Kingdom and the United States of America, forming a broadly based civil engineering and construction combine with an international reputation, being committed to a policy of continuing development in overseas areas. Our operations include tunnelling for drainage and underground railways, sinking of shafts and underground works for mineral development, the building of sewage works, roads and bridges, the control and supply of water, the construction of industrial buildings, wharves and jetties and all civil aspects of petrochemical and oil related industries.

Successful candidates will be those keen to apply themselves to the practical side of the profession, have a preference for a vigorous outdoor life and be prepared to travel throughout the country for work at contract sites.

Types of graduate required
We have a varying number of vacancies each year for graduates who hold a degree or comparable qualification in *civil engineering*, being equally concerned with the personal qualities of the individual coupled with his ability to assume a high degree of responsibility quickly.

Training
Structured training will be given to enable engineers to qualify for membership of the Institution of Civil Engineers. Along with the essential site and office involvement, suitable design experience will also be given either within the group or by arrangement with a leading firm of consulting engineers.

A number of places are also available for indenture pupils under the scheme recognised by the institution.

Location
While appointments can be made from each of our divisions, our contracts are spread throughout Britain, mobility being essential if full advantage is to be taken of career advancement opportunities.

Overseas
Resulting from our overseas policy, opportunities are of course available through the group's international division for employment on our overseas contracts, following a period of initial training within the United Kingdom.

Salaries and prospects
Good starting salaries, based on qualifications and experience, are payable. There is an annual salary review with increases commensurate with progress, responsibilities and application to tasks.

FJC Lilley plc, cont

Promotions are made from within the group whenever possible, with good opportunities for advancement.

Pensions

Non-contributory pension and permanent health insurance schemes are in operation.

Lishman Sidwell Campbell and Price

Activities
Accountants, finance, taxation and management services

Employees
40

Location: UK
North Yorkshire

Opportunities & places
Student trainee accountants 4

Application address
B Price, FCA, Lishman Sidwell Campbell and Price, Lishman Chambers, 12 Princes Square, Harrogate HG1 1LX

We are a practice of accountants with our main office in the conference town of Harrogate and well established in the surrounding rural and farming communities. We have a very friendly and personal working atmosphere. Our approach is to give a comprehensive service on financial, taxation, management and commercial matters in addition to auditing and accounting.

Types of graduate required
Preferably those with degrees recognised by the accountancy profession.

Training and career development
Studies for the examinations of the Institute of Chartered Accountants are with a leading private tutorial establishment which provides full time study in addition to a comprehensive and carefully monitored home study programme. Inside the office instruction is provided on the job with additional in-house training on residential courses. An exchange agreement with the Yorkshire practice of an international firm of chartered accountants enables two periods of three months out of the three year training contracts to be spent seconded into the large firm atmosphere. This ensures that the benefits of personalised training in our office are supplemented with a wide variety of experience. Responsibility is delegated progressively and quickly and students are encouraged to work on their own initiative.

Prospects
An internationally recognised qualification as a member of the Institute of Chartered Accountants and opportunities for future partnerships.

Locations
Harrogate, Ripon, Boroughbridge, Wetherby, Knaresborough and Northallerton.

Salaries
According to individual ability and achievement in work and studies.

The Littlewoods Organisation plc

Littlewoods

Activities
Retailing through chain stores and mail order catalogues; football pools

Employees
30,000 approx

Locations: UK
General

Opportunities
General management; Management services

As one of Britain's major companies, with sales of over £1,000 million per annum, Littlewoods can offer career opportunities to young men and women of widely varying talents.

The mail order division (concerned with the selling of goods by post, through catalogues) and the chain store division (the well known Littlewoods stores seen in most towns and cities) together comprise one of Britain's biggest retail groups. The football pools, although now the smallest division of the company is the largest organisation of its type in the world.

Our head office is in Liverpool and the company is thus one of the relatively few major businesses with its HQ in the provinces.

Upper age limit
26

Application address
Management Appointments Department (Ref DOG) Littlewoods Organisation plc, JM Centre, Old Hall Street, Liverpool L70 1AB

Chain store management

Our chain store management training scheme is highly regarded throughout the retail industry and provides a thorough and professional training in modern retail management. Trainees can expect to progress rapidly and gain early responsibility in a planned training programme which enables them to become the manager of one of our smaller stores within five to six years of joining us. Thereafter opportunities exist to progress to the most senior levels in the organisation: our present managing director and many other senior executives joined the company as chain store management trainees.

Applicants must be prepared to work in any part of the country and should be willing to accept a career which has many advantages but also some drawbacks. It is not everyone's cup of tea! Is it yours? Ask yourself these questions before you decide whether or not to apply.

Am I ambitious and determined to gain real responsibility?
Can I take decisions quickly and with confidence?
Can I successfully organise and motivate other people?
Am I practical and thorough with an eye for detail?
Am I prepared to work most Saturdays?
Am I willing to work anywhere in the UK?
Could I cope with frequent moves?
Will I enjoy a job which demands both energy and commitment?

Management services training scheme

Our management services department, based at JM Centre in Liverpool, already houses the largest commercial Honeywell installation in Europe and we also have a sizable IBM installation. Our systems development section is the largest in the North West and we have a number of vacancies every year for management services trainees.

Initial training lasts a year, the first five months of which are spent at our fully equipped, data processing training department. During this period trainees are familiarised with our computer configurations and with our programming and systems standards. Subsequent training is on the job as part of a project team.

The work includes a large variety of projects, such as real time order processing, merchandising, payments and warehouse control, stock allocation, real time food distribution and point of sale applications, plus the payroll and reporting services essential for an organisation of over 30,000.

With regard to future career development, there are excellent prospects for anyone interested in developing skills in computer programming or systems analysis and ultimately in systems management.

How to apply

If you are interested in these opportunities or would like to see if we have any other vacancies please first consult your careers service. If we are visiting your university or polytechnic you can apply through the careers service. If not apply to us direct using a standard introduction form.

Lloyds Bank plc

The bank has over 2,300 offices throughout England, Wales, Scotland, the Channel Islands and the Isle of Man with a staff numbering approximately 42,000. Of these, approximately 3,000 at present hold managerial or other executive positions with salaries ranging from £11,800 to £28,000 and well beyond. Graduates are accepted only if they are regarded as qualifying for training for early management. They can look forward to a challenging career with positions of responsibility at an early age. In addition to posts in branch management there are limited opportunities to specialise in trust work and overseas banking. The development of computer accounting offers an interesting future to those with special aptitude for this work.

Types of graduate required

Applications will be considered from undergraduates normally aged 24 and under in *any* faculty and final acceptance will be conditional on successful completion of an honours degree course. Great importance is attached to the personal qualities of applicants. The bank is seeking to recruit those with personality and powers of leadership who have the ability to mix easily, who have taken an active part in the corporate life of their university and are prepared to be mobile. Candidates may be asked to have a medical examination prior to entry.

Training

A special work plan covering a period of approximately four years is provided for those considered suitable for accelerated training. The plan includes branch training and courses at the bank's training establishments at appropriate stages of the programme. A few graduates may spend some time in head office departments on working attachments during this time. Graduates are trained to attain junior management by the time they are in their mid 20s. The most promising may attend a course at one of the university business schools or the administrative staff college in preparation for senior management. The bank will expect the associate examinations of the Institute of Bankers to be completed well within the period covered by the work plan, and day release is given.

Activities
A complete banking service for all sections of the community

Employees
42,000

Locations: UK
General

Opportunities
Branch banking; Data processing; Overseas division; Trust division

Vacancies
50 approx

Upper age limit
24

Application address
Appointments Officer, Lloyds Bank pic, Black Horse House, 78 Cannon Street, London EC4P 4LN

Lloyds Bank International

Lloyds Bank International, the international arm of the Lloyds Bank Group, recruits graduates who are prepared to spend a large part of their careers overseas.

For details of our work and training programme, see our entry in the Overseas section.

The Logica Group

The Logica Group works in the broad field of information technology. The company provides a range of consultancy, implementation services and products in computing, communications, electronics and office automation.

Since its foundation in 1969, Logica has maintained a strong record of growth. Annual turnover for 1981 was around £26 million sterling. The group now employs more than 1,000 staff worldwide, operating in Europe, the Middle East, Australasia and North America.

Logica's clients include governments, multinational agencies, major corporations, financial institutions and private companies. Logica services its clients in two principal ways: as consultants, giving advice on policy for both users and suppliers; and as independent contractors, designing and delivering computer based systems. Our hardware, software and engineering capabilities are well established.

Logica's staff is its principal asset. Their overall ability to meet high standards on varied and demanding projects is the company's main strength and forms the basis of the high international reputation Logica

Activities
All aspects of information technology, including computing, communications, electronics and office automation

Employees
1,000 + worldwide

Locations: UK
London; Cobham, Surrey; Swindon

Locations: Overseas
Rotterdam; Brussels; Stockholm; Sydney; Melbourne; New York; Boston; San Francisco

Opportunities
Software and applications programming; Electronic engineering, leading to technical consultancy, project management and sales

Application address
Graduate Recruitment Officer, Logica Limited,
Freepost No 21, 64 Newman Street, London
W1A 4SE
Tel: 01-637 9111

enjoys. That success and our continuing growth contribute towards a stimulating working environment and excellent prospects for the individual within Logica.

Types of graduate required

Logica invites applications from honours graduates or postgraduates in *any* numerate or logical discipline. The most relevant degrees are *computing science, mathematics, natural sciences, engineering* or *management studies*. Appropriate experience either at university or during vacations is considered a major advantage. Applicants must be able to work effectively in teams with minimal supervision, so initiative, drive, enthusiasm and discipline are important. We look for those who can foster and maintain good relationships with clients and colleagues. The ability to communicate, both orally and in written reports, is important in our work and capability in a foreign language is also useful.

Training and career development

When you join Logica you will be assigned to a project team as soon as possible; you will build on your university experience, whilst learning new skills under the supervision of experienced colleagues. Short specialised courses are arranged to meet specific needs. Projects often bring together a wide range of skills, so that interests are broadened by working with experts in different fields. Care is taken to assign staff to projects which utilise their skills and extend their capabilities.

As your experience develops, you will be given increased responsibility within projects, and if your interests are in project management you will be given the opportunity to lead a project team. Thereafter you may choose to develop further technical expertise or to move into other areas such as sales and marketing, or eventually line management. Your career development will be assisted by regular counselling and appraisals. At all levels your salary will be directly related to your skills and performance.

Location

We have offices in London, Cobham (Surrey), Swindon (Wilts), Rotterdam, Brussels, Stockholm, Sydney, Melbourne, New York, Boston and San Francisco. During the last year project work took our staff to many parts of the UK and to other countries. Our clients are derived from all sectors of industry and commerce, the banking and financial community, nationalised industries, British and foreign governments and international agencies. See the Logica Press Cuttings book and Annual Review in your careers office for examples of recent projects at home and abroad.

Selection procedures

Applications should be made directly to our London offices on the Logica application forms obtainable from your career advisors or from us, at the address given.

Selection of candidates for interview is made on the basis of the information you provide on the application form. Initial interviews are carried out in our London offices by experienced members of our professional staff representing the part of our organisation that seems most likely to match your interests. Applicants wishing to be based in Rotterdam, or Swindon should apply to London indicating this on their form.

In addition to this interview you will be asked to demonstrate your communication skills by writing a short report. Offers of employment are normally made within two weeks of the interview. You will have an opportunity to visit the Logica offices in which you will be based, either in conjunction with an interview or subsequently.

GLC
Working for London

Activities
Firefighting services

Employees
6,700 uniformed firefighters

Location: UK
London

Opportunities
Firefighters

Upper age limit
30

Application address
The Chief Officer, Recruiting Centre/GRAD,
London Fire Brigade, 94 Southwark Bridge
Road, London SE1 5BR

London Fire Brigade

The London Fire Brigade is the largest fire service in the country, serving a community of over eight million people in some 620 square miles, and protecting £million's worth of property. On average, someone in London needs the brigade every six minutes. Having an annual budget of over £100 million and employing some 6,700 uniformed staff, its responsibilities as well as the traditional roles of firefighting and fire prevention include a wide range of managerial and technical support services.

Types of graduate required
Applications from graduates of *any* discipline are welcome, but an *engineering* or *science* background would be an advantage.

Training and career prospects
All Fire Brigade recruits, including graduates, join as firefighters and go through an intensive training in basic firefighting skills. The modern firefighter also needs a good working knowledge of building construction, electricity, commercial plant and machinery, chemicals, and even radioactive materials, so further specialist training takes place throughout your career on an ongoing basis. Firefighters can achieve the rank of station officer after five years service by passing the statutory promotion examination – promotion thereafter can lead to the highest senior officer level in command, management and executive positions.

Developing the high level of expertise required in the fire service and keeping pace with the latest trends in new technology represents an absorbing career challenge for graduates.

Entry requirements
Applications are invited from graduates between 18 and 30 years of age prepared to live within 40 miles of central London. The minimum physical requirements are height: 5'6", chest: 36" with a minimum 2" expansion. Good unaided eyesight is also essential as is general all round physical fitness.

Salaries
The salary for recruits is £6,750, a station officer can expect to earn £9,933, thereafter the salary for senior officer ranks are progressively higher – for example an assistant chief officer earns £21,945. These salaries include a London weighting allowance. On retirement, after 30 years service, a two-thirds pension is payable.

Further information
For further details and an application form apply to the address given.

London Transport

London Transport is responsible for the operation of buses and underground trains in London, and is one of the largest and busiest transport systems in the world.

As back-up to these operations we have three major engineering works, a large data processing installation, specialist finance, personnel and supplies management teams and a variety of other activities.

Types of graduate required
We offer careers to graduates in many disciplines. For our engineering management schemes we are looking for *mechanical, electrical, electronic* and *civil engineers*. For our specialist business management schemes,

Activities
Public transport

Employees
60,000

Location: UK
London

Opportunities
Business management trainees; Engineering
management trainees

Vacancies
40

Application address
Trainee Appointments, Management
Development and Training Officer, London
Transport, 55 Broadway, London SW1 0BD

(including bus and rail operations, finance, personnel etc) we need
graduates in *any* discipline.

Training and prospects
All training schemes combine practical training with studies for
professional qualifications. All engineering management schemes are
designed to fulfil the requirements for membership of the appropriate
institution. Future prospects are excellent as it is London Transport's
policy to fill posts from existing staff wherever possible.

Further information
Please see our graduate recruitment literature available from your careers
service or from the address given.

Longcrofts

Activities
Chartered accountancy, including audit, tax
accountancy and other financial services

Employees
120

Locations: UK
City of London; Sutton; Hitchin

Opportunities
Student chartered accountants under training
contracts

Vacancies
10

Application address
Madeleine Messenger, Student Training Officer,
Longcrofts, Capel House, 62 New Broad Street,
London EC2M 1JS
Tel: 01-628 9696

The role of a modern accountant is no longer confined to the basic skills
of preparing and maintaining financial records, but has widened
considerably to include every sphere of economic activity affecting people
and business.

We identify our role in the commercial environment as threefold.
Firstly, as an auditor, secondly as a tax adviser and thirdly as a business
colleague. In our first role we are controlled by legislation but the main
concern of the auditor is that the accounts fully reflect the financial
transactions of a business during the year. Tax work is carried out for
both corporations and individuals in our second role, where tax planning
plays an important part in business decisions and an annually reviewed
tax plan is available to all our clients. Lastly in our role as business
colleague, we offer an opportunity to our clients to discuss ideas,
problems and plans in a totally confidential environment.

The structure of the firm enables the student to gain a broad base of
client experience. The firm is organised into groups, each under a group
partner, and as each group deals exclusively with its own clients, students
have the opportunity to work closely with senior people inside the
practice and also to have contact with management in client companies.

Training
Your training contract with us is for three years, during which time you
study for the professional examinations set by the Institute of Chartered
Accountants in England and Wales. Study entails full time attendance at
an accountancy school combined with private study. We pay your tuition
fees plus a full salary during the periods of study leave.

This study is complemented by a planned programme of courses and
seminars run by our training department. These courses, together with
the practical training we offer, provide the comprehensive knowledge
and experience demanded of the modern accountant.

Salaries and prospects
Starting salaries are competitive and during your three years of training
your salary will be progressive and regularly reviewed.

Our newly qualified chartered accountants are encouraged to stay with
us and take advantage of the excellent opportunities for promotion and
specialisation.

Applications
We are interested in graduates of *all* disciplines who have the
determination integrity and personality to succeed in our challenging
profession.

Lucas Industries plc

Activities
Systems engineering of components for all
types of road, rail, water and air transport

Employees
72,000

Locations: UK
General

Locations: Overseas
Worldwide

Opportunities
Accounts; Administration; Computing; Design
and development; Job evaluation; Production
engineering; Production supervision; Quality
control; Management services; Marketing;
Personnel; Purchasing; Research; Sales
engineering; Systems analysis; Works
engineering; Work study

Vacancies
150–200

Application address
The Appointments Manager, Lucas Industries
plc, Great King Street, Birmingham B19 2XF

Lucas Industries is a worldwide group of light engineering companies.
Employing 72,000 people they are major designers and manufacturers of
electrical, electronic, hydraulic and mechanical equipment used by
petrol, diesel and gas turbine engines, road and rail vehicles, ships and
aircraft. Additional products for a wide range of other markets include
fluid power transmission systems, test calibration and diagnostic
equipment, semiconductors, searchlights and ultrasonic cleansing
equipment.

The organisation
Major manufacturing companies in the organisation include Lucas
Electrical, Lucas CAV, Lucas Girling, Lucas Aerospace, SMEC, Lucas
Batteries and Rists. Distribution outlets are organised through Lucas
Service UK and Lucas World Service.

Operating in a world market, emphasis is placed on international
development. At home and abroad extensive research and development
programmes continue to create opportunities for group expansion, and
ensure that company products are able to meet successfully the challenge
of worldwide competition.

The Lucas Research Centre
Individual Lucas companies are responsible for their own research and
development projects, but additional facilities are provided by the Lucas
Research Centre at Solihull in the West Midlands.

The Research Centre is staffed by physicists, chemists,
mathematicians, metallurgists and a full complement of engineering
specialists.

Its work ranges from tooling developments to electronic systems for
supersonic aircraft, and the techniques it employs vary from computer
aided design to laser holography.

As well as its work for Lucas companies, the Research Centre undertakes
work for industrial and government organisations throughout the world.

Lucas CAV
This principal Lucas company is a world leader in the design and
manufacture of diesel fuel injection and electrical systems for a very wide
range of applications from fork lift trucks to ocean liners. Increased
demand for CAV products, resulting from the pressures to conserve
natural resources, is creating worldwide expansion of investment in the
company's resources, with concomitant opportunities for graduates.

Lucas Girling
Specialising in braking and suspension systems for road, off-road and rail
vehicles, Lucas Girling is a key member of the Lucas group. Recent
advances in the company's area of technology have resulted in the Lucas
Girling Skidchek system, a microprocessor controlled air-actuation
braking system and a compact, technically improved disc brake caliper
for automotive use.

Lucas Electrical
Lucas Electrical is a world leader in the design, development,
manufacture and marketing of a vast range of electrical and electronic
equipment for a multitude of applications in the worldwide automotive
market. Increasingly, Lucas Electrical's technology is finding solutions
in advanced electronics.

Lucas Aerospace
The largest supplier of aerospace equipment outside the USA, Lucas
Aerospace manufactures a range of products which include gas turbine

fuel and combustion systems, small gas turbines and engine starting/ management systems. The company supplies equipment for more than 100 different aircraft types to over 300 operators in 100 countries.

Graduates
The main requirement is for *mechanical, production, electronic* and *electrical engineers, physicists, chemists, mathematicians, metallurgists* and *materials scientists.* Graduates of *any* discipline are recruited for data processing, accounting, management services, purchasing, marketing personnel and other commercial and administrative functions.

Location
Most initial graduate training is based in Birmingham, London and the South East, Cwmbran, Hemel Hempstead, Burnley, Bradford and Newcastle under Lyme.

Training
Lucas training has established a high reputation in industrial and academic circles. Training schemes are designed to meet the individual needs of graduates and include a large element of experience with both training and job objectives. Direct appointments are available for those already possessing relevant experience.

Salary
Salaries are revised annually and are very competitive.

Applications
For further information about opportunities in any Lucas company apply direct to the Appointments Manager at the address given.

The Lummus Company Limited

Activities
Design and construction of petrochemical plant, including heat transfer units and control and automation

Employees
1,000 UK
CE Group 46,000 worldwide

Location: UK
Midlands

Locations: Overseas
Worldwide

Opportunities
Chemical, mechanical, electrical, civil, control and instrumentation engineers, mathematicians and computer scientists

Vacancies
12–15

Application address
Alan H Robson, Personnel Manager (Recruitment), The Lummus Company Limited, PO Box 41, Greyfriars House, Lady's Lane, Northampton NN1 3HZ

CE – Lummus is part of Combustion Engineering Inc, a worldwide US based engineering group. The group designs and constructs power, petrochemical and other plant. CE – Lummus is primarily concerned with petrochemical plant design procurement and construction.

Types of graduate required
There are opportunities for a wide variety of *engineers* wishing to pursue either a professional specialism or interested in developing later into the administrative and management field.

Training and career development
The company provides a two year programme of practical training and experience. Wherever possible, graduates are introduced first to the departments related to their degree discipline and, in the case of engineering graduates, training thereafter will be structured to meet the requirements of the professional institutions and eventually chartered status.

Prospects
The company is keen to recognise and reward ability, and encourage internal promotion.

Locations
UK head office is in Northampton but projects may arise worldwide.

Salaries
Competitive salaries and excellent benefits packages are offered.

Further information
Company information is available from the application address.

McDermott Engineering London

McDermott Engineering London is part of McDermott Incorporated, an international company which began contract construction in the Texas oilfields in 1923, and now provides total energy related services to the petrochemical, processing and power industries around the world. These services encompass the design, construction and project management of giant marine structures, sub-sea pipelines, instrumentation gear, storage installations and generating plants.

The growing importance of North Sea hydrocarbons to Great Britain has meant that the company's European engineering design activities, in this area in particular, have grown steadily during the last ten years. As the original pioneer of offshore platform construction, McDermott has led the technology race against the challenges of a harsh environment where structures and equipment have unprecedented climatic demands placed upon them. These are the challenges which engineering staff at the company's Wembley design office are accepting as an essential element of their work.

Types of graduate required

We seek *engineering* graduates with the potential and enthusiasm to make a tangible contribution to the energy industry through a long term career commitment.

Training

This is geared to the highly specialised and competitive business in which we are engaged. Training programmes have been agreed with the various institutions for all graduate entrants and these are supported by theoretical courses where appropriate.

Salaries and prospects

Starting salaries and employment conditions are highly competitive within the industry. All staff are provided with opportunities for planned career advancement in a dynamic atmosphere of company growth, and encouraged towards assuming progressively greater responsibilities within a short period. Some overseas travel may be involved.

Activities
Engineering design and project management of offshore and onshore oil and gas related facilities

Employees
1,200

Locations: UK
Wembley and Aberdeen

Opportunities
Structural, mechanical, electrical, chemical, instrumentation and control engineering; Naval architecture; Computer science

Vacancies
7–10

Application address
Personnel Officer, McDermott Engineering London, McDermott House, 140 Wembley Park Drive, Wembley, Middlesex HA9 8JD

McDonald's Golden Arches Restaurants Limited

McDonald's is a multinational firm with its head office in Chicago. It was founded in 1955 in the USA, where it is now the largest and most successful of the fast-service food restaurant chains. In 1974 the first UK store was opened in Woolwich. Within seven years there was a total of 68 stores in the UK. The company owns restaurants all over the world, and aims to continue with its rapid expansion programme.

UK operations

The UK head office is in London. There are now over 70 restaurants throughout the UK.

Overseas operations

There are McDonald's restaurants in 28 countries, including the USA, Brazil, France, Sweden, Japan and New Zealand. UK graduate recruits, however, would not normally work abroad.

Disciplines and related jobs

In restaurant management your degree discipline is less important than your personal qualities. We need graduates who have the energy and flair

Activities
High quality, fast-service restaurant chain

Locations: UK
London; South East; Midlands; East Anglia; North West

Locations: Overseas
28 countries worldwide

Opportunities
Restaurant management

Application address
The Personnel Manager, McDonald's Golden
Arches Restaurants Limited, 11–59 High Road,
East Finchley, London N2 8AW
Tel: 01-883 6400

to accept a lot of responsibility after a short time with us. We need lively, demonstrative people who want, and get, results. We need people who are not afraid of hard work. We need people who are able to lead and motivate others.

Training detail

Management trainees begin with a few weeks 'in uniform', doing all the jobs the restaurant staff (crew members) do. After this, you will attend the basic operations course, which covers the practical 'hows and whys' of efficient operations, elements of leadership and the best uses of human resources. Subsequent training is provided, designed to keep managers abreast of new techniques. This culminates in the management operations course which deals with the psychology of motivation, legal obligations of management, advanced leadership training, personnel recruitment and training and financial procedures. Throughout the training period, short seminars are frequently held, often for one day only, with managers and senior management coming together to discuss problems and ideas and to s ure experiences. Managers identified for early development to more senior levels attend our advanced courses.

Career development

If you are the right person for the job, upon successful completion of the basic operations course, you will rise to second assistant manager, and later to first assistant manager. About 18 months to two years after joining, if you meet our high standards, you will be promoted to manager of a McDonald's restaurant. This entails being responsible for sales volume, all costs and overheads, and most importantly, the performance and development of every member of your staff. Given the rapid expansion of McDonald's and the fact that we always promote from within, prospects for those with ability and determination are excellent.

Salaries

The basic starting salary is up to £5,500 in London.

Read on . . .

Ask your careers advisor/local Job Centre for a copy of our brochure and an application form, or contact our personnel manager.

Applications procedure

Send your application form or enquiry to the personnel manager at our head office in London. On receipt of an application form, pre-selected candidates are invited for a first interview. After this interview, candidates come to London, at our expense, and 'join' the staff of a medium sized restaurant for two days. This is part of our selection process and is designed to help both you and us to make an informed decision.

Mallinson-Denny Limited
A member of Brooke Bond Group

Activities
International timber importers and merchants;
manufacturers of wood based products

Mallinson-Denny Limited are a vigorous and expanding group of companies operating in the British Isles, Europe, Thailand, Malaysia, Singapore, Australasia and the USA. The group trade as international timber importers, merchants and manufacturers of wood based products. These products include veneers, plywood, softwood, hardwood, office partitioning systems, building panels, household articles and distribution of timber products and hardware to the retail trade. We also operate DIY establishments and trade counters. We manufacture timber frames and insulation materials.

Mallinson-Denny Limited, cont

Employees
3,500

Locations: UK & Ireland
General

Locations: Overseas
Australia; Holland; Indonesia; Malaysia;
Singapore; Thailand; USA; South America

Opportunities & places
Junior management trainees 5 approx

Upper age limit
25

Application address
KFR Pickering Esq, Group Personnel and
Training Officer, Mallinson-Denny Limited,
130 Hackney Road, London E2 7QR

Training
This consists of a progressive and imaginative course of three years in the
various departments and on interesting projects. Training is arranged so
that the individuals have the ability and maturity to make an effective
contribution after training.

Training and career developments
Selected trainees join the group as university graduates. A wide and
practical work training is given throughout the varied divisions of the
Mallinson-Denny Group. This training, paid for by the group, includes
attendance on product knowledge, wood technology, kiln drying, and
sales courses, on a day release basis. Knowledge and experience gained
during this period of training are rewarded by increased salary and
promotion within the frame of the group. The group has openings for
intelligent, personable and ambitious young people who are aiming to be
company executives, managers and directors. The principal openings are
in sales, manufacturing and general management within the United
Kingdom.

Locations
The group head office is situated in London at the address given, and
there are subsidiary companies and branches at Aberdeen, Arbroath,
Bedford, Belfast, Beverley, Bradford, Bridgwater, Bristol, Cardiff,
Claybrooke Magna, Coleford, Dartford, Doncaster, Dublin,
Dunfermline, Edinburgh, Felixstowe, Gateshead, Glasgow,
Grangemouth, Gravesend, Grimsby, Halifax, Hull, Inverness, King's
Lynn, Leeds, Liverpool, Lydney, Manchester, Newcastle, Nottingham,
Plymouth, Rotherham, Southampton, Wellingborough, Wigan, Wigton,
Wolverhampton, as well as overseas in Australia, Holland, Indonesia,
Malaysia, Singapore, Thailand, USA, and South America.

Prospects and pensions
The group is unusual in that its subsidiaries are largely autonomous, fully
controlled by their local directors. As a growth company, excellent
prospects are offered as opportunities for promotion constantly occur.
Wherever possible, vacancies are filled from within the group and
selection is by merit. Successful trainees can anticipate considerable
responsibility at an early age. There is an excellent pension and life
assurance scheme. Four weeks plus one day's paid holiday is given after
twelve months' continuous service.

Marks & Spencer plc

Marks and Spencer has a turnover exceeding £2,000 million a year from
some 250 stores nationwide, seven stores in Europe, a chain in Canada
and an export division servicing 40 countries throughout the world.

Graduate opportunities
We are interested in graduates from *all* disciplines who possess the
personal and leadership qualities to manage in a demanding commercial
world. There are vacancies in commercial, staff and office management.

Training in all three categories lasts 15–18 months depending on your
progress. It is mainly store based with a number of regional and head
office courses.

Promotion is based on merit and can lead to a variety of career
development opportunities; to senior positions in our largest stores; to
divisional responsibility for a group of stores; to senior roles in the
buying, personnel or administrative areas of head office. Mobility is

Activities
Multiple chain store retailing

Employees
40,000+

Locations: UK
General

Locations: Overseas
Canada and Europe

Opportunities
Store, staff and office management; Buying;
Personnel; Administration

Vacancies
100+

essential, but the company offers a generous financial package when
moving its management staff.

Salaries and benefits
The company offers a very competitive salary and benefits package which
is reviewed annually. Until April 1983 the minimum starting salary is
£5,850 pa plus bonus. Management staff retire at 60 and benefit from a
non-contributory pensions scheme, profit sharing, free life assurance and
a minimum of four weeks holiday a year.

Further information
Yours careers service should have supplies of our literature which
describes each career in detail. Applications should be sent to John
Fortescue at the address given.

The Marley Group

Marley is the largest, most diversified manufacturer of building products
in the UK. They range from roof tiles, the starting point of Marley 50
years ago, and now include the majority of plastics products used in
buildings, together with precast concrete structures from factory made
systems buildings to coal bunkers. Marley are also the largest suppliers to
the motor industry of moulded foam crash pads, door panels, arm rests,
etc. In recent years there has been a steady expansion in our share of the
home improvement market, through our shops, superstores, builders
merchants and specialist plumbing and heating centres.

Types of graduate required
Applications are invited from graduates of *any* discipline who are
prepared initially to be located at any of our sites throughout the country,
and can display the qualities necessary for management.

Training
Individual training programmes are prepared for each management
trainee, examples of which can be seen in our graduate booklet. Nearly
all training is on the job and personal contact is maintained with
individual trainees from the outset.

Locations
It may be anywhere in the UK: at head office in Sevenoaks or at any of
the Marley locations throughout the country.

Salaries and prospects
Commencing salaries for graduates are highly competitive. Successful
graduates should reach junior management level within two years. From
then on achievement is based entirely on merit and will be rewarded with
higher responsibilities. Our exceptional growth record over the past few
years continues to assure excellent prospects to graduates of proven
ability. The fringe benefits are excellent and in accordance with modern
business practice.

Applications
Having read our literature, available from your careers service, please
send a completed standard introduction form or cv, giving full details of
what you have to offer our company to the address given.

Mars Group Services

MARS GROUP SERVICES **MGS**
A division of Mars Limited

Activities
Market research, computer systems
development, data processing and
management sciences services to Mars group
companies in the UK and increasingly in Europe

Employees
250+

Locations: UK
South East; Midlands

Opportunities
Computing and market research

Vacancies
8

Application address
Personnel Officer, Mars Group Services,
132/133 Fairlie Road, Slough, Berks SL1 4JX

We're a young and very fast moving division of the highly successful
Mars Group whose range includes best selling confectionery, pet foods
and grocery products.

We provide centralised computing and market research facilities to all
Mars UK companies and increasingly for our sales/marketing units and
manufacturing operations throughout Europe.

Over the past decade we have maintained an enviable growth rate and
each year we recruit a select number of graduates to play vital roles in our
future expansion programme.

As you would expect, a significant proportion of our employees are
graduates and we are committed to attracting talented people who have
the potential to progress to senior positions in the organisation.

Types of graduate required
Graduates and postgraduates from *all* disciplines will be considered.
Your career will start initially in programming, operations or consumer
research and within these areas, there are many opportunities for
development.

We are looking for graduates who can demonstrate initiative and
energy, and will enjoy the rewards of working in a demanding
commercial environment.

Training and career development
We place great emphasis on training and career development for all our
new and existing employees. Graduates are recruited directly into specific
jobs, for which they receive a comprehensive training which is flexible
and designed to equip them for significant responsibility as early as
possible in their career. Our policy is to promote, wherever possible,
from within the company and progression can be very rapid for those
who demonstrate ability, achievement and future capabilities. Your
performance and career development will be formally appraised and fully
discussed with you twice a year.

Location
Our offices are situated in the Thames Valley at Slough, Berkshire,
(where the majority of our employees work) and in Melton Mowbray,
Leicestershire.

Salaries and benefits
In 1983, a starting salary of around £7,500 per annum will be offered.

We offer a number of generous benefits including a comprehensive
non-contributory associate benefits scheme, which provides life
assurance, pensions and sickness benefits to all employees from the first
day in service with the company.

Mars Limited (Confectionery Division)

Mars

Activities
Manufacture and marketing of confectionery

Employees
3,500

Mars Confectionery is a vigorous and successful company in the food
industry and part of a worldwide, privately owned business. The main
activities of the group are confectionery, other forms of convenience
foods and pet foods. Besides the Mars Bars, we make a wide range of
chocolate and sugar confectionery including Twix, Milky Way, Bounty,
Topic, Marathon, Maltesers, Tunes, Pacers, Opal Fruits, Treets,
Minstrels, Lockets, Spangles, Revels and Galaxy.

We are seeking high calibre graduates of various disciplines who will,

Location: UK
Home Counties

Locations: Overseas
Australia; France; Germany; Austria; Holland;
North and South America

Opportunities
Engineering; Production; Sales; Marketing;
Purchasing; Management sciences

Vacancies
16 approx

Application address
The Personnel Officer (Graduate Recruitment),
Mars Limited, Dundee Road, Slough, Berkshire
SL1 4JX
Tel: 75 23932

after a period of properly designed and organised training become managers in our company. Competition for our graduate scheme is tough and there is no easy ride when you come but for ambitious, successful people the rewards are high.

If you think you would enjoy the demanding training and early responsibility, then read on. . .

Types of graduate required

Any subject although an *engineering* degree is essential for engineering vacancies and a degree in a numerate discipline is necessary for management sciences.

Opportunities

We believe that a business can only be successful if it provides mutual benefits for everyone connected with it. Our objective is to ensure that employees, suppliers, distributors, customers, shareholders and consumers all gain from their association with the company.

The policies of the company are designed to attract, retain and motivate individuals capable of responding to challenging assignments in a demanding work environment.

We are seeking graduates, male or female, who possess enough ability, maturity and determination to become managers in two years. There are opportunities for graduates in the following areas.

Trainee production shift manager

As a production shift manager your main objective is to achieve the planned production schedule within the parameters of safety, hygiene, quality, cost and quantity.

Your objectives include meeting the required production schedules, ensuring that the quality of the product is right and keeping a high standard of general cleanliness and housekeeping in the department. You have to keep adequate control of costs, aiming to minimise any wastage of raw or packaging materials. Safety, too, is one of the major responsibilities of a production shift manager; it is your job to make sure that all machinery is operated safely and that all your team work in a safe manner.

You achieve all your objectives through the people who work with you and for you. Consequently, motivating, organising, controlling and developing your team of people is your most important responsibility. You will be responsible for about 30 people working on a rotating shift system, and for a production line which has a capital cost of up to £10 million and which uses a wide range of technologies with particular emphasis on computer controlled systems.

Engineering trainee

Many engineers do not think of applying to a food manufacturer when they think of a career in engineering. At Mars, however, engineering is one of our major strengths; our engineering is very advanced in its field with many of our production lines incorporating the use of computer controls. Over the past five years we have spent over £50 million on engineering projects with many unique developments.

The reason behind all this investment and activity is the need for efficiency: we aim to reduce our production costs by improving productivity through innovative engineering.

You would join us on a training course tailored to your individual needs for the development of practical skills but also structured to comply with the training requirements of your appropriate engineering institution for acceptance into corporate membership. During the training you would have the opportunity to translate your theoretical knowledge into reality.

We are seeking the best engineering graduates around: those with outstanding creative ability, ingenuity and maturity, plus an honours degree in mechanical, chemical, electrical or control engineering.

Sales trainee

As a field sales manager you will be managing the Mars business in your area. You increase your sales by ensuring that our products are readily available and well displayed in all our trade outlets, whether corner shops or supermarkets.

This is achieved:

● through your team of salesmen whom you will recruit, train, direct, motivate and develop

● through contact and negotiation with local managers of retail and wholesale organisations

● through a marketing plan which provides for special offers and promotions in addition to national advertising.

You will start as a salesman, gaining experience in selling in one or more sectors of the trade. Your management training will be based on that experience and will begin as soon as you are ready to progress. At all stages of your development we provide the necessary technical sales training at our training centre in Slough.

If you are confident, enthusiastic, determined and able to use your own initiative to cope with a multitude of different situations, then selling with Mars could be the career for you.

Marketing trainee

As a brands manager you are responsible for putting the company's marketing principles into practice. This requires the bringing together of resources for the profitable management of specific brands. You respresent the consumer to the company and become involved in every aspect of the company's operation, seeking at all times the profitable growth of your brands through the development and growth of their consumer franchise.

You will start, like the sales trainees, as a salesman gaining experience in selling to different outlets. After six to twelve months you will move into marketing and become involved in the pricing, advertising, promotion and development of one of our brands.

Purchasing trainee

The supplies division is responsible for ensuring that our current and forecast requirements of materials and services are resourced in the most cost effective manner. The basic ingredients of our products represent over half of their cost hence effective buying is crucial to providing better value and ensuring business profitability.

Many of our raw materials are traded on markets which show significant price volatility. Our approach is to carry out research into the factors affecting price movements thereby obtaining an understanding of the fundamentals involved which in turn allows us to use forward buying techniques to reduce our exposure to price changes. This is of particular importance in cocoa buying where we trade on the London and New York terminal markets.

Our marketing strategy requires us to maintain a very flexible approach to the supply of packaging materials where we have around 400 different packaging types and generate up to 800 changes in design each year. In engineering buying we supply over 30,000 items per year, many to our own design using materials and systems in fields of high technology. Success in these specialist areas requires a combination of specific technical knowledge with professional negotiating skills.

As part of an international group we co-ordinate a number of our activities with our sister companies, participating in joint research projects and ensuring that we communicate effectively on local and world events which may affect our ability to resource at competitive prices.

Management sciences trainee

The successful management of a large company like Mars, which operates in a complex and ever changing environment, is dependent upon an understanding of the market, the business, the economy and many other factors. The role of management sciences is to provide the company with an analytical approach to complex business problems and decisions. Consequently the department is intimately involved with all divisions of the company, but in particular marketing, sales and finance.

Most of the activity in management sciences is project based and relates to issues of major strategic importance to the business. There is, however, through the open style of Mars management, a substantial involvement in the tactical day to day activities of the company; indeed this involvement is essential to the ability of the department to understand and successfully analyse problems. Although mathematical and data processing techniques are used extensively the emphasis is on practical solutions to problems in whatever timescale is demanded.

Training

Your training programme will be developed to meet your own particular requirements. It will start with an induction course and you will then work in your nominated division holding a real job as soon as possible. Towards the end of your first year you will attend a review course and following this your further training will be determined.

Career development

Normally graduates take about two years to develop and demonstrate the skills they need for a management job. Sometimes an exceptionally mature graduate develops more rapidly. Providing we have a suitable position we will promote you when we assess that you are ready.

Location

Our factories and offices are at Slough and all our people are based there except for the field sales force which is spread out over the UK.

Salaries

We aim to keep our salaries above average and to reward good job performance quickly. Your starting salary will be around £8,000 pa and £15,000 pa within two years is a realistic target. We have a number of managers who have reached over £20,000 pa in their middle twenties.

Applications

For a copy of our brochure and application form, please contact your careers advisory service or write direct to the Personnel Officer (Graduate Recruitment) at the address given.

Mars Money Systems

A high technology electronics company within the Mars Group, we have a remarkable growth record. Using progressive management techniques we need adaptable energetic graduates to help us sustain that growth and find new answers to the traditional problems of a manufacturing environment.

Training

Training will be geared to the individual and promotion is based on merit, so you should be keen to take on real responsibility from the start of your career.

Activities
Manufacture of sophisticated electronics products
Employees 250
Opportunities
Design and development; Test engineering; Production engineering; Line management; Purchasing; Materials control; Accountancy; Technical sales and marketing
Vacancies 3

Upper age limit 25

Application address
Mars Money Systems, 266 Bath Road, Slough

Salaries
Starting salaries will be from £6,500.

Further information
Enquiries and details to the Personnel Officer.

Matthew Hall Group

Founded in 1848 the Matthew Hall Group is today an expanding engineering based enterprise, established throughout the world. It has the ability to combine the considerable managerial and technical resources necessary to carry out large and complex projects.

Individual companies are involved in feasibility studies, project management, engineering design, procurement and construction services to the energy, chemical and mineral processing industries; design installation and maintenance of mechanical and electrical services, including air conditioning, instrumentation, fire protection and plumbing.

Activities
Engineering contractors

Employees
7,000 UK
10,000 worldwide

Locations: UK
General

Locations: Overseas
Holland; Australia; Saudi Arabia; Singapore;
USA; Brazil

Opportunities
Design engineers; Construction engineers;
Project engineers; Systems analysts; Quantity
surveyors

Vacancies
20

Application address
Group Graduate Development Adviser, Matthew
Hall & Co Ltd, Matthew Hall House, 101–108
Tottenham Court Road, London W1A 1BT

Types of graduate required
Each year member companies of the group recruit graduates in a number of disciplines. Vacancies occur for graduates in *mechanical*, *chemical*, *electrical*, *civil*, *control* and *environmental engineering*, *building services*, *quantity surveying*, *computer sciences*, and *mineral processing*. Opportunities are available for both graduates and postgraduates, particularly those with relevant previous experience who are able to make a contribution to our activities.

Training and career development
Initial training lasts for about 18 months and is planned in accordance with the requirements of the appropriate professional institution. Training is flexible to suit individual needs and interests; it involves gaining experience by working in a number of departments. These planned moves provide the opportunity to develop into a responsible member of an engineering team.

After training the graduate may take up a position in design, project engineering, construction or commercial areas. There is a commitment to develop staff throughout their career and to promotion from within the group, wherever possible.

Location
Training is based in London or the head office of the appropriate group company. Experience in other offices and on sites is normally a part of initial training. For those wishing to travel there will be opportunities to work overseas in the future.

Applications
Further information about the company can be obtained from the group annual report, subsidiary company brochures and the graduate development brochure. A copy of these should be available in your careers office. If you are interested in discussing opportunities with a member of the company, please consult your careers office. If we are not visiting your university or polytechnic please write, enclosing a completed application form, to the relevant group company or to the Group Graduate Development Adviser.

May & Baker Ltd

M&B | May & Baker

Activities
Manufacturers of fine chemicals,
agrochemicals and pharmaceutical products

Employees
4,500

Locations: UK
Dagenham, Essex; Norwich

Opportunities
Pharmacy; Pharmacology; Biology; Chemistry

Vacancies
30

Application address
Personnel Officer, (Scientific and Technical
Staff) May & Baker Ltd, Dagenham, Essex
RM10 7XS

May and Baker's reputation in the field of original research is reflected in a wide range of medical and other chemical products which have benefited the lives of countless thousands of people, throughout the world. In the fields of human medicine, medical research, veterinary science and agriculture these products are widely used to protect human life and combat all manner of diseases. From the surgeon with patients threatened by anaerobic infection to the third world farmer needing to protect his crops and his livelihood against all manner of hazards – May & Baker products are known and respected.

But success in these areas is not won easily. The demands, both in terms of financial investment and human resources, are very substantial.

This is why our parent company, Rhône-Poulenc, earmarked some £165 million in 1982 for a wide ranging research and development programme which will underwrite new research projects in all areas of pharmaceutical, chemical and agrochemical development.

These substantial financial resources need to be complemented with human ones. So, each year we select a number of graduates who can meet the challenge of working in a multi-disciplinary environment with some of the best people in their field.

Types of graduate required
High academic achievement is just one of the things we look for. We need people with resourceful personalities to tackle work that calls for initiative, attention to detail and, as much as anything, a flair for problem solving. It's something of a hothouse environment, but one in which young graduates seem to thrive.

We are primarily interested in *science* graduates, men and women with good honours degrees in the following disciplines: *pharmacy, pharmacology,* the *biological sciences* and *chemistry.*

Training and career development
The demands we make are high, the rewards can be equally substantial. Training programmes are thorough, your development is well monitored and success is both recognised and rewarded. And, not least, what you achieve here could substantially benefit many peoples' lives as well as your career.

Applications
May & Baker is about as demanding an environment as a science graduate could hope to work in. If that's a challenge you could meet, and you are confident of at least a good second class honours degree, then we'd like to hear from you.

John Menzies (Holdings) plc

John Menzies is a nationwide concern specialising in the wholesale distribution of newspapers and magazines and in retailing these products plus a wide range of other goods in their hundreds of shops and bookstalls.

New developments
There are John Menzies shops and warehouses from Inverness to Torquay with large concentrations in Glasgow, Edinburgh and London. A progressive expansion of shops and refitting of older ones goes on throughout the year.

Activities
Wholesale and retail distribution of newspapers,
magazines and associated products

Employees
7,000

Locations: UK
General

Opportunities & places
Retail management trainees 25

Application address
Mr A H Bridge, Group Personnel Manager, John Menzies (Holdings) plc, Hanover Building, Rose Street, Edinburgh EH2 2YQ

John Menzies (Holdings) plc, cont

Types of graduate required
The company takes 25 graduates a year from *all* disciplines. The qualities of leadership and a strong sense of responsibility are looked for in graduates. Those who are to become future managers must be profit conscious and have a flair for assessing market trends and forecasting change.

Training and career development
The final aim for graduates may be to a head office position in accounts, administration, management services or staff management, but for most the path will be shop management. Only by experience will graduates find a good knowledge of retailing to further their career in the company.

Locations
Some graduates will be based at the head office in Edinburgh, others following a career in shop management will be given on the job training at one of the company's outlets throughout the country, but would be required to attend periodic residential courses at the management training centre in Edinburgh.

Salaries and benefits
Salaries depend on age and qualifications and are negotiated at interview. They are reviewed regularly and are based on an individual's progress. The company has good pension and life insurance schemes with provisions for dependents.

Merck, Sharp and Dohme Limited

Activities
Research, development, manufacture and marketing of ethical pharmaceuticals

Employees
1,200 UK
32,000 worldwide

Locations: UK
Hoddesdon, Herts; Terlings Park, East Herts
Sales: General UK

Opportunities
Pharmaceutical research and development; Sales and marketing

Application address
Richard Crookes, Personnel Manager, Merck, Sharp and Dohme Limited, Hertford Road, Hoddesdon, Herts

Merck, Sharp and Dohme Limited is the UK subsidiary of an international pharmaceutical company with its head office in the United States. Although, MSD are recognised within the pharmaceutical industry as a major research institution and one of the world's biggest pharmaceutical manufacturers, their name is probably little known outside it, quite simply because their products are available only on prescription. The company has been established in this country for over 50 years and is now one of the biggest suppliers of drugs to the NHS.

It has an excellent reputation for researching, developing, testing and marketing new drugs and to maintain these high standards, MSD recruits graduates of the highest calibre from a variety of disciplines.

Over the years MSD has made significant contributions to the field of pharmaceuticals in the form of medicines which tackle some of today's widespread health problems: heart conditions, Parkinson's disease, glaucoma, arthritic conditions and infectious diseases like measles, hepatitis and mumps.

In accord with its prominent position in the pharmaceutical world, MSD has a strong commitment to reinvest substantial proportions of its profits in basic and applied research – over 300 million dollars is set aside for this purpose annually – and is currently setting up the largest neuro-biological research centre in the UK at Terlings Park in East Herts. This centre will be dedicated to extensive research leading to the production of new compounds specifically designed to act on the nervous system.

Sales and marketing opportunities
MSD requires graduates of *all* disciplines in this department and provides ample grounding in the scientific aspects of the work, so a technical background is not necessary. More important is a desire for hardwork, an ability to communicate effectively and the potential to sell.

In the first instance, recruits work as medical representatives, selling MSD's drugs to a very specialised group of professional people: GP's hospital consultants and pharmacists. After a year or so of accumulating this essential experience and showing proven sales success, there will be opportunities to progress to a year's further training at headquarters in Hoddesdon. Candidates for this programme are selected from the sales force on merit and proven ability.

This marketing trainee programme encompasses all facets of marketing including; market research, advertising and product management together with experience in all the other relevant aspects of the business, eg finance and operations. At the end of this an assistant product managership should be in prospect.

Research opportunities
To undertake basic and applied research MSD needs graduates with good first degrees or PhD's in the following subjects: *pharmacology, biology* and *medical chemistry* and other related disciplines.

The company seeks intelligent, practical and innovative people to work in both the basic research and development laboratories. Scientists will work in small teams under the direction of an experienced group leader.

MSD fosters links with universities and encourages research scientists to publish their work and keep in contact with the scientific community.

Progress at all stages in the company will be monitored by performance appraisal to ensure that a thorough knowledge is gained and that career progression is made in the direction best suited to an individual's talents.

Applications
In the first instance candidates should write for an employer's application form to the address given.

Merrill Lynch International

Activities
Diversified international financial services

Employees
700 UK
38,000+ worldwide

Location: UK
London

Locations: Overseas
Worldwide

Opportunities
International sales, marketing, banking and operations

Application address
Nigel T Carter, Recruitment Officer, Merrill Lynch House, 3 Newgate Street, London EC1A 7DA

Merrill Lynch International Inc is a subsidiary of Merrill Lynch & Co Inc, one of the world's largest diversified financial services companies. The overseas subsidiaries and offices of Merrill Lynch International employ over 2,500 people and have 45 sales offices located in 32 countries outside North America, as well as banking facilities in a half-dozen countries. Along with its sister companies Merrill Lynch, Pierce, Fenner & Smith Inc (USA) and Merrill Lynch Royal Securities Ltd (Canada), it is part of the largest securities and commodities broker/dealer organisation in the world. As such, it has unrivalled global placement capability for securities issues and is a prominent factor in international investment banking circles.

The business of Merrill Lynch International is divided into three principal areas: the international marketing group provides a broad variety of investment and trading services through its sales offices to institutional and individual clients, and of commodities services to both trade and individual speculative clients. Merrill Lynch International Bank provides financing, market-making, and related banking services to governmental and corporate clients. The operations/finance group provides internal support services as well as certain investment services to clients.

Training
Merrill Lynch International offers several training programmes of potential interest to new graduates.

Merrill Lynch International, cont

Corporate trainee programme

For graduates aged 21–25, with honours degrees in *PPE* or *finance*, this eighteen month course covers all aspects of the MLI organisation. It includes a four month securities account executive training programme, commodities, banking and internal professional services. Training takes place in New York, London and possibly other international financial centres, which will be followed by UK or international assignments, and may lead toward a management career in the future.

Securities account executive training programme

For graduates aged 23–30, with either a *business* degree or some prior work experience in finance or sales. This four month course, taking place in London and New York leads to a career in the sales of sophisticated international financial services to institutional and individual investment clients.

Commodities account executive training programme

For graduates aged 23–30, with a *business* degree and/or with some prior work experience in physical commodities, import/export sales, international trade or with a commodity futures broker. This three month course taking place in London, New York and Chicago, leads to a career in the sales of professional services in the international commodity futures markets to commercial and trade clients and to sophisticated individual speculators.

MLIB operations training programme

For graduates aged 21–25, with a *business* degree or equivalent. This two year London based course covers all phases of internal bank operations including on the job training and participation on outside bank training courses.

Branch operations management training programme

For graduates aged 23–30, with a *business* degree or equivalent. This eighteen month course covers management skills and all phases of branch office operations, both on the job and in New York classroom training. Proficiency in a foreign language, numeracy and willingness to relocate internationally for extended periods are desirable.

Application procedure

Standard introduction forms or cvs should be sent to Nigel T Carter at the address given.

Metal Box plc

Activities
Packaging and packaging machinery, printing, domestic central heating systems, high technology gears and bearings

Employees
25,000 UK

Locations: UK
General

Metal Box is one of the largest manufacturers of packaging and packaging machinery in the world. It is also a world leader in central heating; prints one in four of all UK cheques; and is expanding in Europe, the Far East, Africa and North America.

In our newest factories, microprocessor based systems control whole production lines, sharing work between machines and monitoring their productivity. Such lines will produce up to 60,000 seamless cans per hour, deep-drawn from coils of metal.

We are building a new generation of machinery, using computer aided design to achieve greater speeds with less maintenance. In temperature controlled precision toolrooms we work to two ten-thousandths of an inch.

We also use paper, board and plastics. The development and vigorous worldwide selling of complete packaging systems in all materials ensures

Opportunities
Engineering: mechanical, production, electrical,
electronic and control; Science in R&D; Sales
and commercial; Computer programming;
Production management; Accountancy;
Personnel; Product design; Market research

Application address
Recruitment Services Manager, Metal Box plc,
Queens House, Forbury Road, Reading,
Berkshire RG1 3JH

that the theoretical achievements of new technology are realised in
customers' own factories:

We now have one of the most comprehensive research and
development centres in Europe. This one site has some 250 graduates
dealing with the problems of new materials and processes, through to
testing on pilot production rigs and lines.

Our data network is linking the Worcester computer centre to factories
throughout the UK. Powerful minicomputers provide additional, local
data processing.

For the new graduate, we consider that this all adds up to an
interesting range of opportunities.

Types of graduate required

The graduates we seek are themselves looking for both personal and
intellectual challenges. We are a big industrial company but we operate
through a number of largely autonomous units with a variety of needs.
So, we need *scientists* who wish to continue in science; *engineers* looking
for sophisticated engineering; and graduates of *all* disciplines wanting to
develop their entrepreneurial and management talents.

In all our activities we need broad thinking people who have the
knowledge, desire and initiative to make things happen. This real desire
to make things happen is the most important single quality we will look
for in job interviews.

Meteorological Office

The Meteorological Office conducts a vigorous research programme in
addition to providing a wide range of meteorological services. The Office,
which is part of the Scientific Civil Service, is taking full advantage of the
unprecedented opportunities which the use of computers, rockets,
satellites and the new technology generally provide for research workers
in meteorology. The current programme includes the physics and
dynamics of clouds and rain, laboratory simulation of geophysical fluid
motions, atmospheric turbulence and diffusion, energy exchange
between the atmosphere and the oceans, the global circulation of the
atmosphere, research in applied meteorology and climatology and the
development of advanced instrumentation.

The Meteorological Office has one of the best equipped computing
laboratories in the UK with IBM 360/195 and 370/158 computers, to
which has recently been added a CYBER 205 vector processor. There is
also a PDP 11/40 mini computer.

Types of graduate required

Candidates should have or expect to obtain this year a degree or
HNC/HND in *mathematics, physics, meteorology, computer science* or
electronics.

Training

Professional training, on full pay, is given at the Meteorological Office's
own residential college. There is also a scheme in which approved
research work may be submitted to certain universities for the award of a
higher degree.

Location

Mainly at the headquarters at Bracknell, Berkshire, but there are
Meteorological Office units in many parts of the UK.

Salaries

Starting salaries will mostly be between £5,422 and £5,747, depending

Activities
Meteorological research and services

Employees
2,750

Location: UK
South East

Opportunities
Computer science; Mathematics; Physics;
Meteorology; Electronics

Upper age limit
30

Application address
The Civil Service Commission (Science
Division), Basingstoke, Hants
General information from: The Secretary,
Meteorological Office, Room 609, London
Road, Bracknell, Berkshire RG12 2SZ

upon the class of degree obtained. However, relevant post graduate qualifications could lead to a starting salary of £6,840 or above.

Prospects
Good honours graduates may expect to be initially involved in research, whilst other graduates may also be engaged in computing or forecasting work. Promotion to senior posts will be dependent on individual ability.

Further information
General information can be obtained from the Secretary, at the address given, but applications must be made to the Civil Service Commission.

Montague L Meyer plc

Activities
Timber importers, merchants and manufacturers of timber based products

Employees
7,000

Locations: UK
General

Opportunities
Sales; Importing; Manufacturing

Vacancies
5

Application address
Group Personnel Manager, Montague L Meyer plc, Villiers House, 41–47 The Strand, London WC2N 5JG

Montague L Meyer plc is a major British timber group. As well as being a timber importer, the group is engaged in a wide variety of activities including wholesale distribution of timber and sheet materials, merchanting and retailing of timber, sheet materials and building materials, and manufacturing in related fields. Overseas the company operates in Australia, Malaysia, Singapore, Hong Kong, France, Belgium, the Netherlands, Canada and the USA.

Locations
The group head office is in London in The Strand. The head offices and branches of subsidiary companies are spread throughout the United Kingdom.

Training and development
The initial training is of approximately six months duration and is arranged so that the graduate has an exposure to each of the major functions of the group. This general training is considered very important in introducing the graduate to the timber industry.

Normally, graduates can expect to be placed in their first job after the initial six months training. This could be in a head office trading department, or in one of the subsidiary companies of the group. Subsequent progress will be monitored and will depend upon the ability and contribution of the graduate. The group operates a policy of promotion from within as far as is practicable.

Types of graduate required
Graduates of *all* disciplines are recruited and applications are invited from both men and women. Opportunities are in sales, importing and manufacturing.

Salary
Starting salaries are competitive and regular salary reviews relate to progress, appointment and experience. The group has a contributory pension scheme and other benefits to be expected from a major firm.

Further information
For further details of career opportunities with Montague L Meyer plc please write to the Group Personnel Manager at the address given.

Michelin Tyre plc

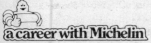

Activities
International manufacturer of radial tyres, tubes and wheels

Employees
15,000 UK
120,000 worldwide

Locations: UK
Midlands; Scotland; North West; Northern Ireland

Locations: Overseas
Europe; USA; Nigeria; Canada; Brazil

Opportunities
Industrial engineering

Application address
MA Sproston, SPM Department, Michelin Tyre plc, Campbell Road, Stoke on Trent ST4 4EY

Michelin is the largest radial tyre manufacturing organisation in the world, with a proven record of technical innovation and success in a highly competitive industry.

In the UK we employ over 15,000 people at our six manufacturing sites using a wide range of technologies in a constant search for improvement in our production processes. But our investment in the future does not stop with plant and equipment. We recognise the need to recruit high calibre young men and women with new ideas to keep us ahead.

Graduate requirements

In 1983, we will be recruiting graduates in *engineering* or associated sciences to train and work as industrial engineers, with open-ended career paths to senior managerial appointments.

Industrial engineering is a key function in any progressive manufacturing organisation. It is directly concerned with the optimum use of the company's resources, requiring problem identification, assessment and innovative solutions. This serves as an ideal introduction for the graduate into industry, providing a unique standpoint from which to study management techniques. An industrial engineer endeavours to improve productivity and reduce production costs by maximising the use of available resources including manpower, materials and plant; assists management control and decision making, supplying information gained through skilled work-measurement; is responsible for the establishment and implementation of realistic and fair incentive schemes.

Finally, you must not expect rigid hierarchies or clearly defined responsibilities. Instead we offer mutual respect and team work; flexibility; personal involvement.

Salaries and benefits

We recognise and reward true ability, offering graduates a very attractive starting salary, with an excellent pension and life assurance scheme and other large company benefits.

Further information

Initial interviews will be held at convenient locations. Contact your university appointments board or write for an application form to the address given.

Micro Focus Limited

1982   1981

Activities
Design, development and marketing of computer software products

Employees 70

Locations: UK
London and South West

Locations: Overseas
California, USA

Micro Focus is a private, British company, formed in 1976 whose rapid growth has been achieved through the company's international significance (70% of the company's business is overseas) combined with the tremendous opportunities created by the microprocessor.

Micro Focus's most well known product – CIS Cobol, an ANSI 74 Cobol Compiler – has become the 'de facto' standard Cobol compiler for micros and thus provides the key to stability and portability within the computing industry.

New development

Building on the success of CIS Cobol, Micro Focus is now engaged in the marketing of a new generation of products – further exploiting the interactive nature of micro computers whilst simultaneously being increasingly receptive to the huge investment in mainframe software development.

Innovation is the guiding principle upon which the Micro Consultants Group has grown so successfully over the past 15 years. It is by working consistently at state-of-the-art, conceiving, designing and implementing new systems that its original contributions to the UK electronics industry have seen it achieve international recognition. The Queen's Award for Technology is the public acknowledgement of these efforts.

The Group's business success is demonstrated by surging exports throughout the world, notably to the United States, Germany and Japan where only high technology can command such response.

The attraction of working on the most advanced available technology has drawn into the Group highly qualified people with exceptional talents in their fields. This has led to the establishment of small specialist project teams which stimulate discussion of new ideas, and generate a strong sense of project identity.

All of the project teams include both software and hardware engineers working together to design and build some of the most sophisticated electronic equipment in the world – often to meet a customer requirement that no one else can meet.

Hardware and software engineering skills required in the work of the Micro Consultants Group include advanced analogue and digital circuit design, operating system design, language definition, signal processing, real time mathematical and engineering programming, image processing and a wide variety of language skills – and superimposed on all of these, the ability to define and solve difficult technical problems in the real world and convert the solutions into well engineered systems.

Particularly significant contributions to the world electronics industry have been made in the development of high speed low level data acquisition turnkey systems, in the field of ultra high speed AD–DA conversion, and in the application of digital techniques to television broadcasting.

The Group of Companies occupy a number of modern, well equipped plants in central Newbury, Berkshire, just off the M4, in a very pleasant rural area. ("in what is often called the Silicon Valley of the UK").

Types of Graduates Required
Excellent career opportunities are open for graduates in Electronic Engineering and Computer Science. Promotion is normally from within and responsibility is given according to ability.

Further Information
As well as attractive salaries, the Company has a comprehensive pension scheme and variety of social activities. If you want to invest in a worthwhile future, please write to the address given below.

The Group Personnel Officer, Micro Consultants Group, West Mills, Newbury, Berkshire RG14 5HG. Telephone (0635) 48222, Ext. 305.

MICRO CONSULTANTS GROUP

Opportunities
Software engineering; Programming; Technical writing; Marketing and market planning; Sales

Application address
Graduate Recruitment Officer, Micro Focus Limited, 10th Floor, David Murray John Tower, Brunel Centre, Swindon, Wiltshire SN1 1NB
Tel: 0793 695891

Micro Focus Limited, cont

Types of graduate required
The continued success of Micro Focus has created new opportunities throughout the company.

Sales/marketing These opportunities are most likely to be suited to graduates with a keen appreciation of business as well as some background knowledge of computing and the computer industry, thus enabling recruits to take early responsibility.

Software development There will be a number of opportunities for graduates to join development teams. Micro Focus' development teams must respond quickly to changes in the computing industry. This requires a very high degree of intellectual competence.

Application procedure
Talented graduates equal to the demands, should apply using standard introduction forms to the Graduate Recruitment Officer.

Opportunities
Design and development engineers; Systems engineers; Test engineers; Computer programmers

Vacancies 6

Employees 350

Application address
Group Personnel Officer, Micro Consultants Limited, West Mills, Newbury, Berkshire RG14 5HG

Micro Consultants Group

The Micro Consultants Group is a highly successful, rapidly expanding group of companies with an international reputation for the design and manufacture of a wide range of advanced electronic equipment used throughout the world in broadcast and other industries. The companies occupy a number of modern, well equipped plants in central Newbury, Berkshire, just off the M4, in a very pleasant rural area.

Further information
For more details on the Micro Consultants Group see the Micro Consultants display opposite.

Activities
Design, development and manufacture of microwave communications and components

Employees
400

Location: UK
South East

Opportunities
Microwave engineers; Communications engineers; Quality engineers

Vacancies
12

Upper age limit
22/23

Microwave Associates Limited

Microwave Associates Limited was established in the UK in 1961 as a sales outlet for the products of our parent company: M/A Com, Burlington, Mass USA. In 1962, an applications laboratory was set up which gained considerable expertise in frequency multipliers, microwave sources, solid state switches and microwave receivers for television link systems. These areas of expertise led to the design and manufacture of transportable and fixed links which are now sold both in the UK and overseas. MA also manufactures components such as microwave diodes and ferrites and has also gained access to valuable markets offering a wide variety of applications for our components and sub-systems in avionics, radar, guided weapons and similar systems.

Types of graduate required
Electronic engineering/physics graduates are required for the following vacancies: microwave engineers (microwave integrated circuits, oscillators, amplifiers, modulators, control devices), communications engineers (microwave analogue and digital radio systems), development engineers (state of the art frequency synthesiser systems encompassing microwave components), quality engineers (liaison with design and production, reliability engineering).

Location
Dunstable, Bedfordshire.

Application address
Vilma Nyss, Personnel Manager, Microwave
Associates Limited, Dunstable
Bedfordshire LU5 4SX
Tel: 0582 601441 ext 18

Salaries and benefits
The company operates a contributory pension/life assurance scheme and
offers a private medical scheme. Starting salaries are competitive and our
policy is to promote from within the company. Other conditions of
employment are kept at an attractive level in order to recruit the well
qualified and ambitious engineers we seek to employ.

Midland Bank plc

Activities
Complete range of banking services

Employees
45,000

Locations: UK
General

Opportunities
General banking; International banking; Trust
company; Computer operations

Upper age limit
25

Application address
Manager, Group Graduate Recruitment,
Midland Bank plc, Courtwood House, Silver
Street Head, Sheffield S1 3RD

Defining the particular qualities of a successful bank manager is about as
difficult as the application of generalised yardsticks of analysis to people
in any other walk of life. Perhaps even more so, at Midland Bank, where
a manager is in effect running his/her own business, he needs to bring to
his job a balanced mixture of business acumen, technical banking
experience and an understanding and ease of communication with people
in all walks of life.

The Midland Bank's total organisation takes in a United Kingdom
establishment of over 3,000 branches, an expanding international
division which is represented in every major world finance centre, a
close-knit association with the Midland Bank Trust Company, Forward
Trust Group and links with various specialist financial organisations in all
parts of the world. It presents, in other words, a very wide spectrum of
opportunity for the future.

As one of the country's major banks, we naturally look to our graduate
intake to give us the majority, and perhaps the best, of our future
managers and specialists. To this end we put them into a special stream
from the start; a policy which aims to reward their potential with a higher
salary but, of course, also increases our expectations of their performance
and progress.

Types of graduate required
Our general practice of considering graduates from *all* disciplines reflects
the strong belief that an applicant's personal qualities are just as
important as his or her degree. The responsibilities of branch
management revolve so closely around aspects of temperament,
flexibility allied to diplomacy, openness in dealing with others and, of
course, intelligence, that the precise nature of previous educational
attainments often becomes a secondary issue. However, in the
requirements of some of our specialist departments, qualifications in *law*,
language or *computer science*, for example, can obviously be seen to confer
an advantage.

For international division we require a number of graduates each year
for management training. An interest in *business studies/economics* is
essential and *modern language* qualifications are advantageous.
Opportunities for secondment abroad are available from time to time.

In computer operations each year a number of graduates is required for
the systems and programming department of computer operations
division based in Sheffield. Aptitude and interest are essential.

Training
In general banking the length of the graduate training programme is
approximately four years, being sufficiently flexible to accommodate
individual progressions.

The first few months are devoted to understanding the whole range of
branch systems and bookkeeping and would include control work and
cashiering experience. The second stage, between 12–18 months, is spent
learning the important work of securities and overseas business. Here is

closer contact with the ever increasing range of customer services, including investments, safe custody facilities, importing and exporting and the various aspects surrounding the taking of security for lending. The final stage is geared much more to the individual, based largely on his or her record. As well as a variety of opportunities within the branch network, experience within a regional head office or head office could also be attained. Full mobility is essential.

Regular assessments are designed to provide objective appraisals of career progress, bearing in mind that progress is rated both in terms of present ability and future potential.

The professional qualification of the Institute of Bankers (AIB) is essential and study leave is arranged to enable you to complete the examinations within approximately three years.

Prospects and salaries

(All salaries are approximate 1982 levels.) Starting salaries are in the range of £5,400 to £7,000 depending on age and location. During training regular increments are received. Following successful completion of the training programme first appointment automatically follows, carrying a salary in the region of £9,000.

In the main, appointments are within the branch network, but opportunities also arise within head office and regional head offices. To have gained sufficient experience for branch managership it is normally necessary to have had three appointment promotions. Managerial appointments are usually achieved in the early 30s, but there are exceptional cases where this level is reached whilst still in the late 20s. Managerial salaries commence at around £12,000; middle management salaries range from £16,000 to £24,000 whereas those of senior management lie between £24,000 and £30,000, and above.

Milliken Industrials Ltd

Activities
Manufacturers of synthetic textile fabrics for industry

Employees
200 UK

Location: UK
North West

Locations: Overseas
Belgium; France

Opportunities
Shift production management normally first appointment; Quality control; Accounts; Industrial engineering; Sales/marketing; Data processing

Vacancies
4

Application address
K Bancroft, Personnel Manager, Milliken Industrials Ltd, Wellington Street, Bury, Lancs

Milliken and Company is a privately owned American organisation established in 1865 which manufactures a wide range of textiles, chemicals and packaging products, supplies the textile, tyre and rubber industries, and produces a range of fashion fabrics. The Milliken Research Corporation, set up in 1945, has invested heavily in resources and personnel for research, benefiting all areas of Milliken's operations in America and Europe.

Milliken Industrials Limited is the headquarters of the European division, with plants situated in England, Belgium and France, specialising in synthetic textiles, particularly for the rubber and tyre industries, and in adhesion technology, meeting the specific needs of industrial consumers. The most recent benefits from our research include the first 100% synthetic v-belt covers, the treatment of synthetic fabrics to give adhesion to a wide range of elastomers and a bead wrap for tyres that drastically reduces time, cost and inefficiency in tyre manufacture.

Types of graduate required

Opportunities exist mainly for graduates with degrees relevant to our fields: *textile technologists*, *rubber technologists*, *production engineers*, *chemists*, *accountants*, *statisticians* and *computer scientists*. Textile experience is not essential, but managerial abilities of leadership, motivation and the handling of people are.

Training and advancement

Initial training is on the job, to give each trainee a thorough understanding of the industry. A graduate's subsequent appointment is

LEADERS BREED LEADERS...

●●● our philosophy is deeply rooted in our experience — experience which spans over 50 years of technological innovation and has demonstrated that outstanding success is directly related to the interdependence of the individual and the organisation.

In other words, to retain our status as a world leader in the semiconductor field, we must continuously top up our reserves with potential young leaders and create the challenges required to bring out the best in them — and us. This way, employee and employer work to each other's mutual advantage.

By paying meticulous attention to career development programmes we have produced some of the top people — and consequently, some of the best products available today.

Our East Kilbride plant is the largest state-of-the-art MOS house in Europe and we have just recently launched the new CMOS and NMOS 4" wafers.
As the demand for Motorola's products continues to increase, we are recruiting more Graduates with the talent and determination to make it to the top with a top organisation.

MOTOROLA

If you want to be among the world leaders in the semiconductor scene write, stating the Division and vacancy in which you are interested to: Recruitment Manager, Motorola Semiconductors Limited, Colvilles Road, East Kilbride, Scotland.

likely to be in shift management, which soon brings a high degree of responsibility.

During the first six months of employment, graduates receive training on our management orientation programme, which acquaints the new employee with all aspects of the company's operations and processes.

Training does not stop after six months; advanced training seminars are available for specialist training in both technical and non-technical areas.

Further information
For company brochures and further information, please contact the Personnel Manager at the address given.

Mobil Oil Company Limited

Activities
Exploration, production, manufacture, distribution and marketing of petroleum and allied products

Employees
3,500

Locations: UK
Head office London
Programmers/analysts Sevenoaks
Others Aberdeen and General

Opportunities
Chemical engineering; Mechanical engineering; Petroleum engineering; Marketing; Personnel; Planning; Supply; Distribution; Accounting; R&D; Technical sales; Exploration and production; Data processing

Vacancies
50

Application address
University Liaison Adviser, Mobil Oil Company Ltd, Mobil House, 54–60 Victoria Street, London SW1E 6OB

The oil industry offers graduates a challenge that is difficult to match. Future world energy supplies depend on decisions taken every day in a company such as Mobil. Consequently, we want graduates who can define problems quickly, offer solutions and act decisively.

Mobil, with business interests in over 100 countries, is one of the world's six largest industrial organisations. The company's products run the gamut of the petroleum industry, from bitumen for asphalt to the most sophisticated jet fuels and synthetic lubricants.

Types of graduate required
Graduates are recruited as follows. Refining: *chemical* and *mechanical engineers;* technical sales: *engineers* and *chemists;* research and technical service: primary and postgraduate *chemists;* marketing and personnel: *any* discipline; planning: *economists;* supply: any *numerate* discipline; distribution: *engineering;* programmer/analysts: any *numerate/logical* discipline; exploration: postgraduate *geologists,* good honours primary or postgraduate *geophysicists;* production: *petroleum, chemical* or *mechanical engineers.*

Training and career development
Graduates are introduced to Mobil and the principles of business theory and practice through an induction programme. They are then given full on the job training programmes in their own departments. To develop promotion potential we offer training schemes and specialist courses such as the Mobil self-study programme, as well as practising systematic job rotation.

Applications and further information
Visit your careers office for our brochure and application forms.

Motorola Limited

Activities
Manufacture of integrated circuits development and of radio communication systems

Employees
2,000

Locations
East Kilbride, Scotland; Basingstoke; Milton Keynes; Wembley

Motorola, Europe's largest MOS house is based in East Kilbride. The organisation produces the broadest range of semiconductor devices available today and is a world leader in linear integrated circuit technology, CMOS and related logic facilities, memory products and systems, as well as LSI microprocessors.

Communications division
The communications division at Basingstoke is responsible for the production and development of FM equipment including mobile and portable radios, paging receivers, fixed station products, point to point

systems, control centres, computer aided despatch systems and component products.

Sales and marketing

The diverse nature of our industry has led us to place great emphasis on market research in order to maximise rapport between customer and suppliers. Milton Keynes and Wembley are the UK centres for market research, new accounts and after sales servicing.

Expansion

Continuing an impressive growth record, we have recently announced the construction of a new module at East Kilbride which will significantly increase our capability through the introduction of innovative technology.

Salaries

Salaries are highly competitive and are commensurate with the level of competence and input we look for in our new graduates. For more details write to either of the addresses given.

Opportunities
Engineering: process, device, development, product; Quality sales: equipment and facilities; Accountants

Application addresses
Graduate Recruitment Manager, Semiconductor Products Division, Colvilles Road, Kelvin Industrial Estate, East Kilbride, Strathclyde, Scotland
Peter Richards, Recruitment Manager, Communications Division, Armstrong Road, Daneshill East, Basingstoke, Hampshire

Moores Furniture Group

Moores Furniture Group is a privately owned group of companies with an excellent record of growth. The group is based in Wetherby, West Yorkshire, with a developing plant in Newton Aycliffe, County Durham. We are perhaps the leading supplier of kitchen, bedroom and living room furniture to builders, local authorities and the retail trade.

This growth has meant that not only have the senior management been promoted from within, but there is now an increasing demand for ambitious graduates who wish to develop with the company.

Types of graduate required

Personal qualities are more important than academic discipline. We look for graduates who are dynamic and hard working with a flexible attitude and good powers of expression both verbally and in writing.

Training

From the first day, graduates will have immediate practical experience in the working life of the company. Training is mainly in-house and graduates are encouraged to learn from working alongside directors and managers, most of whom have progressed through the company in exactly the same way.

Prospects and salaries

Whilst you are learning from your working experience, we will be able to monitor your progress and determine your particular strengths. Thus you could become a senior manager in production as quickly as in sales or many other commercial fields. Salaries are awarded accordingly.

Activities
Manufacturers of kitchen, living room and bedroom furniture

Employees
950

Locations: UK
West Yorkshire and County Durham

Opportunities
Marketing; Product research and development; Production management; Manufacturing services; Commercial and administration operations; Computer; Accountancy

Application address
Mr AD Elsegood, Personnel Manager (Graduate), Moores Furniture Group Ltd, Queen Mary House, Avenue C, Thorp Arch Trading Estate, Wetherby, West Yorkshire

Morgan Brown & Haynes

Activities
Audit, accountancy and taxation services for companies and individuals

Employees 28

Location: UK London

Opportunities & places
Trainee chartered accountants 6

Application address
PF Jackson, Morgan Brown & Haynes,
45 New Broad Street, London EC2M 1PP

We are a City based practice of five partners and 23 professional staff with a wide range of clients including public companies, small to large private companies, solicitors, building societies, etc, very few incomplete record clients, but good experience in company and personal taxation.

Training
As members of the HAT syndicate we are able to offer comprehensive training to our students (see entry under HAT).

Salaries
We offer competitive salaries, which are regularly reviewed.

Murray Noble

Activities
Financial practitioners

Location: UK
London

Opportunities
Accounts; Tax; Investment; Insurance

Vacancies
0

Application address
Murray Noble, Lonsdale Chambers,
27 Chancery Lane, London WC2A 1NF

Murray Noble is a firm of financial practitioners providing integrated financial services in accounts, investment, tax and insurance. We provide a co-ordinated service for individuals over many years.

Types of graduate required
Selection is solely based on personal qualities. Successful candidates will possess initiative, dynamism, the highest level of self-motivation, and the ability to communicate with people.

Training and prospects
Training is both formal and practical. In addition to practical work, trainees attend an intensive three month course at a banking school. This is followed by two to three years practical experience within the firm dealing with clients. To reach partner level, executives will pass the recognised professional exams within their specialist chosen field.

Prospects within the firm are excellent and ambitious executives can expect to progress to partner within five years. Five figure incomes are possible within two years.

Further information and applications
We welcome applications at any time from graduates who are confident of not only succeeding at interview, but also excelling in this innovative and stimulating environment.

Applications should be made using a standard introduction form and supported by a covering letter to John Elderton, Partner.

National Bus Company

Activities
Passenger road transport

Employees
52,000

Locations: UK
England and Wales

Many well known coach and bus companies form the publicly owned National Bus Company group. The pooling of manpower and vehicle resources has resulted in a service which covers England and Wales, with a great awareness of its public obligations and of the need for teamwork and co-operation between management and staff. The NBC subsidiary companies operate some 15,500 vehicles providing a network of stage carriage and express services and undertake coach tours throughout Britain and on the Continent. The number of persons employed is of the order of 52,000.

A transport company as large as ours, offering various kinds of services, naturally has a great many areas of concern, and to help train our selected future managers we have devised a comprehensive training scheme.

Opportunities
Accountancy; Engineering; Traffic management

Vacancies
10–12

Application address
The Secretary, Senior Management Scheme,
National Bus Company, 25 New Street Square,
London EC4A 3AP

Training and career development

Successful candidates embark on a two year course, during which time they will be attached to one company, in any part of England or Wales, which has been designated as a training company.

The trainee's work is monitored by a committee, which is kept abreast of the progress of each individual by regular reports from the general manager of the training company. Every six months the committee also interviews and examines the trainees on the work they have done and the knowledge they have acquired.

This knowledge is acquired by a carefully planned series of steps which takes trainees through the operations/planning, engineering and administration/accounting departments, as well as in direct operations. Subjects covered in this detailed programme include timetables, faretables, publicity, allocation of crews, bookings and enquiries, wages, coach operations, engineering records, central stores and workshops etc. In addition, training is given in responsibility, and two weeks in each year are set aside for special off the job courses on selected subjects such as computer appreciation and modern management techniques. Besides this practical training, trainees are required to undertake studies for membership of professional bodies.

At the end of training, the trainees will be fitted for suitable positions within the group, which will be found for them before training is completed: it will be a position of considerable responsibility, but it will also afford further practical experience in the operation of bus and coach services and thereby stand them in good stead for later and more senior positions. For the right person of capability and ambition, promotion prospects and the opportunities to perform a public service are excellent.

Prospects

Every trainee who successfully completes the course should in later years qualify for appointment to the top managerial posts with the operating companies. Some of the graduates trained under the scheme are now directors of bus companies in the NBC group and a considerable number are general managers.

Types of graduate required

Generally graduates in *arts* subjects are required to train for management posts in traffic operation; graduates in *accountancy* and *automobile engineering* to train for managerial posts in those particular fields. Trainees are also recruited from the staffs of the subsidiary companies and from other sources. Candidates must normally be between 21 and 25 years of age.

Locations

Trainees are posted for the duration of the course to the particular training company in England or Wales which, at the time of admission, has a training place available. Training is received at the training company's headquarters and at its operating depots. The syllabus also provides for off the job courses on specialised subjects.

Salaries and benefits

Salary rates during training are attractive and are reviewed periodically to ensure that they are in line with current trends.

There is a contributory pension and life assurance scheme; we also give assistance in finding lodgings for trainees. Most of the group's companies have staff canteens, all have sports and social clubs. Holidays for trainees are at the rate of three weeks per year.

National Coal Board

Activities
Extraction and processing of coal and by-products

Employees
280,000

Locations: UK
London; Wales; Midlands; Yorkshire; North East; North West; Scotland

Opportunities
Administrative; Computer; Engineering; Operational research; Scientific research

Vacancies
See careers adviser for details

Application address
Peter Hulatt, Staff Department, Room 248D, National Coal Board, Grosvenor Place, London W1X 7AE

Coal provides more than one-third of Britain's total energy requirement. The NCB is one of the largest industrial employers in the UK, with total personnel numbering 280,000 and annual turnover of over £4,000 million. The short term financial problems caused by the recession are now being overcome and the Board's ten-year Plan for Coal, for building a new industry out of the old, is beginning to show results. Major investment of over £2,500 million is providing increased output and greater productivity through the development and modernisation of existing collieries and the sinking of new ones. Work has started on Selby, which is the largest deep mining complex in the world.

This is just the first stage in the long term plans for coal production to the year 2000 and beyond.

Types of graduate required
Within the range of jobs we have available, we are looking for men and women from a wide variety of disciplines including *engineering*, *science*, *technology*, *mathematical subjects* and *social sciences*. For certain posts graduates of *any* discipline can be considered. We are statutorily unable to consider women for certain engineering appointments where the nature of the job and training requires a significant proportion of time to be spent underground at a working mine.

Opportunities normally exist in the Board's engineering training and administrative assistant schemes (both leading to management posts); in the two research establishments; in operational research; in scientific control and in NCB (Coal Products) Ltd, Compower Ltd and Superannuation Investments Department. Your careers adviser will have up to date details of vacancies.

Training
The Board has a number of well established training programmes, some of which lead to professional qualifications. Other vacancies are direct entry posts where the graduate is expected to make an immediate contribution and where training is largely on the job.

Prospects
There are opportunities for progression to the most senior posts with a high level of responsibility. There is plenty of scope for graduates who feel they could help shape the future of one of Britain's largest and most important industries.

National Maritime Institute

Activities
R&D in hydrodynamics, aerodynamics and marine trials

Employees
250

Locations: UK
West London and Hythe

Opportunities
Scientific officers and higher scientific officers

We are a research establishment offering a full range of facilities and resources for research and development in the areas of hydrodynamics, industrial aerodynamics and marine trials. From our three sites at Feltham, Teddington and Hythe (on Southampton Water) we conduct research programmes for both Government Departments and commercial customers.

Types of graduate required
We seek graduates with a marine based degree, ie *naval architecture*, *maritime studies* and *marine engineering*. We also offer employment opportunities for *physics*, *mathematics* and *computer science* graduates.

Graduate training
Graduates will initially join a small project team, with the opportunity of

Application address
Personnel Officer, National Maritime Institute, Faggs Road, Feltham, Middlesex TW14 0LQ
Tel: 01-977 0933

moving to other teams after a period to ensure familiarisation with a range of NMI computing and experimental facilities.

Further information
Please contact the Personnel Officer.

The National Mutual Life Association of Australasia Limited

Activities
Life assurance and pension funds sales and administration

Employees
250

Location: UK
London

Locations: Overseas
Australia; New Zealand; South Africa

Opportunities
Actuarial; Insurance administration

Vacancies
5–10

Application address
Personnel Manager, The National Mutual Life Association of Australasia Limited, Austral House, Basinghall Avenue, London EC2V 5EP

The NMA was established in Australia in 1869 and is now a leading life and general assurance group in Australia and New Zealand with current assets exceeding £1,000 million. The United Kingdom head office was established over 85 years ago.

Types of graduate required
Graduates in *mathematics, statistics* or *economics* who wish to qualify as actuaries, or graduates in *economics* or *business studies* who seek a career in insurance.

Training
Training is given in the actuarial aspects of life assurance and pension work supplemented by experience in other departments. Study release and assistance with tuition and examination fees are given for those who study for the examinations of the Institute of Actuaries or the Chartered Insurance Institute.

Location and opportunities overseas
Vacancies occur at the head office for the United Kingdom in London and there may be opportunities for graduate trainees to transfer to the association in Australia after some years in the London office. Detailed arrangements will be discussed at interviews.

Salaries
Starting salaries depend on age and qualifications and will be at least competitive with market rates at the time of joining the association and subject to annual review according to merit and examination successes. These salary terms may be altered according to market conditions at the time of recruitment.

Prospects
With the growth of the association there are excellent career and promotion prospects for those who qualify and have the ability to accept responsibility and participate in management.

Pensions and other amenities
These include pension and life assurance benefits, four weeks annual leave, long service leave, flexible working hours and a subsidised house purchase loan scheme.

National Nuclear Corporation Limited

NNC

Activities
Design, research and development of power stations

Employees
2,750

Locations: UK
East Midlands; North West; Scotland

Opportunities & places
Trainee mechanical engineers 12; Trainee physicists 12

Upper age limit
23

Application address
Mr P Bailey, Training Manager, National Nuclear Corporation Limited, Warrington Road, Risley, Warrington, Cheshire WA3 6BZ

The nuclear power industry in Britain was rationalised into its present form in 1973. All the skills and experience built up during the earlier years were vested in the National Nuclear Corporation (NNC) which is now the sole British design and construction company for nuclear power plant.

The National Nuclear Corporation carries out design and the management and coordination of construction of nuclear and other electrical power stations, either in part eg nuclear steam supply systems, or the complete station from concept to fully commissioned operational capability.

The design, development, construction and commissioning of power plant demands a wide ranging and high level of professional experience, the utmost technical capability, and thoroughly objective judgement.

NNC meets all these requirements backed by a quarter century of experience in every aspect of power plant engineering for fossil fired, nuclear, gas turbine and diesel generating plant. Its capability ranges from initial studies covering economics, siting and industrial infrastructure through preliminary engineering design, project management, procurement, construction and site services, to operational maintenance of completed facilities.

Corporation structure

The corporation is an independently run joint enterprise of state and industry in the proportions of 35% and 65% respectively and is the sole organisation of its type in Britain. Evolved from a series of industrial consortia begun in the 1950s, NNC embodies all the know-how and experience in designing and building Britain's present 11 commercial nuclear power stations now contributing over 10% of the country's electricity supply. Three large stations are nearing completion and a further two were begun towards the end of 1980. By the end of this decade it is anticipated that 25–30% of the country's electricity will be generated by nuclear power.

Major shareholders in NNC are the British Government (35%), the General Electric Company Limited (30%) and British Nuclear Associates (35%), a holding company representing the interests of the principal manufacturing companies in the nuclear industry.

NNC can call freely on the technical and commercial resources of the shareholding members. These are the General Electric Company Limited (GEC), the UKAEA, and British Nuclear Associates Limited comprising Sir Robert McAlpine & Sons Limited, Babcock and Wilcox Limited, Northern Engineering Industries, Head Wrightson & Co Limited, Strachan & Henshaw Limited, Taylor Woodrow Limited and Whessoe Limited.

Staff distribution

Employees number 2,750 of whom some 1,900 are managerial, professional and technical staff. In addition there are 300 staff on long term secondment to the company, of whom 180 are technically qualified civil engineers and draughtsmen.

The total headquarters resource includes 250 professional staff working in reactor engineering, 200 in general engineering, 230 in systems engineering and 150 in research and development. These are supported by 400 draughtsmen and technical staff. There are 200 professional staff engaged on project management and planning and 60 are employed in computer services. The total site staff of 550 includes 250 professional construction and commissioning engineers.

NNC is established at three centres; Risely near Warrington, Booths Hall, Knutsford Cheshire and at Whetstone near Leicester.

Projects

NNC undertook the responsibility in 1970 under contract from the UKAEA for the design and construction of the 250 megawatt prototype fast reactor (PFR) at Dounreay which has been in successful operation since 1972 and is now engaged on the design and development of the commercial demonstration fast reactor (CDFR) with a net output of 1,300 megawatts based on the PFR.

NNC carried out an exhaustive examination of reactor systems towards identifying the best choice for the UK both in the interests of future nuclear programmes at home and as export potential and this culminated in a report to the Government which was summarised in a public announcement in July 1977 (thermal reactor assessment).

The Government has subsequently authorised the installation of two further AGR stations and at the same time sanctioned design work on the pressurised water reactor (PWR), now being carried out by NNC. A detailed presentation of the safety of the systems (3,500 pages, 2,000 figures) has been completed and work is now concentrated on the forthcoming public inquiry into the siting of a PWR station at Sizewell.

Types of graduate required

Mechanical engineers
A two year training programme is offered to graduates obtaining an honours degree in mechanical engineering. The training scheme is flexible and is designed to meet the requirements of individual engineers and the Institution of Mechanical Engineers.

Physicists
Appointments are for work of a theoretical nature covering a wide range of the company's activities including reactor physics, radiation physics, steady state and kinetic performance of the complete power station, control and safety. Applicants must have at least a second class honours degree in *physics*.

Mathematicians
Appointments exist both as applied mathematicians or as programmers, extensive use being made of large digital computers. Applicants must have at least a second class honours degree.

Successful applicants will initially work under the supervision of an experienced member of staff and receive on the job training.

Every encouragement is given, wherever possible for further study on specialist courses and great attention is paid by the company to career planning and progression.

Salaries

Initial salaries are based on age, qualifications and any relevant experience and are reviewed annually.

National Provident Institution

NPI was established in 1835 and is now a leading company in its field. Business is transacted throughout the UK and with its planned development it can offer excellent opportunities for graduates. Assets at 31 December 1981 exceeded £650 million.

Activities
Life assurance and pensions

Types of graduate required

Graduates in *mathematics*, *statistics*, or *economics* for actuarial training. These disciplines and *accountancy* and *business studies* would be suitable

Employees
950

Location: UK
South East

Opportunities
Actuarial; Accountancy; Computing

Vacancies
10

Upper age limit
22

Application address
W Kingston, Personnel Manager, National
Provident Institution, NPI House, Calverley
Road, Tunbridge Wells, Kent

for accountancy training. Other relevant disciplines are acceptable for training as computer programmers.

Training and career development

The development of graduate trainees includes on the job training and also in-company courses at our training centre in Tunbridge Wells. External courses, where appropriate, are also arranged. Trainees studying for professional examinations are placed in selected departments during training so as to gain the widest possible experience. Study periods are allowed during business hours and upon success in the examinations an honorarium is paid to meet the cost of course fees, exam fees etc. Examination success also attracts a financial reward.

Prospects

Progress during training is carefully monitored. Short and long term development prospects are good and eventual promotion to management positions depends upon demonstrated ability. It is the policy of the company to promote from within.

Salaries and benefits

Commencing salaries will be fully competitive. They are reviewed annually to reflect performance and potential.

In addition to salary we also pay an annual bonus and the benefits we offer include a house purchase scheme at very attractive rates of interest, a non-contributory pension scheme, free permanent health insurance and private treatment in illness. The general conditions of service include generous sick pay, a progressive holiday entitlement (commencing at 20 days per annum) and a subsidised lunch facility. We operate a system of flexible working hours.

There are many sporting and social activities covering a wide range of interests.

Locations

Vacancies occur at our head office in Tunbridge Wells, which is situated in a pleasant part of Kent about 35 miles south of London. The offices are modern and provide excellent working conditions. Applicants selected for interview are invited, at our expense, to spend an informal day at Tunbridge Wells.

Accommodation

We are able to provide accommodation for graduate trainees at our own residential centre. The accommodation comprises fully furnished comfortable single rooms in a well appointed detached house in a quiet area fairly near the town centre. The house is situated in its own grounds. Recreation rooms are also provided.

National Semiconductor

Activities
Design, manufacture and supply of integrated circuits and other semiconductor based products

Employees
1,000 UK
40,000 worldwide

National Semiconductor is one of the world's largest manufacturers of semiconductor products. We design, develop, manufacture and sell semiconductor technology. Our product range encompasses approximately 9,000 types of integrated circuits and discrete transistors, together with memory systems, microcomputer systems, electronic point-of-sale systems, minicomputers and large mainframe computers.

National Semiconductor was founded in Danbury, Connecticut, USA, in 1959. However, its explosive expansion began in 1967 following the move to Santa Clara, California. National soon established a reputation as a world leader in semiconductor technology – pioneering new linear products devices, new process technologies and new production techniques.

Locations: UK
Greenock and Bedford

Locations: Overseas
USA; Far East

Opportunities
Engineering: process, product, design, test;
Supervisors

Application address
Personnel Manager, National Semiconductor
(UK) Ltd, Larkfield Industrial Estate, Greenock,
Scotland PA16 0EQ

National Semiconductor carries out its activities in many locations. From world headquarters in Santa Clara, California, to West Jordan, Utah; Tucson, Arizona to Great Britain, France and West Germany; the Republic of Singapore, Hong Kong, Malaysia, Indonesia, Australia and Brazil. In all, we own or lease over one million square feet of fabrication, assembly and test facilities around the world – facilities manned by around 40,000 National employees.

Our company policy is one of career development and promotion from within. With our current growth, we need a number of top stream aggressive graduates from a variety of backgrounds to join our professional team and develop and grow with us.

Recruitment from UK universities and polytechnics is for our manufacturing plant in Greenock, Scotland. Our northern European sales office in Bedford, England and our European marketing centre near Munich, West Germany occasionally have vacancies.

Greenock

In 1972 National Semiconductor established a manufacturing and design facility at Greenock, Scotland. We quickly recognised the benefits of integrating design, development, manufacturing and testing in one facility. You will therefore have the benefit of working closely with professionals in related fields.

In July 1979, National Semiconductor announced a £45 million plan to extend the Greenock plant. Construction on the new plant is now complete. The basis of semiconductor manufacturing is the economy of scale, processing thousands of chips on one wafer as a single unit. Increasing the size of wafers is the leading edge of production technology. National Semiconductor is one of the first companies in the world to increase the size of wafer fabrication to five inches. Once completed, Greenock will be one of the world's largest and most advanced semiconductor manufacturing facilities.

Working conditions are excellent in modern, air conditioned surroundings and the Greenock plant is situated on a hill overlooking the Clyde estuary. The factory is ideally situated for road, rail and sea and is only 30 minutes from Glasgow airport.

Our requirements for graduates vary to help meet our ambitious expansion plans. You will be joining a young, expanding and progressive team that is involved in a new, exciting and pioneering project. Most jobs are for process and product engineers together with circuit designers. However, to support such a large project, we obviously require graduates from a variety of disciplines. Test, quality control and customer service engineers, for example.

Process engineers

Process engineers at National are very much involved in all aspects of production processing and your responsibilities would be for a part of this process. Typically our engineers are involved in process sustaining, process development, yield improvement, etc.

Product engineers

Product engineers are responsible for ensuring that our completed devices meet the overall specification and this is accomplished by utilising sophisticated electrical testing equipment, as well as by general trouble-shooting. In this role the engineer must liaise very closely with process engineering in order to maximise potential yield improvement and process development.

Design engineers

Our air conditioned design laboratory is fully equipped with all the latest computer aided design facilities including auto frequency and transient analysis programme and an interactive graphics unit for mask layout.

Our new design engineers can expect to undertake a new design project from initial customer contact, through design and layout to the final product under the guidance of one of the senior design engineers.

Test engineer

You will be responsible for optimising throughput and yields at wafer sort and/or final test. You must provide the technical support for on line trouble-shooting of computerised test hardware, product related problems and software.

Your prospects

Ours is the industry of the future and ours is the company that is setting the pace in the industry. Our standards are high and so are the rewards; not only financial but also in terms of job satisfaction and advancement.

If you want to make the fullest use of your qualifications, and be given real responsibility early in your career, you owe it to yourself to find out more about us by writing to the address given.

National Westminster Bank plc

Activities
Banking and financial services

Employees
84,000 worldwide

Locations: Overseas
Worldwide

Opportunities
Management trainees in domestic and international banking; Traineee programmers in data processing and Centre-file Ltd

Vacancies
180 approx

Upper age limit
25

Application address
The Graduate Appointments Officer, National Westminster Bank plc, PO Box 297, Recruitment Department, Drapers Gardens, 12 Throgmorton Avenue, London EC2P 2ES

NatWest is a leading worldwide financial organisation which is seeking graduates to train for senior managerial and executive positions. Graduates of *any* degree discipline are required. The essential requirements are that all graduates are prepared to adapt to a challenging environment and to accept increasing responsibility at any early age.

Training

Graduates obtain accelerated training through our graduate management trainee scheme which is now well established but remains flexible in order to meet the needs of the individual. Training involves a combination of job experience, together with periods at our staff college in Oxfordshire and our technical training centres in London. Those entering domestic banking will gain their basic training in specifically chosen branches throughout England and Wales, whilst those joining international division will normally commence in London. There are a small number of opportunities for graduates to commence as trainee programmers.

Career development

There is considerable variety of job opportunity with career paths reflecting individual performance. Under our staff appraisal system there is careful monitoring of progress, including regular discussions with the individual.

Mobility is an essential prerequisite for training for senior management and where changes of work location involve house moves the bank provides a generous removal expenses package.

Salaries

Salaries are competitive and are reviewed annually. In addition there are allowances paid to staff working in the London area and in certain large towns and a number of attractive fringe benefits.

The selection procedure

We are happy to consider direct applications and we shall endeavour to visit all universities in England and Wales in the spring term to hold preliminary interviews for interested final year undergraduates. Outside the milk round interviews can normally be arranged locally.

National Westminster Bank plc, cont

Further information
Our graduate booklet and application form are available either from your careers advisory service or on request to the address given.

NCR (Manufacturing) Ltd

NCR Corporation Dayton Ohio develop, manufacture, market, install and service total business information processing systems for selected markets. These are primarily in the retail, financial, commercial, industrial, health care, education and government sectors.

NCR Manufacturing Ltd, Dundee is a wholly owned subsidiary of NCR Corporation and has directional business authority to design, develop and manufacture for the worldwide self-service financial terminal market.

Career development
Opportunities for work abroad are limited to short term attachments and training, and the policy of internal promotion and career development is largely dependant on ability.

In an environment of continuous challenge a graduate's potential for personal growth is an essential ingredient for increasing the volume and proportion of intellectual products being developed and manufactured by NCR.

Activities
Design, development and manufacture of self-service financial terminals and computer systems

Employees
800

Location: UK
Dundee, Scotland

Opportunities
Engineering: electrical, electronic, mechanical; Computer science; Manufacturing: industrial, test systems, materials control, quality assurance, MIS; Purchasing

Application address
The Manager, Manpower Development, NCR (Manufacturing) Ltd, Kingsway West, Dundee DD2 3XX

Newey & Eyre Group Limited
A Thomas Tilling Company

The Newey & Eyre Group is an international distributor of industrial equipment and one of the largest members of the Thomas Tilling Group. Less than 30 years has seen our turnover increase from £1 million to £400 million.

The major subsidiary is Newey & Eyre Ltd, distributing industrial and domestic electrical products.

Through three other UK subsidiary companies: Newey & Eyre International Ltd, EC Engineering Supplies Ltd and Newey & Eyre Electronic Distributors Ltd, we have diversified into export and other fields of industrial distribution to keep pace with the specialised needs of today's most up to date industries.

We have acquired three electrical wholesaling companies in the USA and also operate from Singapore.

Training and career development
Your training programme will extend over a minimum of two years. Guidance and counsel will be given regularly and you will be assessed at each stage of your development.

You'll be familiarised with branch activities and group services. Likely experience will include attendance at internal and external courses; project work and special assignments in one or more branches; and attachment to group specialist departments at head office for research and development.

Rapid promotion should follow – depending on your abilities – and you can expect further training right up to director level. Career paths will be mainly sales/marketing oriented.

Activities
International distributors of industrial equipment

Employees
4,000

Locations: UK
General

Opportunities
Sales; Sales management; Branch management

Vacancies
12

Application address
JW Exton, Group Personnel Manager (Ref: DOG 83), Newey & Eyre Ltd, Donne House, Calthorpe Road, Edgebaston, Birmingham B15 1QX

Salary and conditions
Your age, experience and so on will naturally be the main criteria, but as
a broad guide we can tell you that there are few organisations who can
offer so many the chance of securely earning big rewards.

Nielsen Business Services

Activities
Continuous marketing research for
manufacturers of packaged goods to encourage
maximum product performance

Employees
1,100

Location: UK
Oxford

Locations: Overseas
Europe; The Americas; South Africa; Australasia

Opportunities
Sales/service executive; Statistician; Retailer
service executive; Computer programmer

Application address
Mrs DO Nayna, Nielsen Business Services,
Nielsen House, Headington, Oxford OX3 9RX

Nielsen Business Services is the world's largest marketing research
organisation. In 1983 we expect to have a very limited number of
vacancies for high calibre graduates in the following areas.

Sales/service executives pin-point the most significant aspects of a
product's performance and then present this information to the client.
The ideal applicant will have an analytical approach to problems and have
an interest in selling.

Retailer services executives make personal presentations of research
reports to retail organisations, who allow us use of data collected from
their stores. Applicants should be numerate and effective
communicators.

Computer programmers and systems analysts work in small teams
headed by an experienced project manager, full training is given, so
applicants do not need previous programming experience.

Statisticians are concerned with the application of sampling theory,
estimation techniques, regression modelling and the calculation of
sampling errors. Applicants should have a degree in statistics or an
associated discipline with a strong statistics bias. Courses which include
sampling theory and multivariate analyses are particularly relevant.

Applications
If you feel you have the qualities for one of these areas, please consult
your careers adviser to check available vacancies. We do not welcome
speculative applications.

Norris Gilbert Stern & Co

Activities
Chartered accountancy

Employees
35

Location: UK
London

Opportunities & places
Trainee chartered accountants 3

Application address
RH French, FCA, Norris Gilbert Stern & Co,
Dorland House, 18/20 Regent Street,
London SW1Y 4PY

We are a three partner, 35 staff practice, with a lively, friendly and
informal atmosphere. Our modern offices are within 100 metres of
Piccadilly Circus.

We pride ourselves on giving a very personal and all embracing service
to our clients and from early days with us staff find they are dealing with
clients on such topics as accounts preparation, audits, taxation (both
personal and corporate), financial and tax planning, cash flow
forecasting, management accounting and many other varied aspects of
the profession. The installation of our in-house computer will offer
opportunities for experience in this field.

Salaries are highly competitive and are subject to six-monthly reviews.

We believe that a practice of our size and composition is the ideal
training ground in which to gain experience to enable students to qualify
and progress either within or out of the profession.

Types of graduate required
We invite applications from graduates of *any* academic discipline wishing
to train as chartered accountants.

Training
Our wide variety of clients enables students to combine their examination
syllabus studies with a broad and varied experience of practical work
both in our West End office and at clients' premises. This training is on a

Norris Gilbert Stern & Co, cont
very personal basis, and we encourage our students to take as much responsibility, as quickly as their progress permits.

In preparation for the examinations the firm pays for you to attend a full time course of instruction with a leading firm of specialist accountancy tutors.

Further information
We do not issue a brochure, believing in the personal approach and therefore for the opportunity to discuss personally your potential possibilities. Please write to RH French.

Northern Engineering Industries plc

NEI is a multi-discipline engineering group employing 33,000 people in the United Kingdom and overseas. Three of its member companies appear in their appropriate alphabetical positions in DOG.

They are NEI International Combustion Ltd, NEI Overseas Ltd and NEI Thompson Ltd.

Northern Foods plc

Northern Foods

Activities
Food manufacture and distribution

Employees
16,000

Locations: UK
Midlands; North East; North West; Northern Ireland

Opportunities
Production and technical management; Sales management; Accountancy/financial analysis; Personnel management; Distribution management

Vacancies
7–10

Application address
Phil Ward, Group Management Development Adviser, Northern Foods plc, St Stephen's Square, Hull, North Humberside HU1 3XG

Northern Foods is an expanding and diverse Yorkshire based group of companies, with extensive interests in milk and dairy products, cakes, meat products, biscuits, flour and brewing. In addition to manufacturing its own products under brand names such as Northern Dairies, Pork Farms, Park Cakes and Fox's Biscuits it is also a major supplier of own label products to high street shops, including Marks & Spencer, to whom Northern Foods are the biggest food supplier in the UK. It has a reputation for vigorous growth and consistent profitability, both here and in the USA.

Types of graduate required
Our policy in recruiting graduates is to select people who have a clear idea of their career aims and who know what they have to offer. For production and technical posts a science qualification is necessary; in particular a *food technology* or *food science* qualification is a decided advantage. For vacancies in other functions, degree subject is of less importance than personal skills, though a basic numeracy and an ability to communicate verbally and in writing will be required.

Training and career development
All graduates will be given an introductory six months training programme designed to give them some experience in three different functional areas and in three different parts of the group's activities. At the end of the six months the graduate will be given a specific post with both on the job and off the job training.

Further information
For further details and an application form please write indicating your degree course and career preference to Phil Ward, Group Management Development Adviser.

Northern Ireland Civil Service

Activities
Civil Service

Employees
3,000

Location: UK
Northern Ireland

Opportunities
General: Executive officer; Administrative trainee
Specialist: Economist; Scientific officer; Agriculturalist; Architect; Engineer; Solicitor; Barrister; Computer Programmer; Librarian; Pharmacist; Psychologist; Valuer; Veterinary Officer

Application address
The Graduate Recruitment Officer, Civil Service Commission, Rosepark House, Upper Newtownards Road, Belfast BT4 3NR

The work of the Northern Ireland Civil Service is varied and touches on all aspects of life in Northern Ireland. It is this wide and complex range of work which gives opportunities for an increasing number of graduates in all disciplines to play an important part in the administration of public service. All occupations are open to both men and women.

If you obtain a first or second class honours degree in *any* subject the main opening is in the grade of administration trainee. Administrators are concerned not only with the day to day conduct of government business and the management of branches, but also with policy and planning work including the preparation of material for legislation. A pass degree qualifies for entry to the grade of executive officer II. For most specialist posts graduates should have a good honours degree in a relevant subject; initially they will practise within their own discipline and there are opportunities for advancement within all of them. The more senior posts in many cases will offer increasing administrative and managerial responsibilities.

Types of graduate required

Opportunities exist within the Civil Service for *engineers* (mainly *civil* and *structural*) and *architects*. The work is varied and includes motorways, harbour reconstruction, river control, flood prevention and the design, supervision and construction of a wide range of buildings, including factories, office blocks and schools.

The Department of Agriculture requires graduates in appropriate *research* or *natural science* subjects for research, advisory and teaching work and *veterinary* graduates for field investigation and laboratory research and for the prevention, control and eradication of diseases and the welfare of animals. Graduates in *natural sciences* are also needed in the Department of the Environment which is responsible for the water supply, in the Department of Economic Development, Industrial Science Division and in the Northern Ireland Forensic Science Laboratories.

The Departments of Finance & Personnel and Health & Social Services have openings for those with a degree or an HND in *computer science* or an allied discipline.

Graduates also work in the fields of economics, statistics and social research in the Departments of Finance & Personnel and Agriculture.

Training and salaries

Training is given on the job and staff are encouraged to study for higher qualifications, receiving assistance with fees etc for approved courses. The pension scheme is non-contributory apart from a 1·5% deduction in respect of widows benefit in the case of male officers. Flexible working hours are in operation in most departments.

Further information

For further information please write quoting reference DOG/83 to the Graduate Recruitment Officer.

Norwich Union Insurance Group

Activities
A major composite insurance group transacting insurance of all types

Employees
7,900 UK

Location: UK
East Anglia

Opportunities
Accountancy; Actuarial work; Computer programming; Insurance; Investment analysis

Vacancies
20

Application address
Head Office Recruiting Officer, Norwich Union Insurance Group, Surrey Street, Norwich NR1 3NG

The Norwich Union Insurance Group is one of Britain's major insurance organisations. It is run on a mutual basis, without shareholders, and transacts life, fire, accident, marine and aviation insurance. The group has branches, agencies and associated companies in many countries throughout the world.

Types of graduate required
The group offers progressive careers to graduates of many disciplines. Each summer it usually has vacancies for graduates in either *mathematics* or *economics* with *statistics* to train as actuaries; numerate *economists* to specialise in investment analysis and *accounting, economics* or *business studies* graduates as trainee accountants. There are often openings for *computer scientists* as programmers and *business studies, law* and *economics* graduates to make their careers in a number of insurance fields. For details of specific vacancies in 1983, see further information below.

Training and career development
All graduates receive a comprehensive training designed to build on their academic ability, to equip them as speedily as possible with the knowledge necessary to deal with intricate technical problems and to help them acquire the administrative ability to progress to levels of high responsibility. Graduates will be encouraged to obtain the professional qualifications appropriate to their particular careers. They will, of course, be given day release or equivalent study time and other tangible assistance.

Prospects
To an increasing extent the group's future depends on the quality of its graduate intake and advancement is likely to be rapid for men and women with the requisite energy, ability and personality to deal capably with abstruse problems of all types.

Location
The majority of graduates are based at the group's head office in Norwich, a thriving historic city in the heart of rural East Anglia.

Salaries
Salary scales are usually reviewed each April. Details will be available at the interview.

Pensions, benefits and amenities
The many fringe benefits include non-contributory pension, life insurance and permanent health insurance schemes, house purchase on favourable terms after a qualifying period and excellent sports and social facilities at head office.

Further information
Each year at the beginning of October, the group publishes a booklet giving up to date information as to its vacancies for the year ahead. Students may obtain copies from their appointments officers or from the address given. If Norwich Union representatives are visiting your university or polytechnic during the Easter term, you may care to ask your appointments officer to arrange a preliminary interview at that time. If not, or if you prefer to write direct, please address your letter to the Head Office Recruiting Officer.

Edmund Nuttall Group of Companies

Activities
Heavy civil engineering including tunnelling and maritime works; Building construction

Employees
1,300

Locations: UK
General

Opportunities
Civil engineering; Mechanical engineering; Building engineering

Vacancies
12

Application address
Head of Personnel, Edmund Nuttall Ltd,
22 Grosvenor Gardens, London SW1W 0DR

With over a century of experience of civil engineering of all types including tunnelling, maritime work, dam and bridge construction, Edmund Nuttall Limited has recently expanded its activities and range of work with the acquisition of the Mears organisation. Above average engineering and management ability is required to meet the challenge of the major contracts which are carried out.

Types of graduate required
The main requirement is for *civil engineers*. There are sometimes vacancies for engineers who wish to specialise in mechanical engineering or building.

Locations
Edmund Nuttall Limited, which is the main operating company, have their head office in London, with divisional offices in Swindon and Edinburgh. Initial training is usually given on contract sites which are dispersed throughout the UK, and complete freedom of mobility is therefore essential.

Training
Opportunities for civil engineers to train under agreement are available from time to time and the experience they obtain will enable them to qualify for the professional interview of the Institution of Civil Engineers.

Prospects
The line management within the group is generally by professional engineers, and opportunities are provided for suitable engineers to obtain the type of engineering and management experience which leads to senior site appointments. Our aim where possible is to promote from within the company.

Pannell Kerr Forster

PANNELL
KERR
FORSTER

CHARTERED ACCOUNTANTS

Activities
Chartered accountancy

Employees
1,400

Locations: UK & Ireland
General

Locations: Overseas
Worldwide

Opportunities & places
Student chartered accountants 100

Application address
See main text

We are a leading firm of chartered accountants with a long tradition in the City and in other business centres in the British Isles. We are part of a progressive and expanding international organisation and provide a wide range of professional services to our clients. Our London office has a staff of approximately 400 and our offices situated elsewhere in the British Isles are varied in size and offer a variety of training opportunities.

Types of graduate required
A degree of *any* discipline is acceptable but applicants must be numerate. Those selected are chosen for their potential ability to reach a high standard of professional education and training and commensurate position of responsibility.

Training
Our clients are varied in size and in the nature and complexity of their business interests. The firm aims to keep abreast of current developments in methods of professional and business practice and accordingly students are given a wide range of professional training and experience. In addition to this practical experience gained by on the job work we attach importance to our students' training programme.

Each student will be required to attend our internal training courses on the firm's methods and procedures as well as external courses for the purpose of preparation for the professional examinations. These external courses are provided at the firm's expense by a specialist tutorial

Pannell Kerr Forster, cont

organisation and include periods of private study linked with periods of attendance for full time tuition.

Opportunities and prospects

After qualification, we encourage staff to develop their skills by further training and by availing themselves of a wide range of experience and responsibility. There are good prospects for rapid promotion in many different spheres of professional work and there are frequent opportunities to transfer to overseas offices. As it is our policy to select new partners from within, we hope that many of our students will decide to make their career with us and be involved in developing the firm in the future.

Salaries

Good starting salaries are paid and substantial increases follow throughout the training contract. The level of remuneration will vary from office to office depending on the location.

Further information

Application forms and a detailed brochure about our firm are available from your careers adviser or from any of our offices.

Application should be made direct to the office in which you wish to train:

Lee House, London Wall, London EC2Y 5AL
38 Albyn Place, Aberdeen AB9 1US
22 Great Victoria Street, Belfast BT2 7ER
6A Highfield Road, Edgbaston, Birmingham B15 3ED
94 Whiteladies Road, Bristol BS8 2QS
7 St Andrew's Crescent, Cardiff CF1 3PD
6 Laird Street, Coatbridge, Lanarkshire ML5 3LJ
4 Woodland Road, Darlington, Co Durham, DL3 7PJ
83 Friar Gate, Derby DE1 1EP
4 South Parade, Doncaster DN1 2DY
50 Athol Street, Douglas, Isle of Man
Orchard House, Victoria Square, Droitwich, Worcestershire WR9 8EZ
17 Percy Place, Dublin 4.
38 Melville Street, Edinburgh EH3 7HA
31 St David's Hill, Exeter EX4 4DA
85 Claremont Street, Glasgow G3 7RF
6 South Quay, Great Yarmouth, Norfolk NR30 2QL
31 Princes Street, Ipswich 1P1 1PG
Atlas Chambers, King Street, Leeds LS1 2HS
3 Horsefair Street, Leicester LE1 5BA
3 Eastgate, Lincoln LN2 1QA
52 Mount Pleasant, Liverpool L3 5UN
7 St James's Square, Manchester M2 1LB
23 Devon Square, Newton Abbot TQ12 2HU
Regent House, Clinton Avenue, Nottingham NG5 1AZ
Queensway House, Queen Street, St Helier, Jersey
4 Norfolk Park Road, Sheffield S2 3QE
58 The Terrace, Torquay TQ1 1DE

Partco Europe

Partco Europe forms the wholesaling division of Quinton Hazell plc. Over 150 branches wholesale a complete range of automotive components and garage equipment direct to the motor trade.

For further information of our graduate requirements use our entry under Quinton Hazell plc.

Activities
Insurance

Employees
9,000

Locations: UK
General

Upper age limit
23

Opportunities
Actuarial; clerical and district agency duties;
Computer programming

Application address
Pearl Assurance plc, Personnel Department
(R&T), 252 High Holborn, London WC1V 7EB

Pearl Assurance plc

One of the largest companies in this country transacting all classes of life, fire and accident business, the Pearl was established in 1864 and continues to expand year by year.

In addition to its UK organisation the company has important interests overseas. Assets exceed £1,400 million.

The company's business is transacted at its chief offices in London and Peterborough, with regional offices in some provincial cities and district offices throughout the country.

Opportunities available

Graduates of *any* discipline will be considered for positions in London in all branches of insurance, administration and accounting. Successful applicants are expected to study for the examinations of an approved professional body. There are also limited opportunities outside London.

Graduates with degrees in *mathematics*, *statistics* or allied subjects who intend to study for the examinations of the Institute of Actuaries or the Faculty of Actuaries are required for the London office as actuarial trainees.

Vacancies occasionally arise for graduates with *mathematical* or related degrees as trainee computer programmers at the Peterborough office.

Throughout the UK vacancies exist for graduates of *any* discipline interested in a career with the field staff. Appointments are initially as district agents, with opportunities for promotion to specialist jobs.

In contrast to posts in the chief offices and regional offices which lead to an administrative career, agency appointments provide an interesting and rewarding career in selling and servicing all types of Pearl policies.

Training

All new entrants in the London and Peterborough offices attend induction courses designed to provide basic office training and background to the organisation. In the regional offices, introductory training is on a more individual basis.

Daytime release is granted to study for approved professional examinations. Opportunities also arise to attend internal and external training courses covering specialist and technical subjects. An appraisal system encourages the involvement of each member of staff in their own development.

Graduates recruited as district agents receive initial training on a two-week residential course followed by instruction on location. Frequent courses are held for agents to improve selling skills and extend product knowledge.

Prospects

There are many managerial and executive positions and it is the company's policy to fill these by promotion from within the organisation.

Salaries

For those working at the chief and regional offices, commencing salaries

Peat, Marwick, Mitchell & Co.

Aberdeen (2)
Robin Crawford
13 Bon-Accord Square
Aberdeen AB1 2DJ
Aberdeen (0224) 50206

Birmingham (40)
Alastair Jones
45 Church Street
Birmingham B3 2DL
021-233 1666

Bradford & Keighley (5)
John Ridings
Manor Buildings
2 Manor Row, Bradford
West Yorkshire BD1 4HJ
Bradford (0274) 25546

Bristol (7)
Simon Cannell
30 Queen Charlotte Street
Bristol BS1 4HS
Bristol (0272) 292944

*Edinburgh (3)
Iain McLaren
27 Walker Street
Edinburgh EH3 7HX
031-226 2651

*Glasgow (12)
Douglas Boyd
135 Buchanan Street
Glasgow G1 2JG
041-204 1481

Leeds & York (14)
John Mordy
Airedale House, Albion Street
Leeds LS1 5TY
Leeds (0532) 450331

Leicester (6)
Tim Aspell
21 The Crescent, King Street
Leicester LE1 6RX
Leicester (0533) 547272

Liverpool (5)
Michael Jebson
5th Floor, Richmond House
1 Rumford Place
Liverpool L3 9QY
051-236 5052

London (185)
Bruce Bower
1 Puddle Dock
Blackfriars
London EC4V 3PD
01-236 8000

Maidstone (3)
c/o Michael Carter
1 Puddle Dock
Blackfriars
London EC4V 3PD
01-236 8000

Manchester (14)
Alan Benzie
Century House
7 Tib Lane
Manchester M2 6DS
061-832 4221

Middlesbrough & Darlington (6)
Bob Barker
New Exchange Buildings
Queen's Square
Middlesbrough
Cleveland TS2 1AB
Middlesbrough (0642) 242651

Milton Keynes (8)
Peter Mamelok
Norfolk House
433 Silbury Boulevard
Milton Keynes MK9 2HA
Milton Keynes (0908) 661881

Newcastle (7)
David Wilson
27 Grainger Street
Newcastle upon Tyne NE1 5JT
(0632) 28815

Norwich & Ipswich (6)
Patrick Harris
Holland Court
The Close
Norwich NR1 4DY
Norwich (0603) 20481

Nottingham & Derby (8)
Nigel Tamplin
Kingswood House
Pelham Road
Nottingham NG5 1AP
Nottingham (0602) 625011

Plymouth (4)
Rowland Hogg
Phoenix House
Notte Street, Plymouth
Devon PL1 2RT
Plymouth (0752) 25381

Preston (5)
Douglas McMillan
PO Box 22, Unicentre
Lords Walk, Preston
Lancs PR1 1LQ
Preston (0772) 50821

Reading (6)
Andrew Herald
7–11 Station Road
Reading RG1 1LG
Reading (0734) 584121

Sheffield (8)
Peter Scaman
301 Glossop Road
Sheffield S10 2HN
Sheffield (0742) 21071

Southampton (5)
Crawford McKinlay
Richmond House
College Street
Southampton SO1 1EJ
Southampton (0703) 31465

South Wales (Cardiff, Swansea,
Newport, Chepstow &
Carmarthen) (13)
Richard Parkinson
113 Bute Street
Cardiff CF1 6TD
Cardiff (0222) 32245

South West (Camborne,
St Austell & Truro) (4)
Tony Hill
11 Chapel Street, Camborne
Cornwall TR14 8EH
Camborne (0209) 712251

Stoke, Leek and Congleton (11)
Edward Turner
Churchill House, Regent Road
Stoke-on-Trent, Staffs ST1 3RG
Stoke-on-Trent (0782) 271666

Terms and conditions of em
ployment vary from office to
office.
*The exams for the Institute of
Chartered Accountants of
Scotland are different from those
for the Institute of Chartered
Accountants in England and
Wales; full information about
them can be obtained from our
Glasgow office.

are based on academic qualifications. They are reviewed annually and there is also an annual productivity payment. Additional increases are given for success in approved professional examinations.

District agents receive a basic salary plus commissions, with guaranteed minimum annual earnings. The basic salary is related to the size of the agency.

Pensions and other amenities

For all staff: non-contributory pension scheme; mortgage facilities on favourable terms after qualifying period.

Chief office and regional office staff: progressive salary scale; annual productivity payment; free lunches; excellent social and recreational facilities in London and Peterborough; flexible working hours; interest-free annual season ticket loans after an initial period.

Agency staff: car loans at favourable rates after initial period; additional salary supplement for holidays.

Peat Marwick Mitchell & Co

Peat, Marwick, Mitchell & Co.

Activities
Chartered accountancy

Employees
3,500

Locations: UK
General

Locations: Overseas
Worldwide

Opportunities & places
Trainee chartered accountants 400+

Application address
See display page 266

Peat Marwick Mitchell & Co is a leading firm of chartered accountants with some 300 offices in 87 countries. The UK firm operates from 39 offices with 174 partners and 3,500 staff, making it one of the largest firms in the country.

Around 400 students are recruited annually of whom some 185 are required in the London office. Details of the approximate numbers recruited by other offices are given next to the office on the opposite page. The basic business comprises audit and taxation work; however, partly due to close connections with the City, a substantial part of the practice lies in the field of financial consultancy.

Our larger offices are organised into main departments each of which has its own portfolio of clients and each of which provides those clients with all the professional services which we offer, with the assistance of advisory departments where appropriate. Not only does this arrangement provide clients with the most efficient and economic service, it enables our staff to become involved and gain experience in the wide range of our professional work.

Since no one can be an expert in every type of business, some main departments have responsibilities for such specialist areas as insurance and banking. As a matter of policy, however, no more than 25% of any main department's work is in one particular field.

Our London office consists of 26 main departments each with 30 to 40 members. Every department is headed by a senior manager who is responsible for the members of his department both in their professional work and in counselling them in their training and career decisions. Students quickly get to know the members of their own department both socially and in the course of training.

Peats offers the advantages of working for a large firm in terms of wide ranging experience and responsibility yet maintains the friendly atmosphere and close involvement associated with smaller firms.

Each department is responsible for the audits of about 80 different companies, and students will probably be involved in about a dozen audits each year working in teams of perhaps three or four people.

Most audit work is carried out at the client's premises so students also gain detailed knowledge of many different businesses. Typical assignments last around three to four weeks. Some jobs inevitably involve travel away from home but the extent of out of town work can often be arranged to suit individual preferences. Travel, however, is rarely excessive as we have a national network of offices.

The increasing complexity of the business world has led to the development in London and other larger offices of a number of advisory departments dealing with matters such as corporate and personal taxation, computer auditing, insolvency and technical advice. These provide specialist assistance both as a support service for the main departments and direct to our clients.

Training

Practical work is alternated with in-house instruction and formal tuition so that a steady accumulation of knowledge is achieved. The tuition is provided for us by leading firms of tutors. We put considerable emphasis on the quality of practical experience at each level of personal responsibility, and believe that this is a vital element of your training. It is a particular feature of Peats organisation that, where appropriate, staff report directly to partners in respect of the work which they have undertaken.

Your principal and your manager will regularly discuss your progress with you to ensure that you are gaining a variety of experience in your practical work and are also keeping up to date with preparation for the professional exams.

Students joining us may be confident therefore that they are obtaining thorough professional training which will equip them to pass the Institute's examinations and which will be the foundation for a rewarding career.

Your training does not end the moment you qualify. The very nature of the accountant's job means that you must continue to keep up to date. You will attend a series of post-qualification courses at Redfields, our training centre in Hampshire, covering both professional and personal skills.

Career prospects

Qualifying as a chartered accountant requires a great deal of hard work and the direction your career takes you once you are qualified depends very much on the decisions you make. We would strongly advise you to remain with us for at least two further years after qualification because in the early years after qualifying you will gain greater experience of many kinds of businesses and increasing responsibility within the firm. Furthermore, the Institute requires this period after qualification before you are eligible for a practising certificate.

We hope you decide to stay with Peats in the UK where there are a number of different avenues open to you. You may decide to remain involved in the general side of our practice where the concentration towards medium sized listed companies allows staff considerable responsibility shortly after qualification. Alternatively, you may prefer to specialise in taxation, insolvency or computer auditing. There are also opportunities to transfer within the UK.

If you have a desire to travel there are opportunities for you to work abroad. We have offices in every continent and once you are qualified you may consider applying for either secondment or longer term transfer to one of them. About 60 people from our UK offices go to overseas offices each year and members of our staff have recently been transferred to places as diverse as Bahrain, Brussels, Lusaka, Nassau and Singapore as well as to the United States and Canada.

Further information

If you would like to find out more about training with us, please complete an application form and send it to the staff partner of the office for which you wish to be considered.

Pedigree Petfoods

We are part of the Mars group of companies, an international organisation operating primarily in consumer markets. Principally the group manufactures and markets pet foods, confectionery, rice; but also has interests in related service industries. Although Mars is American based, sales in other countries, such as the UK, Europe, and Australia, exceed those inside the United States. Each major company within the group is complete in itself and enjoys a significant degree of autonomy. We at Pedigree Petfoods are British managed and have built up a reputation for consumer marketing, efficient high speed manufacturing, continuous capital investment and new product development.

Products

As our name suggests, we manufacture a wide range of prepared pet foods for dogs, cats, caged and wild birds. Our brands are nationally distributed and advertised and most are household names: Whiskas, Kitekat, Katkins, and Munchies for cats; Pedigree Chum, Pal, Bounce, Chappie, Mick, Bounce Mince Dinner/Chunk Dinner for dogs; Trill and Swoop for birds. The total prepared pet food market has grown by about 70% in the past 10 years, in volume terms. The further potential can be assessed from the fact that of all pet food consumed, the prepared share still only represents around 50%.

Philosophy . . . and people

Pedigree Petfoods is an unusual example of a highly successful British business. Our expectation and drive for excellence is matched by a distinctive management philosophy based on developing and rewarding people effectively. We aim to attract and retain high calibre people in every type of job by ensuring that pay and benefits are well above average. We reward hard work and success corporately through a bonus scheme linked to company growth and profitability, and individually by promotion purely on merit. We operate a single status working environment, and encourage open communication at every level from the board down. The resulting working atmosphere is informal, business like, enjoyable and remarkably free from red tape.

Opportunities for graduates in sales

Our selling function spearheads the company's marketing strategy. It is a highly efficient national operation, capable of responding rapidly to market needs and opportunities. Prepared pet foods represents one of the largest commodity sectors in the grocery trade, having an excellent history of continued growth. It is a fast moving, competitive market where good product distribution, promotion and display are as important as selling and negotiation techniques.

Our attitude to sales is that it is a business function in its own right, needing to be systematic, flexible and highly professional. The calibre of people in the sales force is high, including a significant number of graduates, and our policy is to promote from within into the fifty or so varied sales management positions in the field.

We aim to recruit a small number of graduates each year to join us straight from university. Our training reputation is first class and we believe we offer excellent opportunities to firstly acquire a sound business awareness, and then develop into a management position. The rate at

Activities
Manufacturing and distributing of prepared pet foods

Employees
2,600

Locations: UK
General

Opportunities & places
Sales 8–10

Upper age limit
28

Application address
The Sales Personnel Manager, Pedigree Petfoods, National Office, Waltham on the Wolds, Melton Mowbray, Leicestershire LE14 4RS

which you develop will depend solely on the ability and potential you show us.

If you are interested in sales opportunities now, consult your careers service for further literature or write to our Sales Personnel Manager.

Other opportunities for graduates

Other divisions within Pedigree Petfoods also offer opportunities for graduates, but ask for previous relevant experience, usually a minimum of two years in industry – so we hope that you will bear us in mind as a very pertinent prospect for your future. We recruit for various disciplines: engineers, scientists, computer staff, accountants and so on. Whichever division you join you will be developing your skills within a dynamic organisation with modern technology and management methods, which provide an innovative and stimulating environment.

Perkins Engines Limited

⊗Perkins engines

Activities
Engineering and manufacture of diesel engines

Employees
7,500

Location: UK
Peterborough

Opportunities
Product design; R&D; Production engineering and production management; Finance; Management systems; Sales and marketing; Personnel

Application address
Employee Development Manager, Perkins Engines Limited, Eastfields, Peterborough, Cambridgeshire PE1 5NA

Perkins Engines, founded in 1932, is today established as one of the world's leading manufacturers of high performance diesel engines with the 30–300 bhp range, supplying power for agricultural equipment, road transport, construction and industrial machinery and marine craft. The company is also a world leader in diesel engine research, much of which is concerned with future fuels technology.

Perkins has subsidiary associate and licencee companies extending through 23 countries and builds some 500,000 diesel engines worldwide; over 200,000 of these are produced at Peterborough alone. In the increasingly competitive climate in which the company now operates, maintaining and improving the highest engineering, manufacturing, service, marketing and customer product support is of vital importance to the continued success of the business.

Graduates in Perkins

If you were to join us, you would be included in a graduate training programme, that would, as far as possible, be tailored to meet both your aspirations and abilities to satisfy the company's longer term requirements. The programme lasts for 12 months, up to 18 months for engineers, and is designed to prepare you for a successful and satisfying career with Perkins. Throughout your training programme, you will be assigned a specific tutor in each department who will guide you, help you to obtain maximum benefit from the programme and give you assistance if needed.

The training programme aims to familiarise you with the aspects of Perkins as an international company. Ultimately this will mean that your career scope is very broad and you will have a range of career opportunities from which to choose. For instance, graduate engineers can join us in design, development or research, production engineering or production management. Graduates from any discipline can join us in management systems, finance, personnel or industrial relations, or sales and marketing. Whichever route you choose you can be sure that somewhere along the line you will be asked to put an engine together and get your hands dirty.

Whatever your career choice, the training and experience you gain will be second to none. Our training programmes are well recognised both inside and outside the company and meet the various Institute and EITB requirements. We will certainly give you every encouragement to qualify for membership of your professional body.

Salaries and benefits

Whilst precise figures cannot be quoted here, we can tell you that our graduate salaries are highly competitive and are the subject of regular reviews. In addition to an attractive salary, we can offer you an excellent newly built sports and social club which is very active, subsidised restaurants, good pension, sick pay and welfare schemes.

Peterborough

Peterborough is a developing town which we think you will find attractive. The Development Corporation has learnt by everyone else's mistakes and provides a range of parks, leisure centres, sailing and wind surfing facilities and so on, in a city in which the new has to blend in with the old and traditional character of a riverside market town. Housing is very competitively priced both in the town and in the country and London is just one hour away on the train.

Further information

We cannot hope to tell you everything that you are interested in here. If you want more information, speak to your careers adviser. If you then would still like more information, write to our Employee Development Manager at the address given.

Pfizer Limited

Activities
Pharmaceuticals, fine chemicals, veterinary and agricultural products

Employees
1,500 UK

Location: UK
South East

Opportunities
Research; Development; Production; Marketing; Sales

Vacancies
25

Application address
The Personnel Manager, Pfizer Limited, Sandwich, Kent

Pfizer Limited in the United Kingdom is part of a rapidly growing international organisation with diversified interests covering the following fields: pharmaceuticals, fine chemicals, veterinary and agricultural products.

The administrative headquarters of Pfizer Limited is at Sandwich in Kent, and has close technical, marketing and research links with other Pfizer organisations in Europe and with the parent company in the United States of America.

Also at Sandwich are extensive central research laboratories, employing some 500 scientists, technicians and ancillary staff. In addition, there is on the 40 acre site a large pharmaceutical and manufacturing plant. A further 70 acres are available for expansion when required.

Pfizer central research at Sandwich recently gained the Queen's Award for Technological Achievement for the discovery of Mansil which combats the chronic tropical debilitating disease, schistosomiasis. More than two million sufferers have already been successfully treated with Mansil.

Types of graduate required

Each year the company seeks a limited number of honours graduates and PhDs in *chemistry*, *biochemistry*, *pharmacology*, *pharmacy* and *microbiology* for work in research. Other opportunities for *science* graduates occur from time to time in sales, production and development departments. The company pays particular attention to developing the managerial, scientific and professional ability of its staff, based upon individual capability and potential.

Applicants

Careers advisory service offices are notified each autumn of probable requirements for the following year by function, and by department, discipline and type of degree. If you are interested you should first check with your careers office.

Phillips & Drew

Activities
Stockbroking

Employees
500

Location: UK
London

Opportunities & places
Stockbroking 6–8

Application address
Staff Partner, Phillips & Drew, Lee House,
London Wall, London EC2Y 5AP

This well known firm of stockbrokers was founded in the latter years of the last century. About 90% of its business comes from institutional clients such as banks, insurance companies and pension funds, both at home and overseas. Of the total number of 500 partners and staff over 20% are graduates or hold a professional qualification. The firm has a reputation for the quality of its research work, and some of its activities are in the nature of financial consultancy. It is not a family firm; all the present partners were recruited from staff and the policy is not to take partners' relations into the firm.

Types of graduate required
Aptitude and enthusiasm for the work are the prime considerations, and while a good degree in *economics* or *mathematics* is clearly relevant, other subjects are acceptable for some of the vacancies, provided that the candidate is thoroughly numerate.

Training and prospects
New staff become members of one of the individual specialist departments and training is largely on the job, under the close supervision of one or more partners. Experience of other departments and external courses of instruction are provided at a suitable time. It is hoped that new staff will be capable of decision taking and responsibility within a year to eighteen months. There is considerable delegation from partners to staff, and there is no lack of challenge and scope to the ambitious, with the prospect of rapid promotion to partnership for the successful.

Location
Modern offices are in the City of London and some administrative departments are at Brentwood, Essex.

Salaries
Starting salaries are competitive. For recruits arriving in the autumn, their first review will be in the April following, with a second review the next October. Thereafter salaries are reviewed annually on 1 April. Conditions of service reflect the best modern standards. There is a profit sharing scheme and a contributory pension scheme. A descriptive booklet and application form can be obtained from the address given.

Pilkington Brothers plc

Activities
Manufacture of glass

Employees
40,000 worldwide
19,000 UK

Location: UK
North West

Pilkington, leader in the field of glass technology, is an international group employing about 40,000 people. The main companies in the UK are the parent company, Pilkington Brothers plc, founded in 1826, Pilkington Flat Glass Limited, Triplex Safety Glass Company Limited, Fibreglass Limited, Chance Pilkington Limited, Pilkington PE Ltd and Barr and Stroud Ltd. Flat glass manufacture accounts for half the group's activities which also include toughened and laminated glass (for motor vehicles, aircraft and other uses), glass fibre (for insulation and reinforcement), optical and ophthalmic glass and advanced electro-optical systems. The float process for making flat glass has been licensed to every major flat glass producer in the world.

Types of graduate required
Vacancies occur for graduates in many disciplines, particularly *science*, and *engineering*. Entry to most jobs is direct, giving early responsibility coupled with on the job training. Where further professional training is

Opportunities
Accountancy; Engineering; Marketing; Systems
analysis; Operations research; Industrial
engineering; R&D; Production; Personnel

Vacancies
40

Application address
Dr A Shuttleworth, Recruitment Manager,
Pilkington Brothers plc, Prescot Road, St
Helens, Merseyside WA10 3TT

required eg personnel, engineering and accountancy, there are training
schemes in which job experience and specific professional requirements
are served. The main research and development laboratories at Lathom,
near Ormskirk are among the world's finest in the glass industry. In
management services, graduates are recruited for industrial engineering,
data processing and operations research.

Training

The group is committed to a policy of internal training, transfer and
development of staff. Great importance is attached to the development of
each individual's potential. This is achieved by the planning of successive
appointments, complemented by courses at the group training centre,
St Helens School of Management and at business schools.

Location

The main locations for newly joined graduates are St Helens, in
Merseyside and Lathom in Lancashire. Opportunities may arise later for
service at other places in the UK or overseas.

Salaries

Graduates' starting salaries are reviewed each year and the general level
made known to university careers advisory officers. Subsequently salaries
are subject to annual review. There is a comprehensive superannuation
fund, assisted insurance, a house purchase scheme and excellent
recreational facilities.

 **PLESSEY**

Activities
Telecommunications, office systems, traffic
controls, radar, avionics, radio
communications, marine electronics,
microelectronics, aerospace, hydraulics and
software consultancy

Employees
33,000 UK

Locations: UK
General

Locations: Overseas
Worldwide

Opportunities
Research and development; Hardware
development; Software development; System
design and development; Quality assurance;
industrial and production engineering; Materials
and production control; Marketing; Purchasing;
Selling; Computer programming

Vacancies
260

Application address
(Ref VNU), The Plessey Company plc, Vicarage
Lane, Ilford, Essex

Plessey

Plessey is an international organisation with a worldwide capability in
telecommunications and office systems, defence electronic systems and
equipment, integrated circuit design/manufacture, optoelectronic and
microwave devices, small high performance microcomputer based
systems and electronic components.

Plessey consists of separate autonomous businesses which are grouped
into management and trading companies, each with its own identity and
product interests. The working environment is within a relatively small,
compact, commercially viable business. The management/trading
companies and some of their products are as follows.

Telecommunications and office systems: public and private
telecommunications systems, making increasing use of real-time
computing techniques and digital electronics; transmission systems using
digital, microprocessor and optical fibre technology; computer controlled
office systems; data capture/entry systems; communications and traffic
control systems.

Electronic systems: military, civil and meteorological radars; sonars
and mine-hunting systems; mobile tactical military radio and other
communications systems including C^3I; real-time computer systems for a
variety of military and civil applications; military and civil air traffic
control systems; environmental instrumentation; navigational aids; naval
fire control systems and flight data recording systems.

Electronic components: computer memory systems and small high
performance computers for a wide range of applications; a wide range of
connectors, materials and interference suppressors.

Solid state: design, development and manufacture of silicon integrated
circuits using Bipolar Process I & III, MOS, CMOS and MICROCELL
technology, surface acoustic wave devices, microwave, infra-red and
optoelectronic components and subsystems.

Plessey Research, Caswell: the research laboratory of Plessey. Broad
areas of pure and applied research covering application of solid state

Plessey, cont

physics, electronics, chemistry research to a variety of electronic materials, devices and microelectronics subsystems.

Aerospace: design, development and manufacture of components and systems for the aerospace industry.

Types of graduate required

This year our opportunities in research, design and development will be largely for graduates in *electronics, computer sciences* and related disciplines. There will be some other technological posts for which other science based degrees will be appropriate and in addition a number of posts in other aspects of the organisation's work for which any discipline might be suitable.

Training

A flexible training programme is devised for each graduate. It often includes specific projects carried out under the guidance of experienced managers. Where applicable, the requirements of relevant professional institutions are met. Initial training usually takes between one and eighteen months. Science and technology graduates are given training which provides a vital link between academic studies and industry. Training for careers in production, commerce and administration lasts about eighteen months and gives planned practical experience, supplemented by short internal and external courses on management subjects and by private study.

Salaries and career prospects

The salaries, benefits and career opportunities we offer, taken together, are undoubtedly among the best available in the electronics field. We are above all an innovative company and it is as important to us to recognise and encourage talent as it is to the individual. Our programme of appraisal and counselling ensures that each individual's career progression is directly related to ability.

Applications

Please go first to your careers service, which has copies of our brochure, application form and list of current vacancies, or write to the Graduate Resourcing Manager.

PMA Consultants Ltd

PMA is a computer systems and software company whose work covers a wide range of commercial and technical applications.

Types of graduate required

Computer science graduates with significant practical industrial experience are recruited and trained as programmers. They will join small teams working on projects under the direct supervision of experienced programmers.

Training and career development

Initially promotion will be within programming grades but with experience there are prospects of promotion to systems analysis and design and project leadership.

Salaries

Salaries and progress are reviewed annually and increases awarded

Activities
Investigation, analysis, design, development and implementation of computer systems

Employees
34

Location: UK
South East

Opportunities & places
Trainee programmers 4

Application address
PMA Consultants Ltd, Rhodaus House, Victoria
Road, Horley, Surrey RH6 7AS

Police Service in England and Wales

A graduate is aware of the problems of changing society: as a police
officer you become involved in actually doing something for the world we
live in.

Activities
Police service

Employees
20,000

Locations: UK
England; Wales; N Ireland

Opportunities
Entry at police constable level for all parts of the
police service

Vacancies
25 approx under graduate entry scheme, no
limit under normal entry

Upper age limit
30, but extended to 32 in special
circumstances, for graduate entry scheme and
at the chief officers discretion for normal entry

Application address
Superintendent JM Adams BA, (Ref DOG/1),
The Police Graduate Liaison Officer (Police),
Room 556, Home Office, 50 Queen Anne's
Gate, London SW1H 9AT

Activities
Although the objectives of the police service do not change, its
organisation and methods are being continually re-assessed and
developed. The reason is self-evident. Today our society is changing
faster than ever before. To keep up to date police methods and
techniques are becoming more and more sophisticated. This in turn has
led to the urgent need for men and women of intelligence, education and
character, reflected in recruitment and promotion policies designed to
make the service more attractive to potential future leaders.

In this expanding service, accelerated promotion to inspector may
come in the sixth year of service. Thereafter, there are over 4,600 posts
above the rank of inspector including more than 260 at chief constable,
assistant chief constable and equivalent level. The police service fills
senior posts exclusively from its own ranks. All promotion is on merit
and men and women with good education and ability can look forward to
rapid advancement.

The avenue for accelerated promotion to inspector is the one-year
special course at the Police Staff College at Bramshill in Hampshire.
Constables who do exceptionally well in the examination for promotion to
sergeant and satisfy a very searching and thorough extended interview
procedure are selected to attend this course in the temporary rank of
sergeant. On successful completion of the course they are confirmed in
the rank, and after a further year's satisfactory service are automatically
promoted to inspector.

The police graduate entry scheme
Graduates and final year students in *any* discipline may apply for entry
under the graduate entry scheme. Under this scheme candidates may test
themselves against the selection procedures for the special course before
they commit themselves to a police career.

Those who are successful know in advance, for example, that they are
guaranteed a place on the special course provided that they satisfactorily
complete the two years' probationary training and pass the promotion
examination to sergeant at the first attempt. And, of course, those who
are not successful but still join as ordinary entrants will retain the
opportunity of being considered again for a place on the special course
after passing the same promotion examination.

An applicant must be a British subject, commonwealth citizen or
citizen of the Republic of Ireland, have good health, physique and
eyesight (most forces, including the Metropolitan Police, will consider
applicants who wear glasses or contact lenses). The minimum height for
men is normally 172 cms and women 162 cms.

Familiarisation attachments
People who are seriously considering a career in the police service and
who are in their final year of their full time degree course can take
advantage of a full day familiarisation course into police work which

includes actual patrol with police officers. These courses are staged during the first week in January and are designed to let the students se from the ground what police work is all about. There will normally be choice of attending a centre from one of several force areas throughou the country.

Training

It must be emphasised that the police service has only single tier entry Everyone including the graduate entrant has to complete two vital yea as a constable gaining practical police experience which will form the foundation of their police career. Much of this time will also be spent training and in a series of attachments to specialist departments such a CID, patrol cars, administration and traffic. In the second year there be longer tours of practical duty followed by a further course.

Training continues throughout a police officer's career, both at a lo level and on further command courses at the Police Staff College.

Salaries

New entrants receive at least £5,610 (£6,267 in London) if under 22 or appointment; £6,699 (£7,356 in London) if over 22 on appointment. I addition, free accommodation is provided or a realistic rent allowance paid in lieu.

Basic starting salaries for senior officers range from at least £9,744 t minimum for an inspector (£10,926 in London) to £12,309 (£13,494 i London), the maximum for a chief inspector.

The salaries for superintendents and chief superintendents range fr £15,276 to £18,003 in the provinces and from £16,959 to £19,008 in London. (In addition officers serving in London receive a non-pensionable allowance of £1,011 per annum.)

These rates will be reviewed September 1982.

Pensions

After 25 years' service an officer may retire on a pension payable at 50 years of age, normally equal to half pensionable pay received during th last year of service. After 30 years the pension is two thirds of pensiona pay.

Further information

To obtain more information, including details of familiarisation cours or to arrange an informal interview about a police career get in touch v the chief constable of the force in which you are interested or the Commissioner of Police if you wish to serve in London or write to Superintendent JM Adams at the address given.

The Post Office

The Post Office

Activities
Postal services

Employees 172,000+

Locations: UK
General

Opportunities
General management; Finance; Personnel; Marketing; Engineering; Research and development; Engineering management; Computing; Statistics

The Post Office is one of the UK's largest businesses and one of the biggest employers. Its 23,000 counters provide postal, banking, philatelic, licensing, social benefits and other facilities to the public. Every day the Royal Mail handles more than 35 million letters and parcels to 22 million addresses and, in the past year, we invested over £15 million in new technology and new services to help stay on top of today's job and meet the opportunities of the future. And we aim to ke it that way. Which is why we invest so heavily in training graduates fo the careers of the future.

The Post Office is an international pace-setter in the field of postal technology, such as electronic mail and coding systems, having more

Application address
The Post Office Management Assessment
Centre, Freepost, Coton House, Rugby
CV23 0BR

computer installations than any other UK business. So it is hardly surprising that we provide expert advice and training to overseas postal administrations.

Graduate opportunities
Engineering and engineering management, general management, finance, management services (including business planning, OR statistics and computing), marketing, operations, personnel.

Degree disciplines
There are a wide range of opportunities for all technical and non-technical disciplines.

Types of graduate required
We need men and women who have their eyes firmly fixed on the future. People with the ability to question, find answers and provide new and practical ways of making sure that, in the years to come, we continue to offer our customers the services they need, in every sphere and on every level.

Prospects
Ability is the key to promotion, which can lead to the most senior positions in Post Office management.

Engineering opportunities
Graduates in appropriate subjects such as *electrical, electronic* or *mechanical engineering, mathematics, physics, applied physics* and *computer science* are recruited mainly for vacancies in central London. Work will include involvement in the design and development of computer technology, phosphor technology, electronic technology, etc.

We have already implemented facsimile transmissions and highly advanced hardware and software development. We don't intend to stop there. The scope of our opportunities is extremely varied, demanding a high order of practical engineering skills and offering all kinds of technical challenges with very rewarding results.

Management opportunities
We recruit top flight graduates from *any* academic discipline for management positions in finance, management services, marketing, personnel and the administration and operation of the Post Office mechanisation programme. There are also a few opportunities for graduates with experience in the computer programming and systems analyst fields.

There are also a few opportunities for specialists with degrees in *economics, statistics, mathematics*, and *operational research*. Graduates will work either in central London, or one of our regional headquarters, or in head post offices throughout the UK.

Further training and study
Obviously, the length and depth of training will depend upon work area and background. Generally, however, the Post Office encourages its people to gain professional qualifications. Training is carried out in-house, although there are opportunities for people to gain professional qualifications and the Post Office will support appropriate studies, including postgraduate, where necessary.

Salaries and conditions
Starting salaries, which are excellent, will vary according to age and the type of appointment. There are allowances for working in London.

Conditions of employment are highly competitive, and career

prospects are excellent, leading to some of the most senior jobs in Post Office management.

To find out more about current vacancies with the Post Office, contact your university careers office or write to the address given.

Powell Duffryn Systems Ltd

Powell Duffryn Systems is a member company of Powell Duffryn plc, a major British industrial group employing more than 10,000 people in

Salaries

Salaries are competitive and are reviewed annually, with increases according to merit.

Prospects

Press Computer Systems is part of the Midland News Association Ltd, arguably the country's most successful newspaper publishing group. Established members of staff qualify for the group's own pension scheme and, after a proper term of service, for inclusion in an employee shares participation plan.

You will work as a member of a small project team based at Wolverhampton, but will be required from time to time to work short stints at customers' sites. Elevation to project leadership is open to any person who has acquired the requisite level of skill and experience and who has displayed qualities of dedication and leadership.

The Prison Service

Penal institutions do not exist in isolation. They form part of our society; and it is the task of the Prison Service under the law to hold those committed to custody and to provide conditions for their detention which society currently finds acceptable. Moreover, in dealing with convicted offenders the service has an obligation to do all that may be possible during their time in custody to encourage and assist them to lead a good and useful life.

This applies to all convicted prisoners. A court may properly pass a custodial sentence on one offender to act as a general deterrent to the commission of crime, and on another because the court believes he is in need of training which may be given to him in custody. The duty of the Prison Service in respect of each of them remains unaffected.

Assistant governors

Assistant governors first appeared in the Prison Service under their present title after the last war. Prior to this they had been introduced during the 1930s on the young offender side of the service as housemasters in borstals. After the war borstal housemasters were re-titled assistant governors and integrated into the main managerial structure of the Prison Service.

New developments

During the 1950s and especially the late 1960s assistant governors have been deployed increasingly on the adult offender side of the service, working in prisons as well as continuing to work with young offenders in borstals. 1983 will see the introduction of a new youth custody service.

Types of graduate required

Each year the Civil Service Commission invites applications from graduates aged between 21 and 35* to fill vacancies for assistant governors in the Prison Service. Candidates must possess organising ability associated with a capacity for leadership and a lively interest in social problems. They must be able to organise the efforts of staff involved in handling these problems in a custodial setting and to form good working relationships with professional colleagues. When it is necessary they must be capable of exercising authority firmly and with sensitivity to all the factors present in a given situation.

*(Successful candidates under the age of 24 will be required to serve as prison officers for about a year before taking up appointment and training as assistant governors).

Training and career development

The assistant governor's work derives, as the title implies, from that of the governor. It is essentially a managerial task. The form of the work varies according to the functions of the establishment and the particular role devised for the assistant governor at each establishment. Nevertheless there are elements common to the task wherever performed. A clear understanding of the context in which the prison service works is essential. So too is a sound theoretical background related to the treatment of delinquency and its application to everyday life. A good deal of time has to be devoted to the management of staff and other resources. In essence, assistant governors need to apply skills to the management of the treatment process in whatever form is appropriate. They may be required to work in a variety of types of establishment, ranging from very secure prisons for recidivist adults to open borstals for young offenders. The Prison Service caters for a predominantly male population, but so far as assistant governors are concerned they may be asked to serve in establishments catering for the opposite sex or in those holding both male and female offenders. Successful candidates who are appointed to be assistant governors are on two years probation. During that period training will be given partly in short residential courses at the Prison Service College in Wakefield and partly in supervised training programmes at penal establishments. For those who have had no previous experience of working as a prison officer there will be an attachment to a local prison, following a course of instruction at the Officers' Training School, Wakefield, to gain some experience of this role under supervision. The theoretical course at the Prison Service College will be closely linked to the work of an assistant governor in the establishment to which he or she has been posted. Areas covered will include management, technical and security aspects of the job as well as an understanding of human behaviour, group processes and the theory and practice of social casework. Members of the assistant governor and governor grades are given further training at appropriate stages of their careers. There are also opportunities for attending suitable courses arranged by universities and colleges. In addition there are governors working in HQ who act as career development officers for assistant governors.

Prospects

There are prospects of promotion to higher governor grades in due course. Promotion is based on ability and seniority. In general, assistant governors are considered for promotion after about six years. Promotion is by interview and is competitive. After two years as assistant governor trainee, the promotion path is as follows – assistant governor, governor class IV, class III, class II, class I. There are opportunities at governor class IV level and above for experience not only in penal establishments but also at HQ, regional offices and at the three Prison Service training establishments. Some 70 members of the governor grades are employed in these posts. There are also opportunities for promotion beyond the governor grade. There are at present assistant controllers (equivalent to assistant secretary level in the wider Civil Service – four of whom are regional directors and some members of the Prisons Board (assistant under-secretary level) who have had experience as governors.

Locations

Assistant governors may be required to work anywhere in England, Scotland or Wales, although consideration is given to geographical preferences.

Overseas
Occasionally there are opportunities for secondments overseas but these opportunities are now much less frequent than in former years.

Salaries
Assistant governor trainee, £8,101 at 25 and under rising to £10,207
Assistant governor, £8,494 rising to £10,605
Governor class IV £10,736 rising to £12,254
Governor class III £12,753 rising to £15,266
Governor class II £15,723 rising to £18,507
Governor class I £20,634

Pensions, benefits and amenities
There are generous leave and sick leave terms and a pension which is non-contributory. In addition governor grades are provided with free quarters or a rent allowance in lieu.

Selection procedure
Suitable applicants will be invited to attend a two day extended interview procedure run by the Civil Service Commission.

Further information
For further information apply to the *Recruitment Officer, (HPL), R610, (ABP), Home Office, Freepost, London SW1V 1PU* or
Scotland: The Recruitment Officer, Scottish Home and Health Department, Prisons Division, St Margarets House, London Road, Edinburgh EH8 7TQ

Psychologists
In the Prison Service psychologists are becoming increasingly involved in all the aspects of an organisation where people deal with people. The type of institution influences the types of work that the psychologists undertake as examples below will indicate.

Types of graduate required
Candidates must have one of the following qualifications:
Basic grade psychologist
A degree with first or second class honours in *psychology* or in which psychology was taken as a main subject. A higher degree in psychology, a higher degree in education provided that psychology was taken as a main subject, a postgraduate diploma in psychology which requires at least two years full time study, associate membership of the British Psychological Society. A candidate may be interviewed before the result of his examination is known, but will not be declared successful unless he obtains the prescribed qualification.
Senior psychologists
Candidates must hold one of the qualifications as above (or be fellows of the BPS) and should normally have at least four years relevant experience, but well qualified candidates who have three years especially relevant experience may be considered.
  Mature students are welcome to apply, particularly if they have related experience in other fields.

Training and career development
The first two years of a basic grade psychologist's service is looked upon as a training period. During this time, he or she works under close supervision of an experienced psychologist in an institution and is offered experience in testing techniques, interviewing, report writing and problems of research design and methodology. Attachments to other departments of the institution and to outside agencies are arranged.
  During the first two years training units are taken by the new

psychologist. These units are similar to the open university format. They are tutored by prison psychologists skilled in the relevant area of study.

Once the probation year is completed there are available both internal and external courses. Applications for such courses are assessed according to job requirements.

Prospects

For those who join as a basic grade psychologist there are good prospects of promotion to senior psychologist grade within about four years, or slightly earlier for those with previous relevant experience. Promotion to the next grade, principal psychologist, in charge of one of the larger psychology units, depends upon vacancies.

Locations

The prison department is the principal employer of psychologists in the Home Office. About 80 psychologists of basic, senior and principal grades are in service at the present time. There are also about 30 psychological assistants. Their work is organised by the director of psychological services who is supported at headquarters by three principal psychologists who co-ordinate the work.

In borstals, the psychologists may do some diagnostic work in association with the medical services, and provide treatment and training for individuals or groups of inmates in the form of counselling, behaviour therapy, and social skills training. Increasingly their work involves staff training, research, and advice to the governors and senior management.

In remand establishments, psychologists are involved in research in such areas as bail and the use made of reports to courts, job evaluations and test validation, as well as psychological testing and assessment, and work with the probation service.

In dispersal prisons, the overall task of the psychology unit is to contribute to the design, development and evaluation of the regime. Psychologists are involved in the design and running of staff training programmes. They sometimes help the security of the prison, with the display and use of security and control information systems that are becoming increasingly sophisticated. They will advise the governor on maintaining and improving communication within the prison and assist him with organisational changes and developments. They will also be involved in the assessment and training of inmates.

In an industrial prison, run as much like an ordinary factory as possible, the psychologists are evaluating the effect of the regime on prisoners, in particular its impact on rehabilitation.

In the psychiatric treatment prison psychologists are directly involved with inmates at individual, group, and community levels, and include behaviour therapy and group work among their techniques. They also contribute to the planning of the regime as a whole, with the aim of enhancing social and personal development among the inmates. Research and evaluation are an important part of their work.

In prisons for short term recidivists psychologists provide an information and research service to management, investigating areas such as the effectiveness of liaison between the prison and outside agencies for men about to be discharged. They run therapeutic groups and give training in social skills. The psychology unit also undertakes a regular testing programme and provides assessments of inmates for diagnosis, treatment or research.

Staff training is directed at developing a greater understanding of the individual, of the group behaviour of inmates, and of the psychological characteristics of penal institutions. Advice may be given on the general handling of inmates of specific problems arising, for instance, from the behaviour of a very aggressive individual. This kind of advice occurs in most institutions within the context of the training programme. Psychologists are also on the staff of the Prison Service College and Officers' Training Schools, where they take part in general training courses run for new staff, in in-service training sessions, and help in the development of courses. They cover topics such as human growth and development, psychology of delinquency, and management problems presented by the behaviour of inmates.

Salaries
Salary scales:
Psychologists £5,523 to £7,934
Senior psychologist £8,759 to £10,851
Principal psychologist £11,912 to £15,948
Inner London weighting is £1,087 pa. Outer London weighting is £454 pa. In addition, for those working in establishments an environmental allowance of £374 pa is paid.

Increments are normally granted annually.

Entry will normally be at the minimum of the appropriate scale, but the Civil Service department on the recommendation of the selection board may authorise a higher starting salary, within the limits of the particular scale, for a candidate with additional qualifications or experience considered to be of special value.

Any period of experience approved for this purpose will be deducted from the two years period of satisfactory service which qualifies psychologists for a special increase granted in addition to the normal increment. This will also apply if the successful candidate is already an unestablished civil servant. In the case of an already established civil servant, starting pay will be according to the salary scale mentioned above.

Psychologists normally work a five day week of 41 hours in London, and 42 hours elsewhere, including lunch intervals in both cases.

Probation: The successful candiates will be on probation for at least one year from the day of appointment.

Pension, benefits and amenities
There are generous leave and sick leave terms and a pension which is non-contributory.

Selection procedure
Psychologists for the Prison Service are recruited through open competitions held in the spring and autumn. All candidates who are invited to the selection board are required to visit a prison for a preliminary interview with a senior psychologist. At this informal interview the candidate will be told about the type of work and training newly joined psychologists are expected to undertake.

The vacancies are advertised in the British Psychological Society Bulletin and in the national press.

Candidates must be at least 20 years of age on the advertised closing date for appointment as psychologists and should normally be at least 26 years of age on that date for appointment as senior psychologist, but a candidate under 26 years of age with exceptional qualifications or experience may be considered for appointment as senior psychologist.

Nationality: Candidates are eligible, and this includes citizens of the Commonwealth and of the Irish Republic, if they were at birth a British subject and at least one of their parents is, or was at death, a British subject.

Further information
For further information apply to the *Recruitment Officer, R610 (ABP) Home Office, Freepost, London, SW1V 1PU*

Providence Capitol Life Assurance Company Limited

Activities
Life assurance, pension scheme, investment and savings plan administration

Employees
135 head office

Locations: UK
Head office: London
Branches: General

Opportunities
Actuarial, finance, life and pensions administration; Marketing; Computing

Application address
The Personnel Manager, Providence Capitol Life Assurance Ltd, Providence House, 30 Uxbridge Road, Shepherds Bush, London W12 8PG

Providence Capitol is a young, progressive company with ambitious plans for continued expansion. We need to recruit ambitious people, keen to accept early responsibilities, to help us meet our objectives.

Since our relaunch is September 1978 under the ownership of Gulf and Western, we have sustained an almost unprecedented rate of growth. We already have 22 branch offices throughout the country, and we plan to open more. Our assets exceed £70 million and those of our parent company exceed £2,000 million.

Types of graduate required

We need ambitious graduates in *maths* or allied subjects who intend to study for the examinations of the Institute of Actuaries. There are also openings in our finance, life and pensions administrations, marketing and computer departments. Recruits are encouraged to study for the examinations of the Chartered Insurance Institute, the Pensions Management Institute, or take an equivalent accountancy qualification.

Training

Actuarial students' training is mainly by a broad range of planned experience. Each student is supervised by one of our qualified actuaries, who also provides professional help and guidance.

Trainees will have paid study leave for examinations of the appropriate institutions. We also pay tuition and examination fees.

Salaries and benefits

Starting salaries are very competitive and both merit and responsibility are rewarded. Annual leave is four weeks, and we offer contributory life assurance and pension schemes. There is also a system of flexible working hours at the Shepherds Bush office.

Provident Life Association of London Ltd

Established 1877

Activities
Life assurance and pensions

Employees
500 approx

Location: UK
London

Opportunities
Actuarial work; Sales

Application address
Mr FW Lee, Staff Manager, Provident Life Association of London Ltd, 266 Bishopgate, London EC2M 4QP Ref GB/DOG

Provident Life is an established and progressive life assurance company which has provided life assurance, pensions and mortgages for over 100 years.

We are situated in modern offices close to public transport facilities in the City of London and the company now forms part of the worldwide Winterthur Swiss Insurance Group.

Types of graduate required

The main openings for graduates at Provident Life are for *maths* graduates or allied disciplines, as actuarial students. There are occasionally vacancies in sales or general insurance administration for *any* graduates.

Actuarial trainees are given every encouragement including study leave, to take the examinations of the Institute of Actuaries. The company's practice is to promote from within its existing staff wherever possible.

Salary and benefits

Provident Life offers a good commencing salary along with several excellent fringe benefits, these include: house purchase scheme, non-contributory pension scheme, free lunches, flexible working hours and a Christmas bonus.

Please write giving personal details with an outline of your career plans to the Staff Manager (ref GB/DOG).

The Prudential Assurance Company Limited

Prudential

Activities
All types of insurance and related activities

Employees
25,000 approx UK and overseas

Location: UK
London

Opportunities
Accountancy; Actuarial; Data processing; Estate management; Insurance; Investment analysis; Legal specialists; Personnel management; Pensions management

Vacancies
30 approx

Application address
Stephen LeCras, Personnel Division (PSRJE), Prudential Assurance Company Limited, 142 Holborn Bars, London EC1N 2NH

The Prudential is one of the most powerful forces in the insurance, investment and money markets. Indeed, our performance directly influences the nation's invisible earnings: one of the strongest roots of our economy.

This short entry can be little more than a superficial glance at our activities. However, we hope it will be sufficient to whet your appetite and to prove that the Prudential is committed to growth and to giving graduates the scope and stimulation their intellects demand.

That's not a platitude, it's a promise. In every sector of our business operations, insurance underwriting and claims, investment analysis, law, accountancy, property management, architecture, personnel and pensions, we need people with the potential for top management. For today's graduates are destined to be tomorrow's decision makers, which is why we not only insist on a good degree but also the management temperament, flair, acumen and motivation: qualities which cannot be measured by academic achievement alone.

If you have both the personal qualities and the paper qualifications, we can guarantee one of the most intensive professional training programmes. A training that will develop your talents on some of the most advanced business and management information systems in the country.

Think it over as we tell you something about one of the largest life assurance and general insurance companies in the country. The range of opportunities are described below.

General insurance
Our main business centres around fire and accident cover, motor and personal insurance.

Graduates in a *business* related discipline can move into this sector and be sure of a fascinating and mentally stretching challenge. The work will take you into the legal complexities of public and private liability, the drafting of policies involving a wide range of risks and the negotiation of many different types of claim.

Other areas of our business demand more specific degrees.

Actuaries
Here you will develop the critical skills of assessing and quantifying risks and liabilities. Graduates with special aptitude can go on to work in a variety of actuarial departments both in the UK and overseas.

Graduates with a *mathematically* based degree can apply to become trainee actuaries and will need to take the Institute of Actuaries examinations.

Investment analysts
We are the biggest institutional investor in the country with worldwide funds of thousands of millions of pounds – invested in equities, fixed interest securities as well as land and property. If you have a genuine interest in finance and economics you'll enjoy the intellectual challenge of dealing with these complex investment problems.

The Prudential Assurance Company Limited, cont

Overseas underwriters

This branch of our business appeals particularly to *modern language* graduates. It administers general insurance business written overseas by different organisations, especially in the area of fire and accident insurance. This office also controls a large amount of overseas business placed in the London insurance market by brokers.

Once your initial training is backed by sound practical experience and some success in CII exams, there may well be opportunities to work abroad.

Accountants

The most relevant disciplines are *economics, law, mathematics* and *accounting*. You'll be involved in all aspects of the company's finance, from the general business of insurance and assurance to property and stock exchange investment programmes.

We'll also be looking to you to review accounting procedures where necessary and often to create new ones.

Passing the examinations of the Association of Certified Accountants should be an early goal.

Data processing

As an international, progressive company, we rely heavily upon the most advanced business information systems. *Mathematics* and *science* graduates now have the chance to make a name for themselves in data processing by continuously researching and updating our computer complex in pace with the Prudential's ever changing needs.

Estate management

If you have a degree in *estate management* our growing portfolio of freehold and leasehold properties, currently valued at over one thousand million pounds, will certainly put the professional edge on your academic experience.

You'll be expected to become an associate of the Royal Institute of Chartered Surveyors.

Pensions management

The intricacies of administering pension schemes for many large companies in the country pose fascinating challenges to today's graduates. Vast sums of money are involved and the livelihoods of literally millions of people are directly and indirectly affected by the decisions taken in this department. With much of the routine work now handled by computers, you're free to apply your mind to the intellectually taxing side of this business.

Personnel management

With a UK staff of over 20,000 there will be opportunities to gain a wide ranging experience of every aspect of personnel management including recruitment, job evaluation, appraisal, industrial/employee relations and manpower planning.

Other opportunities include research into future employment policies and organisation structures.

One of your early objectives must be to pass the examinations of the Institute of Personnel Management.

Salaries

Initially salaries are related to class of degree. However, future salary increases or promotion in the Prudential are wholly dependant on performance.

Benefits

These are substantial and include low interest mortgage facilities, a season ticket loan scheme, a non-contributory pension scheme, a subsidised staff restaurant, a wide range of sports and social activities, discounts on all personal insurances, a Christmas bonus and annual productivity bonus and flexible working hours.

Training
Training consists of: induction courses, in-house specialist courses, career development courses, external technician courses and day release for professional examinations.

Quantel Limited

Opportunities
Design and development, test engineers

Vacancies 4

Employees 90

Application address
Group Personnel Officer, Quantel Limited, West Mills, Newbury, Berkshire RG14 5AG
Tel: 0635 48222 ext 205

Quantel Limited is part of the Micro Consultants Group and is a true leader in the field of digital video products for television broadcasting worldwide, marketing an unsurpassed range of superior quality equipment. Their modern unit is situated in Newbury, Berkshire, just off the M4, in a pleasant rural area.

Further information
For more details on Quantel see the entry for Micro Consultants.

Quinton Hazell plc

Activities
International manufacturer, wholesaler and retailer of automotive components

Employees
7,000

Locations: UK
Manufacturing: Midlands and North West
Wholesale and retail: General

Locations: Overseas
Worldwide

Opportunities
Manufacturing: design, development and production engineering; general management training; Marketing: general management training; Wholesale and retail: general management training; Management services: trainee systems analysis; programming

Vacancies
10

Application address
Employee Relations Officer, Quinton Hazell plc, Hazell House, Leamington Spa, Warwickshire CV32 6RF

Quinton Hazell plc is one of Europe's largest manufacturers, wholesalers and retailers of replacement automotive components. Founded in 1946 we are now an international company employing over 7,000 people worldwide.

Types of graduate required
Graduates in *mechanical* or *production engineering* and *any* discipline for marketing management for our manufacturing division. Graduates with a practical *business* bias for Partco Europe, our wholesale division and QH Standard, our specialist retail division. *Any* numerate discipline for positions in our management services function.

In all cases we look for well developed personal skills of communication and self motivation in addition to solid academic achievement. We would be particularly interested in *engineering* graduates with a practical bias in their course of studies.

Training and career development
All our graduates follow a project biased training programme, providing total involvement and early responsibility. Engineering training will be specifically designed over two years to prepare graduates for qualification as chartered engineers. Initial appointments would be in production or in engineering.

In management services, initial projects lasting for 26 weeks lead to appointment as trainee systems analysts or programmers. Whilst for other management trainees, project work generally lasts up to 36 weeks before first appointment.

In Partco Europe and QH Standard, appointments will be to field management positions, or in some cases to head office specialist roles.

Prospects
Really its all up to you, we promote from within whenever possible and your prospects will depend on your own efforts. Demonstrate your potential for career development within this progressive environment and the rewards will be impressive.

Quinton Hazell plc, cont

Location

Our major manufacturing sites are at Colwyn Bay, Lytham St Annes and Redditch, with major computerised distribution centres at Nuneaton and Warton. Our management services function is based at a brand new data centre in Balsall Common, Warwickshire, whilst QH Standard and Partco Europe between them have 260 branches throughout the UK. Mobility is essential particularly in the early part of your career.

Salaries

Salaries and other terms and conditions of employment are fully competitive. Full details will be supplied at interview.

Further information

If your careers service does not have copies of our *Graduate Management Training Scheme* booklet and application forms, then please write to the Employee Relations Officer.

Racal Electronics plc

The Racal Electronics Group, which now includes the Racal–Decca group of companies, has a dominant worldwide position in the electronics industry. Presently radio communications amounts to 31%, data communications 27% and capital goods 28% of the group's total business.

The company

Racal is acknowledged to be one of the most successful companies in the UK. Since its formation in 1950, it has achieved an enviable and continuous record of sustained growth. The Racal success formula is extremely simple: to create compact autonomous companies, each with the specialised knowledge and the ability to respond rapidly to the customers requirements, and allow each employee to feel and be actively engaged in the team activity.

Growth is further stimulated by selective acquisition of complementary high technology companies which are merged into the group whilst retaining full responsibility for their own financial accountability. A large number of such companies have been acquired and they operate the Racal philosophy of recognising technological advancements, applying them to a product requirement and then manufacturing and marketing at the right price. The strength of Racal lies not only in the highly skilled and powerful engineering team which exploits the latest technologies, but also in the well experienced marketing team which covers the world market, demonstrating the quality and efficiency of the group products, and all are ably supported by the finest back-up services.

International organisation

Today Racal is a truly international organisation with a large number of locations in all parts of the world. Gross sales for the year ending 31 March 1982 were over £650 million, 70% of which went to countries outside of the UK. In other words each Racal Employee contributes no less than £24,000 to the export drive. Even greater achievements are anticipated for 1983. Approximately 30% of Racal's staff are permanently based overseas, serving the day to day needs of clients. Many others will be travelling in foreign parts from time to time to discuss directly with customers their requirements.

To date, companies in the Racal Group have been awarded a total of 24 Queen's Awards to Industry for Technological and Export Achievement.

The Electronics Group

1982

Activities
Includes radio and data communications, radar systems, navigation equipment, EW systems, micro-electronics, security systems and ATE

Employees
19,000

Locations: UK
London; Home Counties and South East; South West; Scotland

Opportunities
Accountancy; Commercial/contract officers; Customer training engineers; Design and development engineers (electronic, mechanical and software); Field operations/overseas installation engineers; Marketing engineers; Post-design service engineers; Production engineers/management; Programmers (commercial); Quality assurance engineers; Sales engineers; System engineers; Test engineers

Vacancies
200

Application address
Mr LA Nixon, Training and Education Manager, Racal Group Services Ltd, Western Road, Bracknell, Berkshire RG12 1RG

Products of the Racal Group

Acoustics, antennas, automatic test equipment, avionics, communications and data security, CAD/CAM, data communications, data and communications recording, electronic instrumentation, instrument landing systems, navigation and surveying systems, navigation simulators, radar (airborne, seaborne and land based), safety equipment, security devices, specialised radio communications, strategic and tactical radio communications.

The graduate

After graduation comes the time to put theory into practice. There is just no better way to do this than by joining the Racal Group: the most dynamic and progressive collection of high technology electronic companies in the United Kingdom today. Because Racal firmly believes that the most important asset of any company is the people in that company, any graduate who is accepted for employment is assured of progressive career development within the group. This may occur within the original company or by inter-company transfer. Opportunities may also arise to transfer between different job activities, such as design engineer to marketing engineer.

The Racal Group has an outstanding record of training recognition both by the Engineering Industry Training Board and the professional institutions. Graduates are initially assigned to project leaders and subsequently undergo both in-company and external postgraduate training where this is required. Racal regards its graduate engineers as a valuable asset requiring careful development. To this end, supervision on graduate training for all companies in the group is maintained by the group graduate development manager. His aim is to provide effective training schemes of the highest quality which will give a maximum benefit both to the individual graduate and to the company in which he is employed. This will often provide the means for corporate recognition by the various professional bodies.

Because each one of the autonomous companies in the Racal Group embraces design, production and marketing, graduates are not only concerned with their own contribution in their specialised field, but by being totally involved in the project from concept to customer, soon gain an appreciation of every other aspect of their company. Thus, the realisation of being an integral member of the company team rapidly evolves, strengthened by active participation with the executive management, who are keen to reward ability and enthusiasm.

Formal appraisals of progress are made and discussed, annually by the graduate's manager, and informally on a regular basis.

Racal–Decca

The acquisition by Racal of the Decca group of companies led to a broadening of product base in the Racal Group and provided a much enlarged field for graduate recruitment. Racal–Decca is already well established in the design, manufacture and marketing of navigational, survey and radar systems. The products cover the whole range of the parabolic systems and has been extended to cover low frequency and satellite operated navigation systems. A full range of ancillaries is produced including systems for automatic charting, air navigation, instrument landing systems, doppler navigation, vehicle location, blind pilotage, offshore patrol vessels, minesweepers and navigation training simulators. Radar is produced for marine and air applications, Racal–Decca being one of the worlds foremost suppliers of marine radar equipment. It is estimated that over half the world's radar fitted ships of over 100 gross registered tons, use Racal–Decca radar. Most of the major technical advances in marine radar have come from the laboratories of Racal–Decca. Presently research and development is taking place in the design of microwave components and antennas, the application of lasers, ships instrumentation, radar displays and specialised computer linked radars for harbours, airports and defence. The survey company offers a service to the offshore gas and oil industry in all aspects of surveying and positioning. Clients requirements are closely followed in the research and development of these fascinating projects.

Vacancies

Graduates traditionally seek vacancies in research and development. As this is where future products are created it is therefore the largest area of recruitment. Of equal importance are the other aspects of industry;

Activities
Research, development, manufacture of radiation cross-linked polymer products

Employees
1,250 UK; 8,500 worldwide

Location: UK
South West

Locations: Overseas
USA; Belgium; Germany; France; Eire; Denmark

Opportunities
Chemists; Physicists; Materials technologists; Mechanical and electrical engineers; Polymer scientists; Administration/business; Finance; Marketing; Planning; Patents

Vacancies
20 maximum

Application address
Ian Gray, Personnel Manager, Raychem Ltd, Faraday Road, South Dorcan, Swindon, Wiltshire SN3 5HH

Raychem

Raychem Corporation is now 25 years old and has research and/or development facilities in six countries, manufacturing in 10 countries and has sales /technical services offices in over 50.

The UK operation is based in Swindon, Wiltshire employing over 1,200 people. In Swindon there are three major European manufacturing divisions (materials compounding, wire/cable, heat shrink products); the European research centre; a worldwide marketing/product development group; sales and central administration.

Sales growth has averaged 25% per annum during the last 10 years and this is reflected in the recent and planned expansion of and investment in the UK.

Our technology is the irradiation of polymers giving unique properties and characteristics to our materials which go far beyond the normal limits of untreated plastics. Our products have applications in the electronics, military, aerospace, telecommunication, energy, process, oil and other high technology industries.

Types of graduate required
We principally seek *applied scientists: polymer chemists* and *polymer physicists, electrical, mechanical* and *plastics processing engineers*. Although many choose to make their careers in R&D, career development and progression within the manufacturing and commercial divisions, including overseas appointments, is encouraged.

Salaries and progression
One of the foundations for a strong internal promotion policy is an intake of good honours graduates and postgraduate specialists, and we have an excellent record in giving graduates early responsibility with appropriate salaries.

Activities
Market research

Employees
200

Location: UK
London

Opportunities
Trainee research executive

Upper age limit
23

Application address
Mr T Slinger, Personnel Manager, Research Bureau Limited, PO Box 203, Greenbank, London E1 9PA

Research Bureau Limited

Research Bureau Limited is a separate company within Unilever whose purpose is to develop the use and application of marketing research and to conduct or purchase marketing research both for Unilever and its associated companies and for a wide range of non-Unilever companies. (See the Unilever organisation's entry for further information.)

Marketing research is concerned with the application of scientific techniques to the study of consumer behaviour and attitudes which have a bearing on marketing and advertising problems. This includes the assessment of product ideas, the testing of the products themselves, the measurement of sales performance and consumer attitudes and the study of media and advertising. The main emphasis is on the sample survey; the interests are the consumer and the process of distribution. In addition to tackling ad hoc marketing problems RBL is engaged in a long term research programme into some of the basic problems of methodology. There are opportunities here for offering original contributions to the solution of some of the more difficult areas. RBL's main activities are on the home market but there are strong links with overseas research units and overseas research is carried out by RBL. RBL is a member of the Research International Group of Companies.

Types of graduate required
Trainees have traditionally been recruited from the *social sciences*, but in more recent years students studying more vocational courses, eg *business studies*, have been increasingly accepted, as have graduates from other

Research Bureau Limited, cont

disciplines where they have demonstrated their potential for this sort of work.

Training

On joining RBL, trainee research executives are given a short introductory course and then appointed to a research group and will work on specific problems under guidance. At the end of the first year, he or she should be capable of handling research projects with some supervision, and again after two years should be fully operational as a research executive who plans, organises, and has responsibility for individual projects. During the training period, and afterwards, all trainees will attend special courses on marketing, advertising, statistics, etc.

Salaries

The basic starting salary for first degree graduates is very good and a London allowance is paid in addition. There is a standard increase at the end of the first year of training, after which salary and promotion depend upon individual performance. All employees are included in a contributory superannuation scheme. All completed application forms must be received by the end of January.

Reuters

Reuters, founded in London in 1851, is an international news organisation which supplies news of political, economic, financial, general and sports interest to the media and business communities in most countries of the world. It also produces a wide range of computerised data retrieval services, combining both news and statistical data, using the latest technology to supply banks, brokers, financial institutions and major corporations worldwide with up to the minute information on international money rates, securities, commodities and all factors affecting these markets.

Reuters has one of the largest private communication systems in the world and is a major user of minicomputers to service over 20,000 subscribers in some 150 countries. Its extensive real-time data retrieval networks are among the most sophisticated and reliable in operation, interfacing with high speed communication links and making use of satellites, cables and high frequency radio.

Graduate opportunities

Reuters employs some 2,880 staff including over 500 full time journalists, 1,215 of whom work in the UK. It recruits about 10 graduates each year for training in journalism and about four graduates for training in a wide range of management disciplines. Successful candidates will be expected to have at least a second class honours degree. In addition applicants for the journalist training scheme will be required to speak three languages, one of which should be English. Management trainee applicants should have a good knowledge of at least one foreign lanaguage. Both schemes offer opportunities for posts at home or abroad.

Applications

Apply in writing to the Recruitment Officer at the address given.

Activities
International news and business information organisation

Employees
2,880

Location: UK
London

Locations: Overseas
Worldwide

Opportunities & places
Journalist trainees 10; Management trainees 4

Upper age limit
26

Application address
Recruitment Officer, Reuters Ltd, 85 Fleet Street, London EC4P 4AJ

Activities
Manufacturers and distributors of a wide range of milling, baking, agricultural and convenience food products

Employees
46,000

Locations: UK
General

Opportunities
Production; Distribution; Sales; Marketing; Accountancy (cost and management); Engineering (mechanical, chemical or electrical); Computer programming; Systems analysis; Research and Development

Vacancies
60

Application address
Miss SE Robinson, Graduate Recruitment Manager, RHM plc, King Edward House, PO Box 178, 27/30 King Edward Court, Windsor, Berks SL4 1TJ
Tel: 95 57123

RHM (Ranks Hovis McDougall plc)

RHM means food. Every table in Britain carries an RHM product at one time or another and every kitchen probably stocks something we make.

One of the world's largest foods groups, it presents an unusual profile and an individual style of organisation and management. There are no super factories employing thousands of people, most RHM companies are small or medium sized, which allows for easy contact and communication. For the graduate, RHM presents the advantages of scale in both directions, combining the financial and administrative strength of a very large organisation and a wide spectrum of career opportunities with a working environment of reasonable dimensions.

The group consists of 100 trading companies organised into six trading divisions with combined annual sales of over £1,500 million. RHM Fresh Foods, RHM Groceries and RHM General Products between them are responsible for a wide range of well known names: Mothers Pride, Nimble, Mr Kipling, Bisto, Cerebos, Scotts Porage Oats, Energen, Sharwoods, Paxo and many more. RHM Cereals includes Rank Hovis Ltd which has 17 modern flour mills throughout the UK producing a wide variety of both bulk flour for sale to RHM Fresh Foods and other commercial users and packaged flour for sale to the retail trade. It also includes RHM Ingredient Supplies which produces rusk, crumb and seasonings, and Tenstar Ltd, developing and producing sugar, gluten and starches from flour for other industrial users. RHM Agriculture has about 20 merchanting companies selling animal feeds, cereal and herbage seeds, fertilisers and chemicals, agricultural machinery and a variety of other items used by the farmer. RHM Overseas controls a number of companies producing foods from local sources in the Americas, Australia, South East Asia and Africa.

The six trading divisions are supported by RHM Research, employing about 300 scientific staff, and RHM Management Services consisting of finance, legal, forward planning, organisation and methods, data programming and systems analysis.

Types of graduate required
Graduates from *all* disciplines are required for production management, general commercial management, sales, marketing, distribution, computer work and accountancy, while those with good *scientific*, *engineering* or *agricultural* qualifications are appointed for a range of specialist work.

Training and career development
We are very keen to give graduate entrants early responsibility, although aware that the successful assumption of such responsibility has to be based on experience, knowledge and confidence. The process of acquiring these qualities involves a careful blending of learning and training aimed towards the particular position for which the graduate has been selected. We have our own training centre, where courses and seminars are run for all grades of management throughout the year.

The precise direction of your career and choice of initial appointment is based on a full and frank appraisal in the initial selection procedure of our needs against your evident capabilities and preferences. Further development and career progress is closely linked to regular assessments of performance and monitoring of achievements.

Prospects
RHM operates in a competitive commercial environment. The group's senior positions of tomorrow are likely to be filled by those who have gained a depth of experience, a width of intelligence and outlook and a strength of character and purpose. The acquisition of these qualities is, of

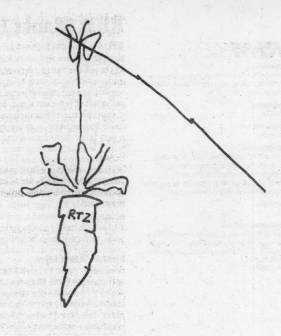

The RTZ Group of companies
welcomes applications from young men
and women who will graduate in
'hard' sciences such as chemical,
mechanical, and production
engineering, chemistry and metallurgy.
Recent graduates considering a career
move may also apply.

Full details of the methods of entry are
given in the reference opposite.

The Rio Tinto Zinc Corporation PLC

RHM (Ranks Hovis McDougall plc), cont

course, largely a private process, but opportunities to demonstrate them will clearly be forthcoming.

Location
RHM has offices and operating companies in most cities and large towns throughout the United Kingdom and it is therefore often possible to employ graduates in their area of choice. However, a degree of mobility may be necessary to ensure that applicants are properly placed in companies and positions appropriate to their future progress and development. Recently qualified graduates are not engaged for work overseas.

Salaries
Starting salaries are determined each year in February and are thoroughly competitive. Salaries are then constantly reviewed and are increased according to individual progress. Proven ability is fully recognised and rewarded.

Pensions
There is an excellent contributory pension scheme which also covers life assurance and dependent's pensions.

Further information
Although we do not visit every university during the year, we welcome applications from all graduates who feel that they might be successful with us. Further information can be obtained in the RHM recruitment booklet which is available along with our 1983 vacancy list from your university careers advisory service or you may write direct to our Graduate Recruitment Manager.

The Rio Tinto Zinc Corporation plc

Activities
Mining (mainly overseas), metal smelting and fabrication, chemical and cement manufacture, light engineering

Employees
18,000 UK
70,000 worldwide

Locations: UK
General

Opportunities
Production engineering; Production management; Technical sales and marketing

Upper age limit
24

Application address
Paul Tebbutt, Personnel Officer, Group Personnel Services, RTZ Services Limited, 6 St James's Square, London SW1Y 4LD

RTZ is the British based parent of a large international group of companies with a track record of growth. Our interests throughout the world are in organisations varying in size and degree of development. You may know of RTZ as a big mining company, but that's only part of what we do. Our worldwide activities include exploration for ore deposits, mining, processing, smelting and fabricating metals, engineering, cement manufacture and the production of chemicals. RTZ has interests in most major metals as well as energy resources such as coal, oil and uranium.

Our non-mining activities are largely broken down into small, local operating companies, each with their own management structure. In the UK alone there are more than 70 operating companies employing about 18,000 people. The largest are the smelting companies, each with a workforce of around a thousand. Most are smaller, with 25–500 employees, working in a specialised area and with their own commercial strategy. Our structure offers the rare opportunity to combine personal commitment and satisfaction, gained from working for a small independent company, with scope for training and career progression more commonly associated with a major group.

Types of graduate required
We welcome applications from all *science* and *technology* graduates, including recent graduates, considering a career move; particularly those with *chemical, mechanical, electrical* and *production engineering, chemistry* and *metallurgy* degrees, to join the group through one of the following methods of entry.

The Rio Tinto Zinc Corporation plc, cont

RTZ training scheme

This scheme is designed to give graduates an insight into different aspects of the group's UK operations, through experience in more than one management function. It provides graduates who are uncertain about their career intentions within industry, an opportunity to delay a decision about their future until they have gained some work experience.

The scheme lasts approximately two years, during which, two major assignments are undertaken. Graduates move from the training scheme into a wide range of positions within the group including sales, marketing, production and technical management.

RTZ chemicals training scheme

This scheme is intended for graduates in chemical engineering, chemistry and engineering who are seeking a career within the group's UK chemical operating companies. The style and duration of training are similar to those of the RTZ training scheme.

Pillar Engineering training scheme

This scheme is restricted to engineering graduates who have had at least 12 months previous industrial experience. It is designed to provide the Pillar Engineering Group, (12 autonomous companies engaged in a wide variety of light engineering activities) with qualified, industrially trained engineers who will ultimately take up production management appointments.

Graduates stay on the scheme between 12–18 months and follow a systematic programme of training which leads to chartered membership of the Institute of Production Engineers.

Direct entry

Some suitably qualified graduates may be recruited into specific vacancies under our direct entry scheme.

Training

Whilst we feel that the best training is a responsible job of work, we also recognise the value of short practical courses of business education. Graduate trainees and other young managers attend periodic residential courses to reinforce experience gained at work.

Career opportunities

Because our group consists of many smaller autonomous operating companies, responsibility tends to come that much earlier. For the individual this means greater personal responsibility, authority, a sense of identity and job satisfaction, coupled with salaries, employee benefits, and progress normally associated with large organisations. Wherever possible, all levels of professional and management personnel are recruited from within the group.

Further information

Copies of our 1983 brochure and application forms are available from your careers service or Paul Tebbutt, Personnel Officer, at the address given.

CONSULTING ENGINEERS

Activities
Internal combustion engine research, design and development

Employees
400

Location: UK
South East

Opportunities
Engine designers; Stress engineers; Computer engineers; Development engineers

Vacancies
6–8

Upper age limit
25

Application address
R Barrow, Personnel & Training Manager, Ricardo Consulting Engineers, Bridge Works, Shoreham by Sea, West Sussex BN4 5FG

Ricardo Consulting Engineers

Ricardo are one of the foremost internal combustion engine establishments in the world and act as consulting engineers to the majority of the major engine manufacturers undertaking a wide variety of engine research, design and development.

New developments
Active interest is being taken in improving engine efficiencies to conserve diminishing oil supplies while meeting increasingly stringent legislation on exhaust gas emissions and noise. Consideration is also being given to alternative fuels.

Types of graduate required
Graduates should have a good honours degree in *mechanical* or *automotive engineering* and must be engine enthusiasts. There are also occasional vacancies for *electronic engineers*.

Training
A training scheme is available which qualifies graduates for corporate membership of the IMechE. The scheme is arranged to meet the needs of graduates wishing to follow a career in engine design and development.

Prospects
The company provides excellent training and prospects for graduates in the IC engine industry.

Location
The design office and engine testing laboratories are on the South Coast at Shoreham by Sea, West Sussex.

Salaries
Salaries are competitive with an annual review related to performance. Starting salaries are dependent on qualifications and experience. The excellent fringe benefits include an annual bonus, contributory pension scheme and free life assurance.

Applications and further information
For further information either contact your appointments board or write direct to Mr R Barrow at the address given.

Richmond Fellowship Therapeutic Communities

The fellowship offers a unique opportunity for a career in the human relations field. It runs 34 communities in various parts of the UK for the mentally or emotionally disturbed, at all age levels. Residents live in a community for periods ranging from three months to three years, participating in a programme of group discussions, counselling and practical skills activities, designed to enable them to reach greater maturity, stability and independence, and a self-awareness that will help them to withstand the pressures and stresses of life.

Types of graduate required
Graduates in the *social sciences* are preferred, and in applying will have to persuade us that they are intelligent, mature, tolerant and sensitive to the feelings of others. A clear understanding of personal motivation for a career in social work, and a firm commitment to an often difficult task is also required.

Activities
Rehabilitation of the mentally ill, education and training in therapeutic community work

Employees
180

Locations: UK
General

Locations: Overseas
United States; Australia; New Zealand; Austria

Opportunities & places
Trainee scholars 10; Some administrative vacancies

Application address
Personnel Assistant, The Richmond Fellowship, 8 Addison Road, Kensington, London W14 8DL
Tel: 01-603 6373

Richmond Fellowship Therapeutic Communities, cont

Training
Those who are offered one-year trainee scholarships (between 5–10% of applicants) will be fully trained in all aspects of therapeutic community work through the fellowship in-service training scheme. For selected trainees, a second year of training is offered. Successful applicants should be prepared to learn all aspects of the work ranging from counselling and groupwork, to homemaking, administrative and public relations skills. After one year trainees are eligible for appointment to permanent posts of assistant warden, and further training to deputy and warden level is available.

Volunteer placements
Applications are welcome from those interested in doing voluntary work in the field of mental health for periods of three months to one year and during vacations.

Grants and salaries
Grants from September 1982: £2,475 per annum for one year trainee scholarship, £3,300 per annum for second year trainee scholarship, with up to £600 supplements depending on qualifications and experience. Salaries from April 1982: £4,200 rising to over £8,000 through progression to higher grades.

Robson Rhodes

Activities
Chartered accountancy

Employees
600

Locations: UK
London; Manchester; Midlands; South West; North West

Locations: Overseas
Associated firms worldwide

Opportunities & places
Trainee chartered accountants 60

Application address
Miss Penny Alison, Director of Personnel, Robson Rhodes, 186 City Road, London EC1V 2NU

Robson Rhodes lies within the top twenty accountancy firms in Britain, having some 64 partners and 600 staff of whom over 300 are based at our London office. At this size we are able to offer first class training facilities and an outstandingly high level of technical support but yet maintain personal involvement with our clients. These range from small family businesses to large public companies with multimillion pound turnovers requiring our professional services in auditing, tax, accountancy, computer services and financial consultancy.

It is essential that students gain a thorough grounding in auditing as this is the basis of our business but you will be given the opportunity to gain experience in the specialist fields during training, should you so wish.

Your practical work will be monitored by those in charge of each assignment and their assessments form the basis of formal half-yearly appraisals at which times every aspect of your work and study will be discussed. The firm's partners take an active interest in students' progress and regular interviews with your principal are built into the three year training programme.

Types of graduate required
The first essential is a good degree in *any* discipline but of equal importance are genuine self-motivation, the ability to communicate with ease and the possession of sound analytical skills. Enthusiasm and enterprise are essential for success in the profession and these qualities are sought in graduate applicants.

Training
Training to meet our rigorous professional standards is of prime importance throughout your career but particularly so during your first three years. Formal tuition is given by professional accountancy tutors with all fees being paid by the firm. This is linked with internal training courses, practical work and home study, the entire programme being monitored and co-ordinated by our training manager.

Salaries
Our salaries are competitive, being based on market rates and rising according to ability, performance and examination success.

Prospects
Qualification as a chartered accountant may be regarded as a springboard to a whole range of top level management careers. Promotion prospects within the firm are excellent and there are opportunities for advancement in such specialised fields as computer and overseas employment. From here, the ambitious young accountant can progress to become a partner, financial controller, computer specialist, management consultant, taxation adviser, teacher or financial journalist.

Further information
The majority of our students join us in late September but we do have a limited number of vacancies for entry in February/March. Although we do not visit every university we welcome applications from all graduates. You can obtain full details of our firm from your careers service or by writing for our brochure and application form to the address given.

NM Rothschild & Sons Limited

Activities
Merchant banking

Employees
680

Locations: UK
London; Manchester; Leeds

Locations: Overseas
USA; South East Asia; Central and South America

Opportunities
Corporate finance; Banking; Investments; Leasing

Vacancies
10

Application address
Personnel Director, NM Rothschild & Sons Ltd, New Court, St Swithin's Lane, London EC4P 4DU

One of the leading London merchant banks, NM Rothschild & Sons Limited is closely linked with other Rothschild banks in Europe, the United States and SE Asia.

The London bank has five principal activities: (i) banking, which includes financing of UK industrial companies by advances or acceptance credits, syndication of Eurocurrency and sterling loans and active participation in the international and London money markets, foreign exchange and bullion dealing; (ii) corporate finance, which includes raising long term funds for corporate clients in the capital market, advising and acting for clients in capital reconstructions, mergers and takeovers; operating actively in the Eurocredit and Eurobond markets and, on a worldwide basis, in export credit transactions, major projects and general international corporate advice; (iii) asset management, ie advising central banks, international companies, pension funds, investment and unit trusts and wealthy individuals on the management of their assets; (iv) trust services, which includes acting as trustee and providing trust and tax advice; (v) leasing, which includes the financing of large items of capital equipment.

Rothschilds acts as banker to several foreign governments and numbers among its clients some of the biggest and best known foreign and domestic industrial companies. In addition, the firm has associated companies offices in many parts of the world including the USA, Europe, Australia, Hong Kong, Malaysia, Brazil, Chile, Mexico, Singapore and the Channel Islands.

Types of graduate required
The bank is only interested in men and women of outstanding ability who wish to make merchant banking their career. The degree subject is not important although a flair for numbers is required. Adaptability and enthusiasm should be coupled with originality and ingenuity.

Training
Graduates are given a short induction course round the bank during their first few months and then appointed to an operating division where their detailed training commences.

Prospects
Within a few years of joining an operating department, graduates would

NM Rothschild & Sons Limited, cont

expect to be in a position of considerable responsibility. There is opportunity for transfer between departments, and exchanges between the London bank and associated banks overseas are increasing. In many divisions of the bank overseas travel may be expected.

Although NM Rothschild & Sons Limited is a privately owned limited company, the majority of the directors are not members of the Rothschild family and for the most part have been promoted from within the bank. The dependence of the firm on intelligence and ingenuity suggests that there is particular scope for graduates.

Salaries and pensions
Salaries are competitive with other merchant banks and terms of employment include a house purchase assistance scheme and non-contributory pension.

Applications, together with a curriculum vitae and a report from the university appointments board/tutor, should be sent by 1 January 1983 to the Personnel Director.

Rowe & Pitman

R&P

Activities
All aspects of stockbroking and investment

Employees
300

Location: UK
London

Vacancies
6

Application address
Mr PN Smith, Staff Manager, Rowe & Pitman, City-Gate House, 39/45 Finsbury Square, London EC2A 1JA

Rowe & Pitman is one of the leading stockbroking partnerships on the London Stock Exchange with a broadly based business that covers most aspects of stockbroking and investment. Our clients are drawn largely from the major UK and European institutions, for whom we provide a wide range of investment services, mainly from our London office but also from smaller offices in San Francisco, Boston, Johannesburg, Hong Kong and Tokyo.

Types of graduate required
A few graduates are recruited each year for positions in various departments throughout the firm. Provided the degree is a good one graduates from almost *any* discipline will be considered, although the nature of our business requires all successful applicants to be numerate and we have a continuing requirement for those with an *economics* and/or *mathematics* background. We have between three and six vacancies for those with the right aptitude and approach to make a career in stockbroking.

Training and career development
Graduates will receive an initial training by working in the relevant departments for the first three/six months with the firm, including a period of training on the floor of the Stock Exchange. Following this, training will continue in one of the particular areas of the firm's activities; gilt-edged, research, institutional equity sales, overseas research and sales and fund management. Subsequent progress will depend on personal preferences so far as these are consistent with the needs of the firm.

Salaries
The initial salary will be competitive and in addition there is an annual bonus based upon the profits of the firm. There is a non-contributory pension scheme incorporating a very good life insurance cover.

Rowland Nevill & Co

Activities
Chartered accountancy

Employees
150

Locations: UK
London and South East

Opportunities & places
Student chartered accountants 12

Application address
Clive Weeks, Rowland Nevill & Co, 53 New Broad Street, London EC2M 1PQ

Rowland Nevill is a firm of chartered accountants with its main office in the City of London and offices at Hove and Hertford. The firm has 20 partners and approximately 150 staff. As a medium sized firm, we offer you the advantages of working with a wide range of clients, to whom we provide audit, accountancy, tax, management consultancy and other services.

Types of graduate required
An ability to communicate with people at all levels, both verbally and on paper is vital. We need graduates who are numerate and who can apply commonsense and logic to the solution of problems. *Any* degree course is useful, and none in particular is favoured.

Professional education
As a graduate, you undertake a three-year training contract which on successful completion will enable you to become a member of the Institute of Chartered Accountants. After this, good opportunities exist for further experience and promotion within the firm.

The training consists of practical work and theoretical study. We use a firm of specialist tutors to provide you with the best available courses and guidance to pass the professional examinations. Working closely with senior members of the firm, particularly partners and managers, you will always have the opportunity to expand your knowledge. The firm is not so large that you will get lost in a sea of people far removed from where the decisions are taken.

Salaries
We pay competitive salaries which are reviewed regularly and which include special incentives for examination success.

The Royal Air Force

RAF officer

Activities
National defence by the operation and support of military aircraft

Employees
80,000

Locations: UK
General

Locations: Overseas
Worldwide, principally W Germany

Opportunities
Air traffic control; Dentistry; Education; Engineering; Fighter control; Medicine; Navigator; Pilot; Secretarial; Supply

Vacancies
300 approx

Upper age limit
23½ for aircrew – higher age limits for other branches

The Royal Air Force plays a vital part in western defence and needs highly trained minds in all branches to carry out this role effectively. The RAF, therefore, has a large annual requirement for graduate entrants.

Ground officers can serve on short service commissions, varying from three to six years, depending on branch; aircrew officers serve a minimum of eight years. Those selected for permanent commissions serve initially for 16 years, or to age 38, whichever is the longer, and thus qualify for retired pay. Officers promoted to the rank of squadron leader may, if they wish for a full career, continue to the age of 55. Most graduate entrants can expect to achieve this rank within 12 years of starting full time service.

Opportunities
The following branches are open to graduates: the general duties (flying) branch in which officers spend much of their early careers in flying and later are responsible for the policy direction of the service; the engineer branch, responsible for the organisation and management of the total engineering task, including various aspects of design, research and development; the supply branch responsible for the logistic support of the RAF, including all aspects of supply and movement; the administrative branch which is responsible for personnel, administration and accounting; the education specialisation of the administrative branch which is responsible for the organisation of continuation training, further education and the teaching of specialised subjects to postgraduate level; the general duties (ground) branch responsible for air traffic and fighter

Application address
The RAF University Liaison Officer, Ministry of Defence, (R4 (RAF)), Room 404, Adastral House, Theobalds Road, London WC1X 8RU

control; the security (RAF Regiment and Provost) branch which is responsible for airfield defence, fire fighting, counter-espionage and intelligence duties; the catering specialisation which is responsible for all aspects of RAF catering including dietetics; the physical education specialisation which provides specialist advice and services on RAF station hospitals and remedial units; the photographic interpretation branch which is responsible for the gathering of airborne intelligence; the medical and dental branches which provide opportunities for general and specialised practise in most fields of medicine and dentistry. There are also occasional vacancies in the marine and legal branch for those with specialist qualifications. There are vacancies for women graduates in all branches other than the general duties (flying), RAF Regiment and Provost branches.

Types of graduate required
Graduates in *any* subject may apply for the general duties, supply, general duties (ground), administrative (secretarial), RAF Regiment and Provost branches. For the engineer branch the principal requirement is graduates in *mechanical, electrical, electronic, aeronautical* and *air transport engineering*. The main requirement in the education specialisation is for graduates in *mathematics, engineering, physics* and *computer science*, preferably with a postgraduate certificate in education or with some teaching experience. There are, however, vacancies for *arts* graduates. Catering and physical education require specialist qualifications and A level mathematics is advisable for the photographic interpretation branch.

Selection
Selection for all branches is by a series of tests and interviews over a period of about three days. Graduate applicants may apply for an initial interview with a university liaison officer. High personal qualities are required.

Cadetships at university
Applications for RAF cadetships for the full three years of a degree course should be submitted with UCCA forms, whilst those for short term, ie one or two years, should be submitted by undergraduates by the 15 May prior to the start of the academic year for which cadetship is required. While at university or polytechnic cadetship holders are commissioned as RAF officers and receive pay and allowances. Tuition and certain other fees are also paid by the RAF. The 1982 cadet pay is £4,398 pa rising to £4,924 pa after one year and to £5,449 pa after two years (1982/83 pay scale).

Training
On entry graduates receive a short course of office training followed by appropriate professional training. Subsequent postings at normally two to three year intervals are designed to provide the experience needed for promotion. In addition to advanced professional training in the service, there are opportunities for postgraduate study for officers of all branches.

Locations
RAF units are situated in all parts of the United Kingdom and some locations overseas. Opportunities to serve abroad are principally in Europe. There are also staff appointments to allied headquarters in both Europe and in the USA. Officers may expect a variety of locations of postings during their careers.

Salaries and prospects
Graduates offered permanent commissions serve initially to the age of 38

or for 16 years service, whichever is the later. These commissions earn retired pay and carry a tax free terminal grant. Short service commissions in the ground branches attract a gratuity of £1,010 pa with £965 pa for women. Graduates enter as officers and in some branches can be granted specially favourable terms for promotion early in their service. Starting salaries after training vary from £6,249 to over £9,574 depending on the branch, type of commission, and qualifications of the officer (1982/83 pay scale).

Retired pay and amenities

Retired pay is non-contributory and terminal grants are three times the rate of annual retired pay. There are six weeks paid leave a year in addition to public holidays and most weekends. Excellent facilities exist for sport and for most other forms of recreational activity.
Accommodation for both single and married personnel is provided at low cost. Married and single quarters are fully furnished.

Further information

RAF university liaison officers visit each university and polytechnic at least once a year. Information about these visits and further details about commissions in the Royal Air Force can be obtained from your careers adviser or appointments officer. Further information can also be obtained by writing to the RAF University Liaison Officer.

The Royal Corps of Naval Constructors

The Royal Corps of Naval Constructors is a wholly civilian team of 500 professional naval architects, electrical engineers and mechanical engineers, who design the warships of the Royal Navy and the engineering equipment fitted therein.

Naval architects

The naval architects of the Royal Corps of Naval Constructors work in close contact with the ship building and allied industries and with research organisations. They must be able to design and equip every type of warship required in the naval service and ensure that their designs can withstand the stresses which will be imposed at sea and function effectively in all weather conditions. They must also be able to assess and turn to practical account technical developments which are likely to influence war at sea. Their duties span a wide range of activities and include the creative work of the ship designer in producing the form and layout of the whole ship, the detailed design of equipment and ship systems, research in hydro-dynamics, structural design and practical ship building and ship repairing in private shipyards and royal dockyards.

Mechanical and electrical engineers

The mechanical engineers and electrical engineers of the Royal Corps of Naval Constructors design the propulsion and electrical engineering equipment of the ships of the Royal Navy, supervise the manufacture of electrical equipment and the installation of mechanical and electrical equipment in ships under construction, and supervise the repair and maintenance of that equipment in ships in the Royal Dockyards. The propulsion machinery, the electrical power and control systems and all the complex electrical and mechanical equipment in HM ships must be designed and manufactured to a very high standard, and the work therefore provides many interesting engineering problems with responsibility attainable at an early age.

Activities
Design and construction of the ships of the Royal Navy and installation of engineering equipment

Employees
500

Locations: UK
London; South West; Scotland

Opportunities
Design – ship and submarine; Maintenance; Repair; Systems control; Engineering

Upper age limit
26

Application address
Civilian Management (Specialists) 2a32, Ministry of Defence, Room 330, Empire Hotel, Bath, Avon BA1 5AB

The Royal Corps of Naval Constructors, cont

Locations

Constructors are liable for service at various locations throughout the UK including the headquarters of the Ministry of Defence at Bath, research and development establishments, shipyards (including the Royal Dockyards) and occasionally in some cases, overseas.

Types of graduate required

Graduates with a first or upper second class honours degree in *electrical engineering, electronic engineering, mechanical engineering, civil engineering, nuclear engineering, mechanical science, naval architecture* or other *maritime sciences* are recruited.

Training

The first year of training is normally spent at the constructors' training office, Plymouth, studying warship design, dockyard organisation, etc. This is followed by further training at other naval establishments and time is also spent at sea on HM ships. There is also a requirement for a further course of study leading to a MSc degree.

Salaries and prospects

Graduates join the RCNC as probationary assistant constructors, 1982 salary £6,358–£6,928; promotion to assistant constructor (salary £7,934–£9,241) usually occurs after about two years. Promotion to constructor (salary £12,697–£15,039) is normally achieved within six years of the assistant constructor appointment. Those of outstanding ability might achieve this promotion within a shorter period. The prospects of promotion to a higher post are very good and the national salaries and grades above constructor are chief constructor (£17,685–£19,927), assistant director (£22,044), deputy director (£25,000).

There is a non-contributory pension scheme and gratuity.

The Royal Electrical and Mechanical Engineers

REME provides engineering support for the Army's equipment, ranging from computers to tanks. The work includes design of maintenance systems, modification of complex equipment to improve its performance, controlling repair systems and project management.

Activities
Responsibility for providing engineering support for the Army's equipment

Employees
14,000

Locations: UK
General

Locations: Overseas
Worldwide

Opportunities
Aeronautical, electronic and mechanical engineers

Vacancies
10

Types of graduate required

If you are reading for, or have attained, a degree in *aeronautical, electronic, mechanical production engineering* or *pure* or *applied science* you will be eligible for selection as an officer in REME. Although employed as an engineering manager you will need to meet the exacting personal and leadership standards demanded of every officer in the Army. Your potential for training to reach these standards will be assessed at a four-day selection process held at the Regular Commissions Board at Westbury.

Training

Although you will specialise in aeronautical, electronic or mechanical engineering your training will cover many aspects of engineering to equip you for the problems you will encounter. The training experience you are given counts towards gaining chartered engineer status at an early opportunity.

Your career in REME

You can join REME on a three-year commission or for a full career. After

Application address
Lieutenant Colonel JC Ashton, REME, Dept
R82/4, HQ REME Training Centre, Arborfield,
Reading RG2 9NN

initial training at the Royal Military Academy, Sandhurst and equipment training, you will be posted to a REME workshop in the UK, Germany or further afield, where you will gain experience of commanding soldiers, and of engineering. Your next step is to command your own workshop of 60 to 100 men, being responsible for them on exercises and in barracks and looking after, for example, Chieftain tanks, missile systems or helicopters. From here, your career will depend on your own ability, it may include appointments in headquarters, as well as commanding soldiers and technical appointments. We offer excellent prospects, responsibility and job satisfaction. The pay is rewarding too: you will start on a lieutenant's salary of about £7,650 but in return we expect a high level of commitment.

The Royal Navy, Royal Marines and WRNS

Types of officers required

Seaman officers are responsible for tactics and ship handling, 'fighting' the ship; only they can command HM ships. They may be selected to sub-specialise in aviation, submarines, aircraft control, mine warfare and clearance diving or hydrographic surveying.

Supply and secretariat officers are the business managers of the fleet. They deal with secretarial, administrative, legal, pay, stores and catering services.

Engineer officers specialise in marine, weapon or aero engineering and their work ranges from the operation, maintenance and performance of systems at sea to design, development, trials, technical support and training ashore.

Flying duties officers (observers and pilots) operate a variety of sophisticated helicopters in roles ranging from anti-submarine warfare to support of the Royal Marines. A few will be selected to fly the Sea Harrier.

Instructor officers provide the general and technical training for ratings and officers up to postgraduate level. They are also responsible for meteorological and oceanographical services and work in automatic data processing, management services and other fields.

The Royal Marines are the Navy's military force and provide commando units for amphibious and helicopter borne operations, mostly on NATO's Northern flank, and detachments for service with the fleet.

WRNS officers are mainly employed in secretarial and administrative duties; other duties are personnel selection, instructor and catering with sub-specialisation for a few in communications, computer work and photographic interpretation. A few opportunities are available for WRNS engineer and instructor officers.

Types of graduate required

Seamen, supply and secretariat, flying duties, Royal Marines and WRNS officers. Any UK recognised degree (or equivalent) acceptable to the Ministry of Defence, and O level passes (or equivalent) at grade C or above in mathematics, English language and, except for Royal Marines and WRNS, a physics based science; age under 26 on entry; RM under 25.

Engineer officers. As above, but the degree must be in a related subject, *physics* and *civil engineering* degrees will be considered. Age under 26 on entry, but for mature applicants satisfying the MOD of continuance of employment in the engineering field 32 will be considered.

Instructor officers. Mainly degrees in *engineering, mathematics* or *physics*

Activities
The maritime and strategic defence of the realm

Employees
65,000

Locations: UK
General

Locations: Overseas
Worldwide

Opportunities
Seaman officers; Engineer officers; Supply or
secretariat officers; Royal Marines; Flying duties
officers; WRNS

Vacancies
150

Application address
The University Liaison Officer (DOG 83), Officer
NTRY Section, Ministry of Defence (Navy), Old
Admiralty Building, Spring Gardens, London
SW1A 2BE

but a few *arts* graduates are accepted each year; age on entry 21 to under 32.

A full career commission is pensionable, for service up to at least age 50. A short career commission is initially for eight years' service (instructors five years and RMs four years), with options to leave after five years (instructors three years). A three-and-a-half year career is available to seaman officers only. WRNS officers may only enter initially on an eight year short career commission with an option to leave after five years. Commissions for flying duties may be as a short career of 12 years with the option to leave after eight, or as a medium, pensionable career of 16 years. A gratuity is payable on completion of short career service. All short career officers have the opportunity to be selected for transfer to a full career commission or, except for RM, to a 16 year pensionable commission.

Bursaries

Sponsorship in the form of a £900 per annum bursary is available to those who wish to join the RN, RM or WRNS after graduation.

Candidates are required to enter into a legal undertaking to serve for a minimum of a short service career as applicable to their chosen specialisation. Failure to graduate or undertake an SCC will entail repayment of the award.

Training

All RN graduates enter as officers and carry out general naval training at Britannia Royal Naval College, Dartmouth, mostly for one term followed by training at sea (flying training for flying duties) and other courses, depending on type of entry and specialisation. Engineer officers then go on to the Royal Naval Engineering College, Manadon, for application courses in naval engineering. RM graduates enter as officers and train for one year at the commando training centre, Lympstone and then in a commando unit for one year. Graduate WRNS train with all other new entry WRNS at HMS Raleigh near Plymouth for five weeks, then for two months as a Wren in a naval establishment and next at BRNC for a 13½ week officer course, before being promoted to officer rank.

Location

Each appointment lasts two to three years. Ship appointments occur more frequently in the junior ranks and more for seaman officers than for others. Instructors on short career commissions are mainly based ashore.

Prospects

Promotion for full career officers to lieutenant commander (or captain RM) is after eight years as a lieutenant (seven years for Royal Marines). Promotion beyond lieutenant commander is by selection to commander (major RM) in mid 30s and to captain (Lt colonel RM) in early forties.

For short career and WRNS officers promotion is by selection at each stage.

Save & Prosper Group

Activities
Unit trust management; Life insurance, pensions and annuities; Investment management

Employees
650

Locations: UK
London and South East

Save and Prosper Group was founded in 1934 and in addition to being Britain's largest unit trust group is also a major force in life assurance, pensions and annuities.

We provide a wide range of plans and services through which differing financial objectives can be achieved in a simple and tax efficient way. By pooling the savings of many people and investing them in stocks and shares, property or government securities, we are able to match the

Opportunities
Investment; Actuarial; Marketing; Sales; Data processing; Administration; Accountancy

Vacancies
6

Application address
G Davies Esq, Group Personnel Manager, Save & Prosper Group Limited, 4 Great St Helens, London EC3 3EP

individual's particular investment requirements with the needs of government and industry for long term finance.

Types of graduate required
Each year Save & Prosper recruit a few graduates as management trainees. Candidates of *all* disciplines and of either sex will be considered provided that they are interested in money matters and show management potential.

Training
New trainees are given a brief overall picture of the company but rather than an elongated tour the individual is allowed responsible and interesting work at an early stage.

Our training manager has designed a programme for graduate entrants to complement their period as management trainees. This includes attendance on external management and educational courses. Encouragement is also given to those prepared to work for professional qualifications.

Salary and benefits
Management trainees are entitled to four weeks annual leave and the usual benefits for Save & Prosper employees. Graduates who joined us in 1982 received a starting salary of £5,500 per annum and we are prepared to increase this basic figure for those with additional qualifications or experience.

Progress in terms of both job content and financial remuneration is limited only by the trainee's capacity to grasp the undoubted opportunities which are available.

J Henry Schroder Wagg & Co Limited

Activities
Commercial banking, investment management, investment research, corporate finance, project finance

Employees
650

Location: UK
London

Locations: Overseas
North America; South America; Australia; Europe; Middle East; Far East

Opportunities
Management trainees

Vacancies
6–8

Application address
Head of Staff and Administration, J Henry Schroder Wagg & Co Limited, 120 Cheapside, London EC2V 6DS

J Henry Schroder Wagg & Co Limited (JHSW) is a member of the Accepting Houses Committee and one of the leading merchant banks in the City of London. It is a subsidiary of Schroders plc, a public company, which has another banking subsidiary in New York, J Henry Schroder Bank & Trust Company. The company has other extensive connections and interests overseas.

The activities of JHSW cover all the main fields of merchant banking. The investment division manages unit and investment trusts, pension funds and other portfolios. The banking division is concerned with the taking of deposits and granting of loans to both domestic and foreign customers in sterling and foreign currencies. The project finance division provides finance for UK exporters and arranges and advises on the raising of finance for projects. The fourth major activity is corporate finance which involves the arrangement of mergers, take-overs and new issues of stocks and shares, but recruitment for this division is in general confined to professionally qualified people, mainly chartered accountants and lawyers.

Types of graduate required
The company welcomes applications from graduates of *all* disciplines. For certain positions fluency in one or more foreign language is an advantage but not an essential.

Training
On joining the company graduates will not immediately be attached to a particular division but during the first few months they will spend time in each of the main divisions. Formal training will comprise presentations by the bank's own staff explaining in detail the complexities of the

Schlumberger-on top of the world in advanced electronic systems and instrumentation.

As an acknowledged international leader in the design, development and manufacture of advanced electronic instruments and systems we can ensure that you get off on the right foot to a satisfying and rewarding career.

We are looking for people with an enthusiastic and lively outlook on life who expect to graduate with a good honours degree in applied physics, computer science, mathematics, electrical or electronic engineering.

You will be closely involved in a small team developing new ranges of products using the latest microprocessor technology.

Your career path will be both varied and interesting with many opportunities for promotion. Advancement to management is encouraged through a policy of promotion from within.

Commencing salaries are always very competitive and are reviewed thrice yearly on performance. Benefits include a relocation package, pension and life assurance cover, over four weeks holiday, a subsidised restaurant and a sports and social club.

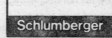

Schlumberger Measurement and Control (U.K.) Ltd.
Victoria Road, Farnborough, Hants.

J Henry Schroder Wagg & Co Limited, cont

activities in which we are engaged, supplemented by a special course in financial appreciation run by professional tutors. In addition, graduates will be given an opportunity to familiarise themselves with all the major activities of the bank through first hand observation and through less formal meetings with key personnel. At the end of this period the graduate will join one of the bank's divisions, and although both divisional requirements and the company's assessment of new entrants' aptitudes must be taken into account, every attempt will be made to meet individual preferences. It is company policy to encourage a degree of movement between divisions and transfers may occur at a later stage. Trainees in all divisions are encouraged to study for relevant professional qualifications and the acquisition of these is suitably rewarded.

Location
The company occupies a modern air conditioned building in the City. Apart from the sister company in New York, there are group companies in Bermuda, Brazil, Lebanon and Switzerland, and associated companies, branch or representative offices in Argentina, Australia, Belgium, Brazil, Colombia, France, Germany, Hong Kong, Japan and Singapore.

Salaries
Salaries are competitive and a wide range of employee benefits include a non-contributory pension scheme, a private medical insurance scheme, a house mortgage subsidy scheme, free lunches in the staff canteen and four weeks' annual holiday.

Prospects
Only a small number of graduates are accepted in each year but the prospects for advancement are excellent. The highest positions in the firm are open to those with the necessary ability.

The closing date for applications is 31 December 1982. Letters of application, enclosing a curriculum vitae or standard introduction form, should be marked 'private and confidential' and addressed to the Head of Staff and Administration.

Schlumberger Measurement and Control (UK) Ltd
Solartron Membrain Weston

Activities
The design and manufacture of electronic measuring instrumentation, radar and weapons simulators, automatic test equipment, industrial systems and a wide range of transducers

Employees
2,500

Locations: UK
Solartron: Farnborough, Hampshire
Membrain: Ferndown, Dorset
Weston: Enfield, Middlesex

Several important British companies have been brought together to form Schlumberger Measurement and Control (UK) Ltd. The group comprises The Solartron Electronic Group Ltd, Membrain Ltd, and Weston Controls. Solartron is the largest of the subsidiaries and is involved in the manufacture of electronic instrumentation, radar simulators, industrial monitoring and control systems and transducers. Membrain is Europe's leading supplier of automatic test equipment and the Weston Controls Group is involved with supplying the aerospace industry with instruments and sensors and is also involved in the manufacture of weapon simulators.

The opportunities
SMC (UK) Ltd requires graduates with relevant degrees (see display). New graduates generally start as a member of a project team with responsibility for a small part of the product. Under the guidance of a senior engineer, their responsibilities will gradually increase as they

Opportunities
R&D; Systems engineering; Software engineering

Vacancies
20 approx

Application address
The Personnel Manager, Schlumberger Measurement and Control (UK) Ltd, Victoria Road, Farnborough, Hants GU14 7PW

acquire an in-depth knowledge of the product backed up with internal and external training courses.

Research and development: Project group teams work with marketing managers conceiving and designing products to meet the cost and performance requirements with the available resources. The work involves close contact with other relevant departments.

Systems engineering: Industrial and simulation systems are designed and developed to meet the needs of customers under cost and time constraints. The engineer is involved from the proposal stage to final acceptance of the equipment on-site.

Software engineering: Opportunities are provided in applications software at Membrain and Solartron at various stages of product development. The engineer is involved in a wide range of programming tasks from simulating weather conditions to providing management information in a power station.

Good performance is rewarded financially and through promotion. Writing for the technical press, giving conference presentations and achieving membership of professional institutions is encouraged.

Applications
Further information is available from your careers office. Enquiries to the address given will be accepted at any time, but the company prefers that applications should be made through the careers service, in conjunction with the visits in the spring. Second interviews are then held at the relevant locations.

Schlumberger Wireline Logging

See our main entry in the Opportunities Overseas section.

Scapa Group plc

Application address
Group Personnel Manager, Scapa Group plc, Oakfield House, 52 Preston New Road, Blackburn, Lancs

Scapa is an international industrial textile group of companies manufacturing highly specialised textile products for use in a wide range of industries.

Its double commitment to both technological and managerial excellence means it can offer rewarding graduate careers in production management, R & D, sales and marketing, and administration. Its graduate trainee schemes are particularly suited to graduates in *textiles* and textile related subjects, *business studies*, *languages* and *marketing*.

Scicon
A member of the BP Group of Companies

Scicon

Activities
Design and implementation of advanced computer systems; Computer services including bureau facilities, data communications, software and turnkey systems

Employees
926

Scicon is an international group of companies providing computer services worldwide. Since its formation in 1960, Scicon has worked on more than 5,000 projects in over 50 countries, developing and using the latest technology to help solve the problems of government, industry and commerce.

We specialise in the design and implementation of the most advanced computer systems, in computer and management consultancy, and in the provision of computer bureau facilities. Our areas of expertise include

Locations: UK
London; Milton Keynes; Nottingham; Aberdeen

Opportunities
Analysts; Programmers; Systems programmers; Mathematicians

Vacancies
68

Application address
Graduate Recruitment Officer, Scicon, Sanderson House, 49 Berners Street, London W1P 4AQ

information systems, business systems, control systems and automation, modelling and simulation, command and control systems, microprocessor technology, product development and communications. Scicon has been a noted leader in the field of mathematical programming for many years.

To maintain our success in these fields we need highly qualified, creative professionals.

Types of graduate required

Scicon mainly recruits graduates with qualifications in *scientific* and *numerate* subjects eg *computer science, mathematics, physics, operational research, electrical* and *electronic engineering*. There are also a few opportunities for non-scientific graduates in our business information systems area.

Prospects and salaries

Assigned to projects where you can quickly make a contribution based on your own existing knowledge, you are strongly encouraged to learn new techniques some of them unique to Scicon.

The speed and extent of advancement depend entirely on you: there is no rigid career and promotion path. Within a couple of years, you could be leading projects in the UK or abroad. In the longer term, participating in national and international projects at Scicon could enable you to progress to posts in marketing, research and development, senior consultancy or management.

Benefits

Scicon consultancy's head office is in London and the computer bureau's head office is in Milton Keynes. These two companies have regional offices in Aberdeen, Nottingham, Weymouth, Ipswich, Bristol and Manchester; and overseas offices in San Francisco, Riyadh, Jeddah, Abu Dhabi, and Rozenburg, Holland.

Amongst other attractive benefits, staff have access to excellent recreational facilities.

Applications

When sending us your completed application form, it would help us if you could indicate the kind of work that interests you and your preference, if any, for software development or computer bureau work.

Scientific Civil Service

Activities
Research, development, equipment trials, provision of scientific advice and services, scientific and technical administration

Employees
17,500

Locations: UK
General

Opportunities
Science engineering and mathematics

Vacancies
400

Upper age limit
32 normally

Application address
Careers Advisory Services, or Mr C Norgrove, Civil Service Commission, Alencon Link, Basingstoke, Hants RG21 1JB

Research, development, advisory duties, technical administration and other scientific work necessary to enable central government to function properly is carried out in over 100 laboratories, many of them very large and many with international reputations, and in headquarters units in London.

Members of the Scientific Civil Service are employed in government departments on a great diversity of topics, ranging from defence operational analysis to specialist support for agricultural advisory services. Styles of activity include research, both fundamental and applied; management of development projects; scientific services and advice for government organisations and for the general public; technical support for scientific staff and quality control; and, at middle and senior levels, administration and management of scientific resources and manpower and provision of scientific and technical contributions to the formulation of government policy.

It is not possible to describe these activities fully within the scope of this article. More detailed information can be obtained from published

Scientific Civil Service, cont

booklets, in particular *Scientists: Civil Service Careers*, and *Defence Science 1982*. These are available from careers services. Specific information is also given elsewhere in this book about work in the Department of Industry, Government Communications Headquarters, and the Meteorological Office.

Each autumn the Civil Service Commission, which is the central recruitment body for the Civil Service, notifies careers services of the anticipated recruitment requirements in the following year. Later it provides details of the main annual recruitment campaign which is also publicly advertised with a closing date. This scheme is designed to offer university and polytechnic students opportunities during the spring to apply for appointments to be taken up later in the year. In addition, further vacancies (many of which demand specialist experience) are advertised individually throughout the year – most opportunities for biologists are handled this way.

Many posts require a good honours degree, or equivalent, but there are others suited to entrants with other degrees or HND/HNC qualifications. Disciplines most in demand are *physics, electronics, electrical* and *mechanical engineering, mathematics, computer science, chemistry* and *chemical engineering*. Vacancies also occur for *civil structural* and *aeronautical engineers, materials scientists, information scientists, health physicists* and *biologists*.

Operational research
The importance of OR is widely recognised in government service. A number of departments have OR units, covering a considerable range of studies: Customs and Excise, Departments of the Environment and Transport, Department of Health and Social Security, Department of Industry, Home Office, Manpower Services Commission, Ministry of Defence, HM Treasury.

Ministry of Defence
Work ranges from pioneering research to design assessment and trials of equipment. The 30 plus research establishments are mainly in the south of England and constitute one of the largest scientific complexes in the western world. They have exceptional facilities.

Departments of the Environment and Transport
Research and professional advice work covers the scientific and engineering requirements of building and construction, fire safety, the environment, the performance of major hydraulics projects, and a wide range of transport studies.

Overseas Development Administration
Tackles the problems of developing countries, ranging from integrated land resource studies, through pest control, to post-harvest handling of agricultural and fish produce. Many of the staff spend periods of time abroad.

Ministry of Agriculture, Fisheries and Food
Carries out research and provides advice relevant to the improvement of agriculture, horticulture and fishing in England and Wales, and on food science and nutrition.

Home Office
Maintains a forensic science service, and caters to the needs of the police, fire and penal services and home defence by developing and evaluating equipment and carrying out operational studies.

Department of Agriculture and Fisheries for Scotland
Responsible for the promotion and development of the agricultural and

fishing industries in Scotland. Scientists undertake relevant research and development, and provide technical assistance and advisory services.

Salaries
Up-to-date information about current levels is available from the Civil Service Commission.

Scottish Equitable Life Assurance Society

The Scottish Equitable was founded in 1831. Its reputation, fostered over many years, is among the most respected in the business world. At the same time it is modern, forward looking and progressive. As a result of expansion in recent years its funds now exceed £598 million. The commitment to future expansion ensures more and bigger jobs in the years ahead – jobs that will be filled by today's recruits. Career prospects are better now than they have ever been.

Types of graduate required
Honours graduates in *mathematics* are suitably qualified to embark on an actuarial career. They are expected to undertake the examinations of the Faculty of Actuaries in Scotland. Graduates in other degree subjects, or with general degrees, are expected to undertake the examinations of the Chartered Insurance Institute; they have scope for career fulfilment either as administrators in a wide variety of fields such as investment, computers, pension scheme administration and the legal side of life assurance; or in marketing and sales promotion.

Training
Administrative trainees do their training in the society's head office in Edinburgh. Courses are arranged and time off is given for daytime study and tuition classes. Trainees are moved periodically between departments in order to furnish their career with a broad base. During this period it is important that examination success should be combined with a genuine and effective contribution to departmental work.

Sales trainees are given an intensive course at head office before being posted to one of the society's branches for further on the job training.

Locations
Head office in Edinburgh, branch offices throughout UK.

Salaries and prospects
Starting salaries depend on the quality of degrees. Both categories can expect substantial increases on passing each part of the examinations, and soon after completion of the examinations there is every chance of appointment to a junior or middle management post. The society operates a modern job related salary system. On present day values in Edinburgh middle management salaries range from about £9,500 to £13,100 and there are prospects of senior appointments at salaries well beyond this level.

Other amenities
We offer non-contributory pension and PHI scheme, house purchase facilities, staff restaurant, good holidays, and flexible working hours.

Activities
Life assurance and pensions business

Employees
540

Location: UK
Scotland

Opportunities
Actuarial; Administration; Computers; Investment research and analysis; Legal; Pension schemes; Marketing and sales

Vacancies
4–5

Application address
Staff Department, Scottish Equitable Life Assurance Society, 31 St Andrew Square, Edinburgh EH2 2QZ

Scottish Provident Institution

Activities
Mutual life assurance and pension business

Employees
600

Location: UK
Scotland

Opportunities
Acturial; Investment; Management; Computer analysts; General insurance

Vacancies
6

Application address
Secretary, Scottish Provident Institution,
6 St Andrew Square, Edinburgh EH2 2YA

We are one of the leading Scottish mutual life assurance offices transacting life assurance, annuity and pensions business through branches in all parts of the United Kingdom and the Republic of Ireland.

Types of graduate required

At our head office in Edinburgh we have a regular though strictly limited requirement for graduates with good honours degrees in *mathematics* or *statistics* who wish to follow an actuarial career and also have occasional vacancies for graduates with appropriate degrees who are seeking careers in general life assurance or as computer or investment analysts.

Location

You will be based at the head office in Edinburgh.

Salaries and prospects

Salaries are fully competitive with those applicable throughout the industry. Fringe benefits include a non-contributory pension scheme, a house mortgage scheme and flexible working hours. Promotion to management at head office or the branches is based entirely on merit and there are excellent prospects for graduates and non-graduates alike.

Scottish Special Housing Association

Activities
Public sector house designing, building and management

Employees
2,000

Location: UK
Scotland

Opportunities & places
Housing management trainees 6

Application address
Recruitment & Training Officer, SSHA,
15/21 Palmerston Place, Edinburgh
Tel: 031-225 1281

The SSHA is a government sponsored organisation which designs, builds, modernises and manages houses in the public sector, supplementing local authority building. It owns nearly 95,000 houses throughout Scotland and is currently involved in urban redevelopment in Glasgow.

Types of graduate required

The association recruits trainees of *any* discipline to train in housing management. Emphasis in selection is on personal qualities since the work demands social commitment; an ability to communicate; numeracy; and an interest in housing.

Training

Trainees gain experience in all aspects of housing management through our individually planned training programme lasting two years. The first year offers experience in house letting; rent accounting; estate management and house maintenance; housing welfare and liaison with social services. Throughout, emphasis is laid on personal contact with tenants. In the second year trainees move to another area office and are allocated specific duties and responsibilities. Graduates must take a correspondence course for the housing professional qualification for which the association pays all fees. Trainees are expected to pass the first part of the course by the end of the two years training. The nature of the training makes mobility a necessity.

Prospects

On completion of the training scheme graduates apply for promotion and with experience, ability and the appropriate professional qualifications (normally membership of the Institute of Housing) graduates can expect steady managerial and financial progress within the department.

Salaries

Competitive salaries are offered.

Benefits
Four weeks annual leave. Flexitime in most offices. 37 hour week.
Superannuation scheme (Local Government). Relocation expenses.

Scottish Widows' Fund and Life Assurance Society

Activities
Life assurance and pension schemes administration

Employees
1,600

Location: UK
Scotland

Opportunities
Actuarial student traineeships

Application address
Mr AM MacIntyre, Staff Manager, Scottish Widows' Fund and Life Assurance Society, 15 Dalkeith Road, Edinburgh EM16 5BU

We are one of the largest and oldest life assurance offices in Scotland, with funds exceeding £1,800 million. As a mutual society having no shareholders, all the profits belong to the policy holders.

Types of graduate required
We are looking for graduates with honours in *mathematics* who are keen to qualify as actuaries. This career is highly recommended to practical mathematicians. In the early stages, training is given in the practical actuarial and statistical aspects of life assurance and pension schemes. Later, experience will be gained in more technical aspects such as investment analysis, computer programming and administration. The initial salary is very competitive. Shortly after qualifying there are good chances of promotion to managerial positions and through an established programme of management development further prospects of promotion to responsible and highly paid posts are excellent. Graduates in other subjects are also employed on administrative work, in some cases with a view to joining the sales staff.

Location
Graduates are employed at our head office in Edinburgh.

Other amenities
Conditions of employment include a generous non-contributory pension scheme, permanent health insurance, house loan facilities, four weeks annual holiday from the outset, productivity bonus and flexible working hours.

Security Pacific National Bank

Activities
Full range of banking and financial services

Employees
185 UK

Location: UK
London

Locations: Overseas
Worldwide

Opportunities
General banking; International banking

With origins dating back to 1871, Security Pacific is now the tenth largest bank in the United States with assets of $33 billion and nearly 700 branches worldwide. From our head office in Los Angeles, we offer a full range of financial services through our branches and subsidiaries in over half of the United States and in 27 foreign countries. Our London office, which houses our Europe, Middle East and Africa headquarters, opened in 1969. We employ 185 staff there engaged in all aspects of international banking. From London we market the bank's services to domestic and multinational corporations, to banks and to public sector entities in Europe, the Middle East and Africa.

Graduate opportunities
We shall be looking for a small number of high calibre graduates of *any* discipline. Although academic ability is undoubtedly important to us, we place an equally strong emphasis on personality and motivation. Whilst most of our credit and marketing officers have at least a first degree qualification, some will be qualified accountants or lawyers. Our management structure worldwide contains graduates from most major universities.

Graduate training programme

The training programme for our UK graduate intake is broadly similar to the programme which is run for US graduates at our head office.

The programme encompasses a broad array of international finance modules, including general commercial lending, cash flow analysis, trade finance, country risk analysis, eurocurrency loan syndication, foreign exchange trading and the services of the merchant banking division. While the programme will for the most part be conducted in London, through both formal course work and on the job training, it will also involve periods of training in Los Angeles and New York.

Career development

It is anticipated that UK graduates, following their period of training, will have the opportunity to follow a career path as international bankers with no geographical limitations, although linguistic abilities as well as performance will tend to govern selection for assignments to non-English speaking parts of the world. The opportunities for travel abroad are excellent and, indeed, officers of the bank can expect to travel as part of their general training and in the normal course of their work.

Terms and conditions of service

Starting salaries will be competitive with those of other US banks in London. Benefits include a non-contributory pension, private medical insurance and house mortgage assistance schemes, together with four weeks annual holiday and free lunches in the staff restaurant.

Applications

If you wish to be considered for one of the vacancies available in 1983 you should submit your letter of application together with a completed university standard introduction form to the address given.

You are encouraged, within reason, to be as full as possible in your submission as selections for interview can only be made on the basis of the information contained in your written application. Initial interviews will be arranged on campus with second interviews taking place in London.

Application address
LM Browning Esq, Vice President
Administrative Services, Security Pacific
National Bank, 2 Arundel Street, London
WC2R 3DF
Tel: 01-379 7355

Seiscom Delta United

SDU is a United States based geophysical contractor engaged by oil companies on a worldwide basis for the exploration, usually by seismic methods, of hydrocarbon deposits. The company employs several hundred staff in managerial and professional grades together with a large number of skilled, semi-skilled and manual workers.

Types of graduate required

At present SDU have no United Kingdom contracts, however there are locations, in remote areas, in Africa, South America, the Far East and Australia, where contracts are at present in progress and where graduates in *electronics/physics* and in *geology/geophysics* are required in addition to graduates in *land surveying*.

Career opportunities

The company is particularly interested in graduates who are looking for an outdoor life in the less developed areas of the world and are willing to put up with a certain amount of hardship and are able to live in a small enclosed community. Training is carried out in the field on a seismic crew. The electronic engineers are recruited as assistant observer/engineers and after a period of a year or less, depending on aptitude and

Activities
Geophysical contractors, engaged by oil companies, for the exploration of hydrocarbon deposits

Locations: Overseas
Worldwide

Opportunities
Engineers; Seismologists; Surveyors

Application address
Seiscom Delta United, 6/7 Rusham Road Industrial Estate, Egham, Surrey

personal progress within the organisation, would progress to observer, possibly in charge of a recording crew of several hundred personnel. The geologist/geophysicist would be employed as assistant seismologist, working as part of a team and liaising with client oil companies with promotional prospects to seismologist. Graduate surveyors also train in the field.

All positions usually lead to promotion into managerial levels starting with the party chief who is in charge of the entire crew or contract, on financial, technical and administrative levels. Positions are all single status.

Applications
Please contact the Regional Manager at the address given.

Seismograph Service Limited

The company was founded in 1946 as a British subsidiary of Seismograph Service Corporation of Tulsa USA, one of the major geophysical exploration contractors to the petroleum industry, and is now a member of the Raytheon Group. It provides a worldwide exploration service, operating only as a contractor for geological exploration by geophysical methods. The exploitation of any discoveries is the business of its clients.

Types of graduate required
Applicants who will become the key geophysical staff to fill the higher technical and managerial positions in the company must have honours degrees in either: *electronics* or *physics with electronics*, for the position of field seismologist in charge of instrumentation and the acquisition of seismic data on seismic field crews; or *physics with geology* or *geophysics*, for the position of seismologist concerned with the processing and analysis of seismic data in field crews and in DP centres both in UK and overseas.

Training
After a short induction course at Holwood, candidates for field work will join a seismic field party in the instrument section, where they will train as assistants to experienced field seismologists, and where they are expected to gain experience of all the work of a seismic party to qualify for the position of party chief. Candidates for seismic processing and analysis will train at head office, and they may be sent overseas quite early in their careers if engaged for worldwide assignment.

Locations
The head office is situated at Holwood, Keston, Kent, a mansion built in 1825. The Holwood estate consists of about 120 acres of parkland in which tests of seismic equipment are carried out. An extensive programme of research and development of new instruments and data processing techniques is conducted by the company's research team.

The data processing centre enables the company to maintain a complete processing service for the presentation of all the seismic field data obtained. To complement this central operation a number of smaller computer installations have been established near overseas field operations, to give a faster turn round of data from the more remote exploration areas.

The seismic exploration carried out by the company is in all the principal areas of petroleum exploration on both land and sea throughout the world. Some of these areas are quite remote, and the work is in many different climates and conditions.

Activities
Worldwide geophysical exploration by seismic methods for minerals (mainly petroleum)

Employees
1,300

Locations: UK
General

Locations: Overseas
Worldwide continents and oceans excluding the USA

Opportunities
Seismologist: processing and analysis of raw seismic data in field and head office locations; Field seismologist: operation and servicing of electronic instrumentation and production of raw seismic data in field locations

Vacancies
85

Upper age limit
26

Application address
Personnel Manager, Seismograph Service Limited, Holwood, Westerham Road, Keston, Kent BR2 6HD

Seismograph Service Limited, cont

Prospects

Starting salaries are in line with those of similar industries and in addition very generous field allowances are paid. The company operates a contributory pension scheme and a free life assurance scheme. A young graduate can anticipate better than average promotion prospects in what is essentially a young person's profession, with all the interest of exploration and overseas travel.

See the booklet *Opportunities for Graduates with Seismograph Service Limited* in your university careers library.

Miss Selfridge Ltd

Miss Selfridge was launched in 1966 and now has over 60 shops in the UK with plans for further expansion. We aim to provide up to the minute young fashions, an instant top to toe look for now which is constantly changing to match the mood and trends of the moment. Everything in the shop is designed and sold by young people who understand today's feeling for fashion and who are enthusiastic about what they are selling and can advise on fashion problems.

Activities
Young fashion retailing

Employees
1,500

Locations: UK
General

Opportunities
Shop and branch management

Upper age limit
25

Application address
Personnel Manager, (DOG 83), Miss Selfridge Ltd, 21–27 Warple Way, Acton, London W3

Types of graduate required

We require a number of graduates both male and female of *any* degree discipline to join our management training scheme. The personal qualities that are important to a successful retailing career are individual creativity and flair combined with an ability to lead staff enthusiastically.

Training

Our management trainee scheme is designed to give sound practical knowledge and experience of our type of retailing. You would be working in one of our branches with the manager and assistant, learning from and assisting with all aspects of retail shop management. This is coupled with regular periods in our training centre, where we aim to back up practical experience with theoretical knowledge. During the training period we would move you frequently to other units to widen your knowledge, so it is essential that you are willing to work and live anywhere in the UK.

Prospects

We endeavour to promote from within the company wherever possible, therefore most of our middle and senior management positions, and some of those on the administrative side, are filled by management trainees who have worked as assistant shop managers or managers within the company. We hope to be able to promote to assistant shop manager within nine months dependent on ability and then to manager within one year.

Further information

We are always pleased to hear from suitable applicants, so if you are young and fashion conscious and feel that Miss Selfridge offers the kind of opportunity to bring out the best in you, please write to us.

Selfridges

Activities
Department store retailing offering a comprehensive range of merchandise and customer services

Employees
2,500

Location: UK
London

Opportunities & places
Retail management 20

Upper age limit
25

Application address
Miss RMB Hall, Training and Development Manager, Selfridges Limited, 400 Oxford Street, London W1A 1AB

Selfridges Ltd

Selfridges Limited – There's no place like it!

Background

Selfridges, a household name and one of the world's great department stores, is in the heart of London's West End. We have an international reputation for the range of our merchandise and customer services, for our many varied, exciting exhibitions and promotions – and for the quality of our staff. We employ 2,500 people and have a turnover in excess of £100 million.

Graduates required

The demands of modern retailing are exciting and challenging. To help us respond to this and keep ahead in a competitive market we are looking for about 20 honours graduates to join our retail management training scheme. This is an intensive programme geared to rapid promotion to junior management positions. We want graduates with at least a lower second class honours degree, who combine intellectual ability with drive, leadership and commonsense.

Management training scheme

You will learn a lot from practical experience in a variety of selling and sales supporting departments but this will be complemented by a number of training courses held in Selfridges and the West London Institute of Higher Education.

For your first three months you will be assigned to a group merchandise manager (GMM) who controls several related departments. During this time you will gain experience of selling and dealing with customer problems. You will learn to use our point of sale, stock control and paperwork systems. The next three-month placement will be in a contrasting selling area where you will have the opportunity to supervise a section of a department or manage a specific project. You will then spend three months in the administrative areas of the store such as personnel, promotions, accounting services and customer relations.

To reinforce this practical experience you will attend a number of training courses on subjects ranging from selling techniques to buying procedures to supervisory skills. A comprehensive programme of weekly tutorials is arranged to cover most aspects of retailing in Selfridges. You will also study for a certificate in management studies (CMS) at the West London Institute of Higher Education. This course will give you an excellent grounding in business management covering subjects from finance and accounting to behavioural science and computers.

Career opportunities

After this training you should be well prepared to assume a junior management role in either selling or sales supporting functions. There are excellent opportunities for those with drive and ambition to progress further within Selfridges.

Benefits

These include attractive salaries, generous discount on merchandise, subsidised staff restaurant, free company dress, medical and dental facilities, company pension and sick pay schemes, interest-free season ticket loans and a wide range of social facilities.

Applications

Please check with your careers service to see if we will be visiting your university and for details of the arrangements. If we are not visiting your university please contact Miss RMB Hall for an application form.

SGRD Limited

SGRD is a research and development company and is part of the Lucas CAV Group. It provides an applied research and new product development service to companies within and without the Lucas Group in the field of high precision hydromechanical and electrohydraulic systems many of which have advanced electronic controls. It is also involved in the design and development of prototype engine management systems for land vehicles.

Activities
Design and development of precision hydraulic, electromechanical and electronically controlled systems

Employees 100+

Opportunities
Hands-on design; New product development

Vacancies 4

Application address
The Engineering Manager, SGRD Ltd, Concord Road, London W3 0SE

Types of graduate required
The company employs *electronic, mechanical* and *control engineers* in small development teams on mainly experimental design and development programmes.

Shand Group

Activities
Building, civil engineering, opencast mining and oil and gas pipeline construction

Employees
1,900

Locations: UK
General

Opportunities & places
Site construction staff 6

Application address
The Director (Civil Engineering), Shand Group, Shand House, Matlock, Derbyshire DE4 3AF

Charter Consolidated Ltd is the ultimate holding company for the Shand Group, a progressive organisation working principally in building, civil engineering, opencast mining, construction plant and oil and gas pipeline sectors of the construction industry, in the UK and overseas.

Construction work undertaken by Shand includes opencast mining, pipelines, reservoirs, river and marine works, main drainage, roads, bridges, tunnelling, industrial buildings and turnkey projects. In Shand, graduates are made to feel part of a team and are given excellent opportunities to gain experience in a variety of work.

Types of graduate required
Graduates are required with degrees in *civil engineering*, and to a lesser extent in *quantity surveying* and *business studies*.

Training
Graduates are encouraged to gain professional qualifications. Most training is carried out on-site under the guidance of qualified staff. Additional technical and management training is given where necessary.

Prospects
Excellent opportunities are available including overseas experience after minimum of two years in the UK. Shand's general policy is to promote from within its own organisation.

Locations
Shand head office is near Matlock, in an attractive part of Derbyshire, with area offices in Leeds, Runcorn, Birmingham and Derby. Most of Shand's work is carried out north of a line from Bristol to London, although it is our policy to progressively extend our areas of operation.

Applications
Any applicant interested in a career with Shand should write for an application form to the address given.

COMPUTER SERVICES

Activities
Computer services in engineering

Employees
250

Locations: UK
London; West Midlands; North East; North West; Scotland

Opportunities
Customer support consultants

Upper age limit
35

Application address
Engineering Systems Manager, Service in Informatics and Analysis Ltd, 23 Lower Belgrave Street, London SW1W 0NW

SIA Computer Services

SIA is one of the leading computing service organisations in the UK. The company was formed in 1968 and after an initial very rapid growth has achieved steady growth over the years. We are now part of the French computer service group called CISI who in turn are owned by the French atomic energy commission. The group turnover is such as to make us, probably, the largest computer service organisation in Europe.

The business
We specialise in offering a computer bureau service in the engineering and scientific fields, and we believe that the key to success is to provide competent engineers and scientists to work on client problems and advise clients on the use of our computer and applications packages. Our service is based on the use of Control Data 170 and 6000 series computers, located at our London, Victoria headquarters, and on IBMs and a CRAY supercomputer located elsewhere within the group in France.

Types of graduate required
Our engineering systems staff comprises engineers with civil, mechanical, aeronautical and chemical background all of whom are graduates mostly with industrial experience. Company policy is to promote from within so prospects of enhancement are good. Our recruitment is reviewed annually and, in certain circumstances, we may have a limited number of vacancies for postgraduate qualifiers with an engineering degree and research relevant to engineering computing applications.

Salaries
The company offers a bonus and profit sharing scheme. Staff assessments are made twice annually.

Activities
Chartered accountants in public practice

Employees
40

Location: UK
London

Opportunities & places
Trainee chartered accountants 4

Application address
NT Prozzer, Silver Altman & Co, High Holborn House, 52/54 High Holborn, London WC1V 6RT

Silver Altman & Co

We are an eight partner firm based in High Holborn with a staff of about 40 and an annual recruitment of four/five. Our clients range from sole traders and partnerships to limited companies, both large and small, including groups of companies.

Our students receive a variety of experience with particular emphasis on accounting and bookkeeping, auditing (including computer audits), taxation and management.

Training
We provide, through our membership of the HAT Training Syndicate, a comprehensive training programme covering both practical techniques and professional examinations. Particulars of other syndicate training arrangements are given in the entry under HAT.

Salaries
Our salary structure is competitive, and individual salaries as well as progress in training are under regular review.

Further information
Please write with brief personal details to NT Prozzer at the address given.

Smallfield Fitzhugh Tillett & Co

Activities
Chartered accountancy

Employees
58

Location: UK
London

Opportunities
Trainee chartered accountants

Application address
Smallfield Fitzhugh Tillett & Co, Chartered Accountants, 24 Portland Place, London W1N 4AU

Smallfields is a medium sized, West End firm of chartered accountants, founded in the late 19th century. The firm is engaged in all aspects of the professional accountant's work as well as providing its clients with general financial advisory services. Our clients range from public companies through to smaller businesses, covering the fields of industry, commerce and the professions. Work on these clients' affairs provides the student with a wide range of experience and a comprehensive professional training in accountancy and auditing.

Types of graduate required
Graduates may be of *any* discipline provided they have the necessary personal qualities to accept responsibility and work as a co-operative member of a team.

Training
During the three years of the training contract graduates follow a specific practical internal programme, and receive six-monthly personal reviews of progress. In addition, the firm finances outside tuition courses in preparation for the Institute's professional examinations.

Prospects
Trainees' prospects will be influenced by their success in the professional examinations and the quality of their work. After qualification students are encouraged to stay with the firm and gain post-qualification experience. Excellent opportunities are available for advancement to management level or higher.

Applications
Applications demonstrating your written communication skills together with details of your academic attainments should be sent to John Maskell at the address given.

The Jefferson Smurfit Group

Activities
Paper, packaging and print manufacturers

Employees
12,000

Locations: UK & Ireland
General

Locations: Overseas
USA; Nigeria; Australia

Opportunities & places
Management trainees 3–5

Application address
The Director of Personnel Services, Smurfit Ltd, PO Box 25, Orford Lane, Warrington WA2 7AD

The Jefferson Smurfit Group is a public company in the paper, packaging and print business, employing some 12,000 people worldwide. The company originated and is based in the Republic of Ireland, 2,500 people are employed there and 3,700 in the UK. The management is decentralised with a sophisticated financial reporting system as the principal means of control; with 55 small operating companies in Ireland and the UK, which are individually profit responsible, the group has the advantages of both large and small companies. The Jefferson Smurfit group has shown spectacular growth over the last five years and intends to continue this expansion.

Types of graduate required
Business studies graduates are preferred, however of more importance are the personal qualities of ambition and leadership.

Training
Initial training consists of a week at group headquarters in Dublin covering all aspects of the group; subsequent training programmes are flexible and tailored to the needs of the individual. The trainee will then be seconded to work on current projects, assuming responsibility at an early stage.

Career progression
Progress is assessed at two or three monthly intervals while the individual

is moved within the group to gain varied experience. This period lasts between 18 months and three years. The trainee is then assigned a junior executive post. Future progress depends upon merit, as further openings occur.

Mobility
Mobility between the UK and the Republic of Ireland is essential.

Further information
Please apply to our UK office, on our application form available from careers offices. Interviews will be arranged to suit candidates.

Software Sciences

Software Sciences

Activities
Leading international computing consulting and implementation organisation serving all sectors of commerce, industry, government

Employees
650

Locations: UK
London; South East; North West

Locations: Overseas
Netherlands; Belgium

Opportunities
Trainee programmers

Upper age limit
29

Application address
Graduate Recruitment Officer, Software Sciences Limited, Abbey House, 282–292 Farnborough Road, Farnborough, Hampshire GU14 7BN
Tel: 0252 44321

Software Sciences has an international reputation for its work with computers in areas as diverse as banking, airline departure control, space research, race horse betting, newspaper production, stock control, personnel information, and industrial process control. Its clients range from first time users to the most experienced government departments and financial institutions. They come to Software Sciences for consultancy, systems design, programming, original software development, complete system implementation, or any other way in which the group's experience can contribute to the more effective application of the computer.

Types of graduate required
We are interested in graduates in *any* discipline. Their individual ability, personality, attitudes, and potential are more important than the subject; although we will build on any specialist knowledge they have acquired at university.

Why Software Sciences?
Software Sciences had practical experience of every type of computer system from main frame to microprocessor. Consultancy and implementation assignments have been undertaken for all ranges of large computer systems; the company has designed and implemented over 150 mini-based systems on a turnkey basis; and has installed many hundreds of microprocessor based point-of-use systems. This work has demanded in-depth knowledge of manufacturers' standard software, and the skills to develop special software – such as operating systems, database handlers, languages, and compilers – to meet specialised operational criteria. It is backed by large scale hardware system text and commissioning facilities, and by a comprehensive hardware design and production facility for microprocessor systems.

Training
Training is both formal and practical and aims at giving you the expertise and experience which our clients expect. Initially, you will acquire a high degree of skill in the tools of the trade, for example computer programming and the techniques of systems analysis. You will very soon put this to practical effect and then build on these basic skills with training and job experience both in applications and in the techniques and technologies of computing and related activities.

Your future
The variety of Software Sciences' activities, which embrace every type of computer at every level of involvement, gives graduate entrants a unique opportunity to gain broad experience at the very earliest stages of their careers. We recognise that our future expansion, and the maintenance of the high standards our clients demand, depend on the individual abilities

Addresses for Applications

BELFAST
Arthur Boyd
Spicer and Pegler, Boyd & Co
Scottish Amicable House
11 Donegall Square South
Belfast BT1 5JT
Telephone (0232) 22861

BIRMINGHAM AND DUDLEY
Peter Bendall
Newater House
11 Newhall Street
Birmingham B3 3NY
Telephone (021) 236 4846

BOURNEMOUTH
Brian Ford
Tregonwell Court
118 Commercial Road
Bournemouth BH2 5LT
Telephone (0202) 291655

BRISTOL
Michael Grant
Queen Anne House
69/71 Queen Square
Bristol BS1 4AE
Telephone (0272) 293082

CAMBRIDGE AND PETERBOROUGH
Richard Summerfield
Leda House
Station Road
Cambridge CB1 2RN
Telephone (0223) 61281

CARDIFF
Malcolm Wilton
3 Castle Street
Cardiff CF1 4ST
Telephone (0222) 22861

EDINBURGH
Thomas Moffet
Spicer Watson & Co
6 Rutland Square
Edinburgh EH1 2AU
Telephone (031) 229 2208

GLASGOW
Sandy Maclaurin
Spicer Watson and Co
65 Renfield Street
Glasgow G2 1NS
Telephone (041) 331 1501

GUERNSEY
John de Putron
Spicer and Pegler
Commerce House
Les Banques
PO Box 119
St Peter Port
Guernsey
Channel Islands
Telephone (0481) 24561

ISLE OF MAN
Michael Rayton
Spicer and Pegler, Clarke & Rayton
10-12 St George's Street
Douglas
Telephone (0624) 25015/8

LEEDS
John Smith
29 Park Place
Leeds LS1 2ST
Telephone (0532) 39021

LONDON AND CROYDON
Anthony Patteson
St Mary Axe House
56/60 St Mary Axe
London EC3A 8BJ
Telephone (01) 283 3070

MANCHESTER AND FARNWORTH
Graham Calder
PO Box 498
12 Booth Street
Manchester M60 3ED
Telephone (061) 236 9721

NEWCASTLE UPON TYNE
Michael Gilbert
Central Exchange Buildings
93a Grey Street
Newcastle upon Tyne NE1 6EA
Telephone (0632) 614111

NOTTINGHAM
Peter Hipperson
Clumber Avenue
Nottingham NG5 1AH
Telephone (0602) 607131

SOUTHAMPTON
Hedley Rossell
Carlton House
Carlton Place
Southampton SO1 2DZ
Telephone (0703) 25042

Spicer and Pegler
Chartered Accountants
INTERNATIONALLY SPICER AND OPPENHEIM

Software Sciences, cont

of our staff. Therefore, having discovered where your skills and interest lie, we will take every opportunity to actively develop them through a positive policy of career development. Your future may be in management, applications specialisation, software research and development, marketing, or any one of a number of equally important areas. Whichever you choose, at Software Sciences we have a common interest; you want to achieve your ambitions, we expect you to.

Salaries and benefits
Salaries are competitive and future prospects excellent. The company operates a contributory pensions scheme; all other benefits are non-contributory and include BUPA family cover, life assurance, and permanent health insurance.
Ultimate holding company, Thorn-EMI plc.

Spicer and Pegler
Internationally Spicer and Oppenheim

Activities
Chartered accountancy

Employees
1,920 UK
4,950 worldwide

Locations: UK
General

Locations: Overseas
Worldwide

Opportunities & places
Trainee chartered accountants 140

Upper age limit
26

Application address
See local office contacts in the display opposite

Spicer and Pegler is a leading firm of chartered accountants, with offices in over 20 cities in England, Wales, Scotland, Northern Ireland, the Channel Islands and the Isle of Man. The firm has 120 partners and 1,800 staff, of which 380 are students under a training contract, and is probably the tenth largest firm in the United Kingdom.

We offer an opportunity to join a thriving and progressive firm which is large enough to provide an excellent range of experience and one of the best training programmes available, but not too large for the individual to make a mark. Our approach to training enables our staff to provide all round financial advice to our clients.

The firm has a broad base of national and international clients which includes a substantial number of medium and large family companies, professional partnerships and entrepreneurial clients who require from us a positive contribution to the running of their business.

Spicer and Pegler is a founding member of the rapidly growing international firm of Spicer and Oppenheim which is administered from London and provides professional services in 55 countries worldwide.

Types of graduate required
Applications are invited from graduates who have a mixture of a high academic ability together with the personal qualities of drive, determination, motivation, common sense, and above all a readiness to accept responsibility. We want people who are confident in their ability to contribute to a very professional and businesslike environment.

Training
High priority is given to the training of students. For the professional examinations, non-residential courses are run by leading firms of accountancy tutors. We supplement these courses by mock exams held in the office and offering guidance on specific problems. In-house training and residential courses covering a wide variety of topics are run by ourselves at Brunel and Cambridge Universities. Our examination success rate is one of the most impressive in the profession.

Practical experience
Upon joining the firm, each student is allocated to a general audit group consisting of between 20 and 40 people. We ensure that each student obtains experience in dealing with the affairs of a wide variety of clients which will usually include listed and private companies, partnerships and

Spicer and Pegler, cont

sole traders engaged in all areas of manufacturing, commerce and finance.

In addition, there are opportunities for students to gain further practical experience by short spell secondments to some of our specialist departments. These are departments dealing with corporate and personal taxation, computer audit, investigation, insolvency, stockbroking, insurance and farming.

Career development

Students' progress is under constant review and performance on both the professional and in-house training courses is assessed following attendance at the course. In addition, reports are prepared upon practical work performance for each assignment lasting more than two weeks. In addition six-monthly meetings are held with the group manager and training partner to discuss past progress and future career development. All qualified staff, managers and partners receive continued comprehensive training.

Upon qualification there are opportunities available for either transfer or secondment to the specialist departments in the UK or to an office within our international firm.

We offer rapid advancement for above average staff who are prepared to accept responsibility. Our salaries have always been in the top range and our regular reviews of performance ensure that salary increases are commensurate with performance.

Further information and applications

Your careers advisory service has copies of our recruitment booklet and introductory form, together with the date of our intended visit to the university. If you would like an interview at the time of our visit, you should liaise with your careers advisory service. If you would prefer to make a direct application for an interview, please send your introductory form to the Student Partner at the address given.

SPL International

SPL is a major international computer consultancy. The company provides the computer industry, computer users and potential users with a wide range of specialised skills and professional services. Contracts are fulfilled for internationally recognised clients in the fields of commerce, finance, industry and government. Since its formation in 1963 SPL has gained a reputation for high quality work which is founded on the careful and consistent application of standards both in technical and managerial control of complex projects.

The company's past growth and development has been made possible through the selection of the right calibre staff and by investing in training and career progression as well as research into the requirements of the computer industry. Our future is dependent upon maintaining these standards. The company's strength is reflected in the high degree of skill and expertise possessed by our 400 plus technical staff.

We provide:
- feasibility studies into company problems
- selection and evaluation of computer equipment
- design and implementation of commercial, industrial and scientific computer systems
- turnkey systems.

SPL is a leader in industrial computing and specialises in the application of mini and micro computers in manufacturing and process

Activities
Computer systems and software consultancy

Employees
500

Locations: UK
London; South East; Midlands; North West

Locations: Overseas
Holland; Italy; Sweden; Denmark; Norway; USA; Belgium; Germany

Opportunities & places
Computer programming 30+

Upper age limit
30

Application address
The Personnel Manager, SPL International, 12–14 Windmill Street, London W1P 1HF
Tel: 01-636 7833

industries. The software and products division at Abingdon near Oxford is engaged in designing and supplying programming languages, software products, operating systems and expert systems.

Locations

The company operates internationally with offices in the UK (London, Oxford, Manchester), Stockholm, Milan and Utrecht. Last year some 65% of revenue was earned abroad. The majority of staff operate from a UK base but may be assigned to projects in any of the European countries in which the company is active. SPL also operates in North America and has associations with Australasia. Periods abroad are usually in excess of six months. We expect a high degree of mobility from our staff.

The bulk of work is carried out on our clients' premises, both in the UK and abroad. Graduates joining the company will normally spend a few weeks at one of our major UK offices but thereafter may be assigned to projects in any part of our operating territories.

Career development and training

Increasingly the major proportion of new recruits are graduates direct from university. Graduates are normally assigned to projects where they can quickly learn skills by working under the supervision of experienced staff. Their career development is carefully monitored and regularly assessed. Experience, assisted by regular management appraisal and both internal and external training courses, can soon lead to positions of responsibility.

Types of graduate required

We are particularly interested in hearing from graduates with qualifications in *mathematics*, *computer science*, *physics* and *engineering*. Those from other disciplines will also be considered. Computing experience whilst reading for degrees is an asset.

Salaries

Attractive salaries and benefits are offered to successful candidates. Both salary and performance are reviewed at least annually.

Stanley A Spofforth & Co

Activities
Accountancy, audit and taxation services to personal and small company clients

Employees
23

Locations: UK
London and South East

Opportunities & places
Trainee chartered accountants 3/4

Application address
G Desler, Stanley A Spofforth & Co, 16/18 New Bridge Street, London EC4V 6AU

We are a small firm of chartered accountants in the Blackfriars area consisting of seven partners and a staff of about 15. Our annual recruitment is three/four.

The services which we provide are accountancy, audit, taxation with some emphasis in the area of trust and estate accounting, personal income tax and small/medium company accounts.

Because of our size, we are able to offer a wide range of experience quickly and a trainee would be encouraged and expected to take on responsibility at an early stage.

Our salary structure is competitive and individual salaries, as well as progress and training, are under regular review.

Training

We provide through our membership of the HAT Training Syndicate, a comprehensive training programme covering both practice techniques and professional examinations. Particulars of our syndicate training arrangements are given in the entry under HAT.

Please write with brief personal details to G Desler at the address given.

E R Squibb and Sons plc

Squibb is a progressive and expanding company manufacturing a wide range of pharmaceutical and veterinary products. The plant in Wallasey has been constructed to utilise the most modern techniques of production and methods study. In the laboratories, a programme of research continues to improve existing drugs and develop new ones.

Types of graduate required

Squibb recruits *arts* and *science* graduates for a wide variety of positions: general administrators, biochemists, microbiologists, pharmacists and analytical chemists.

Training

This varies according to the position, but the company encourages training internally and externally to ensure maximum development of graduate staff.

Locations

Head office including sales administration is based at Hounslow and the production unit at Wallasey. Opportunities in Wallasey include production quality control, research and development, production control, work study, warehousing, data processing, accounting, purchasing, engineering and personnel.

Salaries

Competitive salaries are paid, according to position and degree standard, and progress is according to merit.

Prospects

With plans for future development, the company anticipates excellent opportunities for promotion for graduates.

Pensions

The company operates an excellent non-contributory pension scheme including life assurance.

Activities
Pharmaceutical research, development and manufacture

Employees
800

Location: UK
North West

Opportunities
Chemists; Microbiologists; Pharmacists

Application address
Senior Personnel Adviser, E R Squibb & Sons plc, Reeds Lane, Moreton, Wirral, Merseyside L46 1QW

Standard Telecommunication Laboratories

For information on career opportunities with STL see our advertisement on page 22 and write for our brochure *Ideas that Work*.

Standard Telephones and Cables plc

STC is the major UK subsidiary of the International Telephone & Telegraph Corporation (ITT). It consists of two major product groups: one dealing with telecommunications and electronics, the other with components and distribution. Both are supported by the extensive research and development facilities of Standard Telecommunication Laboratories (STL).

The telecommunications and electronics group is concerned with the development, manufacture and marketing of public telephone switching systems, information terminals and audio products, landline transmission systems, submarine and military communication systems, marine communication and industrial cables and business systems.

Activities of the components group are centred around electron

STC

Activities
Design, manufacture and marketing of telecommunication and electronic equipment, systems and components

Employees
26,000

Locations: UK
General, mainly South East

Opportunities
Product development; Industrial engineering; Installation/commissioning; Quality assurance/testing; Finance; Marketing; Personnel

Application address
Graduate Recruitment Officer, Standard Telephones and Cables plc, STC House, 190 Strand, London WC2R 1DU

devices, capacitors, quartz and hybrid devices, power components and the distribution of components and instruments.

Types of graduate required
We particularly need *electronic engineers, physicists, mathematicians, computer scientists, mechanical* and *production engineers*; also some people from *other* disciplines who can make their way in administrative positions in marketing, manufacture, personnel, accounting and data processing.

Training
Apart from those who join the finance function, graduates are appointed directly into jobs and training is given both on and off the job as appropriate to their needs.

Salaries and benefits
Salary levels are decided in the spring and will be discussed at location interviews. STC's comprehensive benefits package includes 25 days holiday (plus statutory holidays) for each complete calendar year worked, BUPA membership at reduced rates and contributory pensions scheme.

Most sites also offer a subsidised restaurant, employees' shop and active sports and social club.

Applications procedure
Visit your careers service for our graduate brochure or write to the Graduate Recruitment Officer.

Staveley Industries plc

Activities
Mineral extraction and processing; Electrical and mechanical engineering services; Iron making; Foundry work; Machine tools; Weighing equipment and industrial measurement devices

Employees
5,000

Locations: UK
South East; Midlands; North West

Opportunities
Electrical, control, mechanical and production engineering; Metallurgists; Marketing; Personnel; Computing; Commercial management

Vacancies
10 approx

Application address
The Manager, Personnel Development, Staveley Industries plc, Salter House, Spoon Lane, West Bromwich, West Midlands B70 6AD

Staveley Industries plc is a group of companies in the UK and overseas. We are in a wide variety of industries, including many branches of engineering, metal refining, foundry work and minerals extraction and processing. Our activities and our performance are described in detail in literature which is available in all careers advisory services. Please make use of it and write to us if you would like to know more.

High grade technology underlies a lot of what we do and our success has been built upon this, allied to soundly based investment, strict financial control and good management. As yet we cannot claim to be among the best in the world at everything we do, but our sights are firmly set on that sort of pinnacle.

Because our activities are so varied and because we are organised into small, largely autonomous units, we believe that we can offer a wide range of opportunities to graduates. Most of these are currently in the UK, but our activities overseas are expanding and therefore new possiblities will open up.

Entry can be either into the group as a whole or direct into one of the subsidiaries. In whatever way it is accomplished, however, our objective is the same – to match people to jobs as quickly as possible and in a way which will promote their professional development.

Types of graduate required
Principally *engineers* in *electrical, electronic, control, mechanical* and *production engineering* and *metallurgists*. Applications also from other degree disciplines for marketing, personnel, finance, computing and commercial positions, will be fully considered.

Training
As recommended by appropriate professional institutions and training boards. Programmes vary up to two years and full account is always taken of relevant experience. Use is made of project work, off the job training and postgraduate study as relevant and available.

Staveley Industries plc, cont

Salaries and prospects

Starting salaries are competitive. They are normally reviewed annually and generally more frequently for graduates who require a full basic training programme. Future prospects depend on individual performance and job opportunities within the company. The company is in a strong financial position and is able to undertake significant investment and acquisition decisions which will continue to provide exciting employment opportunities.

Stewart Wrightson

Stewart Wrightson is one of the largest UK based international insurance brokers, running a network of 89 offices in 28 countries throughout the world. Its activities include the management of underwriting agencies and the ownership of a number of overseas insurance companies. In addition it has interests in shipping, airbroking and forestry.

Insurance broking is the arrangement of the best insurance protection for the buyer of insurance. This requires the broker to have a detailed knowledge of the buyers' needs to provide advice regarding control of risk and the range of covers offered by the insurance market.

Graduate recruitment

We are interested in recruiting graduates of *any* discipline. More important than your academic achievement is the ability to quickly establish personal relationships and to develop new and imaginative approaches to increasingly complex management problems.

Training and career development

The aim of the initial training programme is to give graduates a broad understanding of the insurance market in the UK and overseas, whilst providing a detailed introduction to our internal organisation and systems. The examinations of the Chartered Insurance Institute form an integral part of the training programme and we expect our graduates to complete the FCII within four years of starting. Whether graduates join as direct entrants or on the graduate training programme we expect them to perform a responsible job, often with client responsibilities, within two years of joining. Subsequent careers exist within the UK and overseas and it is fair to say that progression can be rapid for consistently good performers.

Location

Graduates are trained at our London and Kingston offices. In 1983 one or two vacancies may possibly occur in our larger regional offices which are located in cities throughout the UK.

Salaries and other benefits

Starting salaries will be competitive with those offered by other major employers. Details will be available at interview. A good fringe benefit package includes an employee share scheme, a non-contributory pensions scheme and season ticket loan.

How to apply

Please write to Fiona Kay, Recruitment Administrator at the address given with a completed standard introductory form.

Stewart Wrightson

Activities
International insurance brokers

Employees
2,450 UK
1,300 overseas

Locations: UK
City of London and Kingston

Locations: Overseas
Opportunities for qualified staff can arise in a number of countries

Opportunities & places
Insurance brokers 6

Application address
Fiona Kay, Recruitment Administrator, Stewart Wrightson UK Group Ltd, Kingston Bridge House, Church Grove, Kingston upon Thames, Surrey KT1 4AG

Stoy Hayward & Co

Activities
Chartered accountancy

Employees
550

Location: UK
London

Locations: Overseas
General

Opportunities & places
Student accountants 50

Application address
David Fowler, Personnel Manager, Stoy
Hayward & Co, 54 Baker Street, London
W1M 1DJ

Stoy Hayward & Co is unusual for its size in that it employs as many senior staff in specialist services as in audit and accounting. The firm has grown particularly over the last 10–15 years and the client range tends to reflect the sectors of business which have flourished during that period. The number of partners has increased from 11 to 32 in eight years.

Types of graduate required
The firm does not restrict graduate entry to *any* particular type of degree course.

Training
Examinations The firm offers a link scheme with the Financial Training Co Ltd, combining home study with full time college attendance. All course fees and study leave within the scheme are paid for by the firm.
Practical training The firm has established practical training courses in auditing and accountancy to meet the requirements of students who are expanding their work range and experience on a continuing basis.
Staff development Training and experience records are maintained and used constructively at six-monthly appraisal interviews with partners to ensure that progress continues over a broad spectrum of professional activity, from new businesses to large public companies.

Location
The base for the student is a modern office in the West End of London, but a great deal of the work is carried out on clients' premises.

Salaries
Salary progression during the period of contract is dependent on ability and on successful completion of the various examinations.

Prospects
The firm can offer satisfying careers after qualifying in auditing, specialist services or overseas.

Systime Ltd

Activities
Manufacture of business systems: computer
hardware and software, with full service and
support

Employees
1,600

Locations: UK
General

Locations: Overseas
Africa; India; USA; Eire; Holland; France; Middle
East

Opportunities
Programming: applications, systems; Hardware
designers; General management trainees

Application address
Graduate Recruitment Officer, Systime Ltd,
Concourse Computer Centre, 432 Dewsbury
Road, Leeds, West Yorkshire
Tel: 0532 702211

Systime are now Britain's largest manufacturer of interactive business computer systems. Based in Leeds the company have 13 UK offices and there are offices in the Middle East, Africa, Asia, Europe and the USA.

Expansion through development
Much of the company's success and rapid growth has been due to its continuous high investment in on-going development programmes in both hardware and software applications. And although its earlier developments were directed toward smaller business systems today Systime market a complete range of upgradeable and totally compatible systems for use in the very largest configurations.

Types of graduate required
Systime have a full graduate training programme open to those with suitable qualifications particularly in *business studies*, *computer sciences*, *electrical engineering* or *electronics*.

Training
The company's graduate training programme generally takes the form of an induction course followed by constant on the job training. Further academic education is actively encouraged. The training programme is run from the company's headquarters in Leeds and all trainees undergo an initial six month performance review.

Start at the top of Britain's computer industry.

In only ten years, Systime have become Britain's No. 1 manufacturer of interactive business systems with offices throughout the UK and major overseas countries.

A big part of our success has been our policy of recruiting young talent and providing the conditions and environment to make the most of that talent.

If you've got a degree in computer sciences, business studies or electronic engineering, or even a sound working knowledge of computers, we'd like to hear from you.

Write or phone:
The Graduate Recruitment Officer, Systime Ltd., Concourse Computer Centre, 432 Dewsbury Road, Leeds LS11 7DF. Tel: (0532) 702211.

BIRMINGHAM • BRISTOL • LONDON
MANCHESTER • NORTHAMPTON • NOTTINGHAM • SLOUGH

BELFAST • DUBLIN • ABERDEEN • LEEDS
NEWCASTLE • GLASGOW • FRANCE • HOLLAND • INDIA

Systime Ltd, cont

Prospects
The success of the company and its on-going expansion programme in the UK and overseas means that prospects within the company are excellent. Salaries are in general higher than the norm for the industry and the company offers a first class company bonus scheme and excellent fringe benefits dependent on position.

New head office and factory
The company's new purpose built headquarters in Leeds provide an exceptional working environment incorporating many in-house amenities and is probably one of the most modern factories and office complexes in Europe. Leeds itself is a very attractive modern city at the M62 and M1 interchange set amongst some of the most beautiful countryside in Britain.

Applications
Applicants are asked to use the standard introduction form (SIF) available from the careers department of the university, college or polytechnic.

Further details on Systime and graduate training schemes run by the company can be obtained from the Graduate Recruitment Officer, at the address given.

Sun Life Assurance plc

Activities
Life assurance and pensions business

Employees
2,500

Location: UK
South West

Opportunities
Actuarial; Administration; Pensions schemes; Sales

Vacancies
30

Upper age limit
25

Application address
Personnel Officer, Sun Life Assurance plc, Sun Life Court, St James Barton, Bristol BS1 3TH

The Sun Life Group, with funds in excess of £1,000 million and with 170 years experience to draw upon, is one of the leading life assurance companies in the country.

In this well established company, graduates are given every encouragement to develop their career paths which could, in turn, eventually lead to positions in management.

Types of graduate required
For graduates in *mathematics*, *statistics* and *economics* there are opportunities to train as actuaries. In addition there are often openings for training in accountancy, computer techniques, pension schemes, sales or general administration.

Salaries and prospects
Although starting salaries depend to some extent on qualifications, a job evaluated system is in operation which provides a salary structure based on the requirements and demands of each job. It is the society's practice for appointments to senior positions to be made from within its staff, through a career development programme.

Training
We have our own training staff and various courses are arranged throughout a person's career development. In addition, day release facilities, tuition grants and increases in salary are made for success in professional qualifications such as those of the Institute of Actuaries or the Chartered Insurance Institute and every encouragement is given for staff to obtain such qualifications.

Locations
Most opportunities will be at our administrative headquarters in Bristol, although there may be openings for sales trainees in provincial cities.

Amenities
The company offers excellent working conditions and fringe benefits

including flexible working hours, free lunches, a non-contributory pension scheme, staff house purchase facilities and a sports and social club.

Sun Life Assurance Company of Canada

Activities
Life assurance and pensions

Employees
800

Location: UK
London

Opportunities & places
Actuarial trainees 2

Upper age limit
23

Application address
Mrs CS Ives, Recruitment Adviser, Personnel Dept, Sun Life Assurance Company of Canada, 2–4 Cockspur Street, London SW1

Sun Life Assurance Company of Canada is the largest Canadian life assurance company with assets exceeding £2,906 million. We have been operating in Great Britain since 1893 and the company became mutual in 1962. Our key activities are life assurance and pensions and we have a nationwide network of branch offices providing a back-up to our representatives.

New developments
Our company products are constantly under review to ensure that we are keeping pace with our competitors and marketing plays an important part in determining our future plans.

Types of graduate required
We recruit one or two graduates each year to train with us as actuaries. Applications are invited from undergraduates studying *mathematics* or *statistics*, who have highly developed communication skills and the ability to mix well with all levels of personnel.

Training and career development
Trainees are allowed two half-days a week for study leave and the Institute is easily accessible for occasional lectures. The small number of actuarial trainees means that they benefit from the individual attention of qualified actuaries and get directly involved in special project work. It is hoped that trainees will take early responsibility for some supervisory duties and when qualified will carry the rank of departmental manager.

Location
Actuarial trainees are based at our London administrative office, close to Trafalgar Square.

Pensions, benefits and amenities
Fringe benefits are excellent and include a subsidied staff mortgage scheme, non-contributory pension scheme, flexible working hours and free lunches.

The Sun of Canada Club provides facilities for darts, table tennis, football, rugby and cricket. Social activities include cheese and wine parties, discos etc.

Selection procedure
Standard introduction forms should be sent directly to the personnel department by the end of January. An interview programme will then be arranged and selected applicants will be invited to our London office for interview in February. Offers are usually sent out early in March.

Salaries
Our starting salaries are highly competitive and are reviewed each year. Salary is increased with examination success and for performance at work.

Tandy Corporation (Branch UK)
Known as Radio Shack in the USA

Tandy Corporation (Branch UK) known as Radio Shack in the USA with in excess of 8,000 outlets worldwide, was launched during 1974 and now has 250 stores in the UK, with plans for 500 outlets. We aim to provide the very latest in hi fi, electronics and microcomputer products and are the manufacturers of the worlds largest selling microcomputer, the Tandy TRS-80. Every store is a profit making centre managed by professional people who are enthusiastic not only in the career opportunities offered by a growth company but also about the products they are selling.

Types of graduate required
We require a number of graduates of *any* degree discipline, although *business studies* graduates are preferred, to join our management training scheme. The personal qualities that are important to a successful retailing career are individual ability to lead staff enthusiastically and an entrepreneurial attitude to work.

Training
Our trainee management scheme is designed to give sound practical knowledge and experience in our type of retailing. You would be working in one of our branches with the manager, learning from and assisting with all aspects of retail shop management. This is combined with training periods in our training centre, where we aim to back up practical experience with theoretical and administrative knowledge. Due to the diversity of our operation we are normally able to offer successful applicants a position near to their homes or relocate to another part of the country as required.

Prospects
It is a policy to promote from within the company wherever possible, therefore our middle and senior management positions and most of those on the administrative side are filled by successful trainees who have worked as trainee store managers or store managers within Tandy Corporation. We would hope to be able to promote you to store manager within a 6–12 months' training period dependant on ability.

Further information
We are constantly looking for suitable applicants, so if you feel you would like to make the retailing profession your choice of career and appreciate the opportunity that Tandy Corporation has to offer then please write to us.

Taylor Instrument Limited

Taylor Instrument Limited, a division of Sybron, USA, is a world leader in the manufacture of process control instrumentation and systems for the measurement and control of industrial processes. Our products range from simple pressure and temperature gauges to the most sophisticated digital systems utilising microprocessors and process computers.

Types of graduate required
We seek a limited number of high calibre graduates in the following disciplines: *physics, electronic* and *chemical engineering, instrumentation and control,* and *computer science,* but other disciplines will be considered in certain circumstances.

Taylor Instrument Limited, cont

Application address
Personnel Officer, Taylor Instrument Limited, Gunnels Wood Road, Stevenage, Hertfordshire SG1 2EL
Tel: 0438 2366

Training
Our training programmes take into account individual requirements and where appropriate those of the relevant professional institution. There are some opportunities for two year training assignments in the USA.

Career opportunities
Graduates are principally recruited into our systems engineering department, as project engineers, applications programmers, and hardware or software engineers. Career progression at all levels is based on performance and ability.

Taylor Instrument Ltd Analytics Division

Activities
Analytical instrument manufacturers

Employees
230

Opportunities
Administration; Computing; Research; Design; Development; Finance; Production engineering; Manufacturing; Marketing

Application address
Personnel Department, Taylor Instrument Ltd Analytics Division, Crowborough, Sussex

Taylor Instrument Ltd Analytics Division, a part of the Sybron Corporation of Rochester NY, USA, is firmly established in the analytical instrument market with main product lines being oxygen analysis, gas chromatography and EVT analysers.

Types of graduate required
We need *development*, *application* and *electronic engineers*, *marketing* specialists and *chemists* preferably with GC experience, but other qualifications are considered when the need arises.

Training
This is adapted to suit each person. Exposure to the right experience and on the job and day release for further study can be arranged.

Taylor Woodrow International Limited

Activities
International building, civil and mechanical engineering contractors

Employees
1,000

Location: UK
London

Locations: Overseas
Worldwide outside Common Market area

Opportunities
Civil, mechanical engineers; Builders; Quantity surveyors

Vacancies
12

Application address
The Personnel Manager, Taylor Woodrow International Ltd, Western House, Western Avenue, London W5 1EU

Taylor Woodrow International Limited is one of the world's foremost construction contractors, and is engaged in a programme of ambitious building, civil, and mechanical engineering projects overseas. TWI, which is a member of the Taylor Woodrow Group of companies, is responsible for construction work undertaken outside the Common Market area, in addition to work also carried out by local Taylor Woodrow companies overseas.

At present, the company is engaged on a variety of projects ranging from the construction of housing, multi-storey buildings, marine works, irrigation schemes, road/drainage contracts to the installation of industrial plant for the recovery of various minerals.

In recognition of TWI's achievements, it was presented with the Queen's Award for Industry in 1972 and in 1977 received the Queen's Award for Export Achievement.

Types of graduate required
Graduates with degrees in *civil engineering*, *building* and *quantity surveying* are recruited. Also *mechanical engineers* for work in connection with the maintenance and repair of contractors' plant, with the design and installation of building services, and for the design and construction of industrial complexes which require plant for the processing of materials and minerals.

Training

All graduates follow a programme of work experience which meet the requirements of the various institutions. The programmes are flexible in order to meet the aims and needs of each individual, but follow a well defined pattern designed to give young people the best possible grounding in their chosen field, plus the necessary experience for membership of the appropriate professional institution. Site experience in most instances is gained on our numerous sites overseas.

Taylor Woodrow International is also interested in the further development of team members after they have attained professional status, and makes use of both internal and external courses as appropriate.

Service conditions and salaries

For the first three years, young people working abroad are required to serve on single status, and therefore recruitment is limited to single persons.

Starting salaries are attractive, and are competitive with other UK companies. Salaries are reviewed regularly and reflect both performance and responsibility in the job. Overseas salaries vary with the cost of living and taxes in the country of employment; however, they are adjusted in recognition of the generally difficult climatic conditions, long hours, and often arduous working conditions that can exist abroad compared to those in the UK, and are financially advantageous.

TWI also offers the normal range of benefits that one would expect from a major international company.

Prospects

The policy of promotion on merit from within gives young people the opportunity to attain positions of responsibility at an early age.

Further information

This is contained in the brochures *Students – Join the Team at Taylor Woodrow International Limited* and *Opportunities for Graduates with Taylor Woodrow* and on our film cassette *Taylor Woodrow International*. These are available, together with application forms, at many university and polytechnic careers advisory services, or direct from the Personnel Manager.

The Teaching Profession (Scotland)

Activities
Teaching in Scottish schools

Location: UK
Scotland

Opportunities
Teaching

Application address
The Advisory Service on Entry to Teaching in Scotland, 5 Royal Terrace, Edinburgh EH7 5AF

Teaching remains one of the few professions which enables graduates to embark on a worthwhile career while pursuing their academic and other interests to the full. The long established reputation of Scottish education has been sustained and revitalised in recent years by the introduction of new services and techniques, and by the expansion of the equipment and resources available to a teacher.

Teaching as a career can offer the graduate considerable job satisfaction, but the demands are often great, and a sympathetic understanding of the problems and needs of young people is important.

Although there is now no overall shortage of teachers, teaching vacancies arise every session in primary and secondary schools and there are still shortages of teachers of certain secondary subjects notably business studies, mathematics, the science subjects (especially physics) and technical education.

Training

Scotland has long recognised the value of the professional training of graduates. Such training, given by the colleges of education and normally taking the form of a one session postgraduate course, provides the skills and the background knowledge required for teaching. A graduate successfully completing the course will be eligible to register with the General Teaching Council for Scotland: a pre-requisite for employment in education authority and grant aided schools.

In-service training keeps teachers abreast of new developments in education, and enables them to improve their qualifications or broaden their spheres of interest. Those wishing to take a qualification to teach in special schools normally take this on an in-service basis.

Financial assistance

Awards made under the students' allowances scheme are normally continued during teacher training. Particulars of this scheme may be obtained from the *Scottish Education Department, Awards Branch, Haymarket House, Clifton Terrace, Edinburgh EH12 5DT*.

Prospects

Half the teachers in secondary schools hold promoted posts. Principal teacher and headteacher posts are being offered to men and women at a much earlier stage in their careers. Opportunities also exist for graduate teachers to move to jobs in administration, HM Inspectorate, and the colleges of education.

Pensions

Teachers and employers contribute to a statutory pension scheme. In addition to a lump sum, a teacher with five or more years service will on attaining age 60 and on retiral, receive a pension based on total reckonable service and the highest amount of full salary for a successive 365 days of reckonable service whether continuous or not during the final three years of such service.

Those interested in a career in teaching should speak to their appointments officer or write to the Advisory Service on Entry to Teaching in Scotland at the address given.

Texas Instruments Limited

TEXAS INSTRUMENTS
LIMITED

...where people and technology meet

Activities
Creating, making and marketing semiconductor devices, seismic exploration, computer manufacture

Employeees
2,500

Locations: UK
South East and South West

Locations: Overseas
Europe; United States; South America and Far East after some years experience

Opportunities
Design and development; Computers; Electronic production; Engineering: software, product, manufacturing; Marketing; Sales; Quality assurance; Finance

Vacancies
30

Texas Instruments has been working at the heart of the microelectronics revolution for over a quarter of a century, producing sophisticated semiconductor devices for a wide range of applications.

Maintaining our lead in the world's most dynamic and competitive industry depends on attracting a constant flow of new talent. Men and women with the imagination and technical skills to make a genuine contribution to our success.

Our standards are high, but then so are the rewards we offer. Early responsibility, intensive training, generous salaries and benefits and the chance to play a vital role in our organisation from the moment you join.

A history of innovation

Texas Instruments began life in 1930 as Geophysical Services, the world's first seismic survey contractor. Inaugurated as a separate company in 1951, we produced the first commercial transistor radio in 1954 and established our Bedford plant three years later. Subsequent developments have included the world's first integrated circuit (1958), the single chip microcomputer (1971) and more recently speech synthesis learning aids and the first commercial VLSI products using electron beam direct slice writing.

Application address
Recruitment Manager, Texas Instruments
Limited, Manton Lane, Bedford MK41 7PA
Tel: 0234-67466

The present picture

Our current areas of interest include semiconductors with a continually expanding range of applications; distributed computing, consumer products, industrial control, government projects and geophysical services. We employ over 80,000 people worldwide in more than 50 plants, 16 seismic data centres and 50 product distribution centres. Our global communications network is also the largest private on-line system in the world and is based on our own equipment.

A challenging future

Innovation is the driving force behind our success, and our future as a company will depend on our ability to adapt to the needs of a changing market. Research and development activities include software development for design automation and microsystems, microprocessor and peripheral design and a large microprocessor applications group. Semiconductor materials research covers all aspects of wafer processing and we also have a substantial investment in computer aided design, manufacturing and test.

The Texas philosophy

Our philosophy is based on achieving common goals and enabling every member of our staff to maximise his or her potential within the framework of corporate objectives. The company consists of a group of sharply defined, self-sufficient product centres, which provide early responsibility and a tremendous variety of experience. All salary reviews are results orientated and promotion is based purely on ability. Our job opportunity scheme ensures that all vacancies are published internally and TI staff automatically have preference over equally experienced external candidates. At least once a year every employee is entitled to a full review of past performance and future career goals. At the same time, we encourage you to develop your skills by arranging post graduate release courses and internal training programmes.

The practical rewards

We believe that the best way to keep good people is to offer them highly competitive salaries and benefits and interesting, meaningful jobs. Starting salaries are reviewed after six months and then annually, with special cash awards for outstanding contributions. Company facilities are excellent and working with us will give you access to the most up to date equipment on the market.

Speaking from personal experience

We've found that the best way to give you an insight into the company is to let our graduates speak for themselves. Here are just a few of their impressions:

'The sheer growth of TI is such that opportunity will come at regular intervals. One works incredibly hard not because there is pressure, but because there is a momentum which occurs all of its own. You know when you've succeeded and when you've failed and that's what a career is all about.'

'I've stayed here for nine years and I don't believe there's any length of time when I've been bored. I've always looked forward to coming to work and regarded it as a major interest in my life.'

'Everyone is accessible. It means your performance is visible and you can make a career without waiting for others to get out of the way.'

'The only barrier to your progress is yourself. I'd sum up what TI can offer today's graduates as the greatest amount of experience in the shortest possible time.'

Achieving professional distinction

Professional expertise is hard won. It demands application, self-discipline and a top class programme of training.

As a student chartered accountant with Thomson McLintock you are given an invaluable insight into the way business works. Our range of financial services is constantly developing to match modern commercial needs and the practical experience you gain with us is reinforced by specially designed intensive training courses.

Once qualified, your experience prepares you for any number of financial and management roles both inside and outside the profession. If you stay with us, we naturally plan to make the most of your potential. Our membership of the international firm KMG gives wide scope to our activities and provides additional opportunities for our professional staff.

To find out more about us, contact your careers service or write to the staff partner at the office where you would like to work.

Aberdeen
AG McBain
Blenheim House
Fountainhall Road
Aberdeen AB9 1JE
Tel: 29105

Belfast
DA Bradshaw
Chamber of Commerce House
22 Great Victoria Street
Belfast BT2 7BA
Tel: 21452

Birmingham
RJ Bailey
5 St Philip's Place
Birmingham B3 2PU
Tel: 236 7991

Bournemouth
AJ Meredith
Vandale House
Post Office Road
Bournemouth BH1 1BT
Tel: 294541

Bristol, Cardiff & Exeter
GK Cairns
15 Pembroke Road
Bristol BS8 3BG
Tel: Bristol 732291

Darlington
JD Coish
1 Blackwell Lane
Darlington DL3 8QF
Tel: 66031

Dundee
RT Leslie
Royal Exchange
Dundee DD1 1DZ
Tel: 22763

Edinburgh
BJ Rankin
33/34 Charlotte Square
Edinburgh EH2 4HF
Tel: 225 1516

Glasgow
GN Simpson
24 Blythswood Square
Glasgow G2 4QS
Tel: 226 5511

Leeds
J Padley
Royal Exchange House
City Square
Leeds LS1 5NU
Tel: 450527

Leicester
JRN Lowe
Arlen House
Salisbury Road
Leicester LE1 7QS
Tel: 545123

London & Basingstoke
PL Hogarth
70 Finsbury Pavement
London EC2A 1SX
Tel: 01 638 2777

Manchester, Liverpool & Sheffield
DJ Illingworth
Devonshire House
36 George Street
Manchester M1 4HA
Tel: Manchester 236 8241

Newcastle
JL Hinkley
7 New Bridge Street
Newcastle-upon-Tyne
NE1 8BB
Tel: 328042

Norwich
PF Jeffery
3 Princes Street
Norwich NR3 1AS
Tel: 20516

 the British member of

Thomson McLintock & Co   Klynveld Main Goerdeler

Texas Instruments Limited, cont

Interested?
Then ask you careers advisory centre for our brochure *Graduate to the State of the Art* or write telling us about your academic background, qualifications and career ambitions.

Thomson McLintock & Co

Activities
Chartered accountancy, including audit, tax, general financial advice and other services

Employees
2,000 approx UK
25,000 worldwide

Locations: UK
General

Locations: Overseas
Worldwide

Opportunities & places
200

Application address
See accompanying advertisement

Thomson McLintock is the British member of KMG, a leading international firm represented in over 70 countries.

Our clients operate in every aspect of business and industry and include multinational, public, private and nationalised industries, small businesses, professional firms, banks, unit trusts and other financial institutions.

Each of our offices throughout the country provides a full range of accountancy services – auditing, taxation, financial advice and investigation, management services, including computer consultancy and executive selection and insolvency work. We are constantly monitoring our professional techniques and approach and developing them to match modern commercial needs.

Insight into business
Chartered accountancy offers an unrivalled insight into a wide range of company operations and business systems. When you complete your training your options are still wide open, unlike the recruits to most careers. If you demonstrate ability and ambition there is nothing to stop you reaching the very top financial and commercial positions. Thomson McLintock gives you the opportunity to achieve qualification as a chartered accountant in what we consider a rather special environment. We aim to maintain our reputation as one of the most skilled of leading accounting firms in an atmosphere where the quality of our personal relationships is considered of prime importance.

The graduates we seek
We seek determined young men and women who can apply intellectual ability in a practical way to difficult and wide-ranging problems; people who can work as part of a team, communicate well with others and show potential for development of leadership skills. We look for numeracy although an advanced level of mathematics is not essential. Your degree can be in *any* subject, (except in Scotland, where it must be relevant).

Training
You must take the professional exams set by one of the Institutes of Chartered Accountants. As a graduate it will take you three years to qualify. For details of the differences between the three Institutes in exam syllabi and methods of study see the Institutes' appropriate publications. Wide ranging practical experience during your training contract is reinforced by Thomson McLintock's specially designed intensive training courses which ensure that after your exams you are not only a qualified accountant but an experienced and effective one.

Looking forward
Once you qualify you will have excellent prospects for promotion and specialisation either in the UK or overseas. The pace of advancement very much depends on you. Salaries are competitive. They are based on merit and are reviewed regularly.

Come and meet us
We visit most universities during the autumn and spring terms. Ask your

Thomson McLintock & Co, cont

careers service for dates and for our graduate brochure *Achieving Professional Distinction.* Or write to the staff partner at the office where you would like to work.

Thompson Ltd

Activities
Fabrication; Nuclear components; Friction welding; Process plant; Water treatment

Locations: UK
West Midlands

Oportunities
Mechanical engineers; Production engineers; Business studies

Application address
Mr AP Garbett, Company Training Co-ordinator, NEI Thompson Ltd, Spring Road, Ettingshall, Wolverhampton, West Midlands WV4 6JX

NEI Thompson Ltd

NEI Thompson Limited have built up an enviable reputation for the quality of its products, systems and services and is a member company of the Northern Engineering Industries Group.

The comprehensive product range of NEI Thompson Limited includes the design, manufacture and if necessary the erection and commissioning of bridgework, steel structures, general fabrications, water/hydrogen generation systems, components for the nuclear power industry and friction welding machines.

Types of graduate required
We are seeking to recruit graduates from a variety of disciplines who possess the ability, maturity and determination to become future managers. There are opportunities within the areas of mechanical engineering, production engineering and business studies.
Graduate production engineers who in the long term are aiming for a position in production management after periods in both supervision and management services.
Graduate mechanical engineers who wish to persue their career to management via, design management services and project management.
Business studies graduates who wish to aspire to a management position via a variety of functional appointments.

Training and development
Our training programmes are structured to meet the needs of each individual, taking account of previous training and experience. The duration of training is usually two years after which the progression of the individual depends upon their capacity to advance in a hard working environment.

Graduates are encouraged to undertake the necessary training in order to qualify for membership of the appropriate professional bodies.

Location
NEI Thompson Limited consists of five business units, operating from four sites. The majority of activities are located in the Wolverhampton and Tipton Areas of the West Midlands. Our businesses comprise of Thompson Friction Welding, Thompson Nuclear Engineering, Horseley Bridge, Kennicott Water Treatment and Carter Horseley Engineers.

Salaries
A realistic starting salary will be offered together with first class career opportunities and the benefits of being associated with a large organisation.

THORN EMI plc

THORN EMI

Activities
A major international company with diverse business areas

Employees
100,000+

Locations: UK
General

Opportunities
Electrical and electronic engineers; Mechanical, industrial and production engineers; Test engineers; Computer programmers; Chemists; Physicists; Mathematicians; Applied scientists; Accountants; Economists; Glass technologists; General

Vacancies
100

Application address
The Graduate Recruitment Officer, THORN EMI plc, Angel Road, Edmonton, London N18 3HL

THORN EMI is a major British owned company with worldwide interests and combines the capabilities, resources and vast experience of one of the leading names in British industry.

Our business activities include advanced electronics for the home and industry, defence, domestic appliances, lighting, music, video software, and entertainment, telecommunications and high street retailing and rentals.

We are continually concerned with research and new product development and are responsible for many innovations in the fields in which we operate.

There are over 120 principal locations throughout the world and we are continuing to expand, offering challenging career opportunities in research, development, production, technical sales and services, computing and a wide range of business activities.

Our particular requirements are for *electronics* and *electrical engineers, mechanical* and *production engineers, chemists, physicists, computer scientists, mathematicians, commercial programmers* and *material scientists*. The majority of our vacancies are for *engineering* and *science* graduates, however we also have a limited number of vacancies for graduates in *business studies* and other *arts* subjects.

Organisation

THORN EMI operates through eight principal product groups and business areas, each of which has a high degree of autonomy. It is company policy to devolve responsibility through a decentralised structure allowing individuals at all levels to participate directly in the development of the company's interests and to recognise their contribution to the performance of the subsidiary in which they work.

All subsidiary companies are backed by the full resources of THORN EMI. These include the Central Research Laboratories at Hayes where 300 people work, over half of whom are research engineers and scientists with university degrees or an equivalent qualification.

A brief summary of our main areas of recruitment follows:

Electronics

An important supplier of complex advanced electronic systems to the Ministry of Defence mainly for radar, infra-red and acoustic systems, Electronics also has an increasing capability in industrial and commercial projects for the offshore oil industry, public transport and the oil and gas industries. There are laboratories and manufacturing facilities at Hayes, Feltham, Camberley, Woking and Wells. Design work covers a wide range of functions and applications eg, thermal imaging, airborne reconnaissance, ground surveillance, area protection, proximity fusing for missiles, homing, automatic tracking, underwater imaging and tracking, telemetry, weapon location, electronic warfare, data capture, remote control, simulation and training. Digital methods and the rapidly increasing use of microprocessors still leave a high dependence on analogue circuit techniques and ingenious mechanisms. As the complexity of equipment increases rapid progress is necessarily being made in computer aided design and in automatic test equipment. The company is also associated with the research, development and manufacture of microwave tubes and sub-systems with application work extending from sensitive receivers to high power transmitters.

Technology

Aerospace, industry, communications, defence, medicine, commerce, and nuclear engineering are among the many markets served by the wide range of technologies encompassed by THORN EMI Technology. From

THORN EMI plc, cont

its headquarters in Ashford, Kent, it is responsible for the internatio
operations in four major business areas: Measurement, Components
Systems and Systron Donner Corporation.

Each of these organisations concentrates on particular sectors of th
broad technology market and comprises a number of companies or
operating units specialising in individual areas of engineering experti
Collectively they provide the substantial technological strength which
underlies the worldwide business operations of THORN EMI
Technology.

The Measurement and Components activities are concerned with
virtually every aspect of the markets indicated by their titles. In

and Padiham, THORN EMI Gas graduates will be concerned with making the best use of one of Britain's natural resources.

Heating Appliances
Radiators and boilers for domestic use are manufactured by THORN EMI Heating. Based at Gateshead, County Durham, the company is well established in the field of domestic central heating.

General Engineering
THORN EMI General Engineering employs 12,000 people in the UK and overseas and serves markets and customers in most parts of the world. It is organised into six major business areas: cutting tools, foods and equipment, distribution, security, hydraulics and industrial supplies.

Lighting
THORN EMI Lighting is a world leader in lighting technology and one of the largest producers of lamps and lighting fittings and components. The company employs 10,000 people. There are eight UK factories with regional offices controlling sales and distribution and established overseas subsidiaries in Austria, Belgium, France, Italy, Norway, Sweden, West Germany, USA, Australia, South Africa, New Zealand and Canada. To maintain its position in world markets, THORN EMI Lighting has research laboratories at Enfield and Leicester which provide the best R&D capability in the industry.

Television Rentals
This organisation has constantly updated its product range to stay in the forefront of the domestic and commercial market. Equipment currently supplied in the home entertainment sphere includes tv, with Teletext and viewdata facilities, video recorders, pre-recorded cassettes, electronic games, cameras and home computers.

The company has showrooms in all the major towns and cities throughout the UK and provides a nationwide technical service to some 3·5 million subscribers.

Central services include a large computer installation, with a highly sophisticated electronic data retrieval system, and provides a closed user group viewdata information service.

There are overseas rental interests in many countries including Norway, Sweden, Finland, Denmark, Holland, Belgium, France, Spain, Australia, New Zealand, South Africa, Singapore and Hong Kong.

Retailing
The company has extensive interest in high street retailing through Rumbelows and HMV shops in the UK and Fona in Denmark. This tough, competitive business is about selling, and about buying, marketing, accounting, servicing and distribution, where opportunities abound and early promotion is available.

Video
The company is fully involved in all aspects of this exciting area of growth THORN EMI Video Programmes markets a catalogue of pre-recorded video-cassette tapes and produces original material for video cassettes, videodiscs, and home computers.

Types of graduate required
Electronics engineering Opportunities in product design and development, systems and control engineering, instrumentation and measurement, research and development and quality assurance.

Electrical engineering Power systems and machines, design research and development, manufacturing and technical sales.

THORN EMI plc, cont

Mechanical and production engineering Product design and development, manufacturing engineering and management.

Computer sciences Industrial process control, systems analysis, programming, systems applications.

Applied sciences Research and development work in physics, chemistry, and mathematics; vacancies for *materials scientists* and *metallurgists* in research and manufacturing.

Building services Lighting products and systems design, technical sales.

Business studies and arts Postgraduate training in all aspects of retailing and other commercial areas.

Any discipline Commercial computer programming.

These vacancies exist in a variety of UK locations and specific details of these opportunities will be given during first interviews.

Training and career development

Graduates are offered specific jobs and receive on the job training. Career development is co-ordinated at company level and seeks to ensure that graduates with potential or who wish to broaden their career are given sufficient opportunity to develop.

Our training is designed to meet the needs of the company and the individual as well as the requirements of the professional institutions. Every encouragement is given to staff to further their careers by attending postgraduate technical and administrative courses. We have a strong tradition of promotion from within and career development is designed to meet medium and long term needs for senior staff and management for the company.

Salaries and benefits

Starting salaries are most competitive for the industry with recognition being made for special qualifications and experience. We have a pension fund, a generous sickness benefit scheme and a variety of concessionary facilities.

Locations

The main locations are Greater London, South East, South West, Midlands, North East, North West and Wales.

Further literature

Careers brochures, application forms and vacancy schedules can be obtained from all careers advisory services.

Applications

We will be visiting universities for recruitment interviews and applications should be submitted through your careers service using the company graduate application form. You may, of course, write direct to us for more detailed information.

Thornton Baker

Thornton Baker is among the largest firms of chartered accountants in the UK having 210 partners and over 2,600 staff. Through our international partnership, Grant Thornton International, we also have offices in over 50 countries throughout the world.

Because of the way our firm has developed, each of our 58 offices has its individual character with well established roots in the local business community. Even in the major cities where our larger offices are situated, this means that you won't get lost in an impersonal environment and responsibility comes early. Our clients vary from large international

Locations: UK
General

Opportunities & places
Trainee chartered accountants 150+

Upper age limit
26

Application address
Elizabeth Richards, Recruitment Officer,
Thornton Baker, Fairfax House, Fulwood Place,
London WC1V 6DW

organisations to small traders so you can gain broad experience coupled with a variety of opportunities necessary to make the most of your career.

Training and prospects

We maintain high standards in all offices, not least in training where leading professional tutors are backed up by courses at our own training centre, Bradenham Manor. During and after training your progress will be closely monitored and your development will be as fast as your ability allows. After qualification there are ample opportunities to gain interesting experience before specialisation either within a practice office or in a national department.

Types of graduate required

We recruit 150+ trainees each year and place more emphasis on your ability to communicate and your desire for involvement and responsibility than your degree subject.

Salaries

Salaries are competitive and reviewed regularly to reflect your progress. In addition there is a pension scheme and group medical scheme for the over 25s.

The first step

Copies of our brochure and details of our vacancies can be obtained from your careers advisory service. Please contact the Staff Partner of the office you wish to join, or if you wish to consider more than one location, apply to Elizabeth Richards at the address given.

Activities
Diversified metal industries, engineering and consumer goods group

Employees
37,000 UK

Locations: UK
General

Locations: Overseas
Worldwide after training

Occupations
Accountancy; Financial analysis; Computing; Research and development; Mechanical/ electrical/production engineering; Management services; Sales and marketing; Personnel; Production management; Design; Materials supply/purchasing

Application address
Graduate Recruitment and Training Officer, TI Group plc, Woodbourne Grange, 21 Woodbourne Road, Edgbaston, Birmingham B17 8BZ

TI Group plc

TI is a major British based group of over 120 companies, with five main business areas: aluminium, cycle and toys, domestic applicance, specialised engineering products and steel tube. There are approximately 37,000 employees in the UK and there are associated companies in all five continents. The group produces a wide variety of capital, semi-finished and consumer goods. TI is one of the world's largest producers of precision steel tubes, the principle smelter of aluminium in the UK, the world's leading maker of bicycles and an important manufacturer of machine tools and of gas and electric appliances.

TI encourages maximum delegation of operation and authority to individual company management teams – offering the graduate the opportunity to make a real contribution at an early stage. The TI Group policy for staff development includes the planning of training and experience to provide for management succession.

Types of graduates required

Any discipline and especially all types of *engineers* and *technologists*.

Training

In most cases graduates are recruited to fill an identified vacancy giving you the opportunity to accept real job responsibility at the earliest opportunity. All graduates receive management training through the graduate education programme, a series of three off the job training courses run at our management training centre. These courses cover areas such as the structure of a business, business practice and management skills. In addition individuals will be given in-company training specific to their chosen function, and where appropriate this will be geared to enable membership of the relevant professional institution.

Traineeships are available for engineers on the TI domestic applicance division manufacturing training scheme for engineers, designed to give

Trading Standards Officers

The Trading Standards Officer investigates fraud and other trading charges and enforces the criminal law concerning standards of quantity, quality and some aspects of safety and prices. Officers may be called upon to advise members of the public on problems encountered in everyday commercial transactions as well as traders and businessmen who seek help concerning their responsibilities in law.

Our ideal trading standards officers must be able to apply a balanced judgement to a range of varying situations; must be patient and tactful, diplomatic but firm, resourceful and restrained. Above all they must have an enquiring mind, be tenacious and never accept anything at face value.

Freedom of action, within reasonable bounds, comes to officers at an early age, for, on qualification, they are virtually their own bosses from the time they leave their offices in the morning until they return in the evening. Life is never dull for it is rare for the same job to be done on consecutive days.

TI Group plc, cont

monitored professional training and experience of a variety of functions before appointment in one of the division's operating companies. The TI graduate finance scheme for students of any discipline aims to give a thorough financial training to ICMA standard at company and divisional level, leading to an early managerial appointment.

Benefits
In addition to competitive salaries, TI offers free life assurance, contributory pension, family education schemes and employee sales discounts.

Timex Corporation

ctivities
atch manufacture and repair; personal omputer manufacture, camera manufacture

mployees
000 UK
2,000 worldwide

ocations: UK
ondon; Scotland; North East

pportunities
nance and accounting; Manufacturing;
anagement; Systems and data processing;
ectronics; Purchasing and production control

pplication address
A Cecil, Compensation and Benefits Manager,
mex Corporation, Harrison Road, Dundee

Timex Corporation has for many years led the world as the largest manufacturer of watches. The company is determined to maintain this position in an increasingly competitive market with the challenge posed by the development of new electronic and solid state technology. To assist in meeting this challenge the company is seeking to recruit a limited number of graduates in 1983.

Salary and prospects
Starting salaries will be competitive. During the initial period salaries will be reviewed and reflect the responsibilities of the position held and the individual's own development.

Career advancement will be achieved by means of progression in function or operational areas, with progress being maintained through the company's career development programmes.

Trading Standards Officers
Local Authorities

ctivities
o provide a trading standards service advising
onsumers and traders

mployees
,500 approx

ocations: UK
ounty councils throughout England & Wales,
cottish regional councils, London Boroughs

pportunities & places
rainee trading standards officers 50–60

pplication address
he Administrative Officer, The Institute of
rading Standards, Estate House, 319d London
oad, Hadleigh, Benfleet, Essex SS7 2BN

The profession's principal task is to ensure a fair system of trading between consumers and traders, and between traders themselves. The trading standards officer, as a local authority employee, ensures that traders comply with the legal requirements of consumer orientated legislation such as the Weights and Measures, Trade Descriptions, Fair Trading, Food and Drugs, Consumer Safety and Prices Acts. Officers are also becoming increasingly involved in the field of consumer advice and complaints.

Types of graduate required
The profession is open to graduates of all disciplines, but is particularly suitable for those with a degree in *law, the sciences* or a *numerate* based discipline. A trading standards officer needs a practical outlook combined with critical judgement and an interest in technical and legal matters. Officers are expected to work on their own initiative, accept responsibility for their actions and be capable of communicating with people in many varying circumstances.

Training
Trainees are sponsored to go on the three year, block release diploma in trading standards (DTS). This diploma can be taken at colleges in Manchester, London or Weston super Mare. The syllabus covers criminal and civil law relating to consumer protection; economic and commercial practice; sampling, weighing and measuring technology and professional practice. The block release periods are closely integrated

with structured practical training in the employing local authority, where a chosen project will be completed as part of the qualification.

Further information
During training officers are paid a salary on the general career grade of the local authority. It is usual for a car allowance to be paid.

Touche Ross & Co

Activities
Accounting, auditing, management consultancy, tax, insolvency, research

Employees
2,300

Locations: UK
General

Locations: Overseas
Worldwide

Opportunities & places
Student chartered accountants, 200+

Application address
Graduate Rercruitment Manager, Touche Ross & Co, Hill House, 1 Little New Street, London EC4A 3TR

Touche Ross is one of the largest international groups of professional accountants and has 381 offices in 85 countries in the world. Worldwide there are 20,200 staff including 2,000 partners of whom over 150 partners form the United Kingdom partnership. There are offices in 22 locations. The firm has a wide range of clients covering all types of financial institutions and most spheres of industry and commerce. They range in size from the small business with a few employees to the industrial giants. The firm has grown rapidly and is correspondingly young in attitudes and personnel.

Graduates required
With an annual intake of over 200 students we naturally take on a large number with *accountancy*, *economics* and *business studies* degrees. But many graduates in unrelated subjects make excellent accountants, and we are glad to meet them for exploratory interviews. However, we offer training contracts only to those who have a clear idea of what accountancy training will involve, and who are willing to embark on it with clear career intentions.

Training
First, we prepare you to qualify, paying for your training by professional tutors.

Secondly, you take part in our in-house training. This prepares you for practical work serving our clients, and helps you to reflect on your practical experience. Seven or eight weeks in your first three years will be spent at a regional training centre, and after you have qualified you will take part in our continuing professional education indefinitely.

Career development
Staff partners keep a watch on the progress of all their staff, and formal appraisals occur every six months. Graduate entrants can expect to be considered for manager rank within three years of qualifying; able candidates may become partners in their early 30s; it is the firm's policy to recruit partners internally.

Salaries and benefits
Salaries are competitive, up to date details are available on request. Overtime is compensated by cash or time off in lieu. Staff receive four weeks annual holiday, share in a contributory pensions scheme, receive free life insurance, etc. Qualified staff have the chance to ask for overseas experience; as an international group we have 381 offices in 85 countries.

The first step
We need people with the right potential, but also with the outlook and attitudes that will enable us to click. That's why we invite you to discuss your career prospects with either a partner or a senior member of our staff.

On visiting universities a team of partners, senior staff and students will be available to talk to you informally about the firm. Before interviews take place we hold an informative presentation on the firm and the career prospects. We offer equal opportunities to men and women. If you would like to be considered for interview please apply to your careers service or direct to the Graduate Recruitment Manager, at the address given.

Trower, Still & Keeling

Activities
Solicitors dealing with all aspects of legal work

Employees
160

Location: UK
London

Location: Overseas
Oman

Opportunities
Articled clerks

Application address
Mr RE Stagg, Trower, Still & Keeling,
5 New Square, Lincoln's Inn, London
WC2A 3RP

Trower, Still & Keeling is a long established firm of solicitors in Lincoln's Inn. It has 25 partners and a total staff of approximately 160. The practice is varied and has specialist departments dealing with litigation, conveyancing, probate and trust work.

Types of graduate required
Graduates are required with good honours degrees who have taken the Law Society's final examination. Graduates with *law* degrees are preferred but other graduates with good honours degrees will certainly be considered.

Training
Articled clerks are supervised by a partner and are accommodated in partners' rooms, with senior assistants or in departments. At regular (normally six-monthly) intervals articled clerks are moved within the firm to gain fresh experience. There are also regular meetings of articled clerks at which partners discuss different practical aspects of legal work.

Salaries
Salaries are competitive and take into account individual qualifications and achievement. They are reviewed at six-monthly intervals.

Prospects
The policy is to recruit articled clerks who appear to have career potential with the firm either as future staff or partners. The firm normally requires an articled clerk to agree to stay for a prescribed period after admission as a solicitor, at the firm's option. If the option is exercised, the proper market salaries at the going rate for the area are paid.

TSB Group

Activities
Provide a comprehensive range of banking services

Employees
26,000

Locations: UK
General

Opportunities
Banking and financial services

Vacancies
25–35

Application addresses
See main text

The TSB Group is a major national banking and financial organisation. It is now the country's leading personal banking group with more than 8 million customers and 13 million accounts. A network of regional banks, each with its own administration centre, serves the needs of these customers through a total of 1,650 branches. The growth of the TSB over the past few years has meant that the bank now offers all the major services associated with high street banking, including personal and business loans, insurance, mortgages, travellers cheques and their own credit card facility – the TSB Trustcard.

This rapid expansion of financial services has been supported by the group's central services organisations: Central TSB (the banker to the group), Trustcard, a computer services company and an insurance and unit trust company have all played an invaluable part in the growth of the TSB. With the acquisition of UDT in 1981, previously the largest independent finance house in the UK, the TSB made yet another addition to its range of services.

The policy making body of the group is the TSB Central Board. Through its executive based in London, it acts as the link between all parts of the organisation, and will be responsible for leading the group in its continued development in the 1980s and beyond.

Opportunities for graduates

To assist us in our continuing growth and development, we plan to recruit between 25–35 graduates throughout the group in 1983. The opportunities are varied, but wherever you work career prospects are extremely favourable as we follow a policy of internal promotion whenever possible. Each of our member organisations recruits independently, and applications from graduates of both sexes and any degree discipline should be made to the individuals listed below.

Regional TSBs

A management trainee scheme is currently operated by four of our regional banks. As a member of this scheme you will undertake a planned course of training in all aspects of domestic banking, gaining work experience in a number of branches and regional administrative departments. At the same time we will expect you to study for and pass your professional banking examinations.

We believe that personal qualities are as important as qualifications. A successful manager must have the ability to communicate with people at all levels, and to adapt to the needs of a fast growing and developing organisation.

Our planned requirements for 1983 are as follows.

TSB of Eastern England 3–6 vacancies. Apply March to May 1983 to *Departmental Head – Personnel, TSB of Eastern England, Apex House, Oundle Road, Peterborough PE2 9NW*.

TSB of Lancashire and Cumbria 3–6 vacancies. Apply February to April 1983 to *Departmental Head – Personnel, TSB Lancashire and Cumbria, The Guild Centre, Lords Walk, Preston PR1 1RE*.

TSB South East 10–15 vacancies. Apply February to April 1983 to *Assistant General Manager – Personnel, TSB South East, 49–53 Surrey Row, London SE1 0BY*.

West of Scotland TSB Apply to *Assistant General Manager – Personnel, West of Scotland TSB, 177 Ingram Street, Glasgow G1 1DL*.

Central Trustee Savings Bank Limited

Central Trustee Savings Bank (CTSB) provides the banking, clearing, foreign, investment and corporate lending services to all of the TSB Group. Incorporated in 1973 as the central banker to the TSBs, CTSB is a functional member of the bankers clearing house and has recognised bank status under the Banking Act 1979.

As the TSB Group has grown, so CTSB itself has developed into a major City institution offering a full range of wholesale banking services. It is this expansion which has created the need for a small number of high calibre graduates with the ability and ambition to match our rate of development.

The training scheme concentrates on the major areas of CTSB's banking activities and on the role of CTSB as the group's representative in the City. Lasting for 15 months the scheme allows trainees to work for six months in each of two of CTSB's banking departments together with project work and preparation for the professional banking examinations and leads to both a career in one of CTSB's specialist banking areas and to the opportunity to share in the continued development of CTSB as a major City banking institution.

Apply December to February 1983 to the Departmental Head – Personnel and Training at:

Central Trustee Savings Bank Limited, PO Box 99, St Mary's Court, 100 Lower Thames Street, London EC3R 6AQ

TSB Computer Services (Wythenshawe) Limited

The TSB Group has been a substantial user of computers since the early 1970s and in fact pioneered the user of on-line real time systems using counter terminals. TSB Computer Services is involved in the continuing improvement and development of computer based technology to meet the varied business requirements of the group.

Each year TSB Computer Services takes a number of graduates as trainee programmers. Full training is given on site. All applicants will be required to take an aptitude test prior to being selected for interview, and preference will be given to graduates already residing in the area. Detailed applications should be forwarded to the address below. No telephone calls are accepted. Applications should be made April to June 1983. There are six vacancies.

Personnel Manager, TSB Computer Services (Wythenshawe) Limited, PO Box 1, 1 Cornfield Drive, Poundswick Lane, Wythenshaw, Manchester M22 7QE.

UK Provident

Activities
Life assurance and pensions

Employees
715

Location: UK
Salisbury

Opportunites
Actuarial work

Application address
The Personnel and Training Department, UK Provident, Dolphin House, New Street, Salisbury, Wiltshire SP1 2QQ

UK Provident is an old established mutual life office. From our head office in Salisbury we operate throughout the UK, transacting life assurance and pensions business. Our forward looking policies and attitudes have resulted in an encouraging record of growth: our premium income has increased from £31.1 million in 1977 to £91.1 million in 1981.

The company's main objective is to maintain this growth and provide a good efficient service to our policyholders and the insurance brokers with whom we deal.

Types of graduate required

We are looking for graduates in *mathematics* and *statistics* to train as actuaries. In addition to a good degree, candidates should possess initiative, ambition and leadership ability.

Training

All trainees spend some time in the key areas of both the actuarial and pensions divisions, so as to gain a practical knowledge of the work and also to have the opportunity to utilise increased technical knowledge. The range of tasks is wide and incorporates dealing with the technical aspects of new and altered policies and schemes, actuarial valuation and research.

To supplement practical experience, study leave of up to two half days per week is granted; tuition and examination fees are paid.

Salaries

Starting salaries are competitive and the salary structure is designed to reward ability and responsibility as well as examination success.

Other benefits

There is a non-contributory pension fund, a house purchase scheme at concessionary rates of interest (after a while), a well-supported sports and social club and a minimum of 18 days annual holiday.

Progress

Promotion is based on merit and there are excellent opportunities for able and ambitious people in this thriving office.

Applications

Applications should be submitted in December 1982 and January 1983. At the time of going to press, the exact number of graduates we wish to recruit as actuarial students is rather uncertain, but every application will be considered.

Aiming High in the Business World?

Opportunities in

Accountancy
Buying
Computing Systems
Distribution
Economics
Engineering
Marketing
Market Research
Personnel
Product Development
Production
Research
Sales

Unilever
UK National Personnel Department
Unilever House
London EC4P 4BQ

Unilever

Activities
Manufacture, marketing and distribution of foods, detergents, toilet preparations, animal feeding stuffs, chemicals, floor coverings and packaging materials

Employees
70,000 UK
300,000 worldwide

Locations: UK
General

Opportunities
Accountancy; Buying; Computing systems; Distribution; Economics; Engineering; Marketing; Market research; Personnel; Product development; Production; Research; Sales

Vacancies
120 approx

Upper age limit
27

Application address
Mr GW Prior-Wandesforde, Unilever, UK National Personnel Department, Unilever House, London EC4P 4BQ

Unilever consists of a number of medium sized companies, so that there are early opportunities to show your worth. Add to this Unilever's whole hearted commitment to the concept of training and developing graduates to the highest possible level, and the range of opportunities the worldwide structure provides, and you will see why Unilever is able to offer opportunities matched by few other companies.

The management team
The commercial and technical challenges faced by Unilever managers are exciting and constantly changing. Our companies have short chains of command and that means for the individual manager work which is motivating and challenging, testing abilities and experience to the full.

Training
Unilever pays great attention to training, both off and on the job, and within this the training of graduates receives a particularly high priority. The Unilever companies management development scheme (UCMDS) provides a broad training within a particular function. The Unilever engineering management training scheme (UEMTS) offers engineers a training leading to corporate membership of their appropriate professional institution. Direct entrants have a training programme devised by a particular company or department within the group (see also in this context the separate entries for Unilever Research and Lever Brothers Ltd).

UCMDS and UEMTS trainees and many direct entrants participate in the business education programme which is run in conjunction with two of the principal UK business schools.

Salaries and career development
The objective of our salary policy is, above all, to reward good performance. Starting salaries are very competitive and it is expected that graduates will rise to very senior positions in the company.

Applications
Our booklet *Careers in Unilever 1983* details opportunities in the group and application forms are normally available from your careers service. Company representatives visit most universities in the spring term to hold selection interviews. Alternatively you can contact Geoffrey Prior-Wandesforde, at the address given.

Unilever Research

Activities
Research and development to support a major international manufacturer of consumer goods

Employees
2,500 UK
3,500 total

Locations: UK
South East; North West; Scotland

The major function of Unilever Research is to ensure that optimum use is made of science and technology in developing Unilever's existing businesses profitably and in building new business opportunities for Unilever.

To fulfil this objective, research must develop and evaluate new products and processes, and to ensure the long term future of the business this work must be supported by comprehensive programmes of basic and background research. Scientists and technologists employed by us are therefore assured of a diverse career, and can expect to face interesting and challenging problems. Most of our work is closely related to Unilever's major consumer product industries, namely foods, detergents and toiletries.

Who we are looking for
In 1983 we expect to have vacancies for graduates and postgraduates in

Location: Overseas
Holland

Opportunities
Basic and background research; Product and
process development.

Application addresses
Jill Kenny (DOG), Unilever Research, Colworth
Laboratory, Sharnbrook, Bedford MK44 1LQ

Bill Ashworth (DOG), Unilever Research, Port
Sunlight Laboratory, Quarry Road East, Wirral,
Merseyside L63 3JW

most of the *chemical, physical, biological sciences* and *technologies* and in *chemical* and *mechanical engineering* but in particular *physical chemistry, biophysics* and *physics*. We also have some opportunities for *statisticians* and *mathematicians*.

We will be looking for graduates over a wide spectrum of experience to fill a wide range of job responsibilities. Our selection standards are very high, particularly for the most responsible jobs. Those who follow a scientific career with us at this level usually, but not exclusively, join us at postgraduate level. Other appointments may be appropriate to graduates with less experience, but possessing enthusiasm and skills for experimental work.

Locations

We have two UK Unilever Research laboratories; both are equipped with the most advanced scientific equipment and instrumentation, and have a comprehensive range of supporting services and social facilities.

Port Sunlight is our laboratory on Merseyside and its research programme is primarily concerned with the future development of our soaps, detergents and toilet preparations businesses. There is also some research on chemicals and timber products and effluent problems.

Colworth Laboratory is on a huge country estate in Sharnbrook near Bedford. Its scientific base, strong in the biological sciences, has been developed to meet the needs of Unilever's food companies, and there is a particular interest in the processes and techniques of biotechnology.

Career development and training

A wide variety of careers is possible depending on the opportunities which arise and the individual's ability, interests, experience and flexibility.

Many will see themselves as researchers and future leaders of research teams in the Research Division, whereas some will move out into other functions in Unilever. Management potential as well as high scientific competence is frequently sought in those who join us.

Our appraisal system gives employees the opportunities to discuss their work and career development. Training is an important activity and includes courses covering major business functions, general management and specialist areas. Where appropriate, secondments are arranged as part of a scientist's career development.

Salaries

We aim to ensure that our salaries compare favourably with those paid in similar leading companies. Full details of salary and other benefits will be discussed at second interview stage.

Application procedure

Our brochure *Careers in Unilever Research* is available from your careers service and will give you more detailed information regarding career opportunities with us.

Please apply to us either via your careers advisory service if we are visiting your campus, or direct to one of the addresses shown, where your papers will be considered on behalf of both laboratories.

Unigate plc

Activities
Liquid milk, dairy goods and meat production; transport, engineering and garage activities

Employees
37,000

Locations: UK
London; South East; South West; Wales; Midlands; North West

Opportunities
Accountancy; Sales; Marketing; Personnel; Production; Transport; Engineering; General management

Vacancies
30

Application address
Graduate Recruitment Officer, Unigate plc, Unigate House, Western Avenue, London W3 0SH

We are one of the largest food groups in the UK. Our chief interests are liquid milk and fruit juices, dairy products of all kinds, meat products, transport, garages and contract hire.

Our raw materials and finished products are perishable; the products, processes and locations are many and disparate, and so almost everything we do has to be on the instant, with no second chance.

Dairy products and meat are traditional businesses with long histories. But only mass production and high technology allow us to process eight million pints of milk a day and to sell more meat pies and more ham than anyone else in the country, and almost half the nation's sausages.

With an annual turnover well over £1,000 million we are a big business, and international, with plant in Australia, Denmark, New Zealand and the United States, and markets in 70 more countries.

We employ 37,000 people full time.

However, we depend for our success on small groups; a factory with 500 staff is large by our standards. We are a collection of many distinct business each making and distributing high quality food products which sell at a profit.

Company structure

The UK interests of Unigate are organised into four management companies. St Ivel has six UK trading companies. Five are involved in the processing and distribution of liquid milk: five million pints a day by milkman and float, three million in other ways. The remaining one manufactures and distributes a variety of manufactured dairy products including yogurts, creams, cheese and butter. Scot Bowyers processes over 125,000 tons of meat products a year and sells more meat pies and ham than any other company in the UK. The Wincanton Group operates the transport fleet, garages and engineering services. Giltspur Ltd is an industrial services group involved mainly in specialised transport and engineering services.

Training and career development

We are a practical business. Our policy on graduate recruitment is also practical, we do not hire by the cartload and then put you through 'the scheme', but take specific individuals for specific functions and train through experience giving additional training in context as necessary. Our opportunities are open to both men and women. We expect graduates to be geographically mobile during their early career as that is the way they will make best use of training and promotion opportunities.

The people we want

We recruit graduates from *all* disciplines; however for some positions we need, or prefer, graduates with a relevant degree subject. We look for the sensible, adaptable shrewd character who get things done. We need people who can think on their feet, are ambitious, enthusiastic, approachable and who seek out the opportunities created by change.

How to apply

Either write to us or ask your careers office for our graduate brochure and application form. Closing date for applications is in the middle of January.

The Union International plc

The Union International group of companies employs about 35,000 people throughout the world. Its business is concerned with food and particularly with meat. It embraces the production, processing, transporting, cold storing and selling of meat, its by-products such as wool and leather, as well as fruit, vegetables, oils, fats and egg products. There are associate companies in North and South America, Continental Europe, South Africa, the Far East, Australia and New Zealand. The largest companies in the UK are JH Dewhurst Ltd, W Weddel & Co Ltd, the British Beef Co Ltd and Lonsdale and Thompson Ltd who are in the wholesale cash and carry business. The group head office is in London and has administrative openings for graduates to add to the variety of management opportunities especially in the trading companies.

Activities
Worldwide production, distribution and sales of meat, other foods, wool and leather

Employees
35,000

Locations: UK
London; South East; Midlands; North East; North West

Locations: Overseas
Europe; South America; Australia; New Zealand

Opportunities
Commercial management training; Food production

Vacancies
8

Upper age limit
25

Application address
TP Hanley (DOG 83), The Union International plc, 14 West Smithfield, London EC1A 9JN

Types of graduate required
Each year we recruit a small number of *numerate* graduates for commercial and managerial training. In addition we recruit graduates for specialist and technical careers as vacancies arise. All should have the ability to think on their feet, be ambitious, enthusiastic and approachable.

Training
Basic training for graduate trainees lasts around two years. There is no standard programme and emphasis is on individuality.

Location
Trainees must be prepared to work anywhere in the UK during basic training. There are a limited number of opportunities to work overseas, either in sales in Europe or production in Australia and South America.

Salaries
These are realistic being based on qualifications, age and experience and are reviewed at least annually subject to Government legislation. All members of the staff are required to join the contributory pension scheme after one year's service. Further details will be available at second interview.

Prospects
The progress of each trainee is personally supervised by the manager in charge of management development, particularly during the initial period. The business of the organisation is very diverse and trainees are given the opportunity to develop to the limit of their ability and ambition. We believe strongly in promoting from within the company and the higher positions are within the reach of all.

Selection procedure
Following receipt of completed application forms, obtainable from the application address, as well as any cv or other relevant information, first interviews usually take place in the first quarter of the year, short listed candidates having a second interview as soon as practical thereafter.

United Biscuits (UK) plc

United Biscuits, an international food group, is an amalgamation of the most famous names in the British food industry; McVities, Macdonalds, Crawford, Carrs, KP and many others.

Are you interested in fast moving consumer goods? Did you know that biscuits are the largest packaged item in the grocery trade – larger than tea, frozen foods or detergents? Well, United Biscuits is number one in

Activities
Biscuit, snack and convenience food
manufacture; fast-food retailing and catering

Employees
30,000

Locations: UK
General

Locations: Overseas
Europe; the Middle East; USA; Japan; Australia

Opportunities
Sales management; Production management;
Personnel; Distribution; Marketing; R&D;
Management services, engineering and general
management with Wimpy International and DS
Crawford

Application address
Group Training Officer, United Biscuits (UK)
plc, Grant House, PO Box 40, Syon Lane,
Isleworth, Middlesex TW7 5NN

this huge market, over twice the size of our nearest rivals.

Our most important products are biscuits, cakes, nuts and crisps and our leading brands include: Digestive, Chocolate Home Wheat, Jaffa Cakes, Rich Tea, United, Penguin and KP Nuts.

We are wholly British owned and in the last 10 years United Biscuits has climbed to the forefront of UK companies in terms of management techniques, in marketing, sales, personnel, distribution, production and computer applications.

New developments

We are the second largest biscuit manufacturing group in the world, but biscuits now account for only three quarters of our total output. Over the past few years, we have expanded our KP range of crisps, snacks and nuts. We have moved into the area of convenience foods with the acquisition of companies specialising in frozen and pouch-packed meals. We also extended our chain of restaurants and acquired the franchise for Wimpy Bars and Denny's.

While expanding our product range we have also expanded the geographical area of our operations. In 1974, we acquired the second largest biscuit company in the United States. We also export our products to 92 countries around the world.

Types of graduate required

There are nine main branches of activity where graduates are needed: production, marketing, sales management, computer work, personnel, research and development, distribution, catering management and engineering.

We are just as concerned about personal qualities as with academic excellence. We are looking for graduates who have a confident and enthusiastic manner, powers of good expression and imagination. Some experience of organising or leading people will have helped to develop these characteristics.

Your degree discipline is of less concern but ideally we look for graduates in *management sciences, computer science* or *business studies* for computer work; *economics* or *business studies* for marketing, *social sciences* for personnel work; and *any* discipline for sales management and production.

Training and career development

Training programmes for graduates are planned deliberately to suit individual needs in accordance with the appointment in view. They are comprehensive and intensive and in most cases this will include some time gaining broad experience of the company's operations by planned attachments to various departments, followed by specialised training in your selected field. Progress during training is reviewed at appropriate intervals and following an appointment the career progress of an individual is reviewed each year in the light of his or her own aspirations and achievements.

Prospects

United Biscuits recognises that its single most important asset is its staff and aims to encourage individuals to develop their capabilities to the full so that, as far as possible, promotion can be made within the company. This may involve movement into different functions.

Salaries and benefits

The 1983 starting salary will be competitive, and will depend upon the qualifications and experience offered by individuals.

United Biscuits have adopted a code of practice for job security. We also operate a sickness benefit scheme, a contributory pension plan and a share purchase scheme. Factories have welfare facilities which include

United Biscuits (UK) plc, cont

subsidised canteens, medical centres, dentists, chiropodists, hairdressers, staff shops and one site has a crèche for pre-school age children of working mothers.

Locations
The group head office is in West London; factories and depots are located throughout the United Kingdom. The sales operation is geographically divided into regions covering the United Kingdom. Marketing positions are in London and most of the computer positions are in Liverpool. Other training and appointments may be at any of our locations.

Overseas opportunities
All graduate vacancies are in the UK. However, the continuing policy of expansion overseas may create opportunities for working abroad in the future.

Further literature
Detailed information about the specific opportunities is available from your careers advisory service, or write to the address given indicating your career preference.

Applications
We are entering an exciting period in the history of the group which will create excellent career opportunities for people who can demonstrate potential and ability in a challenging situation. If you are interested in joining United Biscuits please write to the Group Training Officer.

United Kingdom Atomic Energy Authority

Activities
Research, development and assessment work for nuclear power and non-nuclear programmes

Employees
14,000

Locations: UK
London; South East; South West; Scotland; North West

Opportunities
Accountancy; Administration; Chemistry; Chemical engineering; Computer science; Electrical engineering; Electronic emgineering; Instrumental engineering; Metallurgy and materials science; Mathematics; Mechanical engineering; Nuclear engineering; Physics

Vacancies
95

Application addresses
See main text

The Authority is a research and development organisation whose main responsibility is to provide the scientific and technological base for the safe, reliable and economic generation of nuclear power and for the development of new reactor systems. We also carry out high quality fundamental research involving close liaison with universities. In addition, we apply our skills and experience to a wide variety of applied nuclear and non-nuclear projects for industry and government departments. We employ 14,000 people, including over 2,750 with graduate or professional qualifications in science or engineering.

Types of graduate required
Science and engineering: For careers in research, design, development, project engineering and plant operation, we aim to recruit newly or recently qualified graduates in the following main disciplines: *chemical engineering, chemistry, computer science, electrical engineering, electronic engineering, instrument engineering, metallurgy* and *materials science, mathematics, mechanical engineering, nuclear engineering* and *physics*.

   Administration: We require newly or recently qualified graduates in *any* discipline for careers covering such fields as personnel and industrial relations, economic assessment and forecasting, contracts, finance, and commerce and marketing.

   Accountancy: We recruit graduates in *any* discipline, including those whose degrees have included accountancy, for professional training.

Locations
The Northern Division, which is responsible primarily for the development and assessment of nuclear reactor systems with their

associated fuels and materials, consists of four establishments: Risley (Cheshire), the headquarters of the division, which also houses the Risley Nuclear Power Development Laboratories; Dounreay (Highland), the site of the Prototype Fast Reactor; and smaller nuclear power development laboratories at Springfields (Lancashire) and Windscale (Cumbria).

Harwell (Oxfordshire) is the largest of the Authority's laboratories. It carries out research and development in support of the nuclear power programme and applied nuclear and non-nuclear projects sponsored by industry and government departments.

Winfrith (Dorset) undertakes work in support of both thermal and fast reactor systems, and is being developed as the major centre for research and development work on reactor safety.

Culham (Oxfordshire) is the UKAEA centre for plasma physics and nuclear fusion research.

The Safety and Reliability Directorate at Culcheth (Cheshire) is responsible for providing advice on the safety of the design and operation of nuclear reactors and related plants and processes. It also provides a safety and reliability service to industry and government departments in both the nuclear and non-nuclear fields.

The headquarters of the Authority are in London.

Training and career development
Considerable emphasis is placed on training and career development and, as far as possible, vacancies are filled internally. The rate of career progression is related to merit and there are good opportunities for promotion. Both on the job training and formal courses, run by one of the Authority's training centres or externally, are used to help staff to develop their technical knowledge and skills and their managerial abilities to meet the needs of their work, to develop their careers, and, where appropriate, to meet the requirements for corporate membership of professional institutions.

Salaries and other benefits
Starting salaries are related to qualifications, age and experience. Conditions of service include a contributory superannuation scheme and generous leave allowances. Most establishments have well equipped hostels, excellent libraries, sports amenities and social clubs.

Applications and further information
Enquiries concerning scientific and engineering appointments should be addressed to the personnel departments at individual establishments:
UKAEA (Northern Division) FREEPOST, Risley, Warrington WA3 6AT (for appointments at Risley, Springfields and Windscale)
UKAEA (Northern Division) Dounreay NPDE, Thurso, Highland KW14 7TZ
UKAEA, AERE Harwell, Didcot, Oxon OX11 0RA
UKAEA, AEE Winfrith, Dorchester, Dorset DT2 8DH
UKAEA, Culham Laboratory, Culham, Abingdon, Oxon OX14 3DB
UKAEA, Safety and Reliability Directorate, Wigshaw Lane, Culcheth, Warrington WA3 4NE
Applications for administrative posts:
Appointments Board 'B', Personnel Policy Branch, UKAEA, 11, Charles II Street, London SW1Y 4QP
Applicants for accountancy trainee posts should write to either Risley or Harwell.

Vetco Offshore Limited

Vetco Offshore Limited is a subsidiary of an international company supplying valves, wellhead and associated equipment to the oil industry for use in the exploration and production phases of offshore oilfield development.

New developments

The company specialises in subsea equipment for which there is an increasing demand. This has led to the growth of our engineering facility based in Aberdeen.

Types of graduate required

Our main requirement is for graduates qualified in *mechanical engineering* and/or *production engineering*. The design engineers would be involved in work relating to the design of mechanical and structural components for subsea drilling and completion equipment. The project engineers would be part of a team controlling high value subsea drilling and production system projects. The production engineers' main responsibilities would be the provision of production engineering services to manufacturing operations.

Prospects

World engineering demands necessitate the need to explore and produce in deeper waters around the continental shelves, and this will undoubtedly make greater demands for our products. There are excellent opportunities for advancement in both engineering, manufacturing and general management areas, either in the UK or overseas.

Further information

For more details about working for Vetco please contact the personnel department for further information.

Activities
Supplies wellhead and associated equipment to the oil industry

Employees
450

Locations: UK
London and Aberdeen

Locations: Overseas
General

Opportunities
Design engineers; Project engineers; Production engineers

Vacancies
5

Application address
SJ Milligan, Personnel Officer, Vetco Offshore Limited, Broadfold Road, Bridge of Don Industrial Estate, Aberdeen AB2 8EY

VG Isotopes Ltd

VG Isotopes is a member of VG Instruments, a highly successful and profitable vacuum based instruments group; with an outstanding record of product innovation and export achievement.

VG Isotopes specialises in mass spectrometers used mainly in geochronology and nuclear science. Nuclear applications include the commercial measurement of nuclear fuel enrichment, while precision determinations of isotope ratios of Rb/Sr, U/Pb, Sm/Nd, K/Ar are fundamental to the dating of rocks right back to the formation of the earth. The technology involved ranges from exceptionally high performance analogue electronics through to TTL and microprocessors using the Texas Instruments range of software, development systems and devices.

Computers selected from the Hewlett Packard range from the HP85 through to the HP9845T, are used to provide automatic operation of the instruments, and to manipulate the data produced.

Types of graduate required

The pace of growth and innovation dictates the kind of person we need. Relevant degree subjects are *electronics, electronic engineering, physics*, but we also look for a high degree of motivation; the ability to adapt to new situations and a positive attitude to the commercial aspects of our operation.

Your future could be in product or applications engineering, marketing and sales.

Activities
Manufacture of high performance isotope mass spectrometers

Employees
85

Location: UK
North West

Locations: Overseas
Worldwide

Opportunities
Project engineers and scientists; Analogue digital and microprocessor circuit designers; Unit and systems test engineers

Vacancies
6

Upper age limit
26

Application address
The Managing Director, VG Isotopes Ltd, Ion Path, Road Three, Winsford, Cheshire CW7 3BX

If you are a newly qualified engineer/scientist we are able to offer a spectrum of flexible options, agreed objectives, and further training to match a mutually agreed pattern of career development.

Salaries and benefits

Attractive salaries are paid and are reviewed annually on the basis of merit. Generous staff benefits include assistance in reallocation expenses in approved cases; sports and social activities; life assurance, and a comprehensive sickness and pensions scheme.

Further information

If you want to make the fullest use of your qualifications and be given real responsibility early in your career, you owe it to yourself to find out more about us.

Vickers Shipbuilding and Engineering Ltd

A member company of British Shipbuilders

Vickers Shipbuilding and Engineering designs, builds and equips naval vessels and in particular nuclear powered submarines. Examples of our engineering products include missile launchers, cement making machinery and winches for the offshore oil industry. Please refer to the British Shipbuilders entry on page 112 for further details of our requirements and opportunities.

Victor Products (Wallsend) plc

Activities
Hazardproof equipment for mining and industry

Employees
900

Location: UK
North East

Locations: Overseas
USA; South Africa; India;
Resident engineers: Middle East and Australia

Vacancies
2

Applications address
Training Officer, Victor Products (Wallsend) plc, Church Bank, Wallsend, Tyne and Wear, NE28 6PP

The company was founded in 1929. Consistent, steady growth over the past decade has created opportunities in the management team. The company's products are intended for use in the energy industry and fall broadly into four categories: flameproof plugs and sockets for the UK mining industry, lighting fittings for the coal, oil and petrochemical industries, control gear for flourescent lighting and electric and hydraulic drills for the mining and civil engineering industries. A rigorous exporting policy is pursued.

Types of graduate required

An *engineering* degree is preferred but posts will go to those with initiative, regardless of faculty.

Training

Training is tailored to the individual's needs, the company's needs and the requirements of any relevant professional institution. There are no artificial training exercises. Graduates are given authority and responsibility quickly, and are regularly monitored and appraised by the company training officer.

Salaries and benefits

Trainees are paid in line with rates for graduate trainees. Salaries are reviewed annually and employees enjoy five weeks holiday plus the normal statutory days.

A Career in Sales or Journalism

VNU Business Publications BV is a substantial and dynamic Pan European publishing house with an impressive record in a wide field of UK professional and trade media. Amongst the highly successful titles we publish are Computing, Accountancy Age, Datalink, Infomatics, DOG, Microdecision, The Computer Users Yearbook and The International Directory of Software, What Micro, Databusiness.

To continue and accelerate our growth we consistently appoint graduates who will be looking for a career in journalism or sales where self motivation and ambition will provide the opportunity for job satisfaction and rapid advancement, since we operate a policy of internal promotion.

Graduates are given extensive training throughout their careers, whether in sales or journalism.

Remuneration in the form of salary and commission is generous, and graduates can expect to earn over £6,000 in their first year of employment.

If you believe that your talent and personality matches the challenge of operating in the extremely fast moving environment of publishing, then write to or telephone:

The Director of Personnel and Training
VNU Business Publications
53-55 Frith Street
London W1A 2HG
Telephone: 01-439 4242

VNU
BUSINESS PUBLICATIONS

Activities
Publishing

Employees
240

Locations: UK
London and South East

Opportunities
Advertising sales executives; Journalists

Application address
The Director of Personnel and Training, VNU
Business Publications, 53–55 Frith Street,
London W1A 2HG
Tel: 01-439 4242

VNU Business Publications BV

VNU Business Publications BV is a substantial and dynamic pan-European publishing house with an impressive record in a wide field of UK professional and trade media. Amongst the highly successful titles we publish are *Computing, Accountancy Age, Datalink, Infomatics, DOG, Microdecision, The Computer Users Yearbook* and *The International Directory of Software, What Micro, Databusiness IDB* and *Personal Computer World*.

To continue and accelerate our growth we consistently appoint graduates who will be looking for a career in journalism or sales where self-motivation and ambition will provide the opportunity for job satisfaction and rapid advancement since we operate a policy of internal promotion.

Training and prospects
Graduates are given intensive training throughout their career whether in sales or journalism. Remuneration in the form of salary and commission is generous and graduates can expect to earn over £6,000 in their first year of employment.

Applications
If you believe that your talent and personality matches the challenge of operating in the demanding and fast moving environment of publishing then telephone or write to the Director of Personnel and Training at the address given.

Vosper Thornycroft (UK) Limited
A member company of British Shipbuilders

Vosper Thornycroft designs and builds complex modern warships and other crafts ranging from small GRP police boats to major frigates of 4,000 tons carrying sophisticated electronic and conventional weapons. Please see the British Shipbuilders entry on page 112 for further information and vacancies.

Waitrose Limited

 a branch of the John Lewis Partnership

Activities
Retailing

Employees
9,000

Locations: UK
London; Home Counties; South East; West
Midlands

Opportunities & places
Supermarket management 8

Upper age limit
23

Application address
Senior Staff Manager, Waitrose Limited,
Doncastle Road, Southern Industrial Area,
Bracknell, Berkshire RG12 4YA

Waitrose, with over 70 supermarkets, is the food group of the John Lewis Partnership. This differs from most businesses in that its aim is to give all its members the advantages of ownership in terms of profit, knowledge and power. Hence, after costs (including amenities and pensions) have been met and proper reserves set aside for future development, all profits are distributed to the workers, managers and managed alike. These are cash distributions in proportion to their pay, which is taken as the best measure of the contribution to the total results. In the five years to 1980–81 partnership bonus has varied from 13% to 24% of pay.

The partnership is more than profits. Workers are in effect part owners and have influence over the policy and direction of the business through a series of democratically elected councils. We believe that democracy lies in the accountability of the management to the managed, not just as a theory, but as a hard fact of everyday commercial life.

Types of graduate required
We recruit from a wide range of disciplines. All applicants must have adequate physical and mental stamina as work in the retail trade is

Waitrose Limited, cont

exacting. A good eye for detail and a flexibility of mind enablin
recruit to switch quickly from problem to problem are also nece
genuine interest in people and the ability to influence and organ
essential. An *economics* degree is useful but not essential.

Training

The scheme is arranged in five stages consisting of a series of pl
work attachments and project work, integrated with a formal tr
programme of short intensive courses. The attachments are arr
provide trainees with an early opportunity to take responsibility
scope for this will increase as experience is gained. After appro
20 months the trainee should be ready to take up an appointme
assistant branch manager.

Pay and prospects

Pay for trainees joining in September 1982 is £5,400 to £6,000 a
to location. Rates for 1983 were not known at the time of going
On completion of training pay will progress according to appoir
and individual merit. In 1982 the pay range for supermarket ma
expected to be between £10,000 and £16,000. There is also som
for more specialised careers in central departments.

The James Walker Group of Companies

James Walker and Co Ltd are the parent company of an interna
organisation concentrating upon sealing technology that is repr
throughout the industrial world. All manufacturing industries
seals and gaskets for the containment of fluids and over a period
hundred years the trade name of Lion has become synonymous
quality, service and innovation. We are amongst the front runn
that's where we intend to stay. This is why we are increasing ou
intake and why we must reinforce certain sectors where our
manufacturing processes continue to grow in complexity. Prou
history, our future must be better.

Types of graduate required

We need technologists, especially design staff, production engi
polymer chemists, but as our strength lies in teamwork we look
the university degree. Personal initiative, a sense of responsibili
willingness to become a respected member of that team are qua
we admire and demand. In return we regard every graduate as a
member of management.

Training

Our policy on training is essentially one of flexibility. Unvaryin
irrelevant programmes have no place in our schemes. Newcome
under constant review; their progress and requirements are asse
senior company officials at regular intervals, but even during th
graduates will be expected to exercise their professional skills u
guidance and supervision.

Location

Our principal UK manufacturing plant is at Woking, Surrey, b
individuals experience increases travel, including overseas visit
required.

...ies
...anufacture of sealing devices and their
...tion

...yees

...ons: UK
...East; North West

...unities
... engineer; Product development;
...r chemist

...cies

...age limit

...ation address
...nel Department, James Walker & Co Ltd,
...orks, Maybury Hill, Woking, Surrey
...3AP

Prospects

No formula is offered. The future lies in the hands of the individual but our record shows that we favour promotion from within.

Applications and further information

Our personnel department will be happy to give you any additional information you require.

Watney Mann & Truman Brewers Limited

Activities
Beer production, distribution, marketing and retailing

Employees
8,000

Locations: UK
General

Opportunities
Marketing; Sales; Distribution; Personnel; Production and management services

Upper age limit
26

Application address
Applications are made to individual regional companies. Addresses available from: Central Personnel Department, Watney Mann & Truman Brewers Ltd, Central Personnel, 91 Brick Lane, London E1 6QN

We are one of the leading brewers in the UK, involved in beer production, distribution, marketing and retailing through our own tied estate and are part of the brewing and retailing division of Grand Metropolitan plc.

We recruit graduates into most functions both in our regional companies and at head office and can offer career opportunities to those who have the ability and determination to succeed.

Our company

Our business is operated through a group of 10 regional companies each of which is responsible for brewing and supplying beer, wholesaling and marketing it through clubs and public houses in its own area. A large distribution network ensures that our beers are available to meet the needs of our customers while one company specialises in the take home trade supplying supermarkets and other national outlets. We employ around 8,000 people who in 1981 significantly contributed towards the division's trading profit of over £73 million.

Opportunities for graduates

We want men and women who not only possess good degrees but who are numerate, results oriented and are prepared to make a long term commitment and contribution to the growth and development of our company. They must also be totally mobile during the early years of their career.

Our policy is to place graduates into positions of responsibility at the earliest opportunity so that experience can be gained in the best possible way, from handling day to day working situations.

Our management development and training policy aims to equip people with the necessary skills so that progress to senior level can be achieved. Progression, however, will depend on individual performance and the achievement of objectives.

If you would like further details please write to us at the address given, or see your careers centre for our booklet and application form.

R Watson & Sons

Activities
Consulting actuaries

Employees
200

Locations: UK & Ireland
London; South East; Scotland; Republic of Ireland

Location: Overseas
West Indies

R Watson & Sons is a large and expanding professional firm of consulting actuaries which advises its clients on the financial and administrative aspects of pension funds and life offices, and also on various other financial and statistical references. New graduates who intend to study to acquire the fellowship of either the Institute or the Faculty of Actuaries are being recruited each year.

Types of graduate required

Good honours graduates in *mathematics*, *statistics*, *computer science* or *economics* are best equipped to train as actuaries, but other degrees are not

Opportunities & places
Actuarial assistants 6

Application address
JR Wigley MA, FIA, R Watson & Sons,
Watson House, London Road, Reigate,
Surrey RH2 9PQ

Activities
Design, manufacture and marketing of
centrifugal pumps to the world

Employees
3,000

Location: UK
Scotland

Opportunities
Design engineers: mechanical and
hydrodynamic; Application engineers: selection
and tendering; Research engineers: testing,
acoustics, noise and vibration, dynamics, stress
analysis; Commissioning engineers: erection,
installation, trouble shooting; Production
management: supervision and manufacturing
techniques.

Vacancies
6

Application address
Training Manager, Weir Pumps Limited,
149 Newlands Road, Cathcart, Glasgow
G44 4EX (by Friday 11 February 1983)

R Watson & Sons, cont

ruled out provided the candidate has a mathematical background and is
interested in financial matters.

Training
Actuarial students are employed as assistants to the partners and their
work is designed to cover aspects of the examination syllabus which are
currently being studied. Students are also trained in the application of the
firm's computer. Day time study facilities are available and revision leave
is allowed shortly before the professional examinations.

Locations
Actuarial students are employed initially at the principal office in Reigate
but opportunities do arise for work at other offices in the UK and
overseas.

Salaries and prospects
Generous salaries are paid to new graduates, and progress on a scale
closely graded according to examination credits. After qualification,
promotion within the firm depends upon individual ability and all new
partners are appointed from within the staff of the firm.

Pensions
There is a non-contributory pension and death benefit scheme.

Weir Pumps Limited

Weir Pumps Limited is one of the most forward thinking and progressive
engineering companies in the UK. The main factories in Glasgow and
Alloa near Stirling utilise up to the minute methods and manufacturing
techniques and are supported by a worldwide network of branch offices
and agencies. The company occupies a leading position in the design and
manufacture of advanced equipment for prestige markets such as nuclear
and conventional power generation, shipbuilding, the process industries,
public works and oil exploration. Current equipment includes pumping
plant for all duties, heat exchangers, water treatment plant, distillation
units, marine systems, compressors, electric motors and a wide variety of
specialised auxiliaries. The company plays an important role in major
technological developments through a well qualified and experienced
research and development team.

Types of graduate required
The company needs high calibre *mechanical*, *production* and *electrical
engineering* graduates who are eager to accept responsibility.

Training
The company believes in giving a graduate a responsible job
immediately, while tailoring experience and training to meet the
requirements of the professional institutions. This gives a graduate a real
sense of purpose and still enables him to obtain a wide exposure to and
appreciation of the company's operations.

Salaries and prospects
Starting salaries reflect qualifications, ability and experience and are
reviewed twice yearly initially to provide rapid progress and advancement
to those who demonstrate high performance and potential.

Wellcome

Activities
Pharmaceuticals and fine chemicals

Employees
7,000 UK
18,000 worldwide

Locations: UK
North West; London; Home Counties

Opportunities
Finance and accountancy; Chemical engineering; Chemical production; Computer work; UK medical sales; Personnel and training and development; Pharmaceutical production; Pharmaceutical development; Production services; Research

Application addresses
For non-research posts:
Group Personnel Division (Graduate Recruitment), The Wellcome Foundation Limited, Temple Hill, Dartford, Kent DA1 5AH
Tel: 32 23488

For research posts:
The Personnel Officer, The Wellcome Research Laboratories, Langley Court, Beckenham, Kent BR3 3BS
Tel: 01-658 2211

The Wellcome Foundation Limited

The Wellcome Foundation Ltd is the British based parent company of an international group of pharmaceutical and chemical companies concerned with the discovery, development, manufacture and distribution of products to promote the health and hygiene of both mankind and animals. Founded in 1880 as a partnership, Burroughs Wellcome & Co, it was registered under its present title in 1924. It is without parallel in the pharmaceutical industry in that its sole shareholders are The Wellcome Trust, a recognised public charity, which applies all distributed profits to the advancement throughout the world of research into human and veterinary medicine and allied sciences.

Graduate opportunities
Each year we have a limited number of opportunities for top calibre graduates, this year our need is likely to be around 25–35.

We can offer a wide range of excellent career opportunities for graduates in many areas of the company including pharmaceutical production, chemical manufacturing, finance and accountancy, UK sales, personnel, computer division, production services, pharmaceutical development; research.

At the time of going to press, exact areas of application are impossible to define for the next year. The areas listed below are indicative of our possible needs and are not firm and definite.

Opportunities in our research laboratories are limited and our requirements very specific.

Areas of applications
Personnel: *economics, business studies, statistics, science subjects.*
Opportunity to gain broad based experience.
Computer division: *computer science/studies, mathematics, statistics* or any good *science* degree. Enter as trainee programmer.
Finance and accountancy: *mathematics/statistics* or *business studies* associated with *accountancy.* Enter trainee accountant scheme, expect to study for professional qualification by day release/evening class.
Sales: *pharmacy, chemistry, biology* or appropriate combination of *science* subjects. Training given in company products, sales techniques.
Pharmaceutical production: *pharmacy, chemistry.* In-company training provided in production/management techniques.
Chemical manufacturing: *chemistry,* to operate as production chemists.
Chemical engineering to provide technical services to production.
Production services: *life sciences, business studies, economics.* Variety of commercial work including purchase and supply, production control, transport, export shipping, product introduction. Training provided.
Pharmaceutical development: *pharmacy.*

Prospects
On joining the company, you will receive any necessary general or specialised training to equip you to perform your duties successfully.

Appointments are generally to specific positions rather than to project type jobs created for a graduate training scheme.

We have a flexible approach towards training and career development and, wherever possible, attempt to meet individual preferences.

Career development can be in a specialised or general role and there is ample opportunity for changes in career direction within the company.

We operate a management appraisal programme and provide management training on an ongoing basis through internal and external courses.

In the long run, your career prospects/direction will depend on your ability and interests.

The Wellcome Foundation Limited, cont

Locations

UK operations: London: head office. Dartford: chief chemical and pharmaceutical manufacturing unit. Beckenham: research in chemistry, pharmacology, virology, bacteriology, parasitology, vaccine production. Crewe: production; UK sales and marketing. Berkhamstead: exports; pesticides and chemotherapy in veterinary medicine.

Overseas opportunities

We are essentially an international organisation, with associated companies and subsidiaries spread throughout the world. Opportunities overseas occasionally occur for graduates with appropriate qualifications and experience with the company in the UK.

Salaries

Salaries are dependent on age, qualifications and experience and are subject to annual review. The company has a generous pension scheme and general conditions of employment are excellent.

Further literature

Requests for a copy of our graduate literature should be made to your careers office. If you have difficulty in obtaining this please write to the appropriate company site.

West Midlands Fire Service

The West Midlands Fire Service is the largest fire service in the country outside London and as such offers a career structure which enables those of proven ability to rise to the top. For those graduates who are searching for an active interesting career, the fire service can provide this in fulfilling its main objectives of:

Saving life and property from the effects of fire and other hazardous situations;

Enforcing fire protection and fire prevention legislation thus safeguarding the lives of people in all types of buildings.

Types of graduate required

No specific degree is necessary – all that is required is that candidates use the same intelligence and self-discipline which enabled them to obtain their degree in establishing a career in the fire service.

Career structure

Everyone starts as a firefighter but by passing the statutory promotion examination can achieve the rank of station officer after five years' service.

Comprehensive training is given at local and national level. In addition, a chair of fire engineering has been established at Edinburgh University and after a period of service suitably qualified candidates may be given the opportunity to obtain a postgraduate degree.

Rank structure

After completing two years' service and passing the statutory examination, a firefighter may be promoted to leading firefighter; after another two years' service and passing the statutory examination to sub-officer, and after a further one year's service and passing the statutory examination, to station officer.

Promotion beyond the rank of station officer is made according to ability, and an employee may attain one of the following ranks: assistant division officer, divisional officer III, divisional officer II, divisional

Activities
Fire fighting, emergency rescue, fire prevention

Employees
2,500

Location: UK
Midlands

Opportunities & places
Firefighters 25

Upper age limit
30

Application address
Mrs J Adams, Staff and Training Officer, West Midlands Fire Service, Lancaster Circus, Queensway, Birmingham B4 7DE
Tel: 021-300 7907

officer I, senior divisional officer, assistant chief officer, or chief fire officer.

Physical requirements
Firefighters must be generally fit, at least 5ft 6ins tall, have a chest measurement of at least 36ins, with an expansion of not less than two inches; and good eyesight without glasses or contact lenses.

Salaries, pensions and benefits
Salaries start at £5,799 and the salary for a qualified firefighter is £7,260. The annual holiday allowance is initially 24 days, rising to 35 days a year, plus public holidays. The three months of initial training are on full pay. A pension of two-thirds the salary is given, after 30 years' service.

Western Geophysical Company of America

WESTERN GEOPHYSICAL CO. OF AMERICA
Litton

Activities
Worldwide exploration of natural resources using, advanced geophysical methods

Employees
4,500

Location: UK
Isleworth, Middlesex

Locations: Overseas
Europe; Africa and the Middle East

Application address
Personnel Manager, Western Geophysical Company of America, 455 London Road, Isleworth, Middlesex TW7 5AB

Founded in California in 1933 and purchased by Litton Industries in 1960, Western Geophysical is the world's largest geophysical company and leads the field in seismic exploration for oil, gas and other natural resources. We provide a full range of services to the world's major petroleum companies and governments: covering land and marine seismic surveys, data processing, scientific programming and interpretation.

Types of graduate required
Applicants with honours degrees are required to fill key technical and future managerial positions in our two areas of operation:
Isleworth (UK data processing centre for Europe, Africa and the Middle East): a *geophysics, physics, maths* or *computer science* degree.
Overseas seismic field crews (land and marine): a degree in *electronic engineering,* or *physics* with electronic engineering.

Training
All new employees receive appropriate induction training. Those assigned to the DP centre are provided with extensive on the job training in data processing and seismic exploration methods. After their initial period of employment they may receive advanced in-house and external training in the latest technological developments.
Field personnel receive frequent updating in developments pertinent to their particular disciplines.

Location
The UK centre for European, African and Middle Eastern operations is situated in large modern offices in Isleworth, Middlesex. It's here, within our sophisticated DP environment, that all seismic data relayed by field personnel are analysed using the very latest computer technology. A progressive programme of research and development into data processing techniques and seismic interpretation is carred out by a small, highly professional team. Western's seismic exploration activities are truly worldwide, covering all continents, climates and conditions on both land and sea.

Prospects
Competitive local benefits include a pension scheme, BUPA, stock purchase plan and spacious premises offering social and sports facilities. Field crews receive a generous foreign bonus and allowances, tax advantages, frequent paid leaves and are offered benefit plans which include profit sharing, stock purchase, life and medical insurance.

Western Geophysical Company of America, cont

In a profession full of variety, adventure and the excitement of exploration, the future career prospects for young ambitious people are excellent. Details are available in our illustrated and informative booklet, available from the address shown.

Westland plc

Westland

Activities
Designers and manufacturers of helicopters, hovercraft, aircraft systems

Employees
12,000

Location: UK
South West

Opportunities
Accounts; Production; Commerce; Product support; Design; Development; Management services; Research; Training

Vacancies
35

Application address
Recruitment Manager, Westland Helicopters Limited, Yeovil, Somerset (marked Graduate Recruitment)

Westland plc is the parent company of a group which designs and manufactures a wide range of high technology products.

The largest company in the group, Westland Helicopters Ltd, is seeking graduates to work on research and design for a new large helicopter to replace the successful Sea King, and the design and development of the Westland 30 helicopter. In addition, development work continues on the existing range of helicopters, including the world record breaking Lynx.

Types of graduate required
Graduates in *aeronautical, mechanical, electrical/electronic* and *production engineering, business studies* and *applied science* are required for careers in occupations listed alongside.

Training and career development
Traineeships in engineering and commerce are offered for those who wish to satisfy professional bodies or require a wider industrial background to fit them for a career. Selected trainees are sponsored for higher degrees or for the production engineering and management course run by Cambridge University or for training in France.

Shorter training programmes are arranged to prepare other graduates for direct entry to specific posts. Those who join the company immediately after leaving school or university are now found at all levels of management and all graduates are encouraged to develop themselves to the full.

Locations
Most of the graduates required would be located at Yeovil, although a small number are also required at Weston super Mare and the Isle of Wight.

Salaries
Salaries depend upon qualifications, experience and age, eg a person who joined as a direct entrant at 22 would earn not less than about £5,900 per year plus fringe benefits. Salaries are adjusted in June each year.

Further information
Apply to the Recruitment Manager (envelope marked Graduate Recruitment).

Williams & Glyn's Bank plc

Please see our display advertisement on page 20.

Wilson Green Gibbs

Activities
Accountancy, audit and taxation services for companies and individuals

Employees 35

Location: UK London

Opportunities & places
Trainee chartered accountants 4

Application address
RD Ward, Wilson Green Gibbs, 5 Southampton Place, London WC1A 2DA

We are a six partner firm with a staff of about 35 and have a varied clientele, including limited companies, both large and small including subsidiaries of public groups, partnerships and sole traders. The firm has its own computer system and we have computerised many of our clients' accounts.

Training
We are a member of the HAT syndicate, and are able to offer comprehensive training to our students (see entry under HAT).

Salaries
Starting salaries are competitive and are reviewed twice yearly.

YMCA

Activities
Social and community services

Locations: UK
General

Opportunities
Youth and community programme assistants

Application address
YMCA National Personnel Department, 640 Forest Road, London E17 3DZ

Founded in 1844 in London, the YMCA is now a truly international organisation providing facilities and programmes to meet community needs. Through its 10,000 local associations, it sets out to serve a wide variety of communities. Its full time staff should have a genuine concern for people and their welfare, the necessary professional qualifications for social and community work and a personal commitment to Christianity.

Types of graduate required
To work as assistants on our youth and community programmes: we are interested in hearing from students who hope to gain a youth and community work certificate, a teacher's certificate, or a diploma or degree in *social science* (which should include appropriate youth and/or community content and a period of supervised relevant practical work). Previous experience of youth work is clearly an additional benefit.

There are also a number of vacancies for wardens, secretaries and leaders in our hostels and services centres. Here a course related to hotel and catering management would be advantageous, but formal qualifications are not always required.

Training
The YMCA has its own national college in London at which we offer, in association with the North East London Polytechnic, a two year course leading to a certificate in youth and community work.

Prospects
The YMCA can offer worthwhile and satisfying opportunities for both long term and short term service. Further in-service training is always available and you will be given every encouragement to develop your career with us.

Further information
Opportunities with the YMCA are varied and interesting. If you would like to know more, you should write to the National Personnel Department.

Yorkshire Bank

Activities
Commercial banking throughout the North and Midlands

Employees
4,000

Locations: UK
Midlands; North East; North West

Opportunities
Banking; Finance; Administration

Vacancies
15

Upper age limit
23

Application address
The Manager, Personnel Selection, Yorkshire Bank plc, 20 Merrion Way, Leeds LS2 8NZ

Yorkshire Bank plc

Yorkshire Bank has more than 200 branches spread over a wide area in the north of England, with a head office situated in Leeds.

Head office is organised into six divisions: finance, regional control, operations, inspection, marketing and personnel. In addition to administration and banking functions implicit in our type of organisation the divisions comprise a number of specialist functions, eg data processing, organisation and methods, business promotions and research to name but a few. In consequence, after obtaining your professional banking qualifications and gaining experience, there are opportunities for following more than one type of speciality within our bank, and opportunities to change direction during one's career without changing employer.

New developments
Over the past few years, Yorkshire Bank has been expanding rapidly. Each year, new branches are being opened and existing premises are being enlarged and modernised to accommodate the increasing volume of business.

Types of graduate required
Graduates of good degree standard are required, to train for positions of responsibility. Graduation in *economics*, *law* or *business studies* gives a good preparation for the banking professional qualifications. In addition, we are looking for graduates who wish to develop and succeed in a long term career.

Training
Training will be for two years and will take place at branches. A necessary concomitant to the practical and planned training is the attainment of the diploma of the Institute of Bankers.

Prospects
When the planned training programme has been completed satisfactorily graduates cease to belong to a special group. They take their place as normal members of the bank's staff, in competition with others, judged on their own performance and capabilities. Their first jobs will be in job evaluation grades three or four depending upon performance and vacancies (there are six grades for non-managerial staff). Further success is reflected by promotion to grades five and six. There are opportunities for graduate entrants to hold supervisory positions before five years' service has been completed. The essential requirements for success are the attainment of the banking diploma and effective performance of responsibilities.

Locations
Mobility is a condition of service. Graduate training is carried out at one or more of the bank's larger branches. Subsequently, as with all staff, transfer to different branches or head office does occur. The area in which the bank is situated is described above. Moves are not made unnecessarily and are frequently linked with promotion.

Salaries
Particulars of up to date salaries can be obtained from the manager, personnel selection. Salary is reviewed annually during training and, subsequently, at least once a year.

Pensions, benefits and amenities
There is a staff house purchase loan scheme with a rate of interest which reduces considerably the cost of house purchase. Other benefits include a comprehensive non-contributory pensions and annuities fund, and a first class sports ground in Leeds.

Zambia Consolidated Copper Mines Limited

Please see our entry in the Overseas section.

One piece has really wide horizons

Like the Queen on a chessboard, <u>Certified</u> Accountants enjoy real mobility within the economy.

Alone among accountancy trainees, they can train in any or all of the three branches of the profession – industry and commerce, public service and public practice.

They obtain a wide-ranging expertise which they can use in any aspect of money management all over the world.

Find out more about the Association of <u>Certified</u> Accountants from your Careers Adviser or by writing to the address below.

We offer the most versatile qualification in an exciting and creative profession.

Student Services Department,
The Association of Certified Accountants
29, Lincoln's Inn Fields
London WC2A 3EE
Telephone 01-242 6855

Association of <u>Certified</u> Accountants: the modern way to qualify

see also page 378

Professional bodies

Professional bodies describe prospects and conditions in the professions and industries they represent.

The Association of Certified Accountants

Activities
Professional and examining body of accountants

Members
24,000 members
64,000 students

Locations: UK
General

Locations: Overseas
Worldwide

Opportunities
Financial accounting; Management accounting; Auditing; Advice on taxation; Management consultancy; Financial and general management

Application address
Student Services Department, The Association of Certified Accountants, 29 Lincoln's Inn Fields, London WC2A 3EE

The Association of Certified Accountants is one of the largest bodies of accountants with 24,000 members and over 64,000 registered students. Certified accountants work in all branches of the accountancy profession and may quickly progress to management positions.

A degree and a professional qualification
Today the combination of a degree and a professional qualification is seen as the ideal starting point for a successful business career. In the increasingly competitive business world it is essential that senior managers have wide knowledge and experience and the Association's particularly broad based study and training programme in addition to a degree is excellent preparation for prospective managers.

The work of a certified accountant
Trainee certified accountants can train in any branch of the profession, and, once qualified, there are numerous career opportunities in either the private sector or nationalised industry, commerce, public service or in public practice. The majority of the Association's students train in industry and commerce and if you are one of these you will obtain experience of both the financial accounting and management accounting functions, liaising closely with managers over a whole range of decisions.

Alternatively, as a practising certified accountant, you will be recognised by statute as an auditor and can offer to clients (who may be companies or individuals) a range of professional services such as accounting, advice on taxation or data processing system, financial advice or business consultancy. You can also choose to train in either local or central government or with the public utilities, where you will be accounting, budgeting and forecasting for a variety of public services.

Examinations
The Association's examinations are particularly broad based, covering both financial and management accounting in depth. In addition they cover a wide range of legal and management topics which is particularly important in preparing trainees for future management posts.

In June 1982 the Association introduced a new, more flexible examination system, which consists of three levels: the Preliminary Examination from which all UK universities and CNAA graduates will be exempt, the Professional Examination consisting of nine papers and the Final Examination of four papers. A relevant degree in subjects such as accounting or business studies may give exemptions on a subject for subject basis within Level 2. Full time, sandwich, day release and evening class courses are available at polytechnics and colleges throughout the UK and Ireland. Alternatively, it is possible to study by correspondence course.

Training
To become a member of the Association, in addition to passing the examinations, graduate trainees must obtain three years approved accountancy experience which may be in any branch of the accountancy profession. Trainees may follow a formal training scheme where they have regular job rotation or they may gain their experience on a less formal basis. Whichever area students choose to train in they will obtain a wide variety of experience which will prepare them for a broad range of career opportunities.

If you would like further information on a career as a certified accountant, please contact your careers advisory service or write to the Student Services Department.

The Association of Cost & Executive Accountants

The association is a professional body for accountants and trainees in industry and commerce, local government, public service and internal auditing. There are two grades of membership, associate (ACEA) and fellow (FCEA). Study for exams is usually by day or evening release, or through correspondence colleges, and syllabi comply with EEC accountancy specifications. Degree and HND/C holders may be eligible for subject exemptions. For further information write to the address given.

The Chartered Institute of Public Finance and Accountancy

The Institute is the professional body for public sector financial managers. One of the six major professional accountancy bodies in the United Kingdom, it is the only one which specialises in high level accountancy for public bodies.

The Institute's members are employed in senior financial management, accountancy and audit posts in central and local government, the health service, water industry, the nationalised industries and other public sector bodies.

Activities
Accountancy and financial management in the public sector

Locations: UK General

Application Address
The Education and Training Officer, The Chartered Institute of Public Finance and Accountancy, 1 Buckingham Place, London SW1E 6HS

Entrance, education and training programme

Any United Kingdom or Republic of Ireland university or CNAA degree is acceptable. All students undertake an approved minimum three-year training programme and the employer will give educational release for the approved courses. Members use the designatory letters IPFA.

For information on vacancies see the entry Accountancy and Financial Management in the Public Sector.

Incorporated Society of Valuers & Auctioneers

Members
8,000 members
2,000 students

Application address
The Education and Membership Officer, ISVA, 3 Cadogan Gate, London SW1X 0AS
Tel: 01-235 2282

A career in property encompasses the fields of valuation, surveying, planning, estate agency, auctioneering, development and management. Qualification entails practical experience as well as passing the Society's examinations, which are at three levels, Intermediate, Final Part I and Final Part II; there is a Direct Final examination for graduates. Tuition is available on a full time, part time and correspondence basis. For further information contact the Education and Membership Officer.

The Institute of Chartered Accountants in England and Wales

Activities
Professional body for chartered accountants

Members
74,000

Locations: UK
General

Locations: Overseas
Worldwide

Opportunities & vacancies
Chartered accountants 3,500–4,000

Application address
The Student Counsellor, The Institute of Chartered Accountants in England and Wales, PO Box 433, Chartered Accountants Hall, Moorgate Place, London EC2P 2BJ

The Institute of Chartered Accountants in England and Wales, which celebrated its centenary in 1980, is one of the world's leading accountancy bodies and has more than 74,000 members.

Around half the Institute's members work in public practice as sole practitioners, partners or employees in accountancy firms. These firms provide financial services to clients ranging in size and complexity from private individuals to the largest multinational corporations. The services provided include the preparation of accounts, auditing, tax advice, design of systems for financial and management control, advice on computer systems, special investigations and insolvency work. For many firms, particularly the larger ones, auditing represents the greatest part of the work as every company in the UK must have its annual accounts audited by an independent accountant to ensure that the financial statements present a true and fair view to shareholders and other interested parties. Auditing provides an unparalleled opportunity to acquire detailed experience and a practical overview of a wide range of different companies and business activities.

Chartered accountants also play a major role in industry and commerce where their influence extends far beyond the preparation of accounts. They are found at every level of corporate activity from the boardroom to the computer department; they include managing directors, finance directors, financial controllers, management accountants, project analysts and internal auditors.

Training to be a chartered accountant has proved to be an excellent foundation for a career in general management.

Types of graduate

Graduates from *all* disciplines successfully train as chartered accountants. Numeracy is, of course, essential but so is the ability to write well and to work closely with people from all levels and functions within an organisation. A chartered accountant has to be able to communicate ideas, often on complicated technical subjects, to experts and laymen alike and to think in a logical way, distinguishing the significant from the immaterial.

Training

Graduates must undertake a three year training contract with a firm of chartered accountants in the UK and pass the Institute's examinations. During the early part of the contract students have to complete a graduate conversion course unless they hold an approved accountancy degree. All students take Professional Examinations I and II. Examination training is usually provided by independent tutors or polytechnics and firms will normally arrange study courses and pay the fees. All students receive between 22 and 26 weeks paid study leave but also need to devote a considerable amount of time to study in the evenings and at weekends.

In addition to preparation for the examinations most firms provide training in their own methods and procedures.

An essential feature and the greatest part of the training contract is the practical experience gained working on a variety of accounting, auditing or tax assignments for clients of different sizes and in different industries.

Prospects

Chartered accountants provide a service to clients, often to tight deadlines so the life of a student accountant can be very demanding. Students may be required to work overtime, particularly in the winter months, and a full day's work, frequently on clients' premises, has to be followed by concentrated private study for the examinations.

Students should consider carefully whether they have the interest, aptitudes and motivation to undertake and complete the three year training contract. These years of very hard work and demanding pressures do however lay the foundation for a wide range of career opportunities at home and abroad, in commerce, industry, government and in professional firms. The job satisfaction from serving the needs of business and the community is considerable while the financial rewards can be substantial.

The Institute of Chartered Accountants of Scotland

Incorporated by Royal Charter in 1854, the Institute of Chartered Accountants of Scotland confers upon its members the exclusive right to use the letters CA after their names. The Institute is also unique in performing an active teaching role as well as providing a formal structure for the passing of examinations in the shortest effective period and for achieving a high level of professional competence.

Although the basic responsibilities of CAs who are engaged in individual or partnership practice still largely revolve around the carrying out of statutory audits on publicly and privately owned companies, the ever increasing levels of sophistication applicable to those responsibilities have led CAs into many other aspects of modern management activity.

Not only are they involved with the newer techniques of statistical sampling and computerised data processing, but their importance in providing the information on which management decisions are based and in applying their trained abilities to many wider aspects of a company's or organisation's affairs, ensure that their value is generally recognised and rewarded.

Alternatively, working directly in industry, commerce or public service, the professional CAs will make their mark in many different environments and within a wide variety of organisation structures and functions. Decision making positions of accountant, company secretary, financial controller or director, managing director or chairman are open to them; provided of course that they have the personal qualities which will allow them to build on their professional training and knowledge.

Types of graduate required
Graduates from *any* discipline are accepted, but those whose degrees include a sufficient depth of *accountancy*, *law* and *economics* are eligible to commence straight away in a three year training period with a member of the Institute in public practice in the United Kingdom. On the other hand, graduates whose degree subjects have not included accountancy in depth, mercantile law and economics, will be required to attend a one year postgraduate course at a Scottish university, or at the London School of Economics and Political Science, prior to the commencement of their professional training.

Training
The Institute's formal three year training scheme is designed to give graduates a thorough professional training in, and a comprehensive knowledge of, the many different aspects of accountancy. Working in the office of a practising member of the Institute, they undertake simultaneously a course of block release study and home exercises, under the tutelage of the Institute's professional teaching staff, designed to help

Activities
Professional body for chartered accountants

Members
10,500

Locations: UK
General

Locations: Overseas
Worldwide

Opportunities & places
Chartered accountants 500

Application address
The Secretary, The Institute of Chartered Accountants of Scotland, 27 Queen Street, Edinburgh EH2 1LA (please quote DOG 83)

them pass the two part professional examination – a target which should be achieved about half way through the formal training period.

Salaries
You will be paid a starting salary which is competitive to current levels. Subsequent increases are directly linked to performance in examination and to personal capability.

Further information
Further details, including the Institute's *CA Student Guide* and list of current training vacancies, may be obtained from Eric Swift.

Institute of Chartered Secretaries and Administrators

The Institute of Chartered Secretaries and Administrators awards a professional qualification in administration. Chartered secretaries work in a wide range of posts, in both business and public administration; the Institute has 44,000 members worldwide.

The Institute was founded in 1891 by a group of company secretaries, seeking training relevant to their particular role in a company. The secretary is the legal representative of the company, and has been described as its chief administrative officer. As such, he or she must have a clear understanding of law and finance as well as the management of people – the elements of administration. The importance of this role has been recognised in the 1980 Companies Act, which says that the secretary of a public company should be professionally qualified; chartered secretaries hold the qualification specifically relevant to such work.

Currently, about one fifth of members in the UK work as company secretaries; the breadth of studies means that it is also relevant to other administrative functions in companies from accounts to personnel, from sales administration to purchasing, from insurance to pensions administration.

Chartered secretaries are also to be found in other organisations: in educational administration, trade associations, nationalised industries and the Health Service. The public service stream is the recognised professional qualification for administration in local government.

Activities
Professional body offering a qualification for administrators in industry, commerce and the public sector

Members
44,000 members worldwide
26,000 students worldwide

Locations: UK
General

Opportunities
Administration in all kinds of organisation

Application address
Careers Department (D83), Institute of Chartered Secretaries and Administrators, 16 Park Crescent, London W1N 4AH

Examinations and courses
The examinations are in four parts, of four papers each. These cover aspects of law, accounting, economics, personnel, management, finance and office administration.

There are three streams providing special options, one for those wishing to work in the company secretarial department, one for those interested in a broader financial or administrative career and one for those working in the public sector. Whichever stream is followed, all chartered secretaries will have studied a substantial common core of subjects.

Courses for the examinations are available for part time students at many polytechnics and colleges, by block, day release and evening class study. Tuition can also be obtained through correspondence courses. Length of study is about two to three years part time, depending on the number of exemptions granted. There are several one year full time intensive courses.

Entry requirements and exemptions
A university or CNAA degree, in *any* discipline, obtains exemption from

part one; further exemptions on a subject for subject basis may be available for relevant study, eg business/public administration, law, economics, finance, etc. Holders of the BEC Higher National award at certain colleges are normally exempt from part one and may also qualify for substantial further exemptions.

The Institute of Cost and Management Accountants

ICMA

Activities
To provide education and training facilities for young people wishing to enter the profession

Employees
20,000 members
40,000 students

Locations: UK
General

Locations: Overseas
Worldwide

Opportunities
All cost and management accounting positions; General management; Education; General finance consultancy

Application address
The Registrar, ICMA, 63 Portland Place, London W1N 4AB
Tel: 01-637 2311

The Institute, the professional and examining body in cost and management accountancy, was incorporated in 1919 and it now has about 20,000 members and 40,000 registered students. The qualification is a combination of examinations and practical experience and membership is denoted by ACMA (Associate) and FCMA (Fellow).

If you train as a cost and management accountant, in the early part of your career you will work in industry or commerce, involved in finding out the costs, of making products, of running departments or carrying out operations. You will analyse costs against estimates and help management maximise the efficient use of manpower, materials, machines and money. You will be a member of the management team, finding ways in which your business can keep costs low and productivity high. Your particular skill and function will be to pinpoint the real costs of activities, highlighting those which are profitable and those which are not.

As you become more experienced your management responsibilities will grow. Your professional skills will be needed to provide information, analysis and advice to top management for the overall financial control of the enterprise and for corporate planning.

Types of graduate required
Graduates in *any* discipline who are interested in a career in industry or commerce.

Examinations and exemptions
The Institute's examinations are in five parts, with papers in cost and management accountancy, financial accountancy, data processing, economics, business mathematics and statistics, company law and taxation, marketing management, financial management, corporate planning and control. The syllabus is divided into two parts: a foundation stage in two sections and a professional stage in three parts. Graduates will earn some measure of exemption from parts of the syllabus. The extent of exemption will depend on the relevance of the degree subject. Details are available from the Institute. No one is exempt from the third and final part of the professional stage as this is regarded as the ultimate test of ability and competence. Graduates usually study on a part time basis, often using college tuition, but correspondence courses are available.

Practical experience
All ICMA members must have a minimum of three years' experience of cost and management accountancy. Many firms can offer carefully devised training programmes leading to the ICMA qualifications. This may include day release or block release to attend college to prepare for the examinations. You will be paid during training and are not bound by a training contract.

Facilities for students
As an ICMA student you are entitled to attend ICMA courses and branch meetings. A comprehensive specialist library is available at head office.

Puzzled
about your career?

Research

Planning & Design

Development

Packaging

Advertising & Promotion

Public Relations

Pricing

Distribution

Sales

After Sales

Service

Marketing is one of the most exciting, and demanding careers in business today. It offers a large number of both general and specialised jobs, all of these demanding a wide variety of skills and experience.

To improve your job prospects, study for the Diploma in Marketing – the Institute's internationally recognised professional qualification.

Part-time courses are available at many Polytechnics and Colleges.

Want to know more about Marketing? Write to:–
Academic Registrar, The Institute of Marketing, Moor Hall, Cookham, Berks SL6 9QH. Tel (06285) 24922.

Institute of Marketing

Put it together with Marketing

The Institute of Cost and Management Accountants, cont

You will receive the ICMA journal, *Management Accounting*, free of charge.

Pay and prospects
Your starting salary will probably be £4,500–£6,500 (although some firms will offer more). By the time you qualify (three years) you could be earning in the region of £9–10,000. Your ultimate salary ceiling will depend on your career pattern, and for many this will mean five figure salaries. Many cost and management accountants reach the top professional positions such as group financial controller, or financial director. Others reach the top in general management. Some cost and management accountants progress into related fields such as data processing, or systems analysis. Many make their careers in lecturing at universities, polytechnics or colleges. A number of members spend some time in management consultancy.

Further information
You will find ICMA members and staff pleased to help you. A representative may be visiting your careers service, and if so, you should make an appointment. The following literature is available from the Institute's Education Department: *ICMA Graduate Entry, Student's Guide* (includes examination syllabus), a list of companies with vacancies for graduate trainee accountants, an educational facilities list, plus other information produced from time to time.

Institute of Marketing

Did you know that your degree can grant direct entry to the Institute of Marketing's professional diploma course? The diploma in marketing is an internationally recognised professional qualification and there are over 16,000 students currently studying for the Institute examinations throughout the world.

Marketing embraces all those business activities responsible for identifying, developing, promoting, distributing and selling a company's product or service profitably in order to satisfy customer requirements. The likelihood of you taking a job in marketing is therefore very high.

Holders of the diploma in marketing, who have practical experience, are eligible to become members of the Institute of Marketing which is the professional body for all executives engaged in the profession. It was founded in 1911 and is the largest organisation of its kind in Europe with over 21,000 members both in the UK and overseas. Membership benefits include careers advice; research and information service; lending and reference library; marketing publications; marketing courses and seminars; as well as UK branch and industry group activities. Members also have the right to use MInstM after their name.

Activities
Full range of membership services for professional marketing executives

Members
21,000

Locations: UK
General

Locations: Overseas
Worldwide

Application address
Academic Registrar, Institute of Marketing, Moor Hall, Cookham, Berkshire, SL6 9QH
Tel: 06285 24922

Institute of Purchasing and Supply

The field of purchasing and supplies management involves the procurement at the most advantageous prices of the raw materials, components, equipment and services used by manufacturing companies and commercial organisations, or the supplies needed by central and local government departments. As a specialised management function leading to executive status it provides a career, both of interest and variety, to men and women of ability, vision and personality.

Institute of Purchasing and Supply, cont

Activities
Professional body for purchasing and supply personnel

Members
15,000

Locations: UK
General

Locations: Overseas
Worldwide

Opportunities
Commercial; Industrial; Public purchasing and supply; Retail and distribution

Application address
Institute of Purchasing and Supply, IPS House, High Street, Ascot, Berkshire SL5 7HU
Tel: Ascot 0990–23711

The work differs from that of many other professional functions in the endless variety of different transactions and the continuous challenge offered by each. The qualities of initiative, enterprise and imagination are important and the supplies manager of today seeks his requirements throughout the world.

Types of graduate required
Graduates entering purchasing and supply start at a considerable advantage, particularly those who have a *business studies* or a *technical* background, since these are the disciplines many potential employers seek when appointing trainee staff. Some of the companies who offer positions for trainee personnel are listed in the job and employer indexes of this directory.

Training
Appropriate exemptions from some of the Institute's examinations are granted to graduates who have taken degrees in relevant subjects, particularly those with a business studies background.

Opportunities overseas

This is a guide to some major employers who recruit graduates for work abroad.

Anglo American Corporation of South Africa Limited

Activities
Mining and beneficiation of ore for coal, gold, uranium and diamonds

Employees
250,000

Locations: Overseas
South Africa; South West Africa; Botswana; Zimbabwe

Opportunities
Mining, mechanical & electrical, metallurgical/mineral, processing engineers

Vacancies
60

Upper age limit
27 approx

Application address
SA Bryant, Manager, ACIS International Appointments Limited, 40 Holborn Viaduct, London EC1P 1AJ

The Anglo American Corporation group of companies in South Africa comprise 13 producers of gold, 13 producers of diamonds and 15 collieries. There are also a number of industrial ventures. In addition, the group's head office in Johannesburg controls various geological and prospecting companies operating throughout Africa.

Types of graduate required
Mining engineers, metallurgists, chemical engineers, mechanical and *electrical engineers*, and *geologists*.

Training
All graduates except geologists serve two year pupillages which are recognised by the institutions and qualify towards associated membership.

Locations
Field geologists may be posted to any part of Africa; other graduates will work in South Africa or South West Africa.

Salaries
A permanent career with first class pension and medical aid scheme is offered. Geologists are entitled to 55 days leave per annum and a free passage back to the United Kingdom every three years. Leave for other graduates is a rate of not less than 45 calendar days per annum. Graduates will start at a figure in excess of R15,000 per annum. In addition geologists are eligible for various field allowances. Married or single accommodation is available at sub-economic rentals. The initial cost of travel is borne by the company.

The climate is healthy and agreeable, income tax low, cost of living moderate, social and sporting facilities excellent, and prospects of advancement have rarely been better.

Consolidated Gold Fields plc

Activities
Mining, energy, exploration, industry, finance

Employees
100,000 worldwide

Location: Overseas
South Africa

Opportunities
Mining; Engineering; Mineral processing

Vacancies
16 approx

Application address
Personnel Officer (Recruitment for Overseas), Consolidated Gold Fields plc, 49 Moorgate, London EC2R 6BQ

The Gold Fields Group is an international mining finance and industrial group comprising more than 250 companies, most of which are concerned with the development of natural resources. Its principal mining interests include gold, tin, copper, iron ore, construction materials, coal, uranium, rutile, ilmenite and zircon. Mining operations are complemented by a continuous exploration programme and prospects in Europe, South Africa, Australia, the Philippines and North America are currently being examined. Other activities include steel manufacture and distribution, the manufacture of drilling rigs, general trading, insurance, aluminium engineering, road transport, property and portfolio management.

The various parts of the group at home and overseas recruit their own employees but when there are shortages in particular categories, eg graduates in mining engineering and other disciplines related to the mining industry, the group's head office recruits in the United Kingdom on behalf of the overseas companies, mainly Renison Goldfields Consolidated Limited (for Australia) and Gold Fields of South Africa Limited.

Types of graduate required
Depending on current vacancies graduates are required for work in all

aspects of mining: the location of ore bodies, the extraction of the ore and the subsequent recovery of metals and minerals. Degrees required are in *geology*, *mining engineering*, *mineral processing*, *extractive metallurgy*, *chemical engineering* and *mechanical* and *electrical engineering*. There are usually vacancies in Australia and South Africa but currently the vacancies are in South Africa only, on mines managed by Gold Fields of South Africa Limited. There were no vacancies for geologists in 1982.

Training and career development
A well established graduate trainee scheme is in operation in Gold Fields of South Africa Limited, which prepares graduates for operational roles on group mines. The length of training is normally about two years. There are good prospects for advancement within Gold Fields of South Africa Limited. Additionally there are prospects of movement within various parts of the group worldwide but this depends on vacancies available and such restrictions as employment visas.

Salaries
Salaries are in accordance with current local scales and are fully competitive. The starting salary (March 1982) for a newly graduated mining engineer is R12,060 per annum.

Pensions, benefits and amenities
Pensions and other fringe benefits are also in accordance with local scales and fully competitive. There are excellent recreational facilities on most mines in the group in South Africa.

Dowell Schlumberger

Activities
Services to companies performing oil prospecting and production

Employees
5,300

Locations: Overseas
Worldwide

Opportunities
Oilfield engineering

Application addresses
Region Recruiter, Dowell Schlumberger, Marble Arch House, 66/68 Seymour Street, London W1H 5AF
Recruiting Manager, Dowell Schlumberger, 8 rue Bellini, 75782 Paris Cedex 16, France
Tel: 010 331 553 5090

Dowell Schlumberger is a truly international group employing engineers of different nationalities, operating in over 60 different countries. The range of services we offer the oil industry forms part of a comprehensive system offered by the Schlumberger group. We are the leaders in our field and to perform these services with the efficiency our clients expect, we require aggressive, practical minded engineers with a sense of responsibility, a willingness to work in diverse conditions and a degree of professional conscientiousness far beyond the average. Personal qualities are thus important criteria in our selection. Most people are initially attracted to the oil industry by the high salaries it offers. You should, however, carefully consider the type of work and the lifestyle: both are unique.

Dowell Schlumberger engineers need to be fully competent in all our basic services which include: well cementing – cementing into place the steel casing through which the oil flows to the surface; drill stem testing – using special tools to locate the productive zones of an oil reservoir; sand control and well stimulation – improving the porosity and permeability of the oil-containing formation or creating new porosity or permeability.

In addition to these basic services, Dowell Schlumberger also performs directional drilling and fishing services to the mining industry and industrial cleaning services.

Training
New recruits spend an initial training period at one of our four training centres. A 14 week course there is followed by a three year practical application period as part of the engineer's training. From then on, engineers will follow a practical/theoretical programme tailored to their own abilities.

The rapid developments in the industry's techniques and technology are such that the training of our service engineers is a continual process.

Dowell Schlumberger, cont

As engineers progress in their career, they assume responsibilities in all aspects of the business, including sales, technique and organisation.

Personnel required
Academic qualifications are important; in fact the salary you are paid upon joining the company depends on them, but essentially we look for single people with a proven mechanical aptitude and a suitable personality. We recruit on a year round basis and applications are welcome at any time. Candidates should be university graduates in *mechanical, civil, electrical, chemical engineering* or *chemistry, physics,* or *maths.*

Salaries and benefits
Salaries are competitive within the oil industry. The basic salary is generally much higher than salaries in other industries.

International staff are entitled to a full range of benefits which include housing, geographical coefficient, job bonus, insurance, medical expenses, a company pension scheme and our own special system of deferred benefits.

Applications
If you feel you are up to this demanding career, write to us, explaining what has attracted you and what you can offer.

Flopetrol International SA

FLOPETROL
Schlumberger

Activities
Providing services to petroleum companies

Employees
2,400

Locations: Overseas
Worldwide

Opportunities & places
Field engineers 36

Upper age limit
27

Application address
Flopetrol Services Inc, 81 Piccadilly, London W1V 9HF

We have one of the most critical and exciting jobs in the oil industry: testing newly drilled wells for their potential productivity. It is on our findings that the petroleum companies, our clients, decide whether to invest tens of millions of dollars in production facilities. Not only do we test wells; we operate newly discovered wells for clients while permanent production facilities are designed and built; we operate a wireline service – positioning and operating devices down the well, and perform a variety of other down-hole tasks during the productive life of the well. We also extend the life of wells in which the subterranean pressure no longer forces oil to the surface. We provide a range of specialist services to an industry in which slight delays generate huge costs. We are always on 24-hour call, often abandoning recreational plans to fly out to a client site. The sites are often remote and in areas of climatic extremes; in the jungle, deserts and out at sea.

Training
As a new entrant you will attend a 14 week course at one of our three training schools; located at Melun in France, Aberdeen in Scotland, and at Bahrain. You will be paid during training, and receive full training expenses. The first two weeks of the course is an introduction to the oil industry, followed by six weeks on well testing and six weeks on wireline. On successful completion of your basic training you will be assigned to one of our 30 bases abroad, each base covering a geographical region. Normally each assignment lasts two to three years.

Career development
Initially you will work as an operator on well testing and wireline. You should progress through various grades, and if you are successful, to specialist engineer, and even the highest levels of management; within four or five years of joining you could become a base manager.

Types of graduate required
To join us you must have a good honours degree in *engineering* or *applied*

science. You must be able to assimilate information and act on your own initiative, communicate effectively, have a sense of responsibility and be a diplomatic, sociable and even tempered person. A positive desire to travel is essential as is a current driving licence.

You must also have a stable character, be physically strong and in excellent health to cope with constant changes in location, jobs, techniques, bosses, clients and colleagues, and with poor working conditions in a variety of often extreme environments. Working on-site our hours are long, often working 12 to 15 hours a day, and you'll have to work, eat and sleep when you can.

Salaries and benefits
Salaries are generous, and your basic salary will be supplemented by a posting coefficient and by operating bonuses. In addition there is a medical scheme, life assurance, a contributory pension scheme and a profit sharing scheme.

Applications
If the challenge of our work interests you, and you think that you have the qualities described please contact your careers adviser.

General Mining Union Corporation Group (Gencor)

Gencor mines gold, platinum, coal, chrome, manganese; and among its many industrial activities makes steel and manufactures pulp and paper.

Within the mining divisions Impala Platinum Limited is the world's second largest producer of platinum group metals. Sappi Limited is Africa's largest producer of pulp and paper. Gencor is investing heavily in expansion, including the development of new mines with their intrinsic process plants and refineries and in paper mills.

Types of graduate required
Mining, metallurgical, mineral processing, chemical, mechanical and *electrical engineering, metallurgy, chemistry* and *geology* graduates are recruited.

Training
Graduates receive thorough practical training to equip them for operational roles and management, including, where appropriate, preparation for government certificates of competency.

The training period is recognised for qualification by the professional institutions.

Locations
South Africa.

Salaries and benefits
Starting salaries are generous and progressive, accompanied by various loans and allowances. In the mining divisions company housing is provided and, for the single, full board and lodging in quarters. Recreational facilities are excellent. Air passages are paid.

Gencor Group

Activities
Mining and manufacturing

Employees
200,000

Location: Overseas
South Africa

Opportunities
Engineers; Metallurgists; Chemists; Geologists

Vacancies
40

Application address
Gencor Recruitment, 30 Ely Place, London EC1N 6UA

Geophysical Service International

Seismic exploration is an industry that demands of its work force continual technical improvement and high mobility. Because of the comprehensive exploratory and analytical service provided by GSI to the petroleum industry, we are looking for graduates who have two main qualifications: the intellectual ability to keep abreast of technological developments and the willingness to take that expertise anywhere in the world. Our requirements and opportunities are detailed fully on page 180 to which you should refer before making an application.

The Hong Kong Administrative Class

Activities
Formulating and co-ordinating Government policies and programmes, overseeing their implementation and controlling the resources involved

Employees
143,000

Location: Overseas
Hong Kong

Opportunities
Public administration; Personnel management; Economic services; Environmental control; Finance; Housing; Monetary affairs; Security; Social services; Education

Application address
Hong Kong Government Office, 6 Grafton Street, London W1X 3LB

Hong Kong consists of a complex of islands and islets and a stretch of mainland, together making up a land area of some 1,060 square kilometres. Over five million people live there, most of them crowded into about 166 square kilometres.

It is a nation in microcosm; it needs to provide the services that any country would be expected to provide. It supports, or rather demands a Civil Service that almost mirrors that in the United Kingdom. Yet civil servants also have to cope with, or certainly oversee, many jobs that a local council would normally take on.

The administrative functions of the Hong Kong Government are carried out by over 40 departments which employ around 143,000 people. Join the Administrative Class as an administrative officer and you will be helping to play a very significant role in the performance of these functions.

The Administrative Class is one of several general grades and now has about 300 members. They do not belong to one department only, but serve in several departments including the Government Secretariat. However, there is no ministerial system in Hong Kong. This means that the Administrative Class is the central lynchpin in the exercise and operation of Government; as an administrative officer you will not only co-ordinate policies and programmes and see that they are implemented, and control the resources involved, but you could also help formulate these policies personally.

As a junior administrative officer you could be a city district officer in the city area, or an assistant district officer in the New Territories in the City and New Territories Administration. Administrative officers at senior level become head or deputy heads and assistant heads of departments such as that of Trade, Industry and Customs, Housing, Labour, and Social Welfare Departments. They also occupy posts at similar levels in the policy and resource branches of the Government Secretariat.

Types of graduate required
You will tend to specialise somewhat from the the the age of about 40; but much importance continues to be attached to adaptability and versatility, so *any* degree is acceptable. Administrative officers are expected to be able to perform efficiently in a variety of posts. Individual preferences, interest and aptitudes are taken into account in postings and career planning, but the Class does not provide careers in restricted spheres of expertise. As an administrative officer you will almost certainly at some stage of your career be faced with difficult, unfamiliar, and possibly even unwelcome, assignments, and you must take such challenges in your stride. The chief qualities required are a capacity to isolate quickly the essential elements of an argument or problem so as to reach a reasoned

decision or recommendation and an ability to deal effectively with other people at all levels so as to get things done.

Training
On being appointed an administrative officer you will receive on the job training, following a brief induction course to familiarise you with the organisation and workings of the Government. You can expect to study colloquial Cantonese for a period of six months full time. Almost certainly, you will also attend management courses later during the first few years of your career with us.

Salary
You start at HK$8,285 a month (£9,040 pa*), which rises to HK$17,405 a month (£18,990 pa*). But promotion prospects are good in a service that has expanded rapidly in line with the economic growth of the territory, and you should expect to be up in the administrative officer staff grade at the end of some ten years, and earning over HK$25,800 a month (£28,150 pa*).
* On 1 January 1982 the exchange rate was £1.00 to HK$11.00, but this is subject to fluctuation.

Leave
This comes after every 2½ years, except the initial tour, which is three years. It works out at 42 days paid leave for every year served.

Further information
The general standard of the Hong Kong public service depends to a significant degree upon the quality of the Administrative Class. If you are a person of first class ability, with intelligence, adaptability and ambition we hope you will seriously consider applying. If you are accepted, you will have chosen one of the most satisfying careers in the world.
For more information write to the address given.

Johannesburg Consolidated Investment Company Limited

'Johnnies' is a leading mining finance house concerned with the discovery, development and exploitation of mineral deposits. Johannesburg based, the group manages the world's largest producer of platinum at Rustenburg and two large gold mines as well as antimony, nickel, copper and coal mines. Its service departments include a modern mineral processing research laboratory which has an analytical section.

Activities
Discovery, development and exploitation of mineral deposits

Employees
50,000

Location: Overseas
Southern Africa

Opportunities
Mining engineers; Metallurgists (extraction); Chemical engineers; Chemical analysts; Mine geologists; Electrical engineers; Mechanical engineers

Application address
Johannesburg Consolidated Investment Company Limited, Recruiting Office, 99 Bishopsgate, London EC2M 3XE

Training
Mining engineers receive graduate training to prepare them as candidates for the Government certificate of competency which is required for advancement to the senior management jobs. *Electrical* and *mechanical engineering* graduates also receive intensive coaching for the Government certificate of competency.

Locations
All overseas, in the Republic of South Africa and adjoining territories.

Salaries and other benefits
Starting salaries for honours graduates are not less than R14,000 per annum. Appointments are permanent and pensionable. Subsidised quality housing is provided for married graduates. Single men are accommodated in modern staff hostels, or alternatively, where possible, are provided with company flats.
Travelling expenses to South Africa are paid by the company.

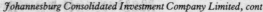

Johannesburg Consolidated Investment Company Limited, cont

Generous baggage grants, settling-in allowances and personal loan facilities (repayable over 30 months, interest free) are given. Excellent contributory pension fund and sickness benefit schemes are provided.

All graduates working underground are entitled to 52 calendar days leave per annum, in addition to a holiday leave allowance equivalent to one month's salary. Surface graduates leave entitlement initially is 45 calendar days per annum, again with a leave allowance of one month's salary.

Kennedy & Donkin

Please see our entry on page 211.

Lloyds Bank International

Activities
International banking operations in 45 countries worldwide

Employees
10,000 (8,700 overseas)

Location: UK
London

Locations: Overseas
Western and Eastern Europe; Latin America; North America; Middle East; Far East; Australasia

Opportunities & places
Banking management including merchant banking 20

Upper age limit
25

Application address
Personnel Development Officer (Graduate Recruitment), Lloyds Bank International Ltd, 40–66 Queen Victoria Street, London EC4P 4EL
Application forms must be received by 12 January

Lloyds Bank International, the international arm of the Lloyds Bank Group, is both a commercial and a merchant bank and, as such, has direct access to major sources of foreign currency in all the great financial centres, plus a substantial role in the Eurocurrency market and is concerned in the financing of important projects throughout the world. A complete range of financial services is offered through a network of overseas branches and representative offices. Applicants must be prepared to spend a large part of their careers overseas and to work in a variety of jobs, possibly including periods of secondment to other units of the Lloyds Bank Group.

Types of graduate required
Any degree subject considered, but most successful candidates will be graduates in *economics, law, business studies, mathematics* or *modern languages*. Candidates should be under 25, and fully mobile. Each year's graduate intake is small in relation to the total staffing needs of the bank and it is to this selective intake that we shall be primarily looking for filling the most senior positions in the bank in the future. Ambition and ability for early responsibility are thus essential qualities.

Training
LBI offers an initial three-month course of instruction in London which provides a good basic knowledge of banking and management, tuition in a foreign language, and an economic, social and political background to international affairs. This is followed by an overseas training programme.

Salaries and benefits
On joining the course in London, trainees are paid a total salary of over £7,000 (subject to review). When posted overseas, staff are paid at rates compatible with expatriate living standards in the country of posting. Generous assistance is also given in the form of rent allowances. The bank pays contributions to the British United Provident Association for all British members of the staff working overseas and their families, in order to assist with possible heavy expenses such as hospital bills, consultants' fees etc.

Applications
Initial interviews are held at various universities and at the bank's head office in London during the period November to mid-March; final interviews, conducted in London by executive directors, follow with minimum delay.

McDermott Engineering

Please see our entry in the main section.

NEI Overseas Ltd

Application address
NEI Overseas Ltd, 49 Park Lane, London
W1Y 3LB

NEI Overseas, part of the Northern Engineering Industries group of companies, is responsible for group manufacturing companies operating overseas.

Opportunities for *engineers* who have already graduated with a good honours degree are occasionally available in Australia, Africa and North America.

Local companies will have particular interest in graduates who are citizens of their own country.

Royal Hong Kong Police Force

Activities
Policing a densely populated British territory in the Far East

Employees
24,000

Location: Overseas
Hong Kong

Opportunities & places
Inspectors of police 100

Upper age limit
27

Application address
The Hong Kong Government Office, 6 Grafton Street, London W1X 3LB
(quoting reference DOG 83)

The Royal Hong Kong Police is a completely modernised police force both in terms of its operational methods and equipment. The force is organised into four regions: Hong Kong Island and Kowloon – busy, urban, commercial and industrial centres; the New Territories – the rural area separating Kowloon from China; and Marine – 700 square miles of sea policed by a fleet of over 60 launches.

Specialist branches of the force, as well as including the usual units such as traffic, special branch and marine district, also include those which Hong Kong's unique problems dictate, such as the Triad societies bureau, narcotics bureau, commercial crime office and juvenile protection office.

Types of graduate required
Graduates should be single men under 27, British citizens of the United Kingdom or the Commonwealth, 5ft 7ins and have good eyesight. They should recognise in themselves qualities of leadership.

Training
On arrival in Hong Kong, inspectors are given nine weeks' intensive language training in the Cantonese dialect, followed by 27 weeks' police training which includes lectures on law and related subjects as well as practical on the job training for police work. Further training is given later in the police tactical unit in the handling of civil disorders and crowd control techniques.

Salary
The starting salary is Hong Kong $7,055 per month (1 April 1982 the exchange rate was HK $10.41 to £1). After an initial tour of duty of three years, four months' vacation leave on full pay is provided with passages paid to country of origin. Subsequent tours are for two and a half years. You may serve on pensionable terms or receive a gratuity of 25% of gross pay for each tour if you serve on agreement terms.

Schlumberger Wireline Logging

Activities
Services to the oil industry

Employees
5,050 (including 1,680 engineers)

Locations: Overseas
Worldwide

Opportunities
Electronic/electrical engineering; Mechanical
engineering; Physics; Geophysics

Upper age limit
28

Application address
The Recruitment Manager, Schlumberger
Wireline Logging, 1 Kingsway, London
WC2 6XH

The eyes of the oil industry.

Schlumberger is the world leader in wireline logging a process which measures physical and seismological data to indicate the likely subsurface conditions and production prospects of oil and gas wells.

It's a service which is vital to the oil industry, for ti represents the most efficient and cost effective method by which vital information about onshore and offshore wells can be gained. Upon its accuracy and interpretation, inferences regarding the viability and likely production difficulties of a given well may be based by the operating companies we serve.

In fact, it is safe to say that nowadays, virtually no well is explored, brought on-stream or exploited without regular wireline logging throughout its life. Across the world, the majority of such operations are carried out by Schlumberger.

Essentially, wireline logging requires that one or more of a range of over 50 highly sensitive and specialised measuring tools be lowered to the base of a well bore which, typically, can mean a depth of over 5,000 metres.

Each tool derives a specific type of data and is attached to a surface unit called a Cyber Service Unit (CSU) by means of a wireline. This extremely strong yet flexible steel cable, in addition to being the method by which the tool is raised and lowered, is also the means by which collected data is transmitted to the surface as the tool, or tools, are drawn slowly up the well bore.

Often, several such logging operations, with tool changes at the surface, are needed before sufficient data to give the required profile is collected.

At the surface, a minicomputer, an integral part of the CSU, receives the transmitted data. Once collected, this is output to digital tape and optical film, both of which are analysed on-site by the Schlumberger field engineer.

From this, one or more well logs, graphical representations of the subsurface conditions, are produced. This is the first tangible result of logging operations which may have gone on for over 36 hours without a break. There are over 100 kinds of well log, each of which shows a particular aspect of well conditions and from which inferences may be drawn.

Once complete, the well logs are passed to the oil company by the Schlumber field engineer. It is with the oil company that final decisions regarding the oil well will finally rest. Even so, the field engineer will usually find himself, or herself, consulted on the results and asked to give an analysis, for Schlumberger field engineers are also advisers whose technical skills and judgements are respected throughout the oil industry.

It's an industry which is wholly international and Schlumberger is to be found wherever there is, or may be, oil or natural gas, employing engineers drawn from over 73 nationalities. Currently, there are over 200 Schlumberger operating bases in some 65 countries around the world to which, as a trainee or field engineer, you could beassigned.

The base is the centre from which you will operate and to which you will return at the end of each job. It is also the place in which you will spend a majority of your time inthe servicing and maintenance of tools and equipment and in self-teaching in order to keep abreast of the latest developments in logging and well technology.

Your trips away, though, will be frequent and, depending on the base from which you work, could take you through the jungles of South

America, the Saudi Arabian desert or to offshore platforms in the North Sea.

Just to get on-site might entail a journey of a couple of days or more, with your equipment, before you and the operating crew over whom you have charge can set up the equipment and begin logging.

Once you do, you'll work hard – very hard, and for days at a time in order to get the results you need. You'll experience extremes of climate and have to operate to tight deadlines.

You'll also get your hands dirty, because the setting up and operating of equipment is a task shared equally by every member of the Schlumberger team.

In addition to physical stamina though, you'll need every one of your technical and intellectual skills. Because it's the Schlumberger field engineer who performs the data processing and produces the well logs required by an impatient and demanding oil company.

To join us and train as a field engineer, you must be a man or woman aged under 28, single, in excellent health and in possession of a full driver's licence. You must also have a good honours degree in *electrical, electronics, mechanical* or *mining engineering, physics* or *geophysics*.

You must also be able to demonstrate a good understanding of practical electrical, electronics and mechanical engineering principals – and be able to use them to solve immediate problems.

If you've got all of these qualities and pass our selection procedure, we'll introduce you to wireline logging with one month at the field location to which, as a qualified field engineer, you will be assigned. There then follows a three month course at one of our training centres, either in the UK or overseas. It will be intensive and consist of a mixture of theory plus a lot of practical work in logging, interpretation and the maintenance of tools and equipment.

Not everyone passes. Those who do return to their field location for a further three months to complete formal training by performing logging operations under the supervision of an experienced field engineer.

Once qualified, you are on your own, but your training does not end. It continues on the field for another two and a half years. On top of that there is an emphasis on self-teaching in order to keep up with the latest developments in both logging and well technology. Learning, in fact, never stops.

Neither does your career, for Schlumberger is a company which promotes from within on the basis of performance alone and irrespective of national origin. All our senior personnel, from vice-president downward, began as field engineers.

To find out more about Schlumberger, either contact your careers adviser, or send your cv to the Recruitment Manager at the address given. Overseas applicants are particularly welcome.

The South African Civil Service

Activities
Advice on government, management, administration, research and development

Employees
65,000

Location: Overseas
Pretoria, South Africa

In the atmosphere of rapid development in South Africa its Civil Service plays a major part. In fulfilling obligations towards society a wide variety of professional and technical research and services are undertaken. Creative and energetic candidates should find this challenging and rewarding.

Types of graduate required
Employment in the Civil Service is usually offered on a contractual basis for an initial three years that can be extended to five. However opportunities exist to join our permanent staff after citizenship has been

Opportunities

Agriculture (soil science); Oceanography; Physics; Chemistry; Mathematics; Hydrology; Geohydrology; Geophysics; Medicine; Meteorology and engineering

Application address

Mr MG Mynhardt, Civil Service Officer, South African Embassy, Trafalgar Square, London WC2N 5DP

The South African Civil Service, cont

granted: this is possible after two years, dependent on age; or five years permanent residence in South Africa. Assistance towards the cost of passage and transport of personal effects is provided on going out, and in the event of five years service contractees will be repatriated if they wish.

We invite enquiries from graduates with training in *oceanography* (especially *chemical and physical*), *agriculture*, *(soil science)*, *physics*, *chemistry*, *maths*, *hydrology*, *geohydrology*, *geophysics*, *medicine and meterology* as well as from *technicians (hydrology)*. There are occasional vacancies in forestry, para-medicine, veterinary science, geology, and civil, electrical, mechanical, chemical and pollution control engineering.

Training

Initially you will train with experienced staff before being assigned to more demanding tasks. Apart from in-service training, ample opportunities exist to further your studies.

Locations

Although most employees begin in Pretoria, employment can be offered in other large centres.

Salary, prospects and benefits

We offer competitive salaries (determined by qualifications and experience) which increase annually. In addition, work of a high standard is also rewarded on an incentive basis. Prospects for promotion are favourable and throughout there are the added benefits of a medical aid scheme, provident fund, annual holiday bonus, settling-in allowance, housing subsidy, generous annual leave and sick leave.

Zambia Consolidated Copper Mines Limited

Activities

Copper and cobalt mining, smelting and refining

Employees

60,000

Locations: Overseas

Zambia

Opportunities

Chemical, electrical, mechanical and mining engineers; Metallurgists; Mineral technologists; Mining geologists

Application address

The General Manager (DOG), Zambia Appointments Limited, Zimco House, 16–28 Tabernacle Street, London EC2A 4BN

Zambia Consolidated Copper Mines Limited (ZCCM), a recent merger of the former Nchanga Consolidated Copper Mines (NCCM) and Roan Consolidated Mines (RCM) is one of the world's biggest producers of copper and cobalt. The government owns about 60% of the shares. ZCCM has seven mining divisions (six copper, one lead-zinc) and two centralised services divisions. The company has 60,000 employees and an annual production capacity of 750,000 tonnes of copper, 4,000 tonnes of cobalt and 76,000 tonnes of lead and zinc.

Conditions of service

Employment is by renewable contract, initially of two years.

Types of graduate required

The mines require *chemical, electrical, mechanical* and *mining engineers, metallurgists, mineral technologists, mining geologists,* and *chemists.* Promotion prospects are excellent. Experience with ZCCM is recognised by institutions and qualifies towards associate membership.

Salaries

Salaries are competitive, and include a 25% tax free gratuity paid annually in the UK or country of recruitment.

Other benefits

Generous baggage allowance, company housing at very low rent, tax free settling-in allowance, interest free car loan, free life assurance, generous leave, company hospitals. Zambia's climate is healthy and agreeable, and the social and sporting amenities excellent.

Graduate recruiters

This is a listing of graduate recruiters who have indicated to us that they are likely to have vacancies in 1983. Since the information was compiled during June of 1982 it is important that you check with your careers service before you take any action.

Information about recruiters is given under the following headings:

Employees
Approximate number to give an idea of company size.

Vacancies
Number of graduate vacancies for 1983 estimated as accurately as possible at time of going to press. Check with your careers services for the current situation. We have broken down the numbers of vacancies into groups and each group is allocated a letter as follows:

V Less than 10   **Y** 50–100
W 10–20   **Z** More than 100
X 20–50

Graduates required
Letters have been used to indicate the general degree categories from which graduates are recruited. Some companies cannot fit into these general categories and a box has been used, consult your careers service for the precise details. The letters are:
A Arts subject
S Sciences and allied subjects
E Engineering and allied subjects
So Social sciences subjects including Business studies
☐ Consult your careers service

We must emphasise that this list is a general indication of recruiters intentions, we suggest that you consult your careers advisory service before you take any action.

Company name	Employees	Vacancies	Graduates required
Abbott Laboratories Queenborough Kent ME11 5EL	700	V	S
AGB Research Ltd The Research Centre West Gate, Hanger Lane Ealing London W5 1DW	1,100	W	Any
Agricultural Research Council 160 Great Portland Street London W1N 6DT	5,300	X	S E
Air Products Ltd Coombe House St George's Square New Malden Surrey KT3 4HH	2,200	X	A E
Airscrew Howden Ltd Weybridge Trading Estate Weybridge Surrey KT15 2QR	512	V	E
Akroyd & Smithers plc Austin Friars House 2–6 Austin Friars London EC2N 2EE	400	V	Any
Albright & Wilson Ltd 1 Knightsbridge Green London SW1X 7QD	8,800	V	Any S E
Alfa-Laval Co Ltd Great West Road Brentford Middx TWB 9BT	700	V	E
WH Allen NEI-APE Ltd PO Box 43 Queens Engineering Wks Bedford MK40 4JB	2,000	V	E
Allen & Overy 9 Cheapside London EC2V 6AD	400	W	A S E
Allied Breweries (UK) Ltd 107 Station Street Burton on Trent Staffs DE14 1BZ	35,000+	W	Any S
Allied Colloids Ltd PO Box 38 Low Moor Bradford W Yorks BD12 0JZ	1,000	V	S
Altergo Ltd 38 Soho Square London W1V 5DF	150	V	Any
Amersham International White Lion Road Amersham Bucks HP7 9LL	1,500	X	S

Company name	Employees	Vacancies	Graduates required
Amey Roadstone Construction Sutton Courtenay Abingdon Oxon OX14 4PP	500	V	E
The Analysts Schlumberger c/o The Analysts Inland Servs 2 Park West Place London W2 2QZ	330	Y	E
Arthur Andersen & Co 1 Surrey Street London WC2R 2PS	2,000	Z	Any
Arthur Anderson & Co Management Consultancy Div 1 Surrey Street London WC2R 2PS	200	X	Any
Anderson Strathclyde Ltd Anderson House 47 Broad Street Glasgow G40 2QW	4,200	V	E
Anglo American Corp of SA Ltd 40 Holborn Viaduct London EC1P 2A	250,000	Y	E
Anglo Continental Educ Group 33 Wimbourne Road Bournemouth BH2 6NA	80	X	A
Maurice Apple & Co 1 Hyde Park Place London W2 2LH	23	V	□
A&P Appledore Ltd Northumbrian Way Newcastle upon Tyne Tyne & Wear NE12 0EH	80	V	E
Applied Computing & Software ACS House 37–39 Bowling Green Lane London EC1R 0BJ	150	V	S
Arlington Motor Holdings 67 High Street Ponders End Enfield Middlesex EN3 4EG	550	X	Any
Arthur Young McClelland Moores & Co Rolls House 7 Rolls Buildings Fetter Lane London EC4A 1NL	2,250	Z	Any
Ove Arup Partnership 13 Fitzroy Street London W1P 6BQ	2,000	X	E
Associated British Foods Weston Centre Bowater House 68 Knightsbridge London SW1X 7LR	72,400	X	Any S E

Company name	Employees	Vacancies	Graduates required
WS Atkins Group Ltd Woodcote Grove Ashley Road Epsom Surrey KT18 5BW	2,000	X	E
Audits of Great Britain Ltd Hanger Lane Ealing London W5 1DW	650	W	Any
Aurora Holdings plc Aurora House Julian Road Sheffield S9 1RA	3,500	V	Any
Austin Knight Ltd Knightway House 20 Soho Square London W1A 1DS	200	□	A
Austin Reed Ltd 103 Regent Street London W1A 2AJ	860	V	So
W&J Avery Ltd Foundry Lane Smethwick Warley W Midlands B66 2LP	2,800	V	E
Avon Rubber Co Ltd Bath Road Melksham Wilts SN12 8AA	6,000	V	S E
Ayerst Laboratories Ltd South Way Andover Hants SP10 5LT	100	V	Any
Babcock International plc Cleveland House St James's Square London SW1Y 4LN	37,000	X	E
Babcock Woodall-Duckham Ltd Crawley Sussex RH10 1UX	700	V	E
Baird Textile Holdings Ltd Broadstone House Broadstone Road Reddish Stockport SK5 7DL	5,000	V	A
Baker Rooke 99 Aldwych London WC2B 4JY	300	V	Any
John Baker Sons & Bell 282 Bishopsgate London EC2M 4UU	60	V	Any
Balfours Yeoman House 63 Croydon Road London SE20 7TW	300	V	E

Company name	Employees	Vacancies	Graduates required
Ball Baker 17 Southampton Place London WC1A 2EH	115	V	Any
Bank of America NT & SA 25 Cannon Street London EC4P 4HN	1,500	V	Any
Bank of Credit & Commerce Int 100 Leadenhall Street London EC3A 3AD	1,500	W	Any
Barclays Bank International Barclays House 1 Wimborne Road Poole Dorset B15 2BB	5,600	X	Any
Barclays Bank plc 54 Lombard Street London EC3P 3AH	70,000	X	Any
Baring Brothers & Co Ltd 88 Leadenhall Street London EC3A 3DT	460	V	Any
Barron Rowles & Bass 12 John Street Holborn London WC1N 2EB	80	V	Any
Ted Bates Ltd 155 Gower Street London WC1E 6BJ	200	V	Any
Bechtel GB Ltd 245 Hammersmith Road London W6 8DP	1,600	Y	E
Beecham Pharmaceuticals Beecham House Great West Road Brentford Middx TW8 9BD	11,000	X	A S E
Beecham Products Beecham House Great West Road Brentford Middx TW8 9BD	12,500	X	A S E
Benton & Bowles Ltd 197 Knightsbridge London SW7 1RP	220	V	Any
Berkshire County Council Shire Hall Shinfield Park nr Reading Berks	25,000	V	Any
Bestobell plc Bestobell House 16 Bath Road Slough Berks SL1 3SS	5,400	V	E

Company name	Employees	Vacancies	Graduates required
BICC plc PO Box 1 Prescot Merseyside L34 5SZ	60,000	Y	S E
Edward Billington & Son Ltd Cunard Building Liverpool L3 1EL	450	V	Any
Binder Hamlyn 8 St Bride Street London EC4A 4DA	450	X	Any
Biorex Laboratories Ltd Biorex House Canonbury Villas London N1 2HB	140	W	S
BIS Applied Systems Ltd York House 199 Westminster Bridge Road London SE1 7UT	140	V	S
Blick Rothenberg & Noble 7 Fitzroy Square London W1P 6AS	100	V	Any
BL Systems Ltd PO Box 5 Grosvenor House Prospect Hill Redditch Worcs B97 4DQ	1,100	X	Any
Blue Circle Industries Ltd Portland House Stag Place London SW1E 5BJ	14,000	W	Any E
BNF Metals Technology Centre Grove Laboratories Denchworth Road Wantage Oxon OX12 9BJ	180	W	S E
Boase Massimi Pollitt Univas 12 Bishops Bridge Road London W2 6AA	160	V	Any
BOCM Silcock Ltd (Unilever Basing View Basingstoke Hants RG21 2EQ	2,700	V	□
Boots Company plc Head Office Thane Road Beeston Nottingham NG2 3AA	64,000	Y	Any S E

Key

Graduates required		Vacancies	
A	Arts	V	1–10
E	Engineering	W	10–20
S	Science	X	20–50
So	Social Sciences	Y	50–100
□	Consult Careers Service	Z	100 plus

Company name	Employees	Vacancies	Graduates required
Bovis Civil Engineering Ltd Bridge House Westbury Wilts BA13 4HS	600+	W	E
Birmingham & Bridgwater Building Society Bridgwater House King Square Bridgwater Somerset TA6 3DF	420	V	Any
Britannia Refined Metals Ltd 98 Cannon Street London EC4N 6EH	450	V	E
British Aerospace Dynamics Group Six Hills Way Stevenage Herts SG1 2DA	17,500	□	S E
British Airports Authority 2 Buckingham Gate London SW1E 6JL	7,000	V	S E
British Airways Employment Services S104 Comet House Heathrow Airport Middx TW6 2JA	42,000	W	Any
British Antarctic Survey High Cross Madingley Road Cambridge CB3 0ET	310	W	S
British Broadcasting Corp Broadcasting House London W1A 1AA	25,000	Z	E
The British Carbonization Research Association Mill Lane Chesterfield S42 6JS	110	□	S
British Cellophane Ltd Bath Road Bridgewater Somerset	3,750	V	Any A S E
British Gas Corporation Star House Mutton Lane Potters Bar EN6 2PD	106,000	Z	Any A S
The British Industrial Research Association Woodmansterne Road Carshalton Surrey SM5 4DS	150	□	□
British Mail Order Corp Ltd Universal House Devonshire Street Manchester M60 6EL	10,000	V	Any
The British Museum (Nat Hist) Cromwell Road London SW7 5BD	800	V	S
British National Oil Corp 150 St Vincent Street Glasgow G2 5LJ	2,500	X	S E
British Nuclear Fuels Ltd Risley Warrington WA3 6AS	16,000	X	S E
British Railways Board Rail House Euston Square PO Box 100 London NW1 2DZ	230,000	Z	A S E So
British Ship Research Assoc Wallsend Research Station Wallsend Tyne and Wear NE28 6UY	233	V	S E
British Shipbuilders Benton House 136 Sandyford Road Newcastle upon Tyne NE2 1QE	67,000	Y	S E
British Steel Corporation Head Office 10 Addiscombe Road Croydon CR9 3JH	100,000	Z	Any
British Sulphur Corporation Ltd Parnell House 25 Wilton Road London SW1V 1NH	60	V	S E
Brooking Knowles & Lawrence Brook House Alencon Link Basingstoke Hants RG21 1QZ	90	V	Any
Brown and Root (UK) Ltd 125 High Street Colliers Wood London SW19 2JR	2,000	W	E
John Brown Engineering Ltd Clydebank Dunbar GB1 1YA	2,000	W	E
John Brown Machine Tool Div Banner Lane Tile Hill Coventry CV4 9GE	1,000	□	□
BTR Industries Ltd Silverton House Vincent Square London SW1P 2PL	12,000	W	E
Burmah Oil Co Ltd Burmah House Pipers Way Swindon Wilts SN3 1RE	27,000	W	Any

Company name	Employees	Vacancies	Graduates required
Burndept Electronics Ltd St Fidelis Road Erith Kent DA8 1AU	490	V	S E
Buzzacott & Co Salisbury Square House 8 Salisbury Square London EC4Y 8HR	100+	W	Any
BHRA Fluid Engineering Cranfield Beds MK43 0AJ	230	V	E
Cadbury Schweppes Ltd Bournville Birmingham B30 2LU	32,000	Y	Any
WJ Calder Sons & Co Park House 22 Park Street Croydon CR9 3HU	20	V	Any
Cambridge Consultants Ltd Science Park Milton Road Cambridge CB4 4DW	140	V	S E
Cambridgeshire Constabulary Hinchingbrooke Park Huntingdon PE18 8NP	1,140	□	Any
Cambridgeshire County Council Finance Department Shire Hall Castle Hill Cambridge CB3 0AS	22,000	V	Any
C & A Modes 64 North Row London W1A 2AX	9,000	W	Any
Cannon Industries Ltd Gough Road Coseley W Midlands WV14 8XR	920	V	Any
Capper Neill Ltd St Helens Merseyside WA9 4TA	4,500	W	E
Carreras Rothmans Ltd Oxford Road Aylesbury Bucks HP21 8SZ	6,000	V	Any
Carrington Viyella Ltd Sagar House Eccleston Chorley Lancs	15,000	V	A
CEGB South Eastern Region Bankside House Sumner Street London SE1 9JU	1,100	V	Any

Company name	Employees	Vacancies	Graduates required
J W Chafer Ltd Chafer House 19 Thorne Road Doncaster DN1 2HQ	400	V	S
Chalmers Impey & Co 6 Long Lane London EC1A 9DP	250	W	Any
Charcon Products Ltd Hulland Ward Derby DE6 3ET	650	V	E
Chillcotts Ltd Prince Street Works Madeley Telford Salop TF7 4PX	200	V	E
Chloride Group Ltd 52 Grosvenor Gardens London SW1 0EH	8,000	V	S E
Christiani & Nielsen Ltd 21–24 Grosvenor Place London SW1X 7JE	230	V	E
Church Commissioners 1 Millbank London SW1P 3JZ	390	V	Any
Church of England Church House Dean's Yard Westminster London SW1P 3NZ	600	V	Any
Ciba-Geigy Plastics & Additives Co 30 Buckingham Gate London SW1E 6LH	2,600	V	S
Civil Service Civil Service Commission Alencon Link Basingstoke Hants RG21 1JB	680,000	Z	Any S E
C & J Clark Ltd 40 High Street Street Somerset BA16 0YA	13,000	V	Any
Clarkson Puckle Group Ibex House Minories London EC3N 1HJ	1,400	V	Any

Key

Graduates required		Vacancies	
A	Arts	**V**	1–10
E	Engineering	**W**	10–20
S	Science	**X**	20–50
So	Social Sciences	**Y**	50–100
□	Consult Careers Service	**Z**	100 plus

Company name	Employees	Vacancies	Graduates required
Cleanaway Ltd Claydons Lane Rayleigh Essex SS6 7UW	1,000	V	S E
Clerical Med & Gen Life Assurance Soc Narrow Plain Bristol BS2 0JH	1,100	V	Any S
Cleveland Bridge & Eng Co Ltd PO Box 27 Smithfield Road Darlington Co Durham DL1 4DG	1,200	V	E
Clydesdale Bank plc 150 Buchanan Street Glasgow G1 2HL	5,500	V	Any
CMG Computer Mngmnt Grp Ltd Sunley House Bedford Park Croydon CR0 2AP	250	V	Any
Coles Cranes Ltd Crown Works Pallion Sunderland SR4 6TT	2,300	V	A E
Colonial Mutual Life Ass Soc Ltd 24 Ludgate Hill London EC4P 4BD	430	V	Any S
Commonwealth Bureau of Dairy Science & Tech Lane End House Shinfield Reading RG2 9BB	15	V	S E
Computation Research & Development 12 Dartmouth Street London SW1H 9BL	16	V	S E
Computer Machinery Co Ltd Maxted Close Hemel Hempstead Herts HP2 7LA	875	X	Any S E
Computer Technology Ltd Eaton Road Hemel Hempstead Herts HP2 7EQ	400	V	S
Confederation Life Ins Co Canada 50–52 Chancery Lane London WC2A 1HE	200	V	S
Conoco Ltd (Humber Refinery) Manufacturing Division South Killingholme S Humberside DN40 3DW	650	V	E
Consolidated Gold Fields Ltd 49 Moorgate London EC2R 6BQ	100,000	W	E

Company name	Employees	Vacancies	Graduates required
Co-operative Bank Ltd PO Box 101 1 Balloon Street Manchester M60 4EP	3,650	V	Any
Coopers & Lybrand Abacus House Gutter Lane Cheapside London EC2V 8AH	2,700	Z	Any
Coopers & Lybrand Associates Shelley House 3 Noble Street London EC2	200	V	S E
Cossor Electronics Ltd The Pinnacles Elizabeth Way Harlow Essex CM19 5BB	2,000	W	E
Coventry City Council Council House Earl Street Coventry CV1 5RR	18,000	V	Any
Courtaulds Ltd 345 Foleshill Road Coventry CV6 5AE	60,000	Y	Any S E
Coward Chance Royex House Aldermanbury Square London EC2V 7LD	400	W	Any
Creasey Son & Wickenden 1 East Street Tonbridge Kent TN9 1AS	27	V	Any A S E
Trevor Crocker & Partners 323–339 London Road Mitcham Surrey CR4 4BE	150	V	E
Cross International AG Knowsley Prescot Merseyside L34 9EZ	350	V	E
Crown Life Assurance Group Crown Life House Woking Surrey SU21 1XW	500	V	S
W G Curtin & Partners 19 Rodney Street Liverpool L1 9EQ	110	V	E
Daresbury Laboratory Science Research Council Daresbury Warrington WA4 4AD	555	W	S E
Data Recall Diamond House 138 South Street Dorking Surrey RH4 2EU	140	V	S E

Company name	Employees	Vacancies	Graduates required
Datapoint (UK) Ltd 400 North Circular Road London NW10 0JG	550	V	S E
Davy McKee Ltd Ashmore House Richardson Road Stockton on Tees Cleveland TS18 3LT	1,090	W	E
Day Smith & Hunster Star House Maidstone Kent ME14 1LT	100	V	Any
Dearden Farrow Serjeants' Inn Fleet Street London EC4Y 1JD	400	X	Any
De La Rue Co Ltd De La Rue House 3–5 Burlington Gardens London W1A 1DL	6,100	V	Any
Deloitte Haskins & Sells PO Box 207 128 Queen Victoria Street London EC4P 4JX	3,000	Z	Any
Derwent Publications Ltd Rochdale House 128 Theobald's Road London WC1X 8RP	415	W	S E
Dickinson Robinson Grp Ltd 1 Redcliffe Street Bristol BS99 7QY	13,500	W	Any
Dounreay Nuclear Power Dev Establishment UKAEA Dounreay Thurso Caithness Scotland KW14 7TZ	2,000	V	S E
Dowty Group Ltd Arle Court Cheltenham Gloucs GL51 0TP	9,000	W	E
Drake & Scull Engineering Ltd Hamlyn House Highgate Hill London N19 5PS	4,000	V	E
Dumfries & Galloway Constab Loreburn Street Dumfries DG1 1HP	308	V	So
Durham Constabulary Aykley Heads Durham DH1 5TT	1,350	V	Any
Dyfed-Powys Police Friars Park Carmarthen Dyfed SA31 3AW	1,000	W	Any

Company name	Employees	Vacancies	Graduates required
Gerald Edelman & Co 25 Harley Street London W1N 2BR	100	W	Any
EEV Ltd Waterhouse Lane Chelmsford Essex CM1 2QU	2,500	W	S E
Electronic Techniques (Anglia) Viking Works Kirton Ipswich Suffolk IP10 0NX	40	V	S E
Engineering Sciences Data Unit 251–259 Regent Street London W1R 7AD	45	V	E
English China Clays plc John Keay House St Austell Cornwall	11,000	V	S E
Epsom Glass Industries Ltd Longmead Epsom Surrey	200	V	E
Equitable Life Ass Soc Ltd Equitable Life House Walton Street Aylesbury Bucks HP21 7QW	730	V	Any
Equity & Law Life Ass Soc plc Amersham Road High Wycombe Bucks	1,500	X	Any
Era Technology Ltd Cleeve Road Leatherhead Surrey KT22 7SA	300	V	S E
Ernst & Whinney Beckett House Lambert Palace Road London SE1 7EU	3,000	Z	Any
Eurotherm Ltd Faraday Close Durrington Worthing W Sussex BN13 3PL	300	V	E

Key

Graduates required		Vacancies	
A	Arts	**V**	1–10
E	Engineering	**W**	10–20
S	Science	**X**	20–50
So	Social Sciences	**Y**	50–100
☐	Consult Careers Service	**Z**	100 plus

Company name	Employees	Vacancies	Graduates required
Ewbank & Partners Ltd Prudential House North Street Brighton E Sussex BN1 1RW	550	V	E
Exploration Logging PO Box 46 Windsor Berks SL4 5JU	1,200	□	S E
Fairey Hydraulics Ltd Cranford Lane Heston Middx TW5 9NG	549	V	E
W A Fairhurst & Partners 11 Woodside Terrace Glasgow G3 7XQ	200	V	E
J H Fenner & Co Ltd Marfleet Hull N Humberside HU9 5RA	1,571	V	E
Fenwick Ltd Northumberland Street Newcastle upon Tyne NE99 1AR	2,500	V	Any
Field Studies Council Preston Montford Montford Bridge Shrewsbury SY4 1HW	45	V	S
Fine Art Developments Queen Street Burton on Trent Staffs DE14 3LP	3,000	V	Any
Finnie Ross Allfields Lee House London Wall London EC2Y 5AX	200	W	Any
First National Bank of Boston 5 Cheapside London EC2P 2DE	207	V	Any
Fisher Controls Ltd Week Street Maidstone Kent ME14 1UQ	3,500	W	S E
Flour Milling & Baking Research Association Chorley Wood Rickmansworth WD3 55H	119	V	S
FMC Ltd 19–23 Knightsbridge London SW1X 7NF	500	V	S
Ford Motor Co Ltd Central Office Eagle Way Brentwood Essex CM13 3BW	66,000	Y	Any
Forward Trust Group Ltd Broad Street House 55 Old Broad Street London EC2M 1RX	2,400	W	Any
Four Square Catering & Vending Ajax Avenue Slough SL1 4DE	1,000	V	Any
Ernest Francis & Son Somerset House Blagrave Street Reading Berks RG1 1QB	55	V	Any
Fraser Keen 4 London Wall Buildings London EC2M 5NT	80	V	Any
Fraser Williams Port of Liverpool Building Pier Head Liverpool L3 1BY	320	X	S
Frazer Whiting & Co City Gate House Finsbury Square London EC2A 1EP	100	V	S
French Kier Ltd Tempsford Hall Sandy Beds SG19 2BD	5,000	W	E
Friends' Provident Life Office Pixham End Dorking RH4 1QA	1,300	W	Any
Fryer Whitehill & Co Buchanan House 24–30 Holborn London EC1N 2PX	250	X	Any
Futters (London) Ltd 16 Acton Lane London NW10 8XA	150	V	E
Gaffney Cline & Associates Ltd GCA International Building Rosemount Avenue West Byfleet Surrey KT14 6JZ	50	V	S E
Gallaher Ltd 65 Kingsway London WC2B 6TG	8,500	V	Any
Gardiners 12 Alma Square Scarborough YO11 1JU	40	V	S
Gearhart Geodata Services MWD Unit 19 Kirkhill Industrial Estate Aberdeen AB2 0ES	500	Z	S

Company name	Employees	Vacancies	Graduates required
GEC Gas Turbines Ltd Cambridge Road Whetstone Leicester LE8 3LH	1,400	V	S E
GEC Industrial Controls Ltd Mill Road Rugby Warwicks CU21 1BD	3,000	X	E
GEC Ltd 1 Stanhope Gate London W1A 1EH	200,000	Z	S E
General Mining Union Corp Gencor Recruitment 30 Ely Place London EC1N 6UA	200,000	X	S E
Geoservices 7 rue Newton 93.150 Le Blanc Mesnil France	1,200	X	S E
Gestetner Ltd Broad Lane Tottenham GeoservicesLondon N17 9LT	1,900	W	S E
Glaxo Group Research Ltd Park Road Ware Herts SG12 0DJ	680	W	S
Glynwed Ltd Headland House New Coventry Road Sheldon Birmingham B26 3AZ	16,000	V	S E
Goodfellow Metals Ltd Science Park Milton Road Cambridge CB4 4DJ	28	V	S E
Goodyear Tyre & Rubber Co GB Goodyear Internl Tech Centre Craigavon Co Armagh N Ireland BT66 6LA	76	V	S E
Government Auditors Audit House Victoria Embankment London EC4Y 0DS	1,400	Y	Any
Grampian Regional Council Woodhill House Ashgrove Road West Aberdeen AB9 2LU	21,000	V	E
Grand Metropolitan Info Svcs Wyvern Way Rockingham Road Uxbridge UB8 2TZ	300	V	S E
Graseby Dynamics Ltd 459 Park Avenue Bushey Watford Herts WD2 2BW	458	V	E
Grassland Research Institute Hurley Maidenhead Berks SL6 5LR	200	V	S
Grindlays Bank Ltd 23 Fenchurch Street London EC3P 3ED	13,000	V	Any
Gross Klein & Co 6 Bream's Buildings Chancery Lane London EC4A 1HP	20	V	S
Guest Keen & Nettlefolds Group Smethwick Warley W Midlands B66 2RZ	42,000	X	S E So
Guiness Mahon & Co Ltd 32 St Mary at Hill London EC3R 8DH	208	V	Any
Hacker Young St Alphage House 2 Fore Street London EC2Y 5DH	180	W	Any
Haden Ltd 7–12 Tavistock Square London WC1H 9LZ	850	W	S E
Haines Watts Sterling House 165–175 Farnham Road Slough SL1 4UZ	50	V	Any
Haiste & Partners Belmont House 20 Wood Lane Headingley Leeds LS6 2AG	250	V	E
Sir William Halcrow & Partners Newcombe House 45 Notting Hill Gate London W11 3JX	1,200	W	E
Hampshire Constabulary West Hill Hants SO22 5DB	3,088		Any

Key

Graduates required		Vacancies	
A	Arts	V	1–10
E	Engineering	W	10–20
S	Science	X	20–50
So	Social Sciences	Y	50–100
□	Consult Careers Service	Z	100 plus

Company name	Employees	Vacancies	Graduates required
Hampshire County Council The Castle Winchester Hants SO23 8UJ	40,000	V	Any
T Harley Haddow & Partners 8 Coates Crescent Edinburgh EH3 7BY	50	V	E
Hawker Siddeley Power Transformers Forest Works Fulbourne Road Walthamstow London E17 4EF	800	W	S E
Haymarket Publishing Ltd 76 Dean Street London W1A 1BU	650	X	Any
HJ Heinz Co Ltd Hayes Park Hayes Middx UB4 8AL	7,000	W	Any
Help the Aged PO Box 4UB London W1A 4UB	300	W	Any
Hepworth Plastics Ltd R & D Division Pollard Moor Works Burnley Lancs BB12 7JR	1,300	V	S E
Hertfordshire Contabulary Stanborough Road Welwyn Garden City Herts AL8 6XF	2,100	X	Any
Hickson & Welch (Holdings) Ltd Ings Lane Castleford W Yorkshire WF10 2JT	1,300	X	S E
Higgs & Hill Ltd Crown House Kingston Road New Malden Surrey KT3 3ST	1,300	V	E
Amos Hinton & Sons Ltd PO Box 24 Master Road Thornaby Stockton on Tees Cleveland TS17 0BD	2,650	V	So
LB Holliday & Co Ltd Leeds Road Huddersfield HD2 1UH	310	V	S E
Holt Lloyd Ltd Lloyds House Alderley Road Wilmslow Cheshire SK9 1QT	270	V	Any
Honey Barrett & Co 45 Gildredge Road Eastbourne BN21 4SF	90	V	Any
Hope Agar & Co Epworth House 25–35 City Road London EC1Y 1AR	70	V	Any
Horizon Exploration Ltd Horizon House Azalea Drive Swanley Kent BR8 8JR	500	X	S E
Hoskyns Group Ltd Africa House 64 Kingsway London WC2B 6BL	900	Y	Any
Howard Tilly & Co Commonwealth House 1 New Oxford Street London WC1A 1PF	180	W	Any
James Howden & Co Ltd 195 Scotland Street Glasgow GS 8PJ	1,300	V	E
Howmet Turbine Components Corporation Kestral Way Exeter Devon EX2 7LG	750	V	E
HSS Hire Group Ltd Warenne House 31 London Road Reigate Surrey	380	V	So
HTV Ltd The Television Centre Cardiff CF1 9XL	820	V	A E
Howard Humphreys & Partners Thorncroft Manor Dorking Road Leatherhead Surrey KT22 8JB	400	V	E
Hymatic Engineering Co Ltd Burnt Meadow Road North Moons Moat Redditch Worcs B98 9HJ	420	V	E
IAL Gemini (Computer Systems) Ltd Gemini House 133 High Street Yiewsley Middx UB7 7QL	80	W	S
ICC Information Group Ltd 81 City Road London EC1Y 1BD	160	V	Any

Company name	Employees	Vacancies	Graduates required
ICI Ltd Imperial Chemical House Millbank London SW1P 3JF	65,000	Y	A S E So
ICFC 91 Waterloo Road London SE1 8XP	250	V	Any
Ilford Ltd Town Lane Mobberley Cheshire WA16 7HA	1,500	W	Any S E
IMI Ltd PO Box 216 Birmingham B6 7BA	20,000	X	Any
Imperial Life Ass Co of Canada 11/13 Young Street London W8	30	V	Any
Inland Revenue M2/4F R443 Bush House (SW Wing) London WC2B 4QN	73,500	Y	Any
Institute of Bankers 10 Lombard Street London EC3V 9AS	80	V	A So
Institute of Engineers & Tech 100 Grove Vale London SE22 8DR	6	V	E
Institute of Medical Lab Sci 12 Queen Anne Street London W1M 0AU	28	V	Any
Institute of Physics 47 Belgrave Square London SW1X 8QX	120	V	S
International Research & Dev Fossway Newcastle upon Tyne NE6 2YD	300	V	E
Inveresk Research Int Ltd Musselburgh East Lothian EH21 7UB	165	V	S
Isopad Ltd Stirling Way Boreham Wood Herts WD6 2AF	160	V	E
ITT-IDEC Canada Life House Mutton Lane Potters Bar Herts EN6 3AR	380	W	S E
Ivory & Sime Ltd 1 Charlotte Square Edinburgh EH2 4DZ	75	V	Any

Company name	Employees	Vacancies	Graduates required
Jaguar Cars Ltd Engine & Transmission Plant Sandy Lane Radford Coventry CB6 3GB	7,500	V	E
Robert Jenkins & Co Ltd Wortley Road Rotherham S61 1LT	593	V	E
Jewitt Sparrow & Swinbank Barrington House 2 Bowesfield Lane Stockton on Tees Cleveland TS18 3ED	35	V	Any
Johnson Matthey & Co Ltd 100 High Street Southgate London N14 6ET	9,000	X	S E
Keane Shaw & Co 10 De Walden Court 85 New Cavendish Street London W1	20	V	□
MW Kellogg Ltd Kellogg House Stadium Way Wembley Middx HA9 0EE	5,000	W	E
Kennedy & Donkin Premier House Woking Surrey GU21 1DG	750	V	E
Kent Ind Measurements Ltd Hanworth Lane Chertsey Surrey KT16 9LF	350	V	S
Kimberley-Clark Ltd Larkfield Maidstone Kent ME20 7PS	3,000	V	Any
KMP Partnership Thomas Archer House 43 King Street London WC2E 8JS	92	V	Any
Knight Frank & Rutley 20 Hanover Square London W1R 0AH	300	V	Any

Key

Graduates required		Vacancies	
A	Arts	**V**	1–10
E	Engineering	**W**	10–20
S	Science	**X**	20–50
So	Social Sciences	**Y**	50–100
□	Consult Careers Service	**Z**	100 plus

Company name	Employees	Vacancies	Graduates required
Kottler & Heron Ltd PO Box 33 Gayton Road Milton Malsor Northants NN7 3AD	300	V	E
John Laing Ltd Page Street London NW7 2ER	14,000	V	E
Lamp Metals Ltd Fourth Avenue Team Valley Trading Estate Gateshead N11 0TY	400	V	S E
Lancashire Tar Distillers Ltd Liverpool Road Cadishead Manchester M30 5DT	400	V	S
Land Rover Ltd Tyburn Road Erdington Birmingham B24 8HJ	10,000	V	S E
Lansdowne Recruitment Ltd Park House 207 The Vale London W3 7QB	25	V	Any
Larking Gowen & Co 7 Queen Street Norwich NR2 4ST	150	W	S E
Lawrence-Allison & Assoc Mitcham House 681 Mitcham Road Croydon London CR9 3AP	137	V	S E
Leach Bright & Co Langton Priory Portsmouth Road Guildford GU2 5EH	83	V	Any
Leatherhead Food Randalls Road Leatherhead Surrey KT22 7RY	230	V	S
Leeds & Northrup Ltd Wharfdale Road Tyseley Birmingham B11 2DJ	265	V	E
Legal & General Ass Soc Temple Court 11 Queen Victoria Street London EC4N 4TP	5,000	W	Any
Leicester City Council New Walk Centre Welford Place Leicester LE1 6ZG	4,000	V	S E
Leicestershire County Council County Hall Glenfield Leicester LE3 8RP	28,000	X	S E So
Lex Service plc 17 Great Cumberland Place London W1H 8AD	9,500	V	Any E
Lincolnshire County Council County Offices Lincoln LN1 1YL	17,500	V	A S So
Linguarama Ltd 53 Pall Mall London SW1Y 5JH	200	X	Any
Lishman Sidwell Campbell & Price Lishman Chambers 12 Princes Square Harrogate HG1 1LX	42	V	So
Littlejohn & Co 19 Curistor Street London EC4 1LT	80	V	Any
Lloyds Bank International Ltd 40–66 Queen Victoria Street London EC4P 4EL	10,000	W	Any
Lloyds Bank Ltd 71 Lombard Street London EC3P 3BS	42,000	Y	Any
Lloyd's Life Assurance Ltd 20 Clifton Street London EC2A 4HX	200	W	Any
Loewy Robertson Engineering 553 Wallisdown Road Poole Dorset BH12 5AG	420	V	E
London Transport Management Development and Training Office 55 Broadway London SW1 0BD	60,000	X	Any
Longcrofts Capel House 62 New Broad Street London EC2M 1JS	120	W	Any
Lonsdale Technical Services 72 Bridge Street Manchester M3 2RJ	700	W	S E
Lovell Construction Group Marsham House Gerrards Cross Bucks SL9 8ER	3,500	V	S
Lucas Group Services Ltd Great King Street Birmingham B19 2XF	72,000	Z	Any S E So
Machine Tool Industry Research Association Hulley Road Macclesfield Cheshire SK10 2NE	72	V	E

Company name	Employees	Vacancies	Graduates required
Macro Marketing Ltd 54 Burnham Lane Slough Berks SL1 6JD	220	V	S
Magnet Joinery Sales Ltd Roydings Avenue Keighley W Yorks BD21 4BY	2,000	W	Any
Makro Self-Service Wholesalers Ltd Emerson House Albert Street Eccles Manchester M30 0LJ	3,500	W	Any
Mallinson-Denny Ltd 130 Hackney Road London E2 7QR	3,500	V	So
Marcol Computer Services Ltd 60 Queen's Gardens London W2 3AF	200	V	S E
Marconi Electronic Devices Ltd Doddington Road Lincoln LN6 0LF	1,200	W	S E
Marconi Research Labs West Hanningfield Great Baddow Chelmsford Essex CM2 8HN	720	X	S E
Markham & Co Ltd Broadoaks Works Chesterfield Derby S41 0DS	600	V	E
Marks & Spencer plc Michael House 47 Baker Street London W1A 1DN	43,000	Z	Any
Marley Group of Cos Riverhead Sevenoaks Kent TN13 2DS	11,000	W	Any
Mars Ltd Confectionery Div Dundee Road Slough Berks S1 4JX	3,400	W	Any E
Mars Money Systems 266 Bath Road Slough Berks SL1 4EB	250	V	S E
Massey-Ferguson Banner Lane Coventry CV4 9GF	6,500	W	Any
Mathers & Bensons Advertg Ltd 86 Lambs Conduit Passage London WC1R 4RH	25	V	Any

Company name	Employees	Vacancies	Graduates required
Matthew Hall Group 101-108 Tottenham Ct Rd London W1A 1BT	10,000	W	E
May & Baker Ltd Dagenham Essex RM10 7XS	4,500	□	S
Thomas May & Co Allen House Newark Street Leicester LE1 5SG	80	V	Any
Meat Research Institute Langford Bristol BS18 7DY	210	V	S E
Mektronic Consultants Linden House 116 Rectory Lane Prestwich Manchester M25 5DB	14	V	E
Mercantile & General Reins Moorfields House Moorfields London EC2Y 9AL	700	V	A
Merck Sharp & Dohme Ltd Hartford Road Hoddesdon Herts EN11 9BU	1,200	W	Any S
Metal Box Ltd Queens House Forbury Road Reading Berks RG1 3JH	25,000	Y	A S E
Metropolitan Police Centre 6 Harrow Road London W2 1XH	26,400	Z	Any
Michelin Tyre Co Ltd Stoke on Trent ST4 4EY	15,000	V	E
Micro Consultants Group 5 West Mills Newbury Berks RG14 5HG	450	W	E
Midland Bank plc Courtwood House Silver Street Head Sheffield S1 3RD	45,000	X	Any

Key

Graduates required		Vacancies	
A	Arts	**V**	1–10
E	Engineering	**W**	10–20
S	Science	**X**	20–50
So	Social Sciences	**Y**	50–100
□	Consult Careers Service	**Z**	100 plus

Company name	Employees	Vacancies	Graduates required
J Miller & Co 296–302 High Holborn London WC1V 7JH	12	V	S E
Robert Miller Tate & Co 15 Sandhill Newcastle upon Tyne NE1 1LD	27	V	Any
Ministry of Defence Eng Career CM(s)3c3, Room 347A The Adelphi John Adam Street London WC2N 6BB	120	X	E
Ministry of Defence: Science Group Room 310, Savoy Hill House Savoy Hill Strand London WC2R 0BX	140,000	Z	Any
Mirrlees Blackstone (Stamford) PO Box 2 Ryhall Road Stamford Lincs PE9 1UH	1,100	V	E
A Monk & Co Ltd PO Box 43 Warrington Cheshire WA1 4JB	65	V	Any
Monsanto Ltd Telford House 14 Tothill Street London SW1	5,500	V	E
Edward Moore & Sons 4 Chiswell Street London EC1Y 4XB	250	W	Any
Samuel Montagu & Co Ltd 114 Old Broad Street London EC2P 2HY	702	V	Any
Moores Furniture Group Ltd Thorpe Arch Trading Estate Wetherby W Yorks LS23 7BW	850	V	Any
Moore, Stephens & Co St Paul's House Warwick Lane London EC4P 4BN	260	X	Any
Morgan Brown & Haynes 35 New Broad Street London EC2M 1PP	20	V	Any
Morison Stoneham & Co 5 Queen Street London EC4N 1SU	70	V	Any
Morley & Scott 13 Marylebone Road London NW1 5JB	170	V	So
Motorola Colvilles Road Kelvin Industrial Estate East Kilbride Glasgow G75 0TG	1,800	W	S E
John Mowlem & Co Ltd Westgate House Ealing Road Brentford Middx TB8 0QZ	5,700	W	E
MTE Ltd Progress Road Leigh on Sea Essex SS9 5LS	500+	V	E
National Adhesives and Resins Galvin Road Trading Estate Slough Berks SL1 4DF	300	V	Any S
National Bus Co 25 New Street Square London EC4A 3AP	52,500	W	Any E
National Children's Home 85 Highbury Park London N5 1UD	2,000	V	So
National Council Training Journalists Carlton House Hemnall Street Epping Essex CM16 4NL	18	V	Any
National Cyrenians 13 Wincheap Canterbury Kent CT1 3TB	300	Z	Any
National Frmrs Union Mut Ins Society Church Street Stratford upon Avon CV3T 6HL	2,000	V	Any S
National Institute Medical Research The Ridgeway Mill Hill London NW7 1AA	545	W	S E
National Provident Institution National Provident House Calverley Road Tunbridge Wells Kent TN1 2UE	950	V	S
National Semiconductor UK Ltd Larkfield Industrial Estate Greenock PA16 0EQ	1,100	X	□
National Vegetable Research Station Wellesbourne Warwks CV35 9EF	226	V	S

Company name	Employees	Vacancies	Graduates required
National Westminster Bank PO Box 297 Drapers Gardens Throgmorton Avenue London EC2P 2ES	84,000	Z	Any
Napier Turbochargers PO Box 1 Lincoln LN2 5DJ	400	V	E
NCR (Manufacturing) Ltd Kingsway West Dundee DD2 3XX	800	W	E
Neville Russell & Co 30 Artillery Lane Bishopsgate London E1 7LT	700	Y	Any
Nevill Long Group North Hyde Wharf Hayes Road Southall Middx UB2 5NL	120	V	Any
AC Neilsen Co Ltd Neilsen House Headington Oxford OX3 9RX	1,200	W	Any
Noble Lowndes & Partners Ltd Norfolk House Wellesley Road Croydon Surrey CR9 3EB	800	W	A S So
NOP Market Research Ltd Tower House Southampton Street London WC2E 7HN	120	V	Any
Northamptonshire Police Wootton Hall Northampton NN4 0JQ	1,006	V	Any
North Eastern Electricity Brd Carliol House Newcastle upon Tyne NE99 1SE	5,900	V	A E
Northern Foods Ltd Beverley House St Stephen's Square Hull HU1 3XG	16,000	V	A S E So
Northumbrian Water Authority Northumbria House Regent Centre Gosforth Newcastle upon Tyne NE3 3PX	2,200	V	Any
Northumbria Police Police Headquarters North Road Newcastle upon Tyne NE20 0BL	3,357	W	Any
North Wales Police Glan-y-Don Colwyn Bay Clwyd LL29 8AW	1,313	V	Any
Norwich Union Insurance Group PO Box 4 Surrey Street Norwich NR1 3NG	7,800	W	A S
Ocean Transport & Trading Ltd India Buildings Water Street Liverpool L2 0RB	12,500	V	Any
Ofrex Group Ltd Ofrex House Stephen Street London W1A 1EA	2,700	V	A So
Package Programs Ltd 91 Blackfriars Road London SE1 8HW	70	V	S
Page Engineering Co Ltd Forge Lane Sunbury on Thames Middx TW16 6EQ	300	V	E
Pannell Kerr Forster Lee House London Wall London EC2Y 5AL	1,400	Y	Any
NEI Parsons Ltd Heaton Works Newcastle on Tyne NE6 2YL	5,000	W	E
Ralph M Parsons Co Parsons House Kew Bridge Road Brentford Middx TW8 0EH	470	V	E
Patent Office (Department of Trade) 25 Southampton Buildings London WC2A 1AY	440		S E
Pauls & Whites Ltd PO Box 39 47 Key Street Ipswich IP4 1BX	2,300	W	S

Key

Graduates required		Vacancies	
A	Arts	V	1–10
E	Engineering	W	10–20
S	Science	X	20–50
So	Social Sciences	Y	50–100
☐	Consult Careers Service	Z	100 plus

Company name	Employees	Vacancies	Graduates required
Pedigree Petfoods National Office Waltham on the Wolds Melton Mowbray Leics LE14 4RS	2,500	V	Any
Pearl Assurance plc High Holborn London WC1V 7EB	1,200	V	A S
Pergamon Press Ltd Headington Hill Hall Oxford OX3 0BW	600	V	S
Perkins Engines Co Eastfield Peterborough PE1 5NA	7,000	W	Any
Peters Elworthy & Moore Salisbury House Station Road Cambridge CB1 2LA	65	V	Any
Petters Ltd The Causeway Staines Middx TW18 3AR	850	V	E
Pfizer Ltd Ramsgate Road Sandwich Kent CT13 9NJ	1,500	W	S
Pilkington Brothers Ltd Prescot Road St Helens Merseyside WA10 3TT	19,000	X	A S E So
Pinchin Denny & Co Salisbury House London Wall London EC2M 5SH	270	V	Any
Pioneer Concrete UK Ltd Pioneer House 56 Northolt Road Harrow Middx HA2 0EY	□	W	Any
PIRA Randalls Road Leatherhead Surrey KT22 7RU	150	V	S
Pitney Bowes plc The Pinnacles Elizabeth Way Harlow Essex CM19 5BD	1,600	V	Any
Playtex Ltd Playtex Park Port Glasgow PA14 5UY	1,100	V	S E
Portsmouth City Council Civic Offices Guildhall Square Portsmouth PO1 2AL	3,165	V	Any E
Powell Duffryn Computer Svcs Faraday Road Basingstoke Hants RG24 0LH	100	V	Any
Press Computer Systems Ltd Albany House Chapel Ash Wolverhampton W Midlands WV3 0UJ	50	V	Any
Pridie Brewster & Co Carolyn House Greville Street London EC1 8RB	96	W	Any
Procter & Gamble Ltd PO Box 1EE Gosforth Newcastle upon Tyne NE99 1EE	3,200	Y	Any S E
Property Services Agency SM2D, Room 546 Lambeth Bridge House Albert Embankment London SE1 7SB	17,000	X	E
Provident Mutual Life Ass Association Wedgewood Way Stevenage Herts SG1 4PU	238	V	Any
Prudential Ass Co Ltd 142 Holborn Bars London EC1N 2NH	20,000	X	Any S So
Public Health Laboratory Svc Headquarters Office 61 Colindale Avenue London NW9 5EQ	2,200	X	S
Pye Telecommunications Ltd St Andrew's Road Cambridge CB4 1DW	2,200	V	E
Pye TVT Ltd PO Box 41 Coldhams Lane Cambridge CB1 3JU	540	V	E
Racal Electronics Ltd Inc Decca Western Road Bracknell Berks RG12 1RG	20,000	Z	E
Rank Precision Industries Ltd PO Box 36 Guthlaxton Street Leics LE2 0SL	800	V	S E
Ranks Hovis McDougall Ltd King Edward House PO Box 178 27–30 King Edward Court Windsor Berks SL4 1TJ	45,000	X	Any E

Company name	Employees	Vacancies	Graduates required
Ransomes Sims & Jefferies Ltd, Nacton Works, Ipswich IP3 PQG	1,350	V	E
Reads & Co, Leith House, 47 Gresham Street, London EC2V 7ET	50	V	Any
Record & Tape Exchange Ltd, 28 Pembridge Road, Notting Hill Gate, London W11 3HL	30	V	Any
Reddie & Grose, 16 Theobalds Road, London WC1X 8PL	45	V	S E
Redifon Telecom Ltd, Broomhill Road, London SW1B 4JQ	620	V	E
Redman Heenan International Ltd, Shrub Hill Road, Worcs WR4 9EQ	2,500	V	E
Reed & Mallik Ltd, Milford Manor, Salisbury, Wilts SP1 2RW	180	W	E
Reeves & Neylan, 37 St Margarets Street, Canterbury CT1 2TU	138	V	S
Reliance Systems Ltd, Turnells Mill Lane, Wellingborough, Northants NN8 2RB	1,500	V	S E
Reuters, 85 Fleet Street, London EC4P 4AJ	3,000	V	Any
Revell Ward, Norwich Union House, Huddersfield HD1 2LN	55	V	Any
Rexco Ltd, Fullarton Lodge, Crowhill Drive, Mansfield, Nottingham NG19 7A2	200	V	S E
Ricardo Consulting Engineers, Bridge Works, Shoreham by Sea, W Sussex BN4 5FG	400	V	E
Richards Butler & Co, 5 Clifton Street, London EC2A 4DQ	180	V	A
Richmond Fellowship Therapeutic Communities, 8 Addison Road, Kensington, London W14 8DL	150	W	So
Rio Tinto Zinc Corp Ltd, 6 St James's Square, London SW1Y 4LD	70,000	X	S E
Robson Rhodes, 186 City Road, London EC1V 2NU	650	Y	Any
Rockware Group Ltd, 13–21 Victoria Street, Windsor, Berks SL4 1HG	3,200	V	A S E
Roffe Swayne & Co, Ashcombe House, Queen Street, Godalming, Surrey GU7 1BB	29	V	Any
Rolls-Royce Motors Ltd, Pym's Lane, Crewe CW1 3PL	5,000	V	E
Roman Catholic Church Eng/Wales, Allen Hall, 28 Beaufort Street, Chelsea, London SW3 5AA	7,000	Y	Any
Rothamstead Experimental Stn, Harpenden, Herts AL5 2JQ	800	W	S
NM Rothschild & Sons Ltd, PO Box 185, New Court, St Swithin's Lane, London EC4P 4DU	650	V	Any
Rowe & Pitman, City Gate House, 39–45 Finsbury Square, London EC2A 1JA	300	V	Any
Rowland Nevill & Co, 53 New Broad Street, London EC2M 1PQ	120	V	Any
Rowntree Mackintosh plc, York YO1 1XY	28,000	W	Any
Royal Air Force, Directorate of Recruitment (RAF), Adastral House, Theobald's Road, London WC1X 8RU	80,000	Z	Any

Key

Graduates required		Vacancies	
A	Arts	V	1–10
E	Engineering	W	10–20
S	Science	X	20–50
So	Social Sciences	Y	50–100
□	Consult Careers Service	Z	100 plus

Company name	Employees	Vacancies	Graduates required
Royal Army Educational Corps Recruiting & Liaison Staff RAEC Centre Wilton Park Beaconsfield Bucks HP9 2RP	650	X	Any
Royal Bank of Scotland Ltd 42 St Andrew Square Edinburgh EH2 2YE	9,320	W	Any
Royal Nat Inst For the Blind 224 Great Portland Street London W1N 6AA	300	V	S
Royal Society of Chemistry Burlington House Piccadilly London W1V 0BN	340	V	Any S
Rubber & Plastics Research Association Shawbury Shrewsbury Salop SY4 4NR	175	V	S E
Ruston Gas Turbines Ltd PO Box 1 Lincoln LN2 5DJ	2,100	V	E
Safeway Foodstores Beddow Way Aylesford Kent ME20 7AT	10,500	X	Any
Saga Senior Citizens Holidays Enbrook House Sandgate Hill Sandgate Kent CT20 3SG	600	V	A
Christian Salvesen Ltd 50 East Fettes Avenue Edinburgh EH4 1EQ	6,000	V	Any
Sandvik Ltd Manor Way Halesowen W Midlands B62 8QZ	2,221	V	E
Save & Prosper Group Ltd 4 Great St Helens London EC3P 3EP	600	V	Any
Schlumberger Measurement Victoria Road Farnborough Hants GU14 4PW	2,600	W	S E
Schlumberger Wireline Svcs 42 rue Saint Dominique 75340 Paris France	2,000	Y	S E
J Henry Schroder Wagg & Co 120 Cheapside London EC2V 6DS	600	V	Any

Company name	Employees	Vacancies	Graduates required
Scottish Education Department 43 Jeffrey Street Edinburgh	59,000	Z	Any
Scottish Equitable Life Ass Soc 31 St Andrew Square Edinburgh EH2 2Q2	540	V	□
Scottish Health Service Management Education & Training Div Crewe Road South Edinburgh EH4 2LF	54,000	X	Any S
Scottish Health Service Common Services Agency Crewe Road South Edinburgh EH4 2LF	100,000	W	Any
Scottish Life Mutual Ass Society 109 St Vincent Street Glasgow G2 5HN	512	V	S
Scottish Prison Service The Scottish Home & Health Dept Prisons Div St Margaret's House London Road Edinburgh EH8 7TQ	2,500	V	So
Scottish Special Housing Association 15–21 Palmerston Place Edinburgh EH12 5AJ	2,000	V	Any
The Scottish Widows Fund & Life Assurance Soc 15 Dalkeith Road Edinburgh EH16 5BU	1,575	V	S
Seismographic Services Ltd Holwood Keston Kent BR2 6HD	1,350	Y	S E
Selfridges Ltd 400 Oxford Street London W1A 1AB	3,000	W	Any
SGRD Ltd Concord Road London W3 0SE	100	V	E
Shepherd Construction Ltd Frederick House Fulford Road York YO1 4EA	3,000	V	E
Sherwood Computer Centre North House 11 St Edward's Way Romford Essex RM1 4AR	280	V	Any S
Shetland Health Board 28 Burgh Road Lerwick Shetland ZE1 0QP	200	V	So

Company name	Employees	Vacancies	Graduates required
Shipley Blackburn 14–16 Regent Street London SW1Y 4PS	130	W	A
Shirley Institute Didsbury Manchester M20 8RX	193	V	S E
Silver Altman & Co High Holborn House 52/54 High Holborn London WC1V 6RT	30	V	Any
Simon Engineering Ltd Bird Hall Lane Cheadle Heath Stockport SK3 0RT	8,000	V	Any
SIRA Institute Ltd South Hill Chislehurst Kent BR7 5EH	170	V	S E
Smallfield Fitzhugh Tillett & Co 24 Portland Place London W1N 4AU	50	V	Any
Smallfield Rawlins & Co Beadle House 47–49 Borough High Street London Bridge London SE1 1EJ	40	V	Any
Smiths Industries Aerospace & Defence Systems Co Cricklewood Works Cricklewood London NW2 6JN	3,000	W	E
Solex (UK) Ltd Honeypot Lane Stanmore Middx HA7 1EG	800	V	E
Sound Attenuators Ltd Eastgates Colchester Essex CO1 2TW	230	V	S E
South African Civil Svce South African Embassy Trafalgar Square London WC2N 5DP	70,000	Z	S E
Southerns-Evans Ltd Sasco House Mill Lane Widnes Cheshire WA8 0UJ	1,500	W	Any
South Wales Constabulary Bridgend Mid-Glamorgam CF31 3SR	3,106	□	Any
South West Water Authority 3–5 Barnfield Road Exeter EX1 1RE	2,400	V	S E

Company name	Employees	Vacancies	Graduates required
South Yorkshire Police Police Headquarters Snig Hill Sheffield S3 8LY	2,872	□	Any
Spicer & Pegler St Mary Axe House 56–60 St Mary Axe London EC3A 8BJ	1,800	Z	Any
Stanley A Spofforth & Co 16/18 New Bridge Street London EC4	12	V	Any
Staffordshire County Council County Buildings Staffs ST16 2LH	38,000	Z	Any
Standard Telecoms Laboratories Ltd London Road Harlow Essex CM17 9NA	1,100	X	E
Staveley Industries plc Salter House Spon Lane West Bromwich W Midlands B70 6AD	5,000	V	S E
Steetley plc Gateford Hill Worksop Notts S81 8AF	7,000	V	S E
Stephenson Harwood Saddlers Hall Gutter Lane London EC2V 6BS	250	W	A
Sterling Varnish Co Ltd Fraser Road Trafford Park Manchester M17 1DU	120	V	S E
Stock Exchange London EC2N 1HP	1,000	W	Any
Stoy Hayward & Co 54 Baker Street London W1M 1DJ	550	Y	Any
Strachan & Henshaw PO Box 103 Ashton Vale Road Bristol BS99 7TJ	1,050	V	E
Strategic Recruitment Ltd 169 Piccadilly London W1E 6YZ	12	W	E

Key

Graduates required		Vacancies	
A	Arts	**V**	1–10
E	Engineering	**W**	10–20
S	Science	**X**	20–50
So	Social Sciences	**Y**	50–100
□	Consult Careers Service	**Z**	100 plus

Company name	Employees	Vacancies	Graduates required
Suffolk Constabulary Police Headquarters Martlesham Heath Ipswich IP5 7QS	1,124	V	Any
Sun Alliance Insurance Group 1 Bartholomew Lane London EC2N 2AB	8,000	X	Any
Sun Life Ass Co of Canada 2–4 Cockspur Street London SW1X 5BH	2,500	W	S
Surrey Constabulary Mount Browne Sandy Lane Guildford GU3 1HG	1,602	Z	Any
Systems Designers Ltd Systems House 105 Fleet Road Fleet Hants GU13 8NZ	350	W	S
Systime Ltd Concourse Computer Centre 432 Dewsbury Road Leeds L11 7DF	1,350	X	S E So
Tandy Corp (UK Branch) Tameway Tower Bridge Street Walsall W Midlands WS1 1LA	1,000	X	Any
Tarmac Construction Ltd Construction House Birch Street Wolverhampton WV1 4HY	6,000	W	E
Taylor Nelson Group 457 Kingston Road Ewell Epsom Surrey KT19 0DH	140	V	S So
Taylor Woodrow International Western House Western Avenue London W5 1EU	1,000	W	E
Tempered Spring Co PO Box 17 Foley Street Sheffield S4 7WS	400	V	E
Joseph Terry & Sons Ltd The Chocolate Works Bishopthorpe Road York YO1 1YE	1,400	V	Any
Texas Instruments Ltd Manton Lane Bedford MK41 7PA	2,250	X	S E
J Walter Thompson Co Ltd 40 Berkeley Square London W1X 6AD	110	V	A S So
Thompson, Jenner & Co 1 Colleton Crescent Exeter EX2 4DQ	35	V	S E
Thomson Organisation 4 Stratford Place London W1A 4YG	18,000	X	Any
Thyssen (GB) Ltd Group of Companies Bynea Llanelli Dyfed SA14 9SU	2,000	V	E
Tilghman Wheelabrator Ltd Broadheath Altrincham Cheshire WA14 5EP	277	V	E
Timex Corp Harrison Road Dundee DD2 3XL	5,000	V	Any E
Titmuss, Sainer & Webb 2 Sergeants' Inn London EC4Y 1LT	140	V	Any
Top Shop Oxford Circus London W1A 2LP	1,500	W	Any
Total Systems Ltd 388 City Road London EC1V 2QA	70	V	S
Travenol Labs Ltd Caxton Way Thetford Norfolk IP24 3SE	1,300	V	S E
TSB Group 3 Copthall Avenue London EC2P 2AB	26,000	W	Any
Tullis Russell & Co Ltd Rothes & Crocker Paper Mills Markinch Glenrothes Fife KY7 6BP	1,200	V	S E
Turner & Newall Ltd 20 St Mary's Parsonage Manchester M3 2NL	14,000	V	Any S
UK Provident Dolphin House New Street Salisbury SP1 2QQ	700	V	S
Unigate Ltd Unigate House Western Avenue London W3 0SH	37,000	X	Any S E
Unilever Research Unilever House London EC4P 4BQ	2,500	X	S E

Company name	Employees	Vacancies	Graduates required
Union International Co Ltd 14 West Smithfield Street London EC1A 9JN	35,000	V	Any
Unionoil Company of GB 32 Cadbury Road Sunbury on Thames Middx TW16 7LX	91	V	E
Unipart Group Unipart House Cowley Oxford OX4 2PG	5,800	V	Any E
United Biscuits Ltd Syon Lane Isleworth Middx TW7 5NN	30,000	X	Any
United Free Church of Scotland 11 Newton Place Glasgow G3 7PR	49	V	Any
United Glass Group 79 Kingston Road Staines Middx TW18 1AD	7,500	V	□
United Kingdom Atomic Energy Authority 11 Charles II Street London SW1	14,000	Y	S E
Vaux Breweries The Brewery Castle Street Sunderland SR1 3AN	2,500	V	Any
Vega-Cantley Instrument Co Unit J Eskdale Road Uxbridge Middx UB8 2RT	20	V	E
Voluntary Service Overseas 9 Belgrave Square London SW1X 8PW	800	Z	A S E So
Volunteer Missionary Movement Shenley Lane London Colney Herts AL2 1AR	200	Y	Any
Warren Point Ltd Babbage Road Stevenage Herts SG1 2EQ	20	V	S E
R Watson & Sons Watson House London Road Reigate Surrey RH2 9PQ	200	V	S
Watson Hawksley Terriers House Amersham Road High Wycombe Bucks HP13 5AJ	130	V	E
Welding Institute Abington Hall Abington Cambridge CB1 6AL	540	V	S E
Western Isles Health Board 37 South Beach Street Stornoway Isle of Lewis PA87 2PB	500	V	□
West Midlands Fire Service Lancaster Circus Queensway Birmingham B4 7DE	2,000	W	Any
Westland plc Westland Helicopters Yeovil Somerset	12,000	X	S E So
West Midlands Police Colmore Circus Queensway Birmingham B4 6NQ	6,684	Z	Any
Whatlings Ltd North Claremont Street Glasgow G3 7LF	650	V	E
Whessoe Ltd Brinkburn Road Darlington Co Durham DL3 6DS	3,450	V	E
Whitbread & Co Ltd The Brewery Chiswell Street London EC1 4SD	40,000	W	Any
Wiggins Teape Group Ltd PO Box 88 Basing View Basingstoke RG21 2EE	9,000	W	Any S E
Sir Owen Williams & Partners 41 Whitcomb Street London WC2H 7DT	250	X	E
Wilson De Zouche & Mackenzie 123 Indian Buildings Water Street Liverpool L2 0SA	30	V	Any
Winthrup Laboratories Production Division Fawdon Newcastle upon Tyne NE3 3TT	850	V	S

Key

Graduates required		Vacancies	
A	Arts	V	1–10
E	Engineering	W	10–20
S	Science	X	20–50
So	Social Sciences	Y	50–100
□	Consult Careers Service	Z	100 plus

Company name	Employees	Vacancies	Graduates required
WIRA Headingley Lane Leeds LS6 1BW	107	V	S
Wolsey-Hughes (Group Services) Ltd PO Box 18 Vines Lane Droitwich WR9 8ND	4,001	V	E
Wood King & Co 1 Old Burlington Street London W1X 2AX	80	V	Any
Wootton Jeffreys & Partners Cemetery Pales Brookwood Woking Surrey GU24 0BL	80	W	S

Company name	Employees	Vacancies	Graduates required
Yorkshire Bank 20 Merrion Way Leeds LS2 8NZ	3,500	W	Any
Yorkshire Regional Health Authority Park Parade Harrogate HG1 5AH	55,000	X	Any
Young & Rubicam Ltd Greater London House Hampstead Road London NW1 7QP	350	V	Any

Occupations index

Employers are listed under the following occupations for which they are recruiting. Professional bodies, trade associations and industrial training boards are also included.

Accountant	421
commercial/industrial	421
professional firm	423
public sector	423
Actuary	423
Advertising/publicity work	423
account executive	423
advertising/promotions executive	423
copywriter/researcher	423
Architect	423
Armed forces personnel	423
Bank work	423
clearing	423
international	423
merchant	423
Biochemist	423
Biologist	423
Buyer (retail/wholesale)	423
Chemist	423
Company secretary	425
Computer work	425
consultant	425
data processor	425
engineer	425
programmer	425
sales person	425
systems analyst	425
Corporate planner	426
Economist	426
Engineering work	426
applications	426
consultant	426
contracts, tendering and commissioning	426
design	426
installation and maintenance	426
plant engineering	427

production, process control	427
project engineering	427
quality control and testing	427
research and development	427
site	429
systems and control	429
technical sales and customer. liaison	429
Fire fighter	429
Geologist/geophysicist	429
Insurance work	429
broker	429
general trainee	429
sales person (inspector)	429
surveyor	429
underwriter	431
Journalist/editorial work	431
Legal executive	431
Librarian/information officer	431
Managerial/administrative work	431
agriculture/fisheries/forestry/ horticulture	431
building society	431
civil service	431
commercial/office	431
consultant	431
distribution/transport/shipping	431
education	431
estate/property	431
financial/investment	431
general	431
hotel	431
housing	431
import/export	431
local government	431
production (excluding engineering)	431
recreation	431
retail	431
Marketing	431
Market researcher	433

Merchanting	433
Metallurgist	433
Organisation and methods	433
Operational researcher	433
Patent agent	433
Personnel/industrial relations/training	433
Pharmacist	433
Physicist	433
Pilot	433
Police force	433
Psychologist	433
Purchasing/supplies officer	433
Scientific work	433
analysis and testing	433
design	433
field work/exploration	433
research/development	433
sales representative	435
scientific production	435
Selling/sales representative	435
Social/community/probation work	435
Solicitor	435
Statistician	435
Stockbroker	435
Surveyor (excluding insurance)	435
Tax inspector	435
Teacher/lecturer	435
Technical writer	435
Town and country planner	435
Work study/ergonomist	435

Accountant

⬤commercial/industrial

Air Products plc	70
Amersham International plc	72
Association of Certified Accountants	378
Association of Cost & Executive Accountants	379
Babcock International plc	82
BICC plc	94
Boots Co plc	99
Bowater Organisation	100
British Gas Corporation	106

British Steel Corporation	115
Cadbury Schweppes	122
Clerical Medical & General Life Assurance Society	131
Coles Cranes Ltd	133
Conoco Group in the UK	137
Dowty Group Ltd	159
Dunlop	157
Esso Group of Cos	163
Ford Motor Co Ltd	169
Gestetner	181
Hughes Microelectronics Ltd	197
IBM United Kingdom Ltd	199

Institute of Chartered Accountants in England & Wales	380
Institute of Cost & Management Accountants	383
Johnson Matthey Group	208
Marley Group	229
John Menzies (Holdings) plc	235
Metal Box plc	238
Milliken Industrials Ltd	245
Moores Furniture Group	248
Motorola Ltd	247
National Provident Institution	254
Northern Foods plc	260

Finnie Ross Allfields
Chartered Accountants

A 31 partner firm of Chartered Accountants with offices in London, Leeds, Glasgow, Newbury, Reading and Sheffield and associated firms in Europe, America, The Middle and the Far East.

We will be recruiting some 30 student accountants to join in 1983. Our clients range from quoted companies to small businesses; the work we undertake for them covers the full range of professional services; training both 'in-house' and external, is good; salaries are competitive and the atmosphere is friendly.

If you're thinking

of

Chartered Accountancy

DON'T!

DON'T decide before considering us

Application addresses
For London, Newbury and Reading:
Michael Robinson
Finnie Ross Allfields
Lee House
London Wall
London EC2Y 5AX

For Leeds and Sheffield:
John Clemmence
Finnie Ross Allfields
Bridge House
Westgate
Leeds LS1 4ND

For Glasgow
John Goudie
Finnie Ross Allfields
Hellenic House
87 Bath Street
Glasgow G2 2HL

Our selection criteria are high, but if you believe you will meet them —

write to the appropriate staff partner for further information and an application form

enclosing a cv, or with brief personal details

specifying particular office of interest

mentioning this publication

Norwich Union Insurance Group 262
Perkins Engines Ltd 270
Pilkington Brothers plc 272
Post Office 276
Prudential Assurance Co Ltd 285
RHM (Ranks Hovis McDougall plc) 293
Royal Insurance 50
Save & Prosper Group 306
Standard Telephones & Cables plc 328
THORN EMI plc 343
TI Group plc 347
Timex Corporation 349
Unigate plc 357
Unilever 355
Watney Mann & Truman Brewers Ltd 367
Wellcome Foundation Ltd 369
Westland plc 372

●professional firm
Arthur Andersen & Co 74
Arthur Andersen & Co Management
 Consultancy Division 74
Armitage & Norton 76
Arthur Young McClelland Moores & Co 79
Association of Certified Accountants 378
Baker Rooke 85
John Baker, Sons & Bell 83
Binder Hamlyn 95
Brebner, Allen & Trapp 101
Brewer & Co 102
Brian Ingram Associates 102
Buzzacott & Co 121
Casson Beckman 125
Clark Pixley 129
Coopers & Lybrand 140
Dearden Farrow 152
Deloitte Haskins & Sells 153
Ernst & Whinney 161
Finnie Ross Allfields 168
Fraser Keen 171
Fryer Whitehill & Co 174
Hacker Young 189
Haines Watts 189
HAT Accountancy Training Syndicate 191
Hughes Allen Payne Stone 198
Institute of Chartered Accountants of
 Scotland 381
Institute of Chartered Accountants in
 England & Wales 380
Kidsons 213
Knill Padgham & Grande 214
Lishman Sidwell Campbell & Price 218
Longcrofts 223
John Menzies (Holdings) plc 235
Morgan Brown & Haynes 249
Murray Noble 249
Norris Gilbert Stern & Co 259
Pannell Kerr Forster 263
Peat Marwick Mitchell & Co 267
Robson Rhodes 298
Rowland Nevill & Co 301
Silver Altman & Co 321
Smallfield Fitzhugh Tillet & Co 322
Spicer & Pegler 325
Stanley A Spofforth & Co 327
Stoy Hayward & Co 331
Thomson McLintock & Co 341
Thornton Baker 346
Touche Ross & Co 350
Wilson Green Gibbs 373

●public sector
Accountancy & Financial Management in
 the Public Sector 68
Association of Certified Accountants 378
Association of Cost & Executive
 Accountants 379

British Rail 111
British Steel Corporation 115
Chartered Institute of Public Finance &
 Accountancy 379
Institute of Chartered Accountants in
 England & Wales 380
Leicestershire County Council 424
London Transport 222
National Bus Co 249
National Coal Board 251
UK Atomic Energy Authority 360

Actuary
Clerical Medical & General Life Assurance
 Society 131
Co-operative Insurance Society Ltd 139
Crown Life 143
Cubie Wood & Co Ltd 146
Equity & Law Life Assurance Society plc 160
Friends' Provident Life Office 173
Guardian Royal Exchange Assurance plc 186
Hymans, Robertson & Co 198
Imperial Life Assurance Co of Canada 203
National Mutual Life Association of
 Australasia Ltd 252
National Provident Institution 254
Norwich Union Insurance Group 262
Pearl Assurance plc 265
Providence Capitol Life Assurance Co Ltd 284
Provident Life Association of London Ltd 284
Prudential Assurance Co Ltd 285
Royal Insurance 50
Save & Prosper Group 306
Scottish Equitable Life Assurance Society 313
Scottish Provident Institution 314
Scottish Widows' Fund & Life Assurance
 Society 315
Sun Life Assurance Co of Canada 334
Sun Life Assurance plc 332
UK Provident 353
R Watson & Sons 367

Advertising/publicity work
●account executive
AGB Research Group 70
Benton & Bowles Ltd 92
Boase Massimi Pollitt 97
Leo Burnett Ltd 120
●advertising/promotions executive
Benton & Bowles Ltd 92
Institute of Marketing 385
●copywriter/researcher
Boase Massimi Pollitt 97

Architect
Civil Service 127
Prudential Assurance Co Ltd 285

Armed forces personnel
Regular Army 77
Royal Air Force 301
Royal Electrical & Mechanical Engineers 304
Royal Navy, Royal Marines & WRNS 305

Bank work
●clearing
Bank of Scotland 87
Barclays Bank plc Group 88
Clydesdale Bank plc 132
Midland Bank plc 244
National Westminster Bank plc 257
Security Pacific National Bank 315
TSB Group 351
Williams & Glyn's Bank plc 20
Yorkshire Bank plc 374

●international
Bank of Credit & Commerce International
 SA 86
Bank of Scotland 87
Barclays Bank plc Group 88
Lloyds Bank International 394
Lloyds Bank plc 219
Merrill Lynch International 237
Midland Bank plc 244
National Westminster Bank plc 257
Security Pacific National Bank 315
Williams & Glyn's Bank plc 20

●merchant
Bank of Scotland 87
British Linen Bank Ltd 107
Hambros Bank Ltd 190
Industrial & Commercial Finance
 Corporation Ltd 204
Lloyds Bank International 394
Lloyds Bank plc 219
NM Rothschild & Sons Ltd 299
J Henry Schroder Wagg & Co Ltd 307
Security Pacific National Bank 315

Biochemist
Amersham International plc 72
Beecham Pharmaceuticals 90
Civil Service 127
May & Baker Ltd 235
Merck, Sharp & Dohme Ltd 236
Pfizer Ltd 271
RHM (Ranks Hovis McDougall plc) 293
ER Squibb & Sons plc 328
Unilever Research 355
Wellcome Foundation Ltd 369

Biologist
Beecham Pharmaceuticals 90
Civil Service 127
Mallinson-Denny Ltd 227
May & Baker Ltd 235
Merck, Sharp & Dohme Ltd 236
ER Squibb & Sons plc 328
Unilever Research 355
Wellcome Foundation Ltd 369

Buyer (retail/wholesale)
Boots Co plc 99
Institute of Purchasing & Supply 385
Moores Furniture Group 248
THORN EMI plc 343

Chemist
Abbott Laboratories Ltd 68
Amersham International plc 72
Beecham Pharmaceuticals 90
Beecham Products 91
British Nuclear Fuels Ltd 109
BXL Plastics Ltd 122
Ciba-Geigy Plastics & Additives Co 126
Civil Service 127
Dearborn Chemicals Ltd 152
Esso Group of Cos 163
Fishburn Printing Ink Co Ltd 168
Foseco Minsep Group 169
General Electric Co plc 177
General Mining Union Corp Ltd (Gencor) 391
Hickson & Welch Ltd 194
Hughes Microelectronics Ltd 197
Ilford Ltd 200
Johannesburg Consolidated Investment Co
 Ltd 393
Johnson Matthey Group 208
May & Baker Ltd 235
Merck, Sharp & Dohme Ltd 236

Leicestershire

Come to the country's centre for creative careers

The Area

Leicestershire is a part of the Midlands renowned for the variety of its landscape and economic activity. The main employment centre is the City of Leicester which also provides a comprehensive range of shopping, business and entertainment facilities for a wide catchment area. The south and east of the County are predominantly agricultural areas which fringe the large recreation centre of Rutland Water; whilst the north and west (containing Charnwood Forest and its picturesque villages) have a more rugged, though still attractive character. The County lies right at the centre of England with excellent communications by rail, M1 and M6 to all parts of the Country.

The Employer

Community services (such as Education, Highways, Social Services, Police and Libraries) are provided for the population of around 850,000 by Leicestershire County Council whose County Hall headquarters are a large modern building on the outskirts of Leicester. The premises include staff restaurant, mini-market and bank, together with a range of sports and social facilities. The staff have an excellent working environment with flexible hours and good holidays. The Authority employs 30,000 people and has a revenue and capital budget exceeding £300 million per annum.

Local Government is, by any standard, a complex area offering numerous challenging opportunities for graduate careers concerned with matters of great social importance and amongst those available at Leicestershire County Council are ones described below located in the Treasurer's Department.

The Jobs

Graduates able to apply energy and imagination to problem solving are required in the Treasurer's Department in the following fields:

Accountancy   Accountants assist in the effective and efficient deployment of the Authority's resources by means of financial advice, project evaluation, audit investigation and budgetary control. Graduate entrants, preferably with relevant degrees, are given full training assistance to become members of the Chartered Institute of Public Finance and Accountancy. The starting salary is within a range of *£5,300 to £5,900 rising after qualification to *£9,500. Opportunities for public finance accountants exist throughout the country, many posts have salaries in excess of £13,000.

Computing   The computer section is responsible for the provision of data processing facilities to all departments of the council and numerous other bodies. Satisfying and creative posts available (to graduates of any discipline with expectations of at least a second class degree) as computer programmers. Career paths into systems analysis and technical support by means of extensive training designed to release full individual potential. Competitive starting salaries with rapid progression within a graduate career structure. Local government computing offers a great variety of system areas which will provide a broad foundation to the experience of any intending computer professional.

Further information and application forms from County Treasurer, County Hall, Glenfield, Leicester. Telephone 0533 871313 Ext 376

* Plus Pay Award pending July 1983.

Metal Box plc 238
Mobil Oil Co Ltd 247
National Coal Board 251
Pfizer Ltd 271
Pilkington Brothers plc 272
Raychem 291
RHM (Ranks Hovis McDougall plc) 293
Rio Tinto Zinc Corporation plc 295
R Squibb & Sons plc 328
Standard Telecommunication Laboratories 328
THORN EMI plc 343
UK Atomic Energy Authority 360
Unilever Research 355
James Walker Group of Cos 366
Wellcome Foundation Ltd 369

company secretary
Association of Cost & Executive
  Accountants 379
British Aerospace-Dynamics Group 103
Institute of Chartered Secretaries &
  Administrators 382

Computer work

●consultant
Arthur Andersen & Co Management
  Consultancy Division 74
BIS Applied Systems Ltd 96
BIS Software Ltd 96
CAP Group Ltd 123
Civil Service 127
Coopers & Lybrand Associates Ltd 141
Data Logic Ltd 149
Fraser Williams 171
Hymans, Robertson & Co 198
IBM United Kingdom Ltd 199
Logica Group 220
Nielsen Business Services 259
Powell Duffryn Systems Ltd 278
SPL International 326

●data processor
AGB Research Group 70
BIS Software Ltd 96
British National Oil Corporation 107
British Shipbuilders 112
Brown & Root (UK) Ltd 117
Civil Service 127
Crosfield Electronics Ltd 145
Cummins Engine Co Ltd 147
Geophysical Service International 180
Horizon Exploration Ltd 195
Leicestershire County Council 424
Littlewoods Organisation plc 218
Logica Group 220
London Transport 222
Lummus Co Ltd 225
National Coal Board 251
Prime Computer (UK) Ltd 438
Scicon 310
Standard Telephones & Cables plc 328
THORN EMI plc 343
Timex Corporation 349
TSB Group 351
UK Atomic Energy Authority 360
Western Geophysical Co of America 371

●engineer
British Aerospace-Dynamics Group 103
British Steel Corporation 115
CASE Computer & Systems Engineering
  plc 126
Civil Service 127
Computer Machinery Company (CMC) Ltd 133
Computer Technology Ltd 136
Cossor Electronics Ltd 142

Crosfield Electronics Ltd 145
Cummins Engine Co Ltd 147
Eurotherm International 164
Ferranti plc 167
Gardline Surveys 177
Hawker Siddeley Dynamics Engineering
  Ltd 192
Hickson & Welch Ltd 194
IBM United Kingdom Ltd 199
International Computers Ltd 206
MW Kellogg Ltd 211
FJC Lilley plc 217
Logica Group 220
Lummus Co Ltd 225
Micro Consultants Group 243
Microwave Associates Ltd 243
Motorola Ltd 247
Providence Capitol Life Assurance Co Ltd 284
Royal Air Force 301
Scicon 310
SIA Computer Services 321
SPL International 326
Standard Telephones & Cables plc 328
Systime Ltd 331
THORN EMI plc 343
UK Atomic Energy Authority 360
VG Isotopes Ltd 362

●programmer
Air Products plc 70
Barclays Bank plc Group 88
BICC plc 94
BIS Applied Systems Ltd 96
BIS Software Ltd 96
Boots Co plc 99
British Aerospace-Dynamics Group 103
British Airways 104
British Gas Corporation 106
British Nuclear Fuels Ltd 109
British Rail 111
British Ship Research Association 111
British Shipbuilders 112
British Steel Corporation 115
Cadbury Schweppes 122
CASE Computer & Systems Engineering
  plc 126
Civil Service 127
Compeda Ltd 135
Computer Machinery Company (CMC) Ltd 133
Conoco Group in the UK 137
Coopers & Lybrand Associates Ltd 141
Cossor Electronics Ltd 142
Crosfield Electronics Ltd 145
Cummins Engine Co Ltd 147
Daresbury Laboratory 148
Data Logic Ltd 149
Easams 58
Esso Group of Cos 163
Eurotherm International 164
Ferranti plc 167
Ford Motor Co Ltd 169
Fraser Williams 171
French Kier Construction Ltd 172
Friends' Provident Life Office 173
Gardline Surveys 177
General Mining Union Corp Ltd (Gencor) 391
Geophysical Service International 180
Gestetner 181
Government Communications HQ 183
Hawker Siddeley Dynamics Engineering
  Ltd 192
Hymans, Robertson & Co 198
IBM United Kingdom Ltd 199
Instron Ltd 205
International Computers Ltd 206
ITT-IDEC 207

Laser-Scan Laboratories Ltd 215
Leicestershire County Council 424
Littlewoods Organisation plc 218
Logica Group 220
Lucas Industries plc 224
Lummus Co Ltd 225
Mars Group Services 230
Meteorological Office 239
Micro Consultants Group 243
Micro Focus Ltd 241
Midland Bank plc 244
Milliken Industrials Ltd 245
Mobil Oil Co Ltd 247
National Coal Board 251
National Provident Institution 254
National Westminster Bank plc 257
Nielsen Business Services 259
NCR (Manufacturing) Ltd 258
Norwich Union Insurance Group 262
Pearl Assurance plc 265
Perkins Engines Ltd 270
Pilkington Brothers plc 272
PMA Consultants Ltd 274
Post Office 276
Powell Duffryn Systems Ltd 278
Press Computer Systems Ltd 278
Prime Computer (UK) Ltd 438
Prudential Assurance Co Ltd 285
Quantel Ltd 287
RHM (Ranks Hovis McDougall plc) 293
Save & Prosper Group 306
Scicon 310
Software Sciences 323
SPL International 326
Standard Telecommunication Laboratories 328
Sun Life Assurance plc 332
Systime Ltd 331
Taylor Instrument Ltd 335
THORN EMI plc 343
TI Group plc 347
TSB Group 351
UK Atomic Energy Authority 360
VG Isotopes Ltd 362
Wellcome Foundation Ltd 369
Western Geophysical Co of America 371
Westland plc 372
Williams & Glyn's Bank plc 20

●sales person
BIS Software Ltd 96
Compeda Ltd 135
Crosfield Electronics Ltd 145
IBM United Kingdom Ltd 199
International Computers Ltd 206
Logica Group 220
Mallinson-Denny Ltd 227
Micro Focus Ltd 241
Unilever 355

●systems analyst
Air Products plc 70
Babcock International plc 82
Barclays Bank plc Group 88
BICC plc 94
BIS Applied Systems Ltd 96
BIS Software Ltd 96
British Aerospace-Dynamics Group 103
British National Oil Corporation 107
British Nuclear Fuels Ltd 109
British Ship Research Association 111
British Shipbuilders 112
British Steel Corporation 115
Brush Electrical Machines Ltd 118
Cadbury Schweppes 122
Civil Service 127
Compeda Ltd 135

Computer Machinery Company (CMC) Ltd 133
Conoco Group in the UK 137
Coopers & Lybrand Associates Ltd 141
Cossor Electronics Ltd 142
Crosfield Electronics Ltd 145
Cummins Engine Co Ltd 147
Daresbury Laboratory 148
Data Logic Ltd 149
Dunlop 157
Easams 58
Equity & Law Life Assurance Society plc 160
Ferranti plc 167
Ford Motor Co Ltd 169
Fraser Williams 171
French Kier Construction Ltd 172
Gestetner 181
Hawker Siddeley Dynamics Engineering
  Ltd 192
International Computers Ltd 206
Johnson Matthey Group 208
Leicestershire County Council 424
Littlewoods Organisation plc 218
Logica Group 220
Lucas Industries plc 224
Lummus Co Ltd 225
Matthew Hall Group 234
Micro Focus Ltd 241
Mobil Oil Co Ltd 247
Moores Furniture Group 248
National Coal Board 251
Perkins Engines Ltd 270
Pilkington Brothers plc 272
Powell Duffryn Systems Ltd 278
Press Computer Systems Ltd 278
Prime Computer (UK) Ltd 438
Prudential Assurance Co Ltd 285
Quinton Hazell plc 287
RHM (Ranks Hovis McDougall plc) 293
Royal Insurance 50
SPL International 326
Staveley Industries plc 329
Systime Ltd 331
THORN EMI plc 343
TI Group plc 347
Timex Corporation 349
UK Atomic Energy Authority 360
Unilever 355
United Biscuits (UK) plc 358
Wellcome Foundation Ltd 369
Westland plc 372
Williams & Glyn's Bank plc 20

Corporate planner
British Airports 104

Economist
Barclays Bank plc Group 88
Beecham Products 91
British National Oil Corporation 107
Civil Service 127
Hong Kong Administrative Class 392
National Coal Board 251
Prudential Assurance Co Ltd 285

Engineering work
● applications
AE Group 69
British Aerospace-Dynamics Group 103
British Nuclear Fuels Ltd 109
Brush Electrical Machines Ltd 118
Civil Service 127
Compeda Ltd 135
Cossor Electronics Ltd 142
Eurotherm International 164

Hawker Siddeley Dynamics Engineering
  Ltd 192
Holset Engineering Co Ltd 195
Kennedy & Donkin 211
London Transport 222
NCR (Manufacturing) Ltd 258
Royal Electrical & Mechanical Engineers 304
Schlumberger Wireline Logging 396
SIA Computer Services 321
THORN EMI plc 343

● consultant
Civil Service 127
Dearborn Chemicals Ltd 152
Kennedy & Donkin 211
McDermott Engineering London 226
National Coal Board 251
Ricardo Consulting Engineers 297
Schlumberger Wireline Logging 396

● contracts, tendering and commissioning
Air Products plc 70
Alfa-Laval Co Ltd 72
Babcock International plc 82
BICC plc 94
British National Oil Corporation 107
British Nuclear Fuels Ltd 109
British Shipbuilders 112
Brown & Root (UK) Ltd 117
John Brown Engiheers & Constructors Ltd 116
Brush Electrical Machines Ltd 118
Burmah Oil plc 118
Cossor Electronics Ltd 142
Davy McKee Ltd 150
Guest Keen & Nettlefolds plc 187
NEI International Combustion Ltd 205
Kennedy & Donkin 211
Kyle Stewart Group 215
Matthew Hall Group 234
Edmund Nuttall Group of Cos 263
NEI Overseas Ltd 395
Shand Group 320
Staveley Industries plc 329

● design
AE Group 69
Air Products plc 70
APV Co Ltd 75
Babcock International plc 82
Baker Perkins Group of Cos 84
Beecham Pharmaceuticals 90
BICC plc 94
British Aerospace-Dynamics Group 103
British Airports 104
British National Oil Corporation 107
British Nuclear Fuels Ltd 109
British Shipbuilders 112
British Steel Corporation 115
Brown & Root (UK) Ltd 117
John Brown Engineers & Constructors Ltd 116
Brush Electrical Machines Ltd 118
Burmah Oil plc 118
C & S Antennas 145
CASE Computer & Systems Engineering
  plc 126
Ciba-Geigy Plastics & Additives Co 126
Civil Service 127
Coles Cranes Ltd 133
Compeda Ltd 135
Cossor Electronics Ltd 142
Crosfield Electronics Ltd 145
Cummins Engine Co Ltd 147
Davy McKee (London) Ltd 151
Davy McKee Ltd 150
Dow Corning Ltd 155
Dowty Group Ltd 159
Dunlop 157

Eurotherm International 164
Fairey Hydraulics Ltd 165
Ferranti plc 167
Ford Motor Co Ltd 169
Four Square 170
General Electric Co plc 177
Gestetner 181
Guest Keen & Nettlefolds plc 187
Hawker Siddeley Dynamics Engineering
  Ltd 192
Holset Engineering Co Ltd 195
Hughes Microelectronics 197
Instron Ltd 205
NEI International Combustion Ltd 205
International Computers Ltd 206
ITT-IDEC 207
Kalamazoo Business Systems 211
MW Kellogg Ltd 211
Kennedy & Donkin 211
Kyle Stewart Group 215
Lucas Industries plc 224
Lummus Co Ltd 225
McDermott Engineering London 226
Mars Ltd (Confectionery Division) 230
Matthew Hall Group 234
Metal Box plc 238
Micro Consultants Group 243
Microwave Associates Ltd 243
National Semiconductor 255
NCR (Manufacturing) Ltd 258
NEI Overseas Ltd 395
Perkins Engines Ltd 270
Pilkington Brothers plc 272
Quantel Ltd 287
Quinton Hazell plc 287
Racal Electronics plc 288
RHM (Ranks Hovis McDougall plc) 293
Ricardo Consulting Engineers 297
Rio Tinto Zinc Corporation plc 295
Royal Corps of Naval Constructors 303
Schlumberger Wireline Logging 396
South African Civil Service 397
Standard Telephones & Cables plc 328
Staveley Industries plc 329
NEI Thompson Ltd 342
THORN EMI plc 343
Timex Corporation 349
UK Atomic Energy Authority 360
Vetco Offshore Ltd 362
VG Isotopes Ltd 362
James Walker Group of Cos 366
Weir Pumps Ltd 368
Westland plc 372

● installation and maintenance
Air Products plc 70
Associated British Foods plc 80
Babcock International plc 82
Beecham Pharmaceuticals 90
BICC plc 94
BOC Ltd 98
British Nuclear Fuels Ltd 109
British Rail 111
British Shipbuilders 112
British Steel Corporation 115
John Brown Engineers & Constructors Ltd 116
C & S Antennas 145
CASE Computer & Systems Engineering
  plc 126
Conoco Group in the UK 137
Cossor Electronics Ltd 142
Crosfield Electronics Ltd 145
Cummins Engine Co Ltd 147
Dunlop 157
Ford Motor Co Ltd 169
General Mining Union Corp Ltd (Gencor) 391

Hawker Siddeley Dynamics Engineering
Ltd 192
NEI International Combustion Ltd 205
MW Kellogg Ltd 211
Lever Brothers Ltd 216
Mars Ltd (Confectionery Division) 230
Matthew Hall Group 234
Metal Box plc 238
National Bus Co 249
Pilkington Brothers plc 272
Racal Electronics plc 288
Rio Tinto Zinc Corporation plc 295
Seiscom Delta United 316
South African Civil Service 397
Standard Telephones & Cables plc 328
THORN EMI plc 343
UK Atomic Energy Authority 360
VG Isotopes Ltd 362
James Walker Group of Cos 366

● plant engineering
Air Products plc 70
Anglo American Corporation of
South Africa Ltd 388
APV Co Ltd 75
Associated British Foods plc 80
Aurora Holdings plc 81
Babcock International plc 82
Beecham Pharmaceuticals 90
BICC plc 94
BOC Ltd 98
British Nuclear Fuels Ltd 109
British Shipbuilders 112
British Steel Corporation 115
Ciba-Geigy Plastics & Additives Co 126
Compeda Ltd 135
Conoco Group in the UK 137
Cummins Engine Co Ltd 147
Dow Corning Ltd 155
Dunlop 157
Esso Group of Cos 163
Ford Motor Co Ltd 169
Johannesburg Consolidated Investment
Co Ltd 393
Mars Ltd (Confectionery Division) 230
National Coal Board 251
NEI Overseas Ltd 395
RHM (Ranks Hovis McDougall plc) 293
Rio Tinto Zinc Corporation plc 295
TI Group plc 347
UK Atomic Energy Authority 360
Unigate plc 357
Unilever 355
James Walker Group of Cos 366

● production, process control
AE Group 69
APV Co Ltd 75
Associated British Foods plc 80
Aurora Holdings plc 81
Babcock International plc 82
Baker Perkins Group of Cos 84
Beecham Pharmaceuticals 90
Beecham Products 91
BICC plc 94
BOC Ltd 98
British Aerospace-Dynamics Group 103
British National Oil Corporation 107
British Nuclear Fuels Ltd 109
British Shipbuilders 112
British Steel Corporation 115
British Sugar plc 115
Brush Electrical Machines Ltd 118
BXL Plastics Ltd 122
Cadbury Schweppes 122
Ciba-Geigy Plastics & Additives Co 126
Coles Cranes 133

Conoco Group in the UK 137
Consolidated Gold Fields plc 388
Crosfield Electronics Ltd 145
Cummins Engine Co Ltd 147
Davy McKee Ltd 150
Dowty Group Ltd 159
Dunlop 157
Esso Group of Cos 163
Ferranti plc 167
Ford Motor Co Ltd 169
Foseco Minsep Group 169
Four Square 170
General Electric Co plc 177
General Mining Union Corp Ltd (Gencor) 391
Gestetner 181
Guest Keen & Nettlefolds plc 187
Holset Engineering Co Ltd 195
Hughes Microelectronics Ltd 197
Imperial Brewing & Leisure Ltd 201
NEI International Combustion Ltd 205
International Computers Ltd 206
Johnson Matthey Group 208
Kyle Stewart Group 215
Lucas Industries plc 224
Marley Group 229
Mars Ltd (Confectionery Division) 230
Mars Money Systems 233
Metal Box plc 238
Michelin Tyre plc 241
Milliken Industrials Ltd 245
Mobil Oil Co Ltd 247
Moores Furniture Group 248
National Coal Board 251
National Semiconductor 255
NCR (Manufacturing) Ltd 258
Perkins Engines Ltd 270
Pilkington Brothers plc 272
Quinton Hazell plc 287
Raychem 291
Rio Tinto Zinc Corporation plc 295
SPL International 326
Standard Telephones & Cables plc 328
Staveley Industries plc 329
NEI Thompson Ltd 342
THORN EMI plc 343
TI Group plc 347
Timex Corporation 349
UK Atomic Energy Authority 360
Unilever 355
United Biscuits (UK) plc 358
Vetco Offshore Ltd 362
Victor Products (Wallsend) plc 363
Weir Pumps Ltd 368
Wellcome Foundation Ltd 369
Westland plc 372
Zambia Consolidated Copper Mines Ltd 398

● project engineering
AE Group 69
Air Products plc 70
Alfa-Laval Co Ltd 72
Amersham International plc 72
APV Co Ltd 75
Babcock International plc 82
Barr & Stroud 89
Beecham Pharmaceuticals 90
BICC plc 94
British Airports 104
British National Oil Corporation 107
British Nuclear Fuels Ltd 109
British Shipbuilders 112
Brown & Root (UK) Ltd 117
John Brown Engineers & Constructors Ltd 116
Cadbury Schweppes 122
Ciba-Geigy Plastics & Additives Co 126
Conoco Group in the UK 137

Crosfield Electronics Ltd 145
Cummins Engine Co Ltd 147
Daresbury Laboratory 148
Davy McKee (London) Ltd 151
Dunlop 157
Ferranti plc 167
Getty Oil (Britain) Ltd 183
Hawker Siddeley Dynamics Engineering
Ltd 192
Holset Engineering Co Ltd 195
Hughes Microelectronics Ltd 197
NEI International Combustion Ltd 205
Kennedy & Donkin 211
Lummus Co Ltd 225
McDermott Engineering London 226
Mars Ltd (Confectionery Division) 230
Matthew Hall Group 234
Metal Box plc 238
National Coal Board 251
NCR (Manufacturing) Ltd 258
NEI Overseas Ltd 395
Post Office 276
Rio Tinto Zinc Corporation plc 295
Schlumberger Wireline Logging 396
Taylor Instrument Ltd 335
THORN EMI plc 343
TI Group plc 347
Timex Corporation 349
UK Atomic Energy Authority 360
Unilever 355
Vetco Offshore Ltd 362
Westland plc 372

● quality control and testing
AE Group 69
Aurora Holdings plc 81
Babcock International plc 82
Barr & Stroud 89
Beecham Pharmaceuticals 90
BICC plc 94
British Aerospace-Dynamics Group 103
British Nuclear Fuels Ltd 109
British Shipbuilders 112
British Standards Institution 113
BXL Plastics Ltd 122
CASE Computer & Systems Engineering
plc 126
Civil Service 127
Cossor Electronics Ltd 142
Crosfield Electronics Ltd 145
Ford Motor Co Ltd 169
Hawker Siddeley Dynamics Engineering
Ltd 192
Hughes Microelectronics Ltd 197
NEI International Combustion Ltd 205
International Computers Ltd 206
Kennedy & Donkin 211
Kyle Stewart Group 215
Lever Brothers Ltd 216
Microwave Associates Ltd 243
Milliken Industrials Ltd 245
Moores Furniture Group 248
National Coal Board 251
National Semiconductor 255
NCR (Manufacturing) Ltd 258
Perkins Engines Ltd 270
Rio Tinto Zinc Corporation plc 295
Standard Telephones & Cables plc 328
THORN EMI plc 343
Timex Corporation 349
UK Atomic Energy Authority 360
Weir Pumps Ltd 368
Westland plc 372

● research and development
AE Group 69
Babcock International plc 82

The Analysts
Schlumberger

We need self-motivated and alert engineering and geology graduates to continue providing our vital and comprehensive well-logging service to the oil and gas industry.

As well as the more conventional services, The Analysts offer the industry the Instantaneous Drilling Evaluation Log (IDEL) programme and a comprehensive Measurements While Drilling (MWD) service.

The IDEL programme uses data gathered from surface sensors to compute among other things drilling porosity and pore pressure on a foot-to-foot basis.

The MWD system uses sensors and electronic cartridges in the lowermost section of the drill-string to give a continuous log-versus-depth reading of the resistivity of formation pore fluids, the formation gamma-ray, annular temperature, down-hole weight, and the directional coordinates and inclination of the well at the bit.

Our training programme, which leads to Total Concept Unit Manager (TCUM) status, integrates seminars with on-site practical training. Each of the four seminars, of 1–2 weeks, is followed by several months experience at the well-site. On-site periods represent a promotion, as well as the opportunity to apply different skills.

For further details please see our entry on page 73.

THE ANALYSTS

Schlumberger

Barr & Stroud   89
Bestobell plc   93
BICC plc   94
British Aerospace-Dynamics Group   103
British Nuclear Fuels Ltd   109
British Rail   111
British Ship Research Association   111
British Shipbuilders   112
British Steel Corporation   115
C & S Antennas   145
CASE Computer & Systems Engineering
  plc   126
Civil Service   127
Computer Machinery Company (CMC) Ltd   133
Cossor Electronics Ltd   142
Crosfield Electronics Ltd   145
Daresbury Laboratory   148
Dept of Industry (Science Group)   154
Dowty Group Ltd   159
Dunlop   157
Eurotherm International   164
Fairey Hydraulics Ltd   165
Ferranti plc   167
Ford Motor Co Ltd   169
Gardline Surveys   177
Gestetner   181
Government Communications HQ   183
Hawker Siddeley Dynamics Engineering
  Ltd   192
Holset Engineering Co Ltd   195
Hughes Microelectronics Ltd   197
IBM United Kingdom Ltd   199
Ilford Ltd   200
International Computers Ltd   206
ITT-IDEC   207
Johannesburg Consolidated Investment
  Co Ltd   393
Johnson Matthey Group   208
Kalamazoo Business Systems   211
Metal Box plc   238
Micro Consultants Group   243
Moores Furniture Group   248
National Coal Board   251
NCR (Manufacturing) Ltd   258
Perkins Engines Ltd   270
Pilkington Brothers plc   272
Post Office   276
Quantel Ltd   287
Quinton Hazell plc   287
Racal Electronics plc   288
Raychem   291
RHM (Ranks Hovis McDougall plc)   293
Ricardo Consulting Engineers   297
Rio Tinto Zinc Corporation plc   295
Royal Corps of Naval Constructors   303
Schlumberger Measurement & Control
  (UK) Ltd   309
Schlumberger Wireline Logging   396
SGRD Ltd   320
South African Civil Service   397
Standard Telecommunication Laboratories   328
THORN EMI plc   343
TI Group plc   347
Timex Corporation   349
UK Atomic Energy Authority   360
Unilever Research   355
United Biscuits (UK) plc   358
Weir Pumps Ltd   368
Westland plc   372

● site
Alfa-Laval Co Ltd   72
Babcock International plc   82
BICC plc   94
British Airports   104
British Nuclear Fuels Ltd   109

Brown & Root (UK) Ltd   117
John Brown Engineers & Constructors Ltd   116
Consolidated Gold Fields plc   388
Richard Costain plc   142
Davy McKee (London) Ltd   151
Dowell Schlumberger   389
Flopetrol International SA   390
French Kier Construction Ltd   172
NEI International Combustion Ltd   205
Kennedy & Donkin   211
Kyle Stewart Group   215
Matthew Hall Group   234
National Coal Board   251
Rio Tinto Zinc Corporation plc   295
Schlumberger Wireline Logging   396
Seiscom Delta United   316
Shand Group   320
Taylor Woodrow International Ltd   336
UK Atomic Energy Authority   360

● systems and control
AE Group   69
Babcock International plc   82
Bestobell plc   93
BICC plc   94
British Aerospace-Dynamics Group   103
British Nuclear Fuels Ltd   109
British Rail   111
British Shipbuilders   112
British Steel Corporation   115
Brown & Root (UK) Ltd   117
John Brown Engineers & Constructors Ltd   116
Cadbury Schweppes   122
Civil Service   127
Compeda Ltd   135
Computer Machinery Company (CMC) Ltd   133
Crosfield Electronics Ltd   145
Easams   58
Esso Group of Cos   163
Ferranti plc   167
Ford Motor Co Ltd   169
General Electric Co plc   177
Government Communications HQ   183
Holset Engineering Co Ltd   195
Instron Ltd   205
Johnson Matthey Group   208
MW Kellogg Ltd   211
Kennedy & Donkin   211
Mars Ltd (Confectionery Division)   230
Matthew Hall Group   234
Metal Box plc   238
Micro Consultants Group   243
National Coal Board   251
NCR (Manufacturing) Ltd   258
NEI Overseas Ltd   395
Pilkington Brothers plc   272
Plessey   273
Schlumberger Measurement & Control
  (UK) Ltd   309
Schlumberger Wireline Logging   396
SPL International   326
Taylor Instrument Ltd   335
THORN EMI plc   343
UK Atomic Energy Authority   360
Unilever   355
Westland plc   372

● technical sales and customer liaison
AE Group   69
Air Products plc   70
Aurora Holdings plc   81
Bestobell plc   93
BICC plc   94
C & S Antennas   145
Compeda Ltd   135
Crosfield Electronics Ltd   145
Dearborn Chemicals Ltd   152

Dowty Group Ltd   159
Esso Group of Cos   163
Eurotherm International   164
Hawker Siddeley Dynamics Engineering
  Ltd   192
Holset Engineering Co Ltd   195
Hughes Microelectronics Ltd   197
Johnson Matthey Group   208
Kalamazoo Business Systems   211
Kyle Stewart Group   215
Lucas Industries plc   224
Milliken Industrials Ltd   245
National Coal Board   251
Newey & Eyre Group Ltd   258
NEI Overseas Ltd   395
Racal Electronics plc   288
Schlumberger Wireline Logging   396
THORN EMI plc   343
TI Group plc   347
Weir Pumps Ltd   368

Fire fighter
London Fire Brigade   222
West Midlands Fire Service   370

Geologist/geophysicist
Analysts Schlumberger   73
British National Oil Corporation   107
Burmah Oil plc   118
Esso Group of Cos   163
Exploration Logging   165
Gardline Surveys   177
General Mining Union Corp Ltd (Gencor)   391
Geophysical Service International   180
Getty Oil (Britain) Ltd   183
Horizon Exploration Ltd   195
Mobil Oil Co Ltd   247
National Coal Board   251
Pilkington Brothers plc   272
Seiscom Delta United   316
Seismograph Service Ltd   317
Western Geophysical Co of America   371
Zambia Consolidated Copper Mines Ltd   398

Insurance work
● broker
CT Bowring & Co Ltd   100
Endsleigh Insurance Services   159
Murray Noble   249
Stewart Wrightson   330

● general trainee
Equity & Law Life Assurance Society plc   160
Friends' Provident Life Office   173
Guardian Royal Exchange Assurance plc   186
National Mutual Life Association of
  Australasia Ltd   252
Norwich Union Insurance Group   262
Pearl Assurance plc   265
Prudential Assurance Co Ltd   285
Royal Insurance   50
Scottish Equitable Life Assurance Society   313
Stewart Wrightson   330
Sun Life Assurance plc   332

● sales person (inspector)
Endsleigh Insurance Services   159
Equity & Law Life Assurance Society plc   160
Royal Insurance   50
Scottish Equitable Life Assurance Society   313
Sun Life Assurance plc   332

● surveyor
Incorporated Society of Valuers &
  Auctioneers   379

UNITED BISCUITS (UK) LTD

United Biscuits is the company that can offer graduates of any discipline a challenging career in all fields of industrial management.

We are looking for young managers with enthusiasm and ability in the areas of production, engineering, personnel, sales, marketing, distribution and computing.

They are needed in all our major companies — UB Biscuits, UB Foods, UB Frozen Foods, UB Restaurants, DS Crawfords, UB Distribution, UB International and Wimpy International.

If you feel up to this challenge, and are keen to pursue an exciting and rewarding career see our entry on page 358 and write to us for further details.

●underwriter
Endsleigh Insurance Services 159
Providence Capitol Life Assurance Co Ltd 284
Prudential Assurance Co Ltd 285

Journalist/editorial work
AGB Research Group 70
Haymarket Publishing Group 193
Institution of Electrical Engineers 204
Reuters 292
VNU Business Publications BV 365

Legal executive
Prudential Assurance Co Ltd 285

Librarian/information officer
Institution of Electrical Engineers 204

Managerial/administrative work
●agriculture/fisheries/forestry/horticulture
RHM (Ranks Hovis McDougall plc) 293

●building society
Bradford & Bingley Building Society 101

●civil service
Civil Service 127
Government Communications HQ 183
Hong Kong Administrative Class 392
Prison Service 279

●commercial/office
AGB Research Group 70
Cummins Engine Co Ltd 147
Gestetner 181
Institute of Purchasing & Supply 385
Marks & Spencer plc 228
Marley Group 229
John Menzies (Holdings) plc 235
Milliken Industrials Ltd 245
Moores Furniture Group 248
Prudential Assurance Co Ltd 285
Reuters 292

●consultant
Coopers & Lybrand Associates Ltd 141

●distribution/transport/shipping
Air Products plc 70
Boots Co plc 99
British Airways 104
British Rail 111
British Steel Corporation 115
Davy McKee (London) Ltd 151
Fenwick Ltd 166
Ford Motor Co Ltd 169
London Transport 222
Montague L Meyer plc 240
Mobil Oil Co Ltd 247
National Bus Co 249
Newey & Eyre Group Ltd 258
RHM (Ranks Hovis McDougall plc) 293
Unigate plc 357
Unilever 355
Union International plc 358
United Biscuits (UK) plc 358
Watney Mann & Truman Brewers Ltd 367

●education
Association of Cost & Executive
  Accountants 379
Royal Air Force 301

●estate/property
British Rail 111
Incorporated Society of Valuers &
  Auctioneers 379
Knight Frank & Rutley 214
National Coal Board 251

Watney Mann & Truman Brewers Ltd 367
●financial/investment
Conoco Group in the UK 137
Ford Motor Co Ltd 169
Friends' Provident Life Office 173
Industrial & Commercial Finance
  Corporation Ltd 204
Murray Noble 249
National Coal Board 251
Norwich Union Insurance Group 262
Providence Capitol Life Assurance Co Ltd 284
Prudential Assurance Co Ltd 285
Save & Prosper Group 306
Unilever 355
Watney Mann & Truman Brewers Ltd 367

●general
AGB Research Group 70
British Shipbuilders 112
BXL Plastics Ltd 122
Four Square 170
Gallaher Ltd 175
Imperial Brewing & Leisure Ltd 201
Institution of Electrical Engineers 204
Lex Service Group plc 216
Lloyds Bank International 394
McDonald's Golden Arches Restaurants
  Ltd 226
Montague L Meyer plc 240
National Coal Board 251
Post Office 276
Scapa Group plc 310
Shand Group 320
Jefferson Smurfit Group 322
THORN EMI plc 343
Timex Corporation 349
UK Atomic Energy Authority 360
Union International plc 358

●hotel
YMCA 373

●housing
Hong Kong Administrative Class 392
Incorporated Society of Valuers &
  Auctioneers 379
Scottish Special Housing Association 314

●import/export
Montague L Meyer plc 240

●local government
Association of Cost & Executive
  Accountants 379
Greater London Council 185
Hong Kong Administrative Class 392
Trading Standards Officers 349

●production (excluding engineering)
AGB Research Group 70
Associated British Foods plc 80
Aurora Holdings plc 81
Boots Co plc 99
British Steel Corporation 115
C & J Clark Ltd 128
Coles Cranes Ltd 133
Dunlop 157
Ford Motor Co Ltd 169
Four Square 170
Lucas Industries plc 224
Mars Ltd (Confectionery Division) 230
Mars Money Systems 233
Montague L Meyer plc 240
Milliken Industrials Ltd 245
Moores Furniture Group 248
Northern Foods plc 260
Pilkington Brothers plc 272
RHM (Ranks Hovis McDougall plc) 293
Scapa Group plc 310

Timex Corporation 349
Unigate plc 357
Unilever 355
Union International plc 358
United Biscuits (UK) plc 358
Watney Mann & Truman Brewers Ltd 367

●recreation
YMCA 373

●retail
Associated British Foods plc 80
BHS (British Home Stores) plc 94
Burmah Oil plc 118
C & J Clark Ltd 128
Littlewoods Organisation plc 218
Marks & Spencer plc 228
John Menzies (Holdings) plc 235
Quinton Hazell plc 287
Miss Selfridge Ltd 318
Selfridges Ltd 319
Tandy Corporation (Branch UK) 335
Waitrose Ltd 365

Marketing
Abbott Laboratories Ltd 68
AE Group 69
AGB Research Group 70
Air Products plc 70
Alfa-Laval Co Ltd 72
Amersham International plc 72
Beecham Pharmaceuticals 90
Beecham Products 91
Bestobell plc 93
BICC plc 94
Boase Massimi Pollitt 97
Boots Co plc 99
Bowater Organisation 100
British Airports 104
British Gas Corporation 106
British Rail 111
British Steel Corporation 115
C & J Clark Ltd 128
Cadbury Schweppes 122
Conoco Group in the UK 137
Dunlop 157
Eurotherm International 164
Ford Motor Co Ltd 169
Friends' Provident Life Office 173
Guest Keen & Nettlefolds plc 187
Hughes Microelectronics plc 197
Imperial Brewing & Leisure Ltd 201
Institute of Marketing 385
Instron Ltd 205
Johnson Matthey Group 208
Mallinson-Denny Ltd 227
Mars Ltd (Confectionery Division) 230
John Menzies (Holdings) plc 235
Merck, Sharp & Dohme Ltd 236
Micro Focus Ltd 241
Mobil Oil Co Ltd 247
Moores Furniture Group 248
Nielsen Business Services 259
Perkins Engines Ltd 270
Pilkington Brothers plc 272
Providence Capitol Life Assurance Co Ltd 284
Quinton Hazell plc 287
RHM (Ranks Hovis McDougall plc) 293
Rio Tinto Zinc Corporation plc 295
Save & Prosper Group 306
Scapa Group plc 310
Standard Telephones & Cables plc 328
Staveley Industries plc 329
Taylor Instrument Ltd Analytics Division 336
TI Group plc 347
Unigate plc 357
Unilever 355

One executive decision that is a matter of life and death.

There can't be many jobs open to graduates in which you'd have as much responsibility as a Police Inspector.

A man, maybe a bank-robber or a murderer, is cornered in a house with a shotgun.

More than likely, he's mentally disturbed and he's probably more scared than he's ever been in his life. And in that state, he's dangerous and unpredictable.

He may try and kill himself or he may have hostages, in which case you've got more problems.

You've got the lives of the public and the lives of your fellow Police Officers to protect.

Somehow you've got to get him out and you'll only be issued with firearms as a last resort. It's a task which is going to take all your skills as a Police Officer to handle.

The only weapon you've got for this situation is your brain. You'll have to act with tact and understanding and organise your team in the best possible way.

It's because of increasingly complex problems such as this that today's Police have an increasing need for highly qualified men and women.

The Graduate Entry Scheme is designed to train and develop people who not only have the potential for accelerated promotion to Inspector, but who may one day have to make a life or death decision.

The scheme is open to graduates or final year undergraduates of any discipline up to the age of 30, who meet the physical requirements.

In order to help us both make the right decision we're inviting final year undergraduates to spend a few days with us, from 3rd to 6th January 1983 on a familiarisation course.

We shan't hide anything, as you'll be expected to accompany Police Officers during their work. As an undergraduate you'll know if you've been accepted under the scheme before you start your last term.

If you're interested in a Police career, don't hesitate too long. The closing date for the familiarisation course is December 3rd, for the Graduate Entry Scheme January 28th.

To Supt. John M. Adams B.A., Room 556, Home Office, Queen Anne's Gate, London SW1l 9AT. Please send me your booklet and application form for:
The Police Graduate Entry Scheme ☐ The Familiarisation Course ☐ (Please tick)
Name_____ Age_____
Address_____
_____
University/Polytechnic/College_____
My Degree Course_____ Ends____ DOG/83

POLICE ⊕ OFFICER

IF YOU'VE GOT A LOT TO OFFER US. WE'VE GOT A LOT TO OFFER YOU.

United Biscuits (UK) plc 358
Watney Mann & Truman Brewers Ltd 367

Market researcher
AGB Research Group 70
Beecham Pharmaceuticals 90
Beecham Products 91
Boase Massimi Pollitt 97
Boots Co plc 99
Johnson Matthey Group 208
Mars Group Services 230
Metal Box plc 238
Nielsen Business Services 259
Research Bureau Ltd 291
Unilever 355

Merchanting
Institute of Purchasing & Supply 385

Metallurgist
AE Group 69
Anglo American Corporation of South
    Africa Ltd 388
Aurora Holdings plc 81
Babcock International plc 82
British Nuclear Fuels Ltd 109
British Steel Corporation 115
Brown & Root (UK) Ltd 117
Civil Service 127
Crosfield Electronics Ltd 145
Foseco Minsep Group 169
General Electric Co plc 177
General Mining Union Corp Ltd (Gencor) 391
Guest Keen & Nettlefolds plc 187
Hughes Microelectronics Ltd 197
Johannesburg Consolidated Investment
    Co Ltd 393
Johnson Matthey Group 208
Metal Box plc 238
Rio Tinto Zinc Corporation plc 295
Standard Telecommunication Laboratories 328
Staveley Industries plc 329
THORN EMI plc 343
TI Group plc 347
UK Atomic Energy Authority 360
Zambia Consolidated Copper Mines Ltd 398

Organisation and methods
British Gas Corporation 106
Crosfield Electronics Ltd 145
Johnson Matthey Group 208

Operational researcher
Air Products plc 70
Barclays Bank plc Group 88
British Airports 104
British Airways 104
British Gas Corporation 106
British Nuclear Fuels Ltd 109
British Rail 111
British Steel Corporation 115
Cadbury Schweppes 122
Easams 58
Mars Ltd (Confectionery Division) 230
National Coal Board 251
Pilkington Brothers plc 272
THORN EMI plc 343
United Biscuits (UK) plc 358
Westland plc 372

Patent agent
Raychem 291

Personnel/industrial relations/training
Air Products plc 70
Associated British Foods plc 80

Bestobell plc 93
Bowater Organisation 100
British Airways 104
British Gas Corporation 106
British Rail 111
British Steel Corporation 115
Cadbury Schweppes 122
Conoco Group in the UK 137
Cummins Engine Co Ltd 147
Dunlop 157
Esso Group of Cos 163
Ford Motor Co Ltd 169
Four Square 170
Hong Kong Administrative Class 392
Imperial Brewing & Leisure Ltd 201
London Transport 222
Marks & Spencer plc 228
Metal Box plc 238
Moores Furniture Group 248
National Coal Board 251
Northern Foods plc 260
Perkins Engines Ltd 270
Pilkington Brothers plc 272
Prudential Assurance Co Ltd 285
Standard Telephones & Cables plc 328
Staveley Industries plc 329
Taylor Instrument Ltd Analytics Division 336
Timex Corporation 349
Unigate plc 357
Unilever 355
United Biscuits (UK) plc 358
Watney Mann & Truman Brewers Ltd 367
Wellcome Foundation Ltd 369

Pharmacist
Abbott Laboratories Ltd 68
Beecham Pharmaceuticals 90
Civil Service 127
May & Baker Ltd 235
Merck, Sharp & Dohme Ltd 236
Pfizer Ltd 271
Wellcome Foundation Ltd 369

Physicist
AE Group 69
Barr & Stroud 89
British Aerospace-Dynamics Group 103
British Nuclear Fuels Ltd 109
British Steel Corporation 115
Civil Service 127
Crosfield Electronics Ltd 145
Daresbury Laboratory 148
Dept of Industry (Science Group) 154
General Electric Co plc 177
Gestetner 181
Government Communications HQ 183
Hughes Microelectronics Ltd 197
Ilford Ltd 200
Johnson Matthey Group 208
Metal Box plc 238
Microwave Associates Ltd 243
National Coal Board 251
National Semiconductor 255
Pilkington Brothers plc 272
Raychem 291
RHM (Ranks Hovis McDougall plc) 293
Standard Telecommunication Laboratories 328
Taylor Instrument Ltd Analytics Division 336
THORN EMI plc 343
UK Atomic Energy Authority 360
VG Isotopes Ltd 362

Pilot
Royal Air Force 301

Police force
British Transport Police 36
Police Service in England & Wales 275
Royal Hong Kong Police Force 395

Psychologist
Prison Service 279
Richmond Fellowship Therapeutic
    Communities 297

Purchasing/supplies officer
British Airways 104
British Gas Corporation 106
British Steel Corporation 115
Coles Cranes Ltd 133
Ford Motor Co Ltd 169
Institute of Purchasing & Supply 385
MW Kellogg Ltd 211
London Transport 222
Lucas Industries plc 224
Mars Ltd (Confectionery Division) 230
Moores Furniture Group 248
THORN EMI plc 343
Westland plc 372

Scientific work
● analysis and testing
Associated British Foods plc 80
British Aerospace-Dynamics Group 103
British Nuclear Fuels Ltd 109
Civil Service 127
Crosfield Electronics Ltd 145
Daresbury Laboratory 148
General Electric Co plc 177
Johannesburg Consolidated Investment
    Co Ltd 393
May & Baker Ltd 235
National Coal Board 251
National Maritime Institute 251
Schlumberger Wireline Logging 396
ER Squibb & Sons plc 328
THORN EMI plc 343
UK Atomic Energy Authority 360

● design
Alfa-Laval Co Ltd 72
British Aerospace-Dynamics Group 103
British Nuclear Fuels Ltd 109
Civil Service 127
Crosfield Electronics Ltd 145
Daresbury Laboratory 148
General Electric Co plc 177
National Coal Board 251
National Maritime Institute 251
THORN EMI plc 343
UK Atomic Energy Authority 360

● field work/exploration
Burmah Oil plc 118
Civil Service 127
Conoco Group in the UK 137
Geophysical Service International 180
Geoservices 180
Schlumberger Wireline Logging 396
Seismograph Service Ltd 317
THORN EMI plc 343

● research/development
Associated British Foods plc 80
Beecham Pharmaceuticals 90
Beecham Products 91
Boots Co plc 99
British Aerospace-Dynamics Group 103
British Gas Corporation 106
British Nuclear Fuels Ltd 109
British Ship Research Association 111
British Steel Corporation 115

A Career
in Sales/Journalism

VNU Business Publications BV is a substantial and dynamic Pan-European publishing house with an impressive record in a wide field of UK professional and trade media. Amongst the highly successful titles we publish are Computing, Accountancy Age, Datalink, Infomatics, DOG, Microdecision, the Computer User's Yearbook and the International Directory of Software, What Micro?, Databusiness, Infomatics Daily Bulletin.

To continue and accelerate our growth we consistently appoint graduates who will be looking for a career in journalism or sales where self-motivation and ambition will provide the opportunity for job satisfaction and rapid advancement, since we operate a policy of internal promotion.

Graduates are given extensive training throughout their careers, whether in sales or journalism.

Remuneration in the form of salary and commission is generous, and graduates can expect to earn over £6,000 in their first year of employment.

If you believe that your talent and personality match the challenge of operating in the extremely fast-moving environment of publishing, then write to or telephone:

The Director of Personnel and Training, VNU Business Publications
53-55 Frith Street, London W1A 2HG. Telephone: 01-439 4242

BUSINESS PUBLICATIONS

Burmah Oil plc	118	
Cadbury Schweppes	122	
Civil Service	127	
Crosfield Electronics Ltd	145	
Daresbury Laboratory	148	
Dept of Industry (Science Group)	154	
Dow Corning Ltd	155	
Dunlop	157	
Fishburn Printing Ink Co Ltd	168	
General Electric Co plc	177	
General Mining Union Corp Ltd (Gencor)	391	
Gestetner	181	
Government Communications HQ	183	
Ilford Ltd	200	
International Computers Ltd	206	
Johnson Matthey Group	208	
Laser-Scan Laboratories Ltd	215	
Lever Brothers Ltd	216	
May & Baker Ltd	235	
Merck, Sharp & Dohme Ltd	236	
Metal Box plc	238	
Meteorological Office	239	
Moores Furniture Group	248	
National Coal Board	251	
National Maritime Institute	251	
Pfizer Ltd	271	
Pilkington Brothers plc	272	
Raychem	291	
RHM (Ranks Hovis McDougall plc)	293	
Scapa Group plc	310	
ER Squibb & Sons plc	328	
Standard Telecommunication Laboratories	328	
Texas Instruments Ltd	338	
THORN EMI plc	343	
UK Atomic Energy Authority	360	
Unilever Research	355	
United Biscuits (UK) plc	358	
VG Isotopes Ltd	362	
Wellcome Foundation Ltd	369	

● sales representative

Dearborn Chemicals Ltd	152	
Dow Corning Ltd	155	
Johnson Matthey Group	208	
Merck, Sharp & Dohme Ltd	236	
Milliken Industrials Ltd	245	
Moores Furniture Group	248	
Motorola Ltd	247	
ER Squibb & Sons plc	328	
Texas Instruments Ltd	338	
THORN EMI plc	343	
Wellcome Foundation Ltd	369	

scientific production

Beecham Pharmaceuticals	90	

British Nuclear Fuels Ltd	109	
BXL Plastics Ltd	122	
Johannesburg Consolidated Investment Co Ltd	393	
Johnson Matthey Group	208	
May & Baker Ltd	235	
THORN EMI plc	343	
Wellcome Foundation Ltd	369	

Selling/sales representative

Boehringer Corporation (London) Ltd	98	
AE Group	69	
AGB Research Group	70	
Aurora Holdings plc	81	
Baker Perkins Group of Cos	84	
Beecham Pharmaceuticals	90	
Beecham Products	91	
Bestobell plc	93	
Bowater Organisation	100	
British Steel Corporation	115	
Cadbury Schweppes	122	
Compeda Ltd	135	
Crosfield Electronics Ltd	145	
Esso Group of Cos	163	
Ford Motor Co Ltd	169	
Four Square	170	
Gallaher Ltd	175	
Gestetner	181	
Habitat	188	
Haymarket Publishing Group	193	
IBM United Kingdom Ltd	199	
Institute of Marketing	385	
Johnson Matthey Group	208	
Mallinson-Denny Ltd	227	
Marley Group	229	
Mars Ltd (Confectionery Division)	230	
Merck, Sharp & Dohme Ltd	236	
Metal Box plc	238	
Montague L Meyer plc	240	
Micro Focus Ltd	241	
Milliken Industrials Ltd	245	
Mobil Oil Co Ltd	247	
Moores Furniture Group	248	
Murray Noble	249	
Newey & Eyre Group Ltd	258	
Nielsen Business Services	259	
Northern Foods plc	260	
Pearl Assurance plc	265	
Pedigree Petfoods	269	
RHM (Ranks Hovis McDougall plc)	293	
Scapa Group plc	310	
ER Squibb & Sons plc	328	
Taylor Instrument Ltd Analytics Division	336	
Union International plc	358	

United Biscuits (UK) plc	358	
VNU Business Publications BV	365	
Watney Mann & Truman Brewers Ltd	367	

Social/community/probation work

Richmond Fellowship Therapeutic Communities	297	
YMCA	373	

Solicitor

Trower, Still & Keeling	351	

Statistician

AGB Research Group	70	
Civil Service	127	
National Coal Board	251	
Nielsen Business Services	259	

Stockbroker

Murray Noble	249	
Phillips & Drew	272	
Rowe & Pitman	300	

Surveyor (excluding insurance)

Civil Service	127	
French Kier Construction Ltd	172	
Gardline Surveys	177	
Geophysical Service International	180	
Incorporated Society of Valuers & Auctioneers	379	
Knight Frank & Rutley	214	
National Coal Board	251	
Prudential Assurance Co Ltd	285	
Seiscom Delta United	316	

Tax inspector

Civil Service	127	

Teacher/lecturer

Teaching Profession (Scotland)	337	

Technical writer

Computer Machinery Company (CMC) Ltd	133	
Prime Computer (UK) Ltd	438	

Town and country planner

British Airports	104	
South African Civil Service	397	

Work study/ergonomist

Pilkington Brothers plc	272	
Timex Corporation	349	
Watney Mann & Truman Brewers Ltd	367	

Your Future is in Our Brochure...

Employer activity index

Employers are listed under their main activity—the product or service they provide. Professional bodies and industrial training boards are also included.

Abrasives	437
Accountancy (private practice)	437
Actuarial	437
Advertising, public relations	439
Agricultural, fisheries, forestry, horticulture	439
Armed services	439
Aviation	439
Banking	439
Broadcasting, TV, films	439
Building, construction	439
Building society	439
Building supplies	439
Charity	439
Chemical and allied industries	439
Civil service	439
Clothing, footwear, leatherwork	439
Computer hardware, business equipment	439
Computer software	439
Consultancy—Computer	439
Consultancy—Engineering	439
Consultancy—Management	439
Cosmetics, toiletries	439
Economic research	439

Engineering—aeronautical	439
Engineering—automotive	441
Engineering—chemical	441
Engineering—civil and structural	441
Engineering—electrical (heavy)	441
Engineering—electrical (light)	441
Engineering—electronics	441
Engineering—mechanical (heavy)	441
Engineering—mechanical (light)	441
Financial services (exc banking, accounting, insurance)	441
Food, drink, tobacco industry	443
Furniture and timber	443
Geophysical exploration	443
Glass, ceramics	443
Hotels, catering, restaurants	443
Insurance	443
Legal and patent work	443
Leisure industry	443
Local government	443
Machine tools	443
Market research, marketing	443
Medical and health care products	443
Metal goods manufacture	443
Metal producers, processors, refiners	443

Mining and extractive industries	443
News agency	443
Oil and petroleum industry	443
Paints and industrial finishes	443
Paper and packaging	443
Pharmaceuticals	443
Photographic good/materials manufacture	443
Plastics, polymers, rubbers	443
Power (gas, electricity, nuclear etc)	443
Professional body/trade association	443
Public services	443
Publishing and printing	445
Retail, wholesale and distribution	445
Scientific research	445
Shipbuilding	445
Social and community services (statutory and voluntary)	445
Surveying, estate management and architecture	445
Telecommunications	445
Textiles	445
Transport services	445
Travel, tourism	445
Vehicle manufacture	445
Water and drainage services	445

Abrasives
Foseco Minsep Group	169

Accountancy (private practice)
Arthur Andersen & Co	74
Armitage & Norton	76
Arthur Young McClelland Moores & Co	79
Association of Cost & Executive Accountants	379
Baker Rooke	85
John Baker, Sons & Bell	83
Binder Hamlyn	95
Brebner, Allen & Trapp	101
Brewer & Co	102
Brian Ingram Associates	102
Buzzacott & Co	121
Casson Beckman	125
Clark Pixley	129
Coopers & Lybrand	140

Dearden Farrow	152
Deloitte Haskins & Sells	153
Ernst & Whinney	161
Finnie Ross Allfields	168
Fraser Keen	171
Fryer Whitehill & Co	174
Hacker Young	189
Haines Watts	189
HAT Accountancy Training Syndicate	191
Hughes Allen Payne Stone	198
Institute of Chartered Accountants of Scotland	381
Kidsons	213
Knill Padgham & Grande	214
Lishman Sidwell Campbell & Price	218
Longcrofts	223
Morgan Brown & Haynes	249
Norris Gilbert Stern & Co	259
Pannell Kerr Forster	263

Peat Marwick Mitchell & Co	267
Rowland Nevill & Co	301
Silver Altman & Co	321
Smallfield Fitzhugh Tillet & Co	322
Spicer & Pegler	325
Stanley A Spofforth & Co	327
Stoy Hayward & Co	331
Thomson McLintock & Co	341
Thornton Baker	346
Touche Ross & Co	350
Wilson Green Gibbs	373

Actuarial
Cubie Wood & Co Ltd	146
Hymans, Robertson & Co	198
National Mutual Life Association of Australasia Ltd	252
Provident Life Association of London Ltd	284
Scottish Equitable Life Assurance Society	313

PR1ME
Computer

Degree behind you ...
What next?

**Start a career in an industry
where there are: * JOBS *
OPPORTUNITIES * CHALLENGES**

PRIME Computer are seeking
graduates in Maths, Computer
Sciences, Physics and Electronic
Engineering at their Research,
Development & Engineering Centre.

Prime can offer you scope and
training to develop technically and
personally, while working with the
latest technology in a friendly and
relaxed atmosphere. A great deal is
expected of the people that we
employ and we give a lot in return.

Software
Computing
Development
Technology
Engineering
Research

IS THIS YOUR SORT OF
CHALLENGE?

**If so, complete this coupon and send to:
Mrs. Debbie Teague, PRIME Computer (UK) Ltd.,
Research, Development & Engineering,
FREEPOST, The Merton Centre, St. Peter's Street,
Bedford. MK40 2YR.** (No stamps required)
quoting Ref DOG 83 on the envelope.

Name: _____

Address: _____

_____

Degree: _____

University/College: _____

We will then send you a copy of our Careers
Brochure and an application form. Closing date
for receipt of applications is 28 February 1983.

PR1ME
Computer

Careers in
Research, Development
and Engineering

Scottish Provident Institution 314
UK Provident 353
R Watson & Sons 367

Advertising, public relations
Benton & Bowles Ltd 92
Boase Massimi Pollitt 97
Leo Burnett Ltd 120

Agricultural, fisheries, forestry, horticulture
RHM (Ranks Hovis McDougall plc) 293

Armed services
Regular Army 77
Royal Air Force 301
Royal Navy, Royal Marines & WRNS 305

Aviation
British Airports 104
British Airways 104
Royal Air Force 301

Banking
Bank of Credit & Commerce International
SA 86
Barclays Bank plc Group 88
British Linen Bank Ltd 107
Clydesdale Bank plc 132
Hambros Bank Ltd 190
Industrial & Commercial Finance
Corporation Ltd 204
Lloyds Bank International 394
Lloyds Bank plc 219
Merrill Lynch International 237
Midland Bank plc 244
National Westminster Bank plc 257
NM Rothschild & Sons Ltd 299
J Henry Schroder Wagg & Co Ltd 307
Security Pacific National Bank 315
TSB Group 351
Williams & Glyn's Bank plc 20
Yorkshire Bank plc 374

Broadcasting, TV, films
C & S Antennas 145
Quantel Ltd 287
THORN EMI plc 343

Building, construction
Robert M Douglas Holdings plc 155
French Kier Construction Ltd 172
Kyle Stewart Group 215
FJC Lilley plc 217
Shand Group 320
Taylor Woodrow International Ltd 336

Building society
Bradford & Bingley Building Society 101

Building supplies
Bowater Organisation 100
Marley Group 229
Montague L Meyer plc 240

Charity
Help the Aged 194
Richmond Fellowship Therapeutic
Communities 297
Voluntary Service Overseas 62

Chemical and allied industries
Boehringer Corporation (London) Ltd 98
Air Products plc 70
Alfa-Laval Co Ltd 72
Amersham International plc 72
Boots Co plc 99

John Brown Engineers & Constructors Ltd 116
Burmah Oil plc 118
BXL Plastics Ltd 122
Ciba-Geigy Plastics & Additives Co 126
Davy McKee (London) Ltd 151
Dearborn Chemicals Ltd 152
Dow Corning Ltd 155
Fishburn Printing Ink Co Ltd 168
Foseco Minsep Group 169
Hickson & Welch Ltd 194
Ilford Ltd 200
Johnson Matthey Group 208
Lever Brothers Ltd 216
May & Baker Ltd 235
Rio Tinto Zinc Corporation plc 295
UK Atomic Energy Authority 360
Unilever 355
Wellcome Foundation Ltd 369

Civil service
Civil Service 127
Dept of Industry (Science Group) 154
Government Communications HQ 183
Hong Kong Administrative Class 392
Joint Technical Language Service 209
Meteorological Office 239
Prison Service 279
South African Civil Service 397

Clothing, footwear, leatherwork
C & J Clark Ltd 128
Union International plc 358

Computer hardware, business equipment
Computer Machinery Company (CMC) Ltd 133
Computer Technology Ltd 136
Data Logic Ltd 149
Ferranti plc 167
General Electric Co plc 177
Getty Oil (Britain) Ltd 183
IBM United Kingdom Ltd 199
International Computers Ltd 206
ITT-IDEC 207
Kalamazoo Business Systems 211
Laser-Scan Laboratories Ltd 215
John Menzies (Holdings) plc 235
NCR (Manufacturing) Ltd 258
PMA Consultants Ltd 274
Press Computer Systems Ltd 278
Standard Telephones & Cables plc 328
Systime Ltd 331
Tandy Corporation (Branch UK) 335
Texas Instruments Ltd 338

Computer software
AGB Research Group 70
Barclays Bank plc Group 88
BIS Software Ltd 96
BOC Ltd 98
British Shipbuilders 112
CAP Group Ltd 123
CASE Computer & Systems Engineering
plc 126
Compeda Ltd 135
Data Logic Ltd 149
Easams 58
Eurotherm International 164
Ferranti plc 167
Fraser Williams 171
General Electric Co plc 177
Hawker Siddeley Dynamics Engineering
Ltd 192
Hymans, Robertson & Co 198
IBM United Kingdom Ltd 199
International Computers Ltd 206
ITT-IDEC 207

Laser-Scan Laboratories Ltd 215
Micro Focus Ltd 241
NCR (Manufacturing) Ltd 258
PMA Consultants Ltd 274
Powell Duffryn Systems Ltd 278
Press Computer Systems Ltd 278
Prime Computer (UK) Ltd 438
Scicon 310
SIA Computer Services 321
Software Sciences 323
SPL International 326
Standard Telecommunication Laboratories 328
Systime Ltd 331
THORN EMI plc 343
UK Atomic Energy Authority 360

Consultancy—computer
BIS Applied Systems Ltd 96
Coopers & Lybrand Associates Ltd 141
Easams 58
Fraser Williams 171
Hymans, Robertson & Co 198
IBM United Kingdom Ltd 199
ITT-IDEC 207
Leicestershire County Council 424
Logica Group 220
Mars Group Services 230
PMA Consultants Ltd 274
SIA Computer Services 321
SPL International 326
Timex Corporation 349

Consultancy—engineering
Easams 58
ITT-IDEC 207
Kennedy & Donkin 211
Matthew Hall Group 234
National Maritime Institute 251
NEI Overseas Ltd 395
Ricardo Consulting Engineers 297
Royal Air Force 301
Schlumberger Wireline Logging 396
Scicon 310
UK Atomic Energy Authority 360

Consultancy—management
Arthur Andersen & Co Management
Consultancy Division 74
Association of Cost & Executive
Accountants 379
BIS Applied Systems Ltd 96
Coopers & Lybrand Associates Ltd 141
Easams 58
Hong Kong Administrative Class 392
Institute of Purchasing & Supply 385
Lishman Sidwell Campbell & Price 218
John Menzies (Holdings) plc 235
Nielsen Business Services 259

Cosmetics, toiletries
Beecham Products 91

Economic research
Barclays Bank plc Group 88

Engineering—aeronautical
Bestobell plc 93
Engineering Careers Information Service 24
Fairey Hydraulics Ltd 165
Holset Engineering Co Ltd 195
Rio Tinto Zinc Corporation plc 295
Royal Air Force 301
Royal Electrical & Mechanical Engineers 304
Royal Navy, Royal Marines & WRNS 305
Westland plc 372

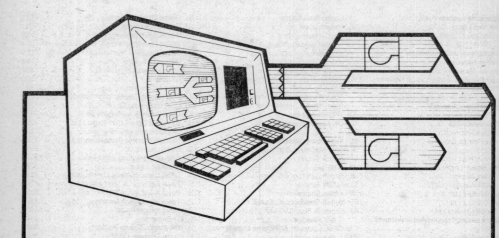

Engineers—A Sales Career

Throughout the building services market we design, sell and maintain control systems for heating and ventilation, security, fire and energy conservation systems.

The Johnson Control Systems operation in the UK is part of the International Division of the parent company which has it's headquarters in Milwaukee, Wisconsin. Established in the UK since 1960, growth has been consistent and has made us a leader in our business in this country as well as world wide.

Our success has been built upon professional engineering expertise applied in the selling environment. We are therefore looking for engineers who wish to train as professionals for a career in selling our systems and products. Training will be provided and will be comprehensive. Particular subject areas which will be considered most relevant are electronic/electrical engineering, computer science or computer engineering.

Future prospects and career development are first rate, with a comprehensive salary and benefits package which is regularly reviewed.

For further information and how to apply please contact Peter Adamson, Training Manager, Johnson Control Systems Limited, PO Box 79, Stonehillgreen, Westlea Down, Swindon, Wiltshire SN5 7DD. Telephone Swindon (0793) 26141.

JOHNSON CONTROLS

Engineering—automotive
Cummins Engine Co Ltd 147
Dunlop 157
Engineering Careers Information Service 24
Holset Engineering Co Ltd 195
Quinton Hazell plc 287
Ricardo Consulting Engineers 297
Royal Electrical & Mechanical Engineers 304
SGRD Ltd 320

Engineering—chemical
Air Products plc 70
Alfa-Laval Co Ltd 72
Babcock International plc 82
Baker Perkins Group of Cos 84
BOC Ltd 98
Brown & Root (UK) Ltd 117
John Brown Engineers & Constructors Ltd 116
Burmah Oil plc 118
Davy McKee (London) Ltd 151
Davy McKee Ltd 150
Dow Corning Ltd 155
Getty Oil (Britain) Ltd 183
Johannesburg Consolidated Investment
Co Ltd 393
Johnson Matthey Group 208
MW Kellogg Ltd 211
McDermott Engineering London 226
SIA Computer Services 321
UK Atomic Energy Authority 360

Engineering—civil and structural
BICC plc 94
British Airports 104
Brown & Root (UK) Ltd 117
Richard Costain plc 142
Davy McKee Ltd 150
Robert M Douglas Holdings plc 155
French Kier Construction Ltd 172
Kyle Stewart Group 215
FJC Lilley plc 217
McDermott Engineering London 226
Edmund Nuttall Group of Cos 263
Shand Group 320
SIA Computer Services 321
Taylor Woodrow International Ltd 336

Engineering–electrical (heavy)
Babcock International plc 82
BICC plc 94
British Airports 104
British Shipbuilders 112
Brown & Root (UK) Ltd 117
Brush Electrical Machines Ltd 118
Davy McKee Ltd 150
Engineering Careers Information Service 24
General Electric Co plc 177
McDermott Engineering London 226
National Nuclear Corporation Ltd 253
NEI Overseas Ltd 395
Royal Corps of Naval Constructors 303
Royal Navy, Royal Marines & WRNS 305
UK Atomic Energy Authority 360

Engineering—electrical (light)
Babcock International plc 82
BICC plc 94
British Aerospace-Dynamics Group 103
British Airports 104
British Shipbuilders 112
British Standards Institution 113
Brown & Root (UK) Ltd 117
C & S Antennas 145
Dunlop 157
Engineering Careers Information Service 24
Eurotherm International 164

Exploration Logging 165
Ferranti plc 167
Four Square 170
General Electric Co plc 177
Gestetner 181
Instron Ltd 205
Lucas Industries plc 224
NEI Overseas Ltd 395
Royal Air Force 301
Royal Corps of Naval Constructors 303
Royal Navy, Royal Marines & WRNS 305
THORN EMI plc 343
UK Atomic Energy Authority 360

Engineering—electronics
Babcock International plc 82
Barr & Stroud 89
BICC plc 94
British Aerospace-Dynamics Group 103
British Airports 104
British Shipbuilders 112
British Standards Institution 113
Brown & Root (UK) Ltd 117
C & S Antennas 145
CASE Computer & Systems Engineering
plc 126
Cossor Electronics Ltd 142
Crosfield Electronics Ltd 145
Davy McKee Ltd 150
Easams 58
Engineering Careers Information Service 24
Eurotherm International 164
Exploration Logging 165
Fairey Hydraulics Ltd 166
Ferranti plc 167
General Electric Co plc 177
Hawker Siddeley Dynamics Engineering
Ltd 192
Holset Engineering Co Ltd 195
Hughes Microelectronics Ltd 197
Instron Ltd 205
International Computers Ltd 206
Kalamazoo Business Systems 211
Lucas Industries plc 224
Micro Consultants Group 243
Microwave Associates Ltd 243
Motorola Ltd 247
National Semiconductor 255
NEI Overseas Ltd 395
Plessey 273
Quantel Ltd 287
Racal Electronics Ltd 288
Royal Air Force 301
Royal Corps of Naval Constructors 303
Royal Electrical & Mechanical Engineers 304
Royal Navy, Royal Marines & WRNS 305
Schlumberger Measurement & Control
(UK) Ltd 309
SIA Computer Services 321
Standard Telecommunication Laboratories 328
Standard Telephones & Cables plc 328
Taylor Instrument Ltd 335
Taylor Instrument Ltd Analytics Division 336
Texas Instruments Ltd 338
THORN EMI plc 343
Timex Corporation 349
UK Atomic Energy Authority 360
VG Isotopes Ltd 362
Weir Pumps Ltd 368

Engineering—mechanical (heavy)
Alfa-Laval Co Ltd 72
Aurora Holdings plc 81
Babcock International plc 82
BOC Ltd 98
British Airports 104

British Shipbuilders 112
British Steel Corporation 115
Brown & Root (UK) Ltd 117
John Brown Engineers & Constructors Ltd 116
Brush Electrical Machines Ltd 118
Burmah Oil plc 118
Coles Cranes Ltd 133
Davy McKee (London) Ltd 151
Davy McKee Ltd 150
Engineering Careers Information Service 24
General Electric Co plc 177
Guest Keen & Nettlefolds plc 187
NEI International Combustion Ltd 205
McDermott Engineering London 226
National Nuclear Corporation Ltd 253
NEI Overseas Ltd 395
Ricardo Consulting Engineers 297
Royal Air Force 301
Royal Corps of Naval Constructors 303
Royal Electrical & Mechanical Engineers 304
Royal Navy, Royal Marines & WRNS 305
Taylor Woodrow International Ltd 336
NEI Thompson Ltd 342
TI Group plc 347
UK Atomic Energy Authority 360
Vetco Offshore Ltd 362
Weir Pumps Ltd 368

Engineering—mechanical (light)
AE Group 69
APV Co Ltd 75
Aurora Holdings plc 81
Babcock International plc 82
Baker Perkins Group of Cos 84
Barr & Stroud 89
Bestobell plc 93
BICC plc 94
British Aerospace-Dynamics Group 103
British Airports 104
British Standards Institution 113
Brown & Root (UK) Ltd 117
Dunlop 157
Engineering Careers Information Service 24
Eurotherm International 164
Fairey Hydraulics Ltd 165
Ferranti plc 167
Four Square 170
General Electric Co plc 177
Gestetner 181
Holset Engineering Co Ltd 195
Instron Ltd 205
Johnson Matthey Group 208
Lucas Industries plc 224
Metal Box plc 238
NEI Overseas Ltd 395
Perkins Engines Ltd 270
Ricardo Consulting Engineers 297
Royal Air Force 301
Royal Navy, Royal Marines & WRNS 305
Taylor Instrument Ltd Analytics Division 336
NEI Thompson Ltd 342
THORN EMI plc 343
TI Group plc 347
Timex Corporation 349
Victor Products (Wallsend) plc 363
Weir Pumps Ltd 368

**Financial services (exc banking, accounting,
insurance)**
Bradford & Bingley Building Society 101
Getty Oil (Britain) Ltd 183
Industrial & Commercial Finance
Corporation Ltd 204
Merrill Lynch International 237
Murray Noble 249
Rowe & Pitman 300

Protech International.

The name to remember in oil and gas engineering

Protech International was formed in Holland in 1964 to provide engineering and construction management services to the oil/gas production industries.

Protech commenced operations in Holland as a wholly owned subsidiary of the VMF-Stork Group of engineering companies, an organisation with over 20,000 employees. The need to provide direct on the spot services has led to the opening of further offices in London, Singapore, Abu Dhabi and Houston.

A highly specialised technical staff form the basis for providing a complete engineering service for onshore and offshore oil and gas production and transportation systems.

Protech International (UK) Ltd.,
Pheonix House, The Green,
Southall, Middx. UB2 4BZ.

||||| Protech
International

ave & Prosper Group	306	Sun Life Assurance plc	332	Esso Group of Cos	163
t Watson & Sons	367	UK Provident	353	Exploration Logging	165
				Flopetrol International SA	390
ood, drink, tobacco industry		**Legal and patent work**		Gardline Surveys	177
PV Co Ltd	75	Trower, Still & Keeling	351	Getty Oil (Britain) Ltd	183
ssociated British Foods plc	80			MW Kellogg Ltd	211
eecham Products	91	**Leisure industry**		Lummus Co Ltd	225
ritish Sugar plc	115	Dunlop	157	Mobil Oil Co Ltd	247
adbury Schweppes	122	THORN EMI plc	343	Schlumberger Wireline Logging	396
our Square	170	YMCA	373	Vetco Offshore Ltd	362
allaher Ltd	175				
mperial Brewing & Leisure Ltd	201	**Local government**		**Paints and industrial finishes**	
Mars Ltd (Confectionery Division)	230	Accountancy & Financial Management in		Fishburn Printing Ink Co Ltd	168
Nielsen Business Services	259	the Public Sector	68		
Northern Foods plc	260	Association of Cost & Executive		**Paper and packaging**	
edigree Petfoods	269	Accountants	379	General Mining Union Corp Ltd (Gencor)	391
HM (Ranks Hovis McDougall plc)	293	Chartered Institute of Public Finance &		Gestetner	181
nigate plc	357	Accountancy	379	Jefferson Smurfit Group	322
nilever	355	Greater London Council	185		
nilever Research	355	Leicestershire County Council	424	**Pharmaceuticals**	
nion International plc	358	Trading Standards Officers	349	Abbott Laboratories Ltd	68
nited Biscuits (UK) plc	358			Alfa-Laval Co Ltd	72
atney Mann & Truman Brewers Ltd	367	**Machine tools**		Beecham Pharmaceuticals	90
		THORN EMI plc	343	Boots Co plc	99
urniture and timber				May & Baker Ltd	235
Mallinson-Denny Ltd	227	**Market research, marketing**		Merck, Sharp & Dohme Ltd	236
Montague L Meyer plc	240	AGB Research Group	70	Pfizer Ltd	271
Moores Furniture Group	248	Beecham Products	91	ER Squibb & Sons plc	328
		Institute of Marketing	385	Wellcome Foundation Ltd	369
eophysical exploration		Mars Group Services	230		
urmah Oil plc	118	Nielsen Business Services	259	**Photographic goods/materials manufacture**	
ardline Surveys	177	Research Bureau Ltd	291	Ilford Ltd	200
eophysical Service International	180	Taylor Instrument Ltd Analytics Division	336		
etty Oil (Britain) Ltd	183			**Plastics, polymers, rubber**	
orizon Exploration Ltd	195	**Medical and health care products**		BXL Plastics Ltd	122
chlumberger Wireline Logging	396	Boehringer Corporation (London) Ltd	98	Dunlop	157
eiscom Delta United	316	Beecham Products	91	Mallinson-Denny Ltd	227
eismograph Service Ltd	317			Marley Group	229
estern Geophysical Co of America	371	**Metal goods manufacture**		Michelin Tyre plc	241
		Aurora Holdings plc	81	Raychem	291
lass, ceramics		Dunlop	157	Standard Telecommunication Laboratories	328
arr & Stroud	89	Johnson Matthey Group	208	James Walker Group of Cos	366
ilkington Brothers plc	272	Rio Tinto Zinc Corporation plc	295		
		THORN EMI plc	343	**Power (gas, electricity, nuclear etc)**	
otels, catering, restaurants				Alfa-Laval Co Ltd	72
our Square	170	**Metal producers, processors, refiners**		British Gas Corporation	106
mperial Brewing & Leisure Ltd	201	Aurora Holdings plc	81	British Nuclear Fuels Ltd	109
McDonald's Golden Arches Restaurants		British Steel Corporation	115	General Electric Co plc	177
Ltd	226	Foseco Minsep Group	169	UK Atomic Energy Authority	360
HORN EMI plc	343	Johannesburg Consolidated Investment			
MCA	373	Co Ltd	393	**Professional body/trade association**	
		Johnson Matthey Group	208	Accountancy & Financial Management in	
nsurance		Rio Tinto Zinc Corporation plc	295	the Public Sector	68
T Bowring & Co Ltd	100			Association of Certified Accountants	378
lerical Medical & General Life Assurance		**Mining and extractive industries**		Association of Cost & Executive	
Society	131	Anglo American Corporation of South		Accountants	379
o-operative Insurance Society Ltd	139	Africa Ltd	388	Chartered Institute of Public Finance &	
rown Life	143	Consolidated Gold Fields plc	388	Accountancy	379
ndsleigh Insurance Services	159	General Mining Union Corp Ltd (Gencor)	391	Incorporated Society of Valuers &	
quity & Law Life Assurance Society plc	160	Johannesburg Consolidated Investment		Auctioneers	379
riends' Provident Life Office	173	Co Ltd	393	Institute of Chartered Accountants in	
uardian Royal Exchange Assurance plc	186	National Coal Board	251	England & Wales	380
mperial Life Assurance Co of Canada	203	Zambia Consolidated Copper Mines Ltd	398	Institute of Chartered Secretaries &	
Murray Noble	249			Administrators	382
National Mutual Life Association of		**News agency**		Institute of Marketing	385
Australasia Ltd	252	Reuters	292	Institution of Electrical Engineers	204
National Provident Institution	254				
Norwich Union Insurance Group	262	**Oil and petroleum industry**		**Public services**	
earl Assurance plc	265	Analysts Schlumberger	73	Accountancy & Financial Management in	
rovidence Capitol Life Assurance Co Ltd	284	British National Oil Corporation	107	the Public Sector	68
rovident Life Association of London Ltd	284	Brown & Root (UK) Ltd	117	Association of Cost & Executive	
rudential Assurance Co Ltd	285	John Brown Engineers & Constructors Ltd	116	Accountants	379
Royal Insurance	50	Burmah Oil plc	118	British Transport Police	36
cottish Equitable Life Assurance Society	313	Conoco Group in the UK	137	Chartered Institute of Public Finance &	
tewart Wrightson	330	Davy McKee (London) Ltd	151	Accountancy	379
Sun Life Assurance Co of Canada	334	Dowell Schlumberger	389	Greater London Council	185

COMMUNITY TRANSPORT

The School House,
6 Cambrian Street,
Beswick,
Manchester M11.

061 273 4645

Dear Friend,

We want to interest you in Community Transport so that you might consider volunteering to work with us.

C.T. has six projects in the North and Midlands, running lorries and minibuses for community benefit. We collect and deliver furniture to families in need, transport goods for voluntary groups and carry pensioners, childminders, youth clubs and handicapped people in our minibuses. We also help other organisations with their vehicles, run a garage and an information service.

Volunteers live communally in a project house, receiving £12 per week (rise expected) pocket money above full board. The work is hard and rewarding — many past volunteers maintain contacts with the projects. Volunteers play a full part in managing and developing the projects, and involve themselves with other groups in the community. The experience of inner city poverty leads some volunteers into community or social work jobs.

We are looking for people who feel that they can contribute positively to this developing field, ideally aged over 21 with a clean driving licence. We like potential volunteers to visit one of the projects to get a realistic picture of what we do, so if this has interested you, then contact us and we'll arrange a visit.

Community Transport

Registered Charity No. 247331

Hong Kong Administrative Class 392
London Fire Brigade 222
National Bus Co 249
Police Service in England & Wales 275
Post Office 276
Royal Hong Kong Police Force 395
Scottish Special Housing Association 314
Trading Standards Officers 349
West Midlands Fire Service 370

Publishing and printing
AGB Research Group 70
Crosfield Electronics Ltd 145
Haymarket Publishing Group 193
Institution of Electrical Engineers 204
VNU Business Publications BV 365

Retail, wholesale and distribution
Associated British Foods plc 80
BHS (British Home Stores) plc 94
Burmah Oil plc 118
Fenwick Ltd 166
Guest Keen & Nettlefolds plc 187
Habitat 188
Lex Service Group plc 216
Littlewoods Organisation plc 218
Marks & Spencer plc 228
John Menzies (Holdings) plc 235
Newey & Eyre Group Ltd 258
Quinton Hazell plc 287
Miss Selfridge Ltd 318
Selfridges Ltd 319
Tandy Corporation (Branch UK) 335

THORN EMI plc 343
Union International plc 358
Waitrose Ltd 365

Scientific research
Barr & Stroud 89
British Ship Research Association 111
Daresbury Laboratory 148
May & Baker Ltd 235
Meteorological Office 239
National Maritime Institute 251
VG Isotopes Ltd 362

Shipbuilding
British Ship Research Association 111
British Shipbuilders 112
Royal Corps of Naval Constructors 303

Social and community services (statutory and voluntary)
Richmond Fellowship Therapeutic Communities 297
Voluntary Service Overseas 62
YMCA 373

Surveying, estate management and architecture
Incorporated Society of Valuers & Auctioneers 379
Knight Frank & Rutley 214

Telecommunications
British Standards Institution 113
C & S Antennas 145

Cossor Electronics Ltd 142
Ferranti plc 167
General Electric Co plc 177
Government Communications HQ 183
ITT-IDEC 207
Microwave Associates Ltd 243
Prime Computer (UK) Ltd 438
Standard Telecommunication Laboratories 328
Standard Telephones & Cables plc 328
THORN EMI plc 343

Textiles
Milliken Industrials Ltd 245
Scapa Group plc 310

Transport services
Bowater Organisation 100
British Airways 104
Cleanaway 130
Lex Service Group plc 216
London Transport 222
National Bus Co 249
Unigate plc 357
Union International plc 358

Travel, tourism
British Airways 104

Vehicle manufacture
Ford Motor Co Ltd 169
General Motors Ltd 179

Water and drainage services
Babcock International plc 82

Degree subject index

This index lists employers under specific degree subjects where these are absolutely essential to the jobs offered. Where a particular degree is required for entry to a profession the relevant professional body or trade association is listed.

Any degree subject	447	
Accountancy	449	
Actuarial science	449	
Aeronautical engineering	449	
Agricultural engineering	451	
Agricultural science	451	
Applied industrial chemistry	451	
Applied physics	451	
Architecture	451	
Automobile engineering	451	
Bacteriology	451	
Biochemistry	451	
Biology	451	
Botany	451	
Brewing	451	
Building technology	451	
Business studies	451	
Ceramics	451	
Chemical engineering	451	
Chemistry	453	
Civil and structural engineering	453	
Communication engineering	453	
Computer engineering	453	
Computer science	453	
Construction engineering	455	
Control engineering	455	
Cybernetics	455	
Economics	455	

Electrical engineering	455	
Electronic engineering	457	
Engineering	457	
Engineering science	457	
Environmental control	457	
Environmental and earth sciences	457	
Environmental engineering	457	
Ergonomics	457	
Estate management and land economics	458	
Food science/dietetics	458	
Food technology	458	
Fuel science	458	
Gas engineering	458	
Geology	458	
Geophysics	458	
Geotechnical engineering	458	
Glass technology	458	
Hotel and catering management	458	
Hydraulic engineering	458	
Instrument engineering	458	
Librarianship/information science	458	
Law	458	
Materials science/technology	458	
Mathematical physics	458	
Mathematics	458	
Mechanical engineering	459	
Medicine and health studies	459	

Metallurgy	459	
Meteorology	459	
Microbiology	459	
Mineral processing and technology	459	
Mining	461	
Modern languages	461	
Naval architecture/marine engineering	461	
Oceanography	461	
Oil technology	461	
Operational research	461	
Paper science	461	
Personnel	461	
Pharmacology	461	
Pharmacy	461	
Physics	461	
Polymers	461	
Production engineering	461	
Psychology	463	
Quantity surveying	463	
Rubber technology	463	
Sociology, social work/studies	463	
Statistics	463	
Surveying	463	
Textile engineering/technology	463	
Transportation engineering	463	

Any degree subject

Accountancy & Financial Management in the Public Sector	
AGB Research Group	68
Arthur Andersen & Co	70
Arthur Andersen & Co Management Consultancy Division	74
Armitage & Norton	74
BIS Software Ltd	76
Regular Army	77
Arthur Young McClelland Moores & Co	79
Associated British Foods plc	80
Association of Certified Accountants	378
Baker Rooke	85
John Baker, Sons & Bell	83
Bank of Credit & Commerce International SA	86

Bank of Scotland	87
Barclays Bank plc Group	88
Beecham Products	91
Benton & Bowles Ltd	92
BHS (British Home Stores) plc	94
BICC plc	94
Binder Hamlyn	95
BIS Software Ltd	96
Boase Massimi Pollitt	97
Boots Co plc	99
CT Bowring & Co Ltd	100
Bradford & Bingley Building Society	101
Brebner, Allen & Trapp	101
Brewer & Co	102
Brian Ingram Associates	102
British Airports	104

British Airways	104
British Gas Corporation	106
British Linen Bank Ltd	107
British Rail	111
British Steel Corporation	115
British Transport Police	36
Burmah Oil plc	118
Leo Burnett Ltd	120
Buzzacott & Co	121
C & J Clark Ltd	128
C & S Antennas	145
CAP Group Ltd	123
Casson Beckman	125
Chartered Institute of Public Finance & Accountancy	379
Clark Pixley	129

Clerical Medical & General Life Assurance Society 131
Clydesdale Bank plc 132
Coopers & Lybrand 140
Coopers & Lybrand Associates Ltd 141
Cummins Engine Co Ltd 147
Davy McKee (London) Ltd 151
Dearden Farrow 152
Deloitte Haskins & Sells 153
Endsleigh Insurance Services 159
Equity & Law Life Assurance Society plc 160
Ernst & Whinney 161
Esso Group of Cos 163
Fenwick Ltd 166
Finnie Ross Allfields 168
Ford Motor Co Ltd 169
Four Square 170
Fraser Keen 171
Fryer Whitehill & Co 174
Gallaher Ltd 175
Gestetner 181
Government Communications HQ 183
Greater London Council 185
Guardian Royal Exchange Assurance plc 186
Habitat 188
Hacker Young 189
Hambros Bank Ltd 190
HAT Accountancy Training Syndicate 191
Haymarket Publishing Group 193
Help the Aged 194
Hong Kong Administrative Class 392
Hughes Allen Payne Stone 198
IBM United Kingdom Ltd 199
Imperial Brewing & Leisure Ltd 201
Incorporated Society of Valuers & Auctioneers 379
Institute of Chartered Accountants of Scotland 381
Institute of Chartered Accountants in England & Wales 380
Institute of Chartered Secretaries & Administrators 382
Institute of Cost & Management Accountants 383
Institute of Marketing 385
Institute of Purchasing & Supply 385
Institution of Electrical Engineers 204
International Computers Ltd 206
Kidsons 213
Knill Padgham & Grande 214
Leicestershire County Council 424
Lex Service Group plc 216
Littlewoods Organisation plc 218
Lloyds Bank International 394
Lloyds Bank plc 219
London Fire Brigade 222
London Transport 222
Longcrofts 223
Lucas Industries plc 224
Marks & Spencer plc 228
Marley Group 229
Mars Group Services 230
Mars Ltd (Confectionery Division) 230
McDonald's Golden Arches Restaurants Ltd 226
Merck, Sharp & Dohme Ltd 236
Metal Box plc 238
Montague L Meyer plc 240
Midland Bank plc 244
Mobil Oil Co Ltd 247
Morgan Brown & Haynes 249
Murray Noble 249
National Bus Co 249
National Coal Board 251
National Westminster Bank plc 257
Newey & Eyre Group Ltd 258

Nielsen Business Services 259
Norris Gilbert Stern & Co 259
Northern Foods plc 260
Pannell Kerr Forster 263
Pearl Assurance plc 265
Peat Marwick Mitchell & Co 267
Pedigree Petfoods 269
Perkins Engines Ltd 270
Pilkington Brothers plc 272
Police Service in England & Wales 275
Post Office 276
Powell Duffryn Systems Ltd 278
Press Computer Systems Ltd 278
Prison Service 279
Provident Life Association of London Ltd 284
Reuters 292
RHM (Ranks Hovis McDougall plc) 293
Richmond Fellowship Therapeutic Communities 297
Robson Rhodes 298
NM Rothschild & Sons Ltd 299
Rowe & Pitman 300
Rowland Nevill & Co 301
Royal Hong Kong Police Force 395
Royal Insurance 50
Royal Navy, Royal Marines & WRNS 305
Save & Prosper Group 306
J Henry Schroder Wagg & Co Ltd 307
Scottish Equitable Life Assurance Society 313
Scottish Special Housing Association 314
Security Pacific National Bank 315
Miss Selfridge Ltd 318
Silver Altman & Co 321
Smallfield Fitzhugh Tillet & Co 322
Software Sciences 323
Spicer & Pegler 325
ER Squibb & Sons plc 328
Standard Telephones & Cables plc 328
Stewart Wrightson 330
Stoy Hayward & Co 331
Tandy Corporation (Branch UK) 335
Thomson McLintock & Co 341
THORN EMI plc 343
Thornton Baker 346
TI Group plc 347
Timex Corporation 349
Touche Ross & Co 350
Trower, Still & Keeling 351
TSB Group 351
UK Atomic Energy Authority 360
Unigate plc 357
Unilever 355
Union International plc 358
United Biscuits (UK) plc 365
VNU Business Publications BV 367
Watney Mann & Truman Brewers Ltd 367
R Watson & Sons 367
West Midlands Fire Service 370
Westland plc 372
Williams & Glyn's Bank plc 20
Wilson Green Gibbs 373
Yorkshire Bank plc 374

Accountancy
Accountancy & Financial Management in the Public Sector 68
Air Products plc 70
Armitage & Norton 76
Arthur Young McClelland Moores & Co 79
Association of Cost & Executive Accountants 379
Babcock International plc 82
Bowater Organisation 100
Brewer & Son 102
Brian Ingram Associates 102
British Steel Corporation 115

CAP Group Ltd 123
Chartered Institute of Public Finance & Accountancy 379
Coles Cranes Ltd 133
Conoco Group in the UK 137
Coopers & Lybrand Associates Ltd 141
Dunlop 157
Ernst & Whinney 161
Finnie Ross Allfields 168
Fryer Whitehill & Co 174
Gestetner 181
Getty Oil (Britain) Ltd 183
Hacker Young 189
Haines Watts 189
HAT Accountancy Training Syndicate 191
Hughes Allen Payne Stone 198
Hughes Microelectronics Ltd 197
Industrial & Commercial Finance Corporation Ltd 204
Johnson Matthey Group 208
Kalamazoo Business Systems 211
Knill Padgham & Grande 214
Leicestershire County Council 424
Lishman Sidwell Campbell & Price 218
Lloyds Bank International 394
Longcrofts 223
Lummus Co Ltd 225
John Menzies (Holdings) plc 235
Milliken Industrials Ltd 245
Moores Furniture Group 248
National Bus Co 249
National Coal Board 251
National Provident Institution 254
Norris Gilbert Stern & Co 259
Northern Foods plc 260
Norwich Union Insurance Group 262
Pilkington Brothers plc 272
Prudential Assurance Co Ltd 285
Royal Insurance 50
Silver Altman & Co 321
Spicer & Pegler 325
Stanley A Spofforth & Co 327
Thomson McLintock & Co 341
THORN EMI plc 343
Touche Ross & Co 350
UK Atomic Energy Authority 360
Unilever 355
Watney Mann & Truman Brewers Ltd 367
Wellcome Foundation Ltd 369
Westland plc 372
Wilson Green Gibbs 373

Actuarial science
Brian Ingram Associates 102
Clerical Medical & General Life Assurance Society 131
Co-operative Insurance Society Ltd 139
Crown Life 143
Friends' Provident Life Office 173
Hymans, Robertson & Co 198
National Mutual Life Association of Australasia Ltd 252
National Provident Institution 254
Pearl Assurance plc 265
Providence Capitol Life Assurance Co Ltd 284
Provident Life Association of London Ltd 284
Prudential Assurance Co Ltd 285
Royal Insurance 50
Save & Prosper Group 306
Sun Life Assurance plc 332
UK Provident 353
R Watson & Sons 367

Aeronautical engineering
British Aerospace-Dynamics Group 103
Civil Service 127

Dowty Group Ltd	159
Easams	58
Engineering Careers Information Service	24
Fairey Hydraulics Ltd	165
Holset Engineering Co Ltd	195
Michelin Tyre plc	241
National Maritime Institute	251
Royal Electrical & Mechanical Engineers	304
SIA Computer Services	321
Westland plc	372

Agricultural engineering

Civil Service	127
Voluntary Service Overseas	62

Agricultural science

Civil Service	127
May & Baker Ltd	235
RHM (Ranks Hovis McDougall plc)	293
Voluntary Service Overseas	62

Applied industrial chemistry

British National Oil Corporation	107
British Nuclear Fuels Ltd	109
Civil Service	127
Dearborn Chemicals Ltd	152
Fishburn Printing Ink Co Ltd	168
Ilford Ltd	200
ITT-IDEC	207
Johnson Matthey Group	208
May & Baker Ltd	235
Milliken Industrials Ltd	245
National Coal Board	251
Raychem	291
THORN EMI plc	343
UK Atomic Energy Authority	360

Applied physics

Barr & Stroud	89
British Aerospace-Dynamics Group	103
British National Oil Corporation	107
British Nuclear Fuels Ltd	109
British Shipbuilders	112
Civil Service	127
Cossor Electronics Ltd	142
Crosfield Electronics Ltd	145
Daresbury Laboratory	148
Dept of Industry (Science Group)	154
Ferranti plc	167
Geophysical Service International	180
Gestetner	181
Government Communications HQ	183
Hawker Siddeley Dynamics Engineering Ltd	192
Horizon Exploration Ltd	195
Hughes Microelectronics Ltd	197
Ilford Ltd	200
Johnson Matthey Group	208
Motorola Ltd	247
National Maritime Institute	251
National Semiconductor	255
Perkins Engines Ltd	270
Pilkington Brothers plc	272
Raychem	291
Schlumberger Measurement & Control (UK) Ltd	309
Schlumberger Wireline Logging	396
Standard Telecommunication Laboratories	328
Standard Telephones & Cables plc	328
Taylor Instrument Ltd Analytics Division	336
THORN EMI plc	343
Trading Standards Officers	349
UK Atomic Energy Authority	360
VG Isotopes Ltd	362
Westland plc	372

Architecture

Prudential Assurance Co Ltd	285

Automobile engineering

Cummins Engine Co Ltd	147
Dunlop	157
Engineering Careers Information Service	24
Ford Motor Co Ltd	169
Holset Engineering Co Ltd	195
Ricardo Consulting Engineers	297
Royal Electrical & Mechanical Engineers	304

Bacteriology

Civil Service	127
Pfizer Ltd	271
Unilever Research	355

Biochemistry

Boehringer Corporation (London) Ltd	98
Amersham International plc	72
APV Co Ltd	75
Beecham Pharmaceuticals	90
Boots Co plc	99
Civil Service	127
Dearborn Chemicals Ltd	152
May & Baker Ltd	235
Merck, Sharp & Dohme Ltd	236
Northern Foods plc	260
Pfizer Ltd	271
RHM (Ranks Hovis McDougall plc)	293
ER Squibb & Sons plc	328
Unilever Research	355
Wellcome Foundation Ltd	369

Biology

Associated British Foods plc	80
Beecham Pharmaceuticals	90
Civil Service	127
Mallinson-Denny Ltd	227
May & Baker Ltd	235
Merck, Sharp & Dohme Ltd	236
ER Squibb & Sons plc	328
Trading Standards Officers	349
Unilever Research	355
Voluntary Service Overseas	62
Wellcome Foundation Ltd	369

Botany

Civil Service	127
Mallinson-Denny Ltd	227
May & Baker Ltd	235

Brewing

Alfa-Laval Co Ltd	72
Imperial Brewing & Leisure Ltd	201
Watney Mann & Truman Brewers Ltd	367

Building technology

Richard Costain plc	142
Robert M Douglas Holdings plc	155
French Kier Construction Ltd	172
FJC Lilley plc	217
National Coal Board	251
Taylor Woodrow International Ltd	336

Business studies

Accountancy & Financial Management in the Public Sector	68
Air Products plc	70
Beecham Products	91
Bestobell plc	93
Bowater Organisation	100
Bradford & Bingley Building Society	101
Brian Ingram Associates	102
British Aerospace-Dynamics Group	103
British National Oil Corporation	107

British Steel Corporation	115
BXL Plastics Ltd	122
CAP Group Ltd	123
Chartered Institute of Public Finance & Accountancy	379
Cleanaway	130
Coles Cranes Ltd	133
Conoco Group in the UK	137
Cossor Electronics Ltd	142
Crosfield Electronics Ltd	145
Data Logic Ltd	149
Dunlop	157
Engineering Careers Information Service	24
Eurotherm International	164
Finnie Ross Allfields	168
Friends' Provident Life Office	173
Hacker Young	189
Haines Watts	189
Imperial Brewing & Leisure Ltd	201
Industrial & Commercial Finance Corporation Ltd	204
Institute of Marketing	385
Johnson Matthey Group	208
Leicestershire County Council	424
Lloyds Bank International	394
Mallinson-Denny Ltd	227
Marley Group	229
Merrill Lynch International	237
Micro Focus Ltd	241
Milliken Industrials Ltd	245
Moores Furniture Group	248
National Provident Institution	254
Newey & Eyre Group Ltd	258
Nielsen Business Services	259
Norris Gilbert Stern & Co	259
Norwich Union Insurance Group	262
Pilkington Brothers plc	272
Prudential Assurance Co Ltd	285
Quinton Hazell plc	287
Research Bureau Ltd	291
Royal Insurance	50
Scapa Group plc	310
Selfridges Ltd	319
Shand Group	320
Jefferson Smurfit Group	322
Stanley A Spofforth & Co	327
Standard Telephones & Cables plc	328
Staveley Industries plc	329
Sun Life Assurance plc	332
Systime Ltd	331
Tandy Corporation (Branch UK)	335
Texas Instruments Ltd	338
NEI Thompson Ltd	342
THORN EMI plc	343
Timex Corporation	349
Voluntary Service Overseas	62
Wellcome Foundation Ltd	369
Westland plc	372
Yorkshire Bank plc	374

Ceramics

Raychem	291
Standard Telecommunication Laboratories	328

Chemical engineering

Air Products Ltd	70
Alfa-Laval Co Ltd	72
APV Co plc	75
Babcock International plc	82
Baker Perkins Group of Cos	84
Beecham Pharmaceuticals	90
BOC Ltd	98
British National Oil Corporation	107
British Nuclear Fuels Ltd	109
British Steel Corporation	115
British Sugar plc	115

DEGREE SUBJECT INDEX 451

The appointments system that beats the system

Finding the right job can all too easily become more a test of your endurance rather than your capabilities.

In fact, you could be forgiven for thinking the entire recruitment system is geared to work against you.

Those attractive, well-paid positions that feature strongly on the appointments pages more often than not fall far short of your expectations. Or else they're already inexplicably filled. You spend a small fortune on phone calls, postage, stationery and travel expenses. And then there's the big question of your time . . . .

We're well aware of all the difficulties. Working with 3,000 UK client companies and thousands of ambitious people in every professional field has given us a full appreciation of the problems – and led us to evolve the definitive recruitment solution. The Lansdowne Appointments Register.

Whatever your degree discipline, it could now enable you to bypass completely the usual long drawn out applications and interview procedures – and get the kind of position you're looking for in record time, and with minimum hassle.

Speed is of the essence. Contact us immediately for our concise Confidential Career Summary Form, to be completed in your own time.

Once we have your details we'll see to it that they're put in front of interested employers the instant a suitable opening arises. From this point, the companies will get in touch with you directly.

What could be simpler?

Or more effective?

Write or telephone:
Stuart Tait,
Lansdowne Appointments Register,
Park House, 207 The Vale, Acton, London W3 7QB
Telephone: 01-743 6321 (24 hour answering service)

...wn & Root (UK) Ltd	117
...n Brown Engineers & Constructors Ltd	116
...rmah Oil plc	118
...L Plastics Ltd	122
...a-Geigy Plastics & Additives Co	126
...il Service	127
...anaway	130
...mpeda Ltd	135
...noco Group in the UK	137
...nsolidated Gold Fields plc	388
...vy McKee (London) Ltd	151
...vy McKee Ltd	150
...arborn Chemicals Ltd	152
...pt of Industry (Science Group)	154
...well Schlumberger	389
...o Group of Cos	163
...petrol International SA	390
...seco Minsep Group	169
...neral Mining Union Corp Ltd (Gencor)	391
...ckson & Welch Ltd	194
...anson Matthey Group	208
...W Kellogg Ltd	211
...er Brothers Ltd	216
...mmus Co Ltd	225
...Dermott Engineering London	226
...tthew Hall Group	234
...y & Baker Ltd	235
...bil Oil Co Ltd	247
...tional Coal Board	251
...rthern Foods plc	260
...zer Ltd	271
...kington Brothers plc	272
...ychem	291
...M (Ranks Hovis McDougall plc)	293
... Tinto Zinc Corporation plc	295
...rlor Instrument Ltd	335
... Atomic Energy Authority	360
...ilever	355
...ilever Research	355
...llcome Foundation Ltd	369
...mbia Consolidated Copper Mines Ltd	398

...emistry

...bott Laboratories Ltd	68
...ersham International plc	72
...sociated British Foods plc	80
...echam Pharmaceuticals	90
...ots Co plc	99
...tish National Oil Corporation	107
...tish Nuclear Fuels Ltd	109
...tish Standards Institution	113
...tish Steel Corporation	115
...rmah Oil plc	118
...L Plastics Ltd	122
...a-Geigy Plastics & Additives Co	126
...il Service	127
...eanaway	130
...arborn Chemicals Ltd	152
...pt of Industry (Science Group)	154
...w Corning Ltd	155
...well Schlumberger	389
...so Group of Cos	163
...shburn Printing Ink Co Ltd	
...seco Minsep Group	169
...neral Electric Co Ltd	177
...neral Mining Union Corp Ltd (Gencor)	391
...stetner	181
...ckson & Welch Ltd	194
...ughes Microelectronics Ltd	197
...ord Ltd	200
...T-IDEC	207
...hnson Matthey Group	208
...ver Brothers Ltd	216
...gica Group	220
...ay & Baker Ltd	235

Merck, Sharp & Dohme Ltd	236
Metal Box plc	238
Milliken Industrials Ltd	245
Mobil Oil Co Ltd	247
National Coal Board	251
National Semiconductor	255
Pfizer Ltd	271
Pilkington Brothers plc	272
Raychem	291
RHM (Ranks Hovis McDougall plc)	293
Rio Tinto Zinc Corporation plc	295
Standard Telecommunication Laboratories	328
THORN EMI plc	343
Trading Standards Officers	349
UK Atomic Energy Authority	360
Unilever Reserach	355
Voluntary Service Overseas	62
James Walker Group of Cos	366
Wellcome Foundation Ltd	369

Civil and structural engineering

British Airports	104
British National Oil Corporation	107
Brown & Root (UK) Ltd	117
John Brown Engineers & Constructors Ltd	116
Civil Service	127
Cleanaway	130
Richard Costain plc	142
Davy McKee Ltd	150
Robert M Douglas Holdings plc	155
French Kier Construction Ltd	172
MW Kellogg Ltd	211
Kyle Stewart Group	215
FJC Lilley plc	217
Lummus Co Ltd	225
McDermott Engineering London	226
Matthew Hall Group	234
Michelin Tyre plc	241
Edmund Nuttall Group of Cos	263
Shand Group	320
SIA Computer Services	321
South African Civil Service	397
Taylor Woodrow International Ltd	336
Voluntary Service Overseas	62

Communication engineering

British Aerospace-Dynamics Group	103
CAP Group Ltd	123
Civil Service	127
Cossor Electronics Ltd	142
Engineering Careers Information Service	24
Ferranti plc	167
Ford Motor Co Ltd	169
General Electric Co plc	177
Government Communications HQ	183
International Computers Ltd	206
ITT-IDEC	207
Leicestershire County Council	424
Prime Computer (UK) Ltd	438
Scicon	310
Standard Telecommunication Laboratories	328
THORN EMI plc	343

Computer engineering

British Steel Corporation	115
CAP Group Ltd	123
CASE Computer & Systems Engineering plc	126
Civil Service	127
Computer Technology Ltd	136
Crosfield Electronics Ltd	145
Dow Corning Ltd	155
Engineering Careers Information Service	24
Eurotherm International	164
Ferranti plc	167
Ford Motor Co Ltd	169

General Electric Co plc	177
Hawker Siddeley Dynamics Engineering Ltd	192
International Computers Ltd	206
ITT-IDEC	207
Kalamazoo Business Systems	211
Logica Group	220
Micro Focus Ltd	241
National Coal Board	251
Prime Computer (UK) Ltd	438
Raychem	291
Standard Telephones & Cables plc	328
Taylor Instrument Ltd	335
THORN EMI plc	343

Computer science

Air Products plc	70
APV Co Ltd	75
Babcock International plc	82
BIS Applied Systems Ltd	96
BOC Ltd	98
British Aerospace-Dynamics Group	103
British National Oil Corporation	107
British Nuclear Fuels Ltd	109
British Ship Research Association	111
British Shipbuilders	112
British Steel Corporation	115
Brown & Root (UK) Ltd	117
Brush Electrical Machines Ltd	118
CAP Group Ltd	123
CASE Computer & Systems Engineering plc	126
Civil Service	127
Compeda Ltd	135
Computer Machinery Company (CMC) Ltd	133
Computer Technology Ltd	136
Conoco Group in the UK	137
Coopers & Lybrand Associates Ltd	141
Crosfield Electronics Ltd	145
Daresbury Laboratory	148
Data Logic Ltd	149
Dept of Industry (Science Group)	154
Dunlop	157
Easams	58
Eurotherm International	164
Ferranti plc	167
Finnie Ross Allfields	168
Ford Motor Co Ltd	169
Fraser Williams	171
French Kier Construction Ltd	172
Gardline Surveys	177
General Electric Co plc	177
General Mining Union Corp Ltd (Gencor)	391
Getty Oil (Britain) Ltd	183
Government Communications HQ	183
Hawker Siddeley Dynamics Engineering Ltd	192
Horizon Exploration Ltd	195
Hymans, Robertson & Co	198
Institution of Electrical Engineers	204
International Computers Ltd	206
ITT-IDEC	207
Johnson Matthey Group	208
Laser-Scan Laboratories Ltd	215
Leicestershire County Council	424
Littlewoods Organisation plc	218
Logica Group	220
Lummus Co Ltd	225
Matthew Hall Group	234
John Menzies (Holdings) plc	235
Meteorological Office	239
Micro Consultants Group	243
Micro Focus Ltd	241
Midland Bank plc	244
Milliken Industrials Ltd	245
Mobil Oil Co Ltd	247

Moores Furniture Group 248
Motorola Ltd 247
National Coal Board 251
National Maritime Institute 251
National Provident Institution 254
NCR (Manufacturing) Ltd 258
Norwich Union Insurance Group 262
Pearl Assurance plc 265
Perkins Engines Ltd 270
Pilkington Brothers plc 272
Plessey 273
PMA Consultants Ltd 274
Powell Duffryn Systems Ltd 278
Prime Computer (UK) Ltd 438
Prudential Assurance Co Ltd 285
Quantel Ltd 287
Raychem 291
RHM (Ranks Hovis McDougall plc) 293
Schlumberger Measurement & Control (UK) Ltd 309
Scicon 310
SPL International 326
Standard Telecommunication Laboratories 328
Standard Telephones & Cables plc 328
Staveley Industries plc 329
Systime Ltd 331
Sun Life Assurance plc 332
Taylor Instrument Ltd 335
Taylor Instrument Ltd Analytics Division 336
Texas Instruments Ltd 338
THORN EMI plc 343
Simex Corporation 349
UK Atomic Energy Authority 360
Unilever 355
Watson & Sons 367
Wellcome Foundation Ltd 369
Western Geophysical Co of America 371
Westland plc 372

Construction engineering
Civil Service 127
Compeda Ltd 135
French Kier Construction Ltd 172
MW Kellogg Ltd 211
Pyle Stewart Group 215
Matthew Hall Group 234

Control engineering
Air Products plc 70
Babcock International plc 82
British Aerospace-Dynamics Group 103
British National Oil Corporation 107
British Steel Corporation 115
Brown & Root (UK) Ltd 117
CAP Group Ltd 123
Civil Service 127
Crosfield Electronics Ltd 145
Davy McKee Ltd 150
Casams 58
Engineering Careers Information Service 24
Esso Group of Cos 163
Eurotherm International 164
Ferranti plc 167
Ford Motor Co Ltd 169
Hawker Siddeley Dynamics Engineering Ltd 192
MW Kellogg Ltd 211
Kennedy & Donkin 211
Lummus Co Ltd 225
McDermott Engineering London 226
Matthew Hall Group 234
Metal Box plc 238
Micro Consultants Group 243
National Coal Board 251
Pilkington Brothers plc 272
Scicon 310

SGRD Ltd 320
Staveley Industries plc 329
Taylor Instrument Ltd 335
THORN EMI plc 343
Westland plc 372

Cybernetics
British Aerospace-Dynamics Group 103
Civil Service 127

Economics
AGB Research Group 70
Air Products plc 70
Armitage & Norton 76
Barclays Bank plc Group 88
Beecham Products 91
Bestobell plc 93
Brian Ingram Associates 102
British Aerospace-Dynamics Group 103
British National Oil Corporation 107
British Steel Corporation 115
Brown & Root (UK) Ltd 117
Cleanaway 130
Clerical Medical & General Life Assurance Society 131
Crown Life 143
Dunlop 157
Finnie Ross Allfields 168
Friends' Provident Life Office 173
Fryer Whitehill & Co 174
Guardian Royal Exchange Assurance plc 186
Hacker Young 189
Haines Watts 189
Hymans, Robertson & Co 198
Imperial Life Assurance Co of Canada 203
Johnson Matthey Group 208
Knill Padgham & Grande 214
Leicestershire County Council 424
Lloyds Bank International 394
Mallinson-Denny Ltd 227
Mobil Oil Co Ltd 247
Moores Furniture Group 248
National Coal Board 251
National Mutual Life Association of Australasia Ltd 252
National Provident Institution 254
Norris Gilbert Stern & Co 259
Norwich Union Insurance Group 262
Pearl Assurance plc 265
Phillips & Drew 272
Pilkington Brothers plc 272
Prudential Assurance Co Ltd 285
Research Bureau Ltd 291
NM Rothschild & Sons Ltd 299
Scapa Group plc 310
Spicer & Pegler 325
Standard Telephones & Cables plc 328
Staveley Industries plc 329
Sun Life Assurance plc 332
THORN EMI plc 343
Waitrose Ltd 365
R Watson & Sons 367
Wellcome Foundation Ltd 369
Yorkshire Bank plc 374

Electrical engineering
Air Products plc 70
Anglo American Corporation of South Africa Ltd 388
Aurora Holdings plc 81
Babcock International plc 82
Baker Perkins Group of Cos 84
Beecham Pharmaceuticals 90
Bestobell plc 93
British Aerospace-Dynamics Group 103
British Airports 104

British National Oil Corporation 107
British Nuclear Fuels Ltd 109
British Shipbuilders 112
British Standards Institution 113
British Steel Corporation 115
British Sugar plc 115
Brown & Root (UK) Ltd 117
John Brown Engineers & Constructors Ltd 116
Brush Electrical Machines Ltd 118
Burmah Oil plc 118
C & S Antennas 145
CAP Group Ltd 123
Civil Service 127
Coles Cranes Ltd 133
Compeda Ltd 135
Computer Technology Ltd 136
Conoco Group in the UK 137
Consolidated Gold Fields plc 388
Cummins Engine Co Ltd 147
Daresbury Laboratory 148
Davy McKee Ltd 150
Dept of Industry (Science Group) 154
Dunlop 157
Engineering Careers Information Service 24
Esso Group of Cos 163
Eurotherm International 164
Exploration Logging 165
Ferranti plc 167
Ford Motor Co Ltd 169
General Electric Co plc 177
General Mining Union Corp Ltd (Gencor) 391
Geophysical Service International 180
Geoservices 180
Institution of Electrical Engineers 204
NEI International Combustion Ltd 205
ITT-IDEC 207
Johnson Matthey Group 208
MW Kellogg Ltd 211
Kennedy & Donkin 211
Logica Group 220
Lummus Co Ltd 225
McDermott Engineering London 226
Matthew Hall Group 234
Metal Box plc 238
Michelin Tyre plc 241
Motorola Ltd 247
National Coal Board 251
NCR (Manufacturing) Ltd 258
Newey & Eyre Group Ltd 258
NEI Overseas Ltd 395
Pilkington Brothers plc 272
Plessey 273
Prime Computer (UK) Ltd 438
Raychem 291
RHM (Ranks Hovis McDougall plc) 293
Rio Tinto Zinc Corporation plc 295
Royal Corps of Naval Constructors 303
Schlumberger Measurement & Control (UK) Ltd 309
Schlumberger Wireline Logging 396
Scicon 310
Seiscom Delta United 316
SIA Computer Services 321
South African Civil Service 397
SPL International 326
Standard Telephones & Cables plc 328
Staveley Industries plc 329
Texas Instruments Ltd 338
THORN EMI plc 343
UK Atomic Energy Authority 360
Unilever 355
United Biscuits (UK) plc 358
Voluntary Service Overseas 62
Westland plc 372
Zambia Consolidated Copper Mines Ltd 398

Electronic
engineering
overseas

Seismograph Service Limited
see also page 317

Electronic engineering

Analysts Schlumberger 73
APV Co Ltd 75
Babcock International plc 82
Baker Perkins Group of Cos 84
Barr & Stroud 89
Bestobell plc 93
British Aerospace-Dynamics Group 103
British Airports 104
British National Oil Corporation 107
British Nuclear Fuels Ltd 109
British Shipbuilders 112
British Standards Institution 113
British Steel Corporation 115
Brown & Root (UK) Ltd 117
Burmah Oil plc 118
C & S Antennas 145
CAP Group Ltd 123
CASE Computer & Systems Engineering plc 126
Civil Service 127
Compeda Ltd 135
Computer Machinery Company (CMC) Ltd 133
Computer Technology Ltd 136
Cossor Electronics Ltd 142
Crosfield Electronics Ltd 145
Daresbury Laboratory 148
Data Logic Ltd 149
Davy McKee Ltd 150
Dept of Industry (Science Group) 154
Dow Corning Ltd 155
Dunlop 157
Easams 58
Engineering Careers Information Service 24
Eurotherm International 164
Exploration Logging 165
Fairey Hydraulics Ltd 165
Ferranti plc 167
Flopetrol International SA 390
Ford Motor Co Ltd 169
Gardline Surveys 177
General Electric Co plc 177
Geophysical Service International 180
Geoservices 180
Gestetner 181
Government Communications HQ 183
Hawker Siddeley Dynamics Engineering Ltd 192
Holset Engineering Co Ltd 195
Horizon Exploration Ltd 195
Hughes Microelectronics Ltd 197
Institution of Electrical Engineers 204
International Computers Ltd 206
ITT-IDEC 207
Kennedy & Donkin 211
Logica Group 220
Mars Money Systems 233
Metal Box plc 238
Meteorological Office 239
Michelin Tyre plc 241
Micro Consultants Group 243
Microwave Associates Ltd 243
Motorola Ltd 247
National Coal Board 251
National Semiconductor 255
NCR.(Manufacturing) Ltd 258
Newey & Eyre Group Ltd 258
NEI Overseas Ltd 395
Pilkington Brothers plc 272
Plessey 273
Prime Computer (UK) Ltd 438
Quantel Ltd 287
Racal Electronics plc 288
Raychem 291
RHM (Ranks Hovis McDougall plc) 293
Ricardo Consulting Engineers 297

Royal Electrical & Mechanical Engineers 304
Schlumberger Measurement & Control (UK) Ltd 309
Schlumberger Wireline Logging 396
Scicon 310
Seiscom Delta United 316
Seismograph Service Ltd 317
SGRD Ltd 320
SIA Computer Services 321
SPL International 326
Standard Telecommunication Laboratories 328
Standard Telephones & Cables plc 328
Staveley Industries plc 329
Systime Ltd 331
Taylor Instrument Ltd 335
Taylor Instrument Ltd Analytics Division 336
Texas Instruments Ltd 338
THORN EMI plc 343
Timex Corporation 349
UK Atomic Energy Authority 360
Unilever 355
VG Isotopes Ltd 362
Weir Pumps Ltd 368
Western Geophysical Co of America 371
Westland plc 372

Engineering

AE Group 69
Air Products plc 70
Associated British Foods plc 80
Aurora Holdings plc 81
Baker Perkins Group of Cos 84
Bestobell plc 93
Boots Co plc 99
British National Oil Corporation 107
British Nuclear Fuels Ltd 109
British Ship Research Association 111
British Steel Corporation 115
Brown & Root (UK) Ltd 117
BXL Plastics Ltd 122
Civil Service 127
Crosfield Electronics Ltd 145
Cummins Engine Co Ltd 147
Davy McKee Ltd 150
Dowell Schlumberger 389
Dowty Group Ltd 159
Engineering Careers Information Service 24
Fairey Hydraulics Ltd 165
Ford Motor Co Ltd 169
General Electric Co plc 177
General Motors Ltd 179
Geophysical Service International 180
Getty Oil (Britain) Ltd 183
Government Communications HQ 183
Haines Watts 189
Hickson & Welch Ltd 194
Holset Engineering Co Ltd 195
Instron Ltd 205
Johnson Matthey Group 208
Kalamazoo Business Systems 211
Logica Group 220
London Transport 222
Lummus Co Ltd 225
McDermott Engineering London 226
Mars Ltd (Confectionery Division) 230
Metal Box plc 238
Michelin Tyre plc 241
Mobil Oil Co Ltd 247
Moores Furniture Group 248
National Bus Co 249
National Coal Board 251
NEI Overseas Ltd 395
Perkins Engines Ltd 270
Pilkington Brothers plc 272
Quinton Hazell plc 287
Raychem 291

RHM (Ranks Hovis McDougall plc) 293
Ricardo Consulting Engineers 297
Rio Tinto Zinc Corporation plc 295
Royal Electrical & Mechanical Engineers 304
South African Civil Service 397
Standard Telephones & Cables plc 328
THORN EMI plc 343
TI Group plc 347
UK Atomic Energy Authority 360
Unilever 355
James Walker Group of Cos 366
Westland plc 372

Engineering science

AE Group 69
Air Products plc 70
Aurora Holdings plc 81
Brian Ingram Associates 102
British Aerospace-Dynamics Group 103
British National Oil Corporation 107
British Nuclear Fuels Ltd 109
British Steel Corporation 115
Civil Service 127
Crosfield Electronics Ltd 145
Davy McKee Ltd 150
Dunlop 157
Easams 58
Eurotherm International 164
Fairey Hydraulics Ltd 165
Ferranti plc 167
Ford Motor Co Ltd 169
General Electric Co plc 177
Guest Keen & Nettlefolds plc 187
Holset Engineering Co Ltd 195
Johnson Matthey Group 208
Lummus Co Ltd 225
Metal Box plc 238
Michelin Tyre plc 241
National Maritime Institute 251
Perkins Engines Ltd 270
Pilkington Brothers plc 272
Raychem 291
Ricardo Consulting Engineers 297
Schlumberger Wireline Logging 396
Scicon 310
Standard Telephones & Cables plc 328
THORN EMI plc 343
UK Atomic Energy Authority 360
Unilever 355
Westland plc 372

Environmental control

Civil Service 127
Kyle Stewart Group 215
THORN EMI plc 343

Environmental and earth sciences

British National Oil Corporation 107
Civil Service 127
Gardline Surveys 177

Environmental engineering

Bestobell plc 93
British Aerospace-Dynamics Group 103
British National Oil Corporation 107
Civil Service 127
Engineering Careers Information Service 24
Kennedy & Donkin 211
Matthew Hall Group 234
NEI Overseas Ltd 395
THORN EMI plc 343

Ergonomics

Civil Service 127
Pilkington Brothers plc 272

Estate management and land economics

Incorporated Society of Valuers & Auctioneers	379
Knight Frank & Rutley	214
National Coal Board	251
Prudential Assurance Co Ltd	285
Watney Mann & Truman Brewers Ltd	367

Food science/dietetics

Alfa-Laval Co Ltd	72
Associated British Foods plc	80
Civil Service	127
Northern Foods plc	260
RHM (Ranks Hovis McDougall plc)	293
Unigate plc	357

Food technology

Alfa-Laval Co Ltd	72
APV Co Ltd	75
Associated British Foods plc	80
Civil Service	127
Metal Box plc	238
Northern Foods plc	260
RHM (Ranks Hovis McDougall plc)	293
Unigate plc	357
Unilever Research	355

Fuel science

British Steel Corporation	115
Civil Service	127
Davy McKee Ltd	150
National Coal Board	251
Perkins Engines Ltd	270

Gas engineering

British Gas Corporation	106

Geology

Analysts Schlumberger	73
Anglo American Corporation of South Africa Ltd	388
British National Oil Corporation	107
Burmah Oil plc	118
Civil Service	127
Conoco Group in the UK	137
Esso Group of Cos	163
Exploration Logging	165
Gardline Surveys	177
General Mining Union Corp Ltd (Gencor)	391
Geophysical Service International	180
Geoservices	180
Getty Oil (Britain) Ltd	183
Horizon Exploration Ltd	195
Mobil Oil Co Ltd	247
National Coal Board	251
Pilkington Brothers plc	272
Zambia Consolidated Copper Mines Ltd	398

Geophysics

Analysts Schlumberger	73
British National Oil Corporation	107
Burmah Oil plc	118
Civil Service	127
Conoco Group in the UK	137
Esso Group of Cos	163
Gardline Surveys	177
General Mining Union Corp Ltd (Gencor)	391
Geophysical Service International	180
Getty Oil (Britain) Ltd	183
Horizon Exploration Ltd	195
Mobil Oil Co Ltd	247
Schlumberger Wireline Logging	396
Seiscom Delta United	316
Seismograph Service Ltd	317
Western Geophysical Co of America	371

Geotechnical engineering

Civil Service	127
Zambia Consolidated Copper Mines Ltd	398

Glass technology

British Nuclear Fuels Ltd	109
Pilkington Brothers plc	272
Standard Telecommunication Laboratories	328
THORN EMI plc	343

Hotel and catering management

THORN EMI plc	343
YMCA	373

Hydraulic engineering

Civil Service	127
Dowty Group Ltd	159
James Walker Group of Cos	366

Instrument engineering

Air Products plc	70
Babcock International plc	82
British National Oil Corporation	107
British Steel Corporation	115
Brown & Root (UK) Ltd	117
John Brown Engineers & Constructors Ltd	116
Civil Service	127
Davy McKee Ltd	150
Dow Corning Ltd	155
Esso Group of Cos	163
MW Kellogg Ltd	211
Lummus Co Ltd	225
McDermott Engineering London	226
Matthew Hall Group	234
National Coal Board	251
Pilkington Brothers plc	272
Staveley Industries plc	329
Taylor Instrument Ltd	335
THORN EMI plc	343
UK Atomic Energy Authority	360

Librarianship/information science

Leicestershire County Council	424
Raychem	291

Law

Brian Ingram Associates	102
British Aerospace-Dynamics Group	103
British National Oil Corporation	107
Friends' Provident Life Office	173
Getty Oil (Britain) Ltd	183
Industrial & Commercial Finance Corporation	204
Lloyds Bank International	394
Midland Bank plc	244
Norwich Union Insurance Group	262
Pearl Assurance plc	265
Prudential Assurance Co Ltd	285
Trading Standards Officers	349
Trower, Still & Keeling	351
Yorkshire Bank plc	374

Materials science/technology

Aurora Holdings plc	81
British Aerospace-Dynamics Group	103
British Steel Corporation	115
BXL Plastics Ltd	122
Civil Service	127
Crosfield Electronics Ltd	145
Daresbury Laboratory	148
Davy McKee Ltd	150
Dunlop	157
Foseco Minsep Group	169
General Electric Co plc	177
General Mining Union Corp Ltd (Gencor)	391

Johannesburg Consolidated Investment Co Ltd	393
Johnson Matthey Group	208
Metal Box plc	238
Moores Furniture Group	248
National Coal Board	251
NCR (Manufacturing) Ltd	258
Pilkington Brothers plc	272
Raychem	291
Rio Tinto Zinc Corporation plc	295
Standard Telecommunication Laboratories	328
Standard Telephones & Cables plc	328
THORN EMI plc	343
Trading Standards Officers	349
UK Atomic Energy Authority	360
Westland plc	372

Mathematical physics

Barr & Stroud	89
British Aerospace-Dynamics Group	103
British National Oil Corporation	107
CAP Group Ltd	123
Civil Service	127
Crosfield Electronics Ltd	145
Crown Life	143
Daresbury Laboratory	148
Ford Motor Co Ltd	169
General Electric Co plc	177
Geophysical Service International	180
ITT-IDEC	207
Micro Consultants Group	243
National Maritime Institute	251
National Nuclear Corporation Ltd	253
Pilkington Brothers plc	272
Scicon	310
THORN EMI plc	343
Trading Standards Officers	349
UK Atomic Energy Authority	360

Mathematics

AE Group	69
AGB Research Group	70
Air Products plc	70
Beecham Products	91
Brian Ingram Associates	102
British Aerospace-Dynamics Group	103
British National Oil Corporation	107
British Nuclear Fuels Ltd	109
British Ship Research Association	111
British Shipbuilders	112
CAP Group Ltd	123
Civil Service	127
Clerical Medical & General Life Assurance Society	131
Co-operative Insurance Society Ltd	139
Compeda Ltd	133
Computer Machinery Company (CMC) Ltd	133
Coopers & Lybrand Associates Ltd	141
Crosfield Electronics Ltd	145
Crown Life	143
Cubie Wood & Co Ltd	146
Daresbury Laboratory	148
Data Logic Ltd	149
Dept of Industry (Science Group)	154
Dowell Schlumberger	389
Dunlop	157
Easams	58
Equity & Law Life Assurance Society plc	160
Esso Group of Cos	163
Ferranti plc	167
Finnie Ross Allfields	168
Ford Motor Co Ltd	169
Friends' Provident Life Office	173
General Electric Co plc	177
Geophysical Service International	180
Government Communications HQ	183

Guardian Royal Exchange Assurance plc 186
Hacker Young 189
Haines Watts 189
Horizon Exploration Ltd 195
Hymans, Robertson & Co 198
Imperial Life Assurance Co of Canada 203
Instron Ltd 205
International Computers Ltd 206
ITT-IDEC 207
Johnson Matthey Group 208
Leicestershire County Council 424
Littlewoods Organisation plc 218
Lloyds Bank International 394
Logica Group 220
Lummus Co Ltd 225
Meteorological Office 239
Milliken Industrials Ltd 245
Mobil Oil Co Ltd 247
National Coal Board 251
National Mutual Life Association of
   Australasia Ltd 252
National Nuclear Corporation Ltd 253
National Provident Institution 254
National Semiconductor 255
NCR (Manufacturing) Ltd 258
Norwich Union Insurance Group 262
Pearl Assurance plc 265
Perkins Engines Ltd 270
Phillips & Drew 272
Pilkington Brothers plc 272
Prime Computer (UK) Ltd 438
Provident Life Association of London Ltd 284
Prudential Assurance Co Ltd 285
Research Bureau Ltd 291
Royal Insurance 50
Schlumberger Measurement & Control
   (UK) Ltd 309
Scicon 310
Scottish Equitable Life Assurance Society 313
Scottish Provident Institution 314
Scottish Widows' Fund & Life Assurance
   Society 315
Spicer & Pegler 325
SPL International 326
Standard Telecommunication Laboratories 328
Standard Telephones & Cables plc 328
Sun Life Assurance Co of Canada 334
Sun Life Assurance plc 332
Taylor Instrument Ltd 335
Texas Instruments Ltd 338
THORN EMI plc 343
Trading Standards Officers 349
UK Atomic Energy Authority 360
UK Provident 353
Voluntary Service Overseas 62
R Watson & Sons 367
Wellcome Foundation Ltd 369
Western Geophysical Co of America 371
Westland plc 372

Mechanical engineering
AE Group 69
Air Products plc 70
Alfa-Laval Co Ltd 72
Analysts Schlumberger 73
Anglo American Corporation of South
   Africa Ltd 388
Aurora Holdings plc 81
Babcock International plc 82
Barr & Stroud 89
Beecham Pharmaceuticals 90
BOC Ltd 98
British Aerospace-Dynamics Group 103
British Airports 104
British National Oil Corporation 107
British Nuclear Fuels Ltd 109

British Shipbuilders 112
British Standards Institution 113
British Steel Corporation 115
British Sugar plc 115
Brown & Root (UK) Ltd 117
John Brown Engineers & Constructors Ltd 116
Brush Electrical Machines Ltd 118
Burmah Oil plc 118
BXL Plastics Ltd 122
Ciba-Geigy Plastics & Additives Co 126
Civil Service 127
Coles Cranes Ltd 133
Compeda Ltd 135
Conoco Group in the UK 137
Consolidated Gold Fields plc 388
Richard Costain plc 142
Cummins Engine Co Ltd 147
Daresbury Laboratory 148
Davy McKee (London) Ltd 151
Davy McKee Ltd 150
Robert M Douglas Holdings plc 155
Dow Corning Ltd 155
Dowell Schlumberger 389
Dowty Group Ltd 159
Dunlop 157
Engineering Careers Information Service 24
Esso Group of Cos 163
Eurotherm International 164
Fairey Hydraulics Ltd 165
Ferranti plc 167
Flopetrol International SA 390
Ford Motor Co Ltd 169
French Kier Construction Ltd 172
General Electric Co plc 177
General Mining Union Corp Ltd (Gencor) 391
Gestetner 181
Guest Keen & Nettlefolds plc 187
Holset Engineering Co Ltd 195
Ilford Ltd 200
NEI International Combustion Ltd 205
Johnson Matthey Group 208
MW Kellogg Ltd 211
Kennedy & Donkin 211
Lummus Co Ltd 225
McDermott Engineering London 226
Matthew Hall Group 234
Metal Box plc 238
Michelin Tyre plc 241
Mobil Oil Co Ltd 247
Moores Furniture Group 248
Motorola Ltd 247
National Coal Board 251
National Nuclear Corporation Ltd 253
NCR (Manufacturing) Ltd 258
NEI Overseas Ltd 395
Perkins Engines Ltd 270
Pilkington Brothers plc 272
Raychem 291
RHM (Ranks Hovis McDougall plc) 293
Ricardo Consulting Engineers 297
Rio Tinto Zinc Corporation plc 295
Royal Corps of Naval Constructors 303
Royal Electrical & Mechanical Engineers 304
Schlumberger Measurement & Control
   (UK) Ltd 309
Schlumberger Wireline Logging 396
SGRD Ltd 320
South African Civil Service 397
SPL International 326
Standard Telecommunication Laboratories 328
Standard Telephones & Cables plc 328
Staveley Industries plc 329
Taylor Woodrow International Ltd 336
NEI Thompson Ltd 342
THORN EMI plc 343
Timex Corporation 349

UK Atomic Energy Authority 360
Unilever 355
Unilever Research 355
United Biscuits (UK) plc 358
Vetco Offshore Ltd 362
Victor Products (Wallsend) plc 363
Voluntary Service Overseas 62
James Walker Group of Cos 366
Weir Pumps Ltd 368
Westland plc 372

Medicine and health studies
Voluntary Service Overseas 62

Metallurgy
AE Group 69
Anglo American Corporation of South
   Africa Ltd 388
Aurora Holdings plc 81
Babcock International plc 82
British National Oil Corporation 107
British Nuclear Fuels Ltd 109
British Steel Corporation 115
Brown & Root (UK) Ltd 117
Civil Service 127
Crosfield Electronics Ltd 145
Davy McKee Ltd 150
Foseco Minsep Group 169
General Electric Co plc 177
General Mining Union Corp Ltd (Gencor) 391
Guest Keen & Nettlefolds plc 187
Hughes Microelectronics Ltd 197
Johannesburg Consolidated Investment
   Co Ltd 393
Johnson Matthey Group 208
Metal Box plc 238
Michelin Tyre plc 241
National Coal Board 251
Rio Tinto Zinc Corporation plc 295
Standard Telecommunication Laboratories 328
Staveley Industries plc 329
THORN EMI plc 343
TI Group plc 347
UK Atomic Energy Authority 360
Zambia Consolidated Copper Mines Ltd 398

Meteorology
Meteorological Office 239
South African Civil Service 397

Microbiology
Associated British Foods plc 80
Beecham Pharmaceuticals 90
Civil Service 127
May & Baker Ltd 235
Metal Box plc 238
Northern Foods plc 260
Pfizer Ltd 271
RHM (Ranks Hovis McDougall plc) 293
Unilever Research 355

Mineral processing and technology
Anglo American Corporation of South
   Africa Ltd 388
Civil Service 127
Consolidated Gold Fields plc 388
Davy McKee Ltd 150
Dept of Industry (Science Group) 154
General Mining Union Corp Ltd (Gencor) 391
Johannesburg Consolidated Investment
   Co Ltd 393
Johnson Matthey Group 208
Matthew Hall Group 234
National Coal Board 251
Staveley Industries plc 329
Zambia Consolidated Copper Mines Ltd 398

Mining
Anglo American Corporation of South
Africa Ltd 388
British National Oil Corporation 107
Consolidated Gold Fields plc 388
Flopetrol International SA 390
French Kier Construction Ltd 172
General Mining Union Corp Ltd (Gencor) 391
Johannesburg Consolidated Investment
Co Ltd 393
National Coal Board 251
Zambia Consolidated Copper Mines Ltd 398

Modern languages
Air Products plc 70
British National Oil Corporation 107
Fryer Whitehill & Co 174
Johnson Matthey Group 208
Joint Technical Language Service 209
Lloyds Bank International 394
Midland Bank plc 244
Moores Furniture Group 248
Perkins Engines Ltd 270
Prudential Assurance Co Ltd 285
Royal Insurance 50
Scapa Group plc 310

Naval architecture/marine engineering
British National Oil Corporation 107
British Ship Research Association 111
British Shipbuilders 112
Brown & Root (UK) Ltd 117
Civil Service 127
McDermott Engineering London 226
National Maritime Institute 251
Royal Corps of Naval Constructors 303

Oceanography
British National Oil Corporation 107
Gardline Surveys 177

Oil technology
British National Oil Corporation 107
Brown & Root (UK) Ltd 117
Conoco Group in the UK 137
Flopetrol International SA 390
Geoservices 180
Getty Oil (Britain) Ltd 183
Lummus Co Ltd 225
Mobil Oil Co Ltd 247

Operational research
Air Products plc 70
British Steel Corporation 115
CAP Group Ltd 123
Civil Service 127
Easams 58
Esso Group of Cos 163
Ford Motor Co Ltd 169
Johnson Matthey Group 208
Leicestershire County Council 424
National Coal Board 251
Pearl Assurance plc 265
Pilkington Brothers plc 272
Scicon 310

Paper science
General Mining Union Corp Ltd (Gencor) 391

Personnel
Air Products plc 70
Association of Cost & Executive
Accountants 379
Bowater Organisation 100
Conoco Group in the UK 137
Mobil Oil Co Ltd 247

Moores Furniture Group 248
Pilkington Brothers plc 272
Prudential Assurance Co Ltd 285
Standard Telephones & Cables plc 328
Staveley Industries plc 329
UK Atomic Energy Authority 360
Wellcome Foundation Ltd 369

Pharmacology
Beecham Pharmaceuticals 90
May & Baker Ltd 235
Merck; Sharp & Dohme Ltd 236
Wellcome Foundation Ltd 369

Pharmacy
Abbott Laboratories Ltd 68
Beecham Pharmaceuticals 90
May & Baker Ltd 235
Pfizer Ltd 271
ER Squibb & Sons plc 328
Wellcome Foundation Ltd 369

Physics
Amersham International plc 72
Barr & Stroud 89
British Aerospace-Dynamics Group 103
British National Oil Corporation 107
British Nuclear Fuels Ltd 109
British Ship Research Association 111
British Shipbuilders 112
British Standards Institution 113
British Steel Corporation 115
Civil Service 127
Crosfield Electronics Ltd 145
Crown Life 143
Daresbury Laboratory 148
Dept of Industry (Science Group) 154
Dowell Schlumberger 389
Dunlop 157
Easams 58
Eurotherm International 164
Ford Motor Co Ltd 169
General Electric Co plc 177
Geophysical Service International 180
Gestetner 181
Government Communications HQ 183
Haines Watts 189
Hawker Siddeley Dynamics Engineering
Ltd 192
Hughes Microelectronics Ltd 197
Ilford Ltd 200
Institution of Electrical Engineers 204
Instron Ltd 205
International Computers Ltd 206
ITT-IDEC 207
Johnson Matthey Group 208
Logica Ltd 220
Meteorological Office 239
Micro Consultants Group 243
Microwave Associates Ltd 243
National Coal Board 251
National Nuclear Corporation Ltd 253
National Semiconductor 255
Perkins Engines Ltd 270
Pilkington Brothers plc 272
Plessey 273
Prime Computer (UK) Ltd 438
Raychem 291
RHM (Ranks Hovis McDougall plc) 293
Schlumberger Measurement & Control
(UK) Ltd 309
Schlumberger Wireline Logging 396
Scicon 310
Seismograph Service Ltd 317
SPL International 326
Standard Telecommunication Laboratories 328

Standard Telephones & Cables plc 328
Texas Instruments Ltd 338
THORN EMI plc 343
Trading Standards Officers 349
UK Atomic Energy Authority 360
Unilever Research 355
VG Isotopes Ltd 362
Voluntary Service Overseas 62
Western Geophysical Co of America 371

Polymers
BXL Plastics Ltd 122
Civil Service 127
Dunlop 157
Fishburn Printing Ink Co Ltd 168
Ilford Ltd 200
Metal Box plc 238
Pilkington Brothers plc 272
Raychem 291
Standard Telecommunication Laboratories 328

Production engineering
AE Group 69
Aurora Holdings plc 81
Babcock International plc 82
Beecham Products 91
British Aerospace-Dynamics Group 103
British National Oil Corporation 107
British Steel Corporation 115
Brush Electrical Machines Ltd 118
BXL Plastics Ltd 122
Coles Cranes Ltd 133
Compeda Ltd 135
Cossor Electronics Ltd 142
Crosfield Electronics Ltd 145
Cummins Engine Co Ltd 147
Dowty Group Ltd 159
Dunlop 157
Engineering Careers Information Service 24
Eurotherm International 164
Ferranti plc 167
Ford Motor Co Ltd 169
General Electric Co plc 177
Gestetner 181
Guest Keen & Nettlefolds plc 187
Holset Engineering Co Ltd 195
Hughes Microelectronics Ltd 197
Imperial Brewing & Leisure Ltd 201
Instron Ltd 205
NEI International Combustion Ltd 205
Johnson Matthey Group 208
Marley Group 229
Mars Money Systems 233
Metal Box plc 238
Michelin Tyre plc 241
Milliken Industrials Ltd 245
Moores Furniture Group 248
National Coal Board 251
NCR (Manufacturing) Ltd 258
NEI Overseas Ltd 395
Perkins Engines Ltd 270
Pilkington Brothers plc 272
Plessey 273
RHM (Ranks Hovis McDougall plc) 293
Rio Tinto Zinc Corporation plc 295
Standard Telephones & Cables plc 328
Staveley Industries plc 329
Taylor Instrument Ltd Analytics Division 336
NEI Thompson Ltd 342
THORN EMI plc 343
Timex Corporation 349
Unilever 355
Weir Pumps Ltd 368
Westland plc 372

Psychology
AGB Research Group 70
Prison Service 279
Research Bureau Ltd 291
Richmond Fellowship Therapeutic
  Communities 297

Quantity surveying
British National Oil Corporation 107
Robert M Douglas Holdings plc 155
French Kier Construction Ltd 172
Kyle Stewart Group 215
Matthew Hall Group 169
Shand Group 320

Rubber technology
Civil Service 127
Dunlop 157
Milliken Industrials Ltd 245
James Walker Group of Cos 366

Sociology, social work/studies
John Menzies (Holdings) plc 235
Moores Furniture Group 248
Richmond Fellowship Therapeutic
  Communities 297
YMCA 373

Statistics
AGB Research Group 70
Air Products plc 70
Brian Ingram Associates 102
British National Oil Corporation 107
CAP Group Ltd 123
Civil Service 127
Clerical Medical & General Life Assurance
  Society 131
Co-operative Insurance Society Ltd 139
Crown Life 143
Cubie Wood & Co Ltd 146
Ford Motor Co Ltd 169
Friends' Provident Life Office 173
Hymans, Robertson & Co 198
Imperial Life Assurance Co of Canada 203
Knill Padgham & Grande 214
Leicestershire County Council 424
Milliken Industrials Ltd 245
National Coal Board 251
National Mutual Life Association of
  Australasia Ltd 252
National Provident Institution 254
Nielsen Business Services 259
Pearl Assurance plc 265
Pilkington Brothers plc 272
Prudential Assurance Co Ltd 285
Research Bureau Ltd 291

Scicon 310
Scottish Provident Institution 314
Scottish Widows' Fund & Life Assurance
  Society 315
Sun Life Assurance plc 332
UK Provident 353
Unilever Research 355
R Watson & Sons 367
Wellcome Foundation Ltd 369

Surveying
Gardline Surveys 177
Geophysical Service International 180
Incorporated Society of Valuers &
  Auctioneers 379
National Coal Board 251
Seiscom Delta United 316

Textile engineering/technology
Civil Service 127
Milliken Industrials Ltd 245
Scapa Group plc 310

Transportation engineering
Civil Service 127
Cummins Engine Co Ltd 147
Dunlop 157
South African Civil Service 397

Geographical index

The map indicates the regions into which the index is divided.
Organisations will be listed under the region *or* county where employment is offered.

General England	466
1 **Greater London**	466
2 **South East**	467
Beds	467
Berks	467
Bucks	467
E Sussex	467
Essex	467
Hants	467
Herts	467
IoW	467
Kent	467
Oxon	467
Surrey	467
W Sussex	467
3 **South West**	467
Avon	468
Channel Islands	468
Devon	468
Dorset	468
Glos	468
Som	468
Wilts	468
4 **Wales**	468
Clwyd	468
Dyfed	468
Gwent	468
M Glamorgan	468
S Glamorgan	468
W Glamorgan	468
5 **Midlands**	468
Derby	468
Leics	468
Lincs	468
Northants	468
Notts	468
Salop	468
Staffs	469
W Midlands	469
Warwicks	469
6 **East Anglia**	469
Cambs	469
Norfolk	469
Suffolk	469
7 **North East**	469
Cleveland	469
Durham	469
Humberside	469
N Yorks	469
S Yorks	469
W Yorks	469
Tyne & Wear	469
8 **North West**	469
Cheshire	469
Cumbria	470
Gtr Manchester	470
IoM	470
Lancs	470
Merseyside	470
9 **Northern Ireland**	470
Antrim	470
Down	470
10 **Scotland**	470
Border	470
Central Region	470
Grampian	470
Dumfries & Galloway	470
Fife	470
Highland	470
Lothian	470
Strathclyde	470
Tayside	470
11 **Republic of Ireland**	470
13 **Overseas**	470

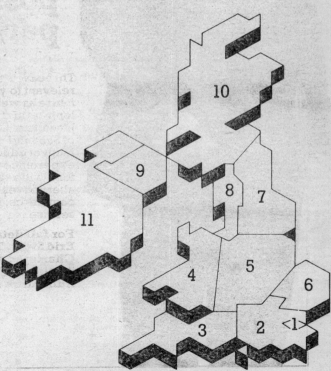

GENERAL ENGLAND

Accountancy & Financial Management in
the Public Sector — 68
Air Products plc — 70
Associated British Foods plc — 80
Association of Certified Accountants — 378
Babcock International plc — 82
Barclays Bank plc Group — 88
BHS (British Home Stores) plc — 94
BICC plc — 94
Binder Hamlyn — 95
CT Bowring & Co Ltd — 100
Bradford & Bingley Building Society — 101
British Gas Corporation — 106
British Shipbuilders — 112
British Transport Police — 36
C & J Clark Ltd — 128
Chartered Institute of Public Finance &
Accountancy — 379
Civil Service — 127
Cleanaway — 130
Deloitte Haskins & Sells — 153
Robert M Douglas Holdings plc — 155
Equity & Law Life Assurance Society plc — 160
Ernst & Whinney — 161
Four Square — 170
French Kier Construction Ltd — 172
Guardian Royal Exchange Assurance plc — 186
Horizon Exploration Ltd — 195
IBM United Kingdom Ltd — 199
Industrial & Commercial Finance
Corporation Ltd — 204
Institute of Chartered Accountants in
England & Wales — 380
Institute of Cost & Management
Accountants — 383
Institute of Marketing — 385
Institute of Purchasing & Supply — 385
FJC Lilley plc — 217
Littlewoods Organisation plc — 218
Lucas Industries plc — 224
Marks & Spencer plc — 228
Marley Group — 229
Mars Ltd (Confectionery Division) — 230
John Menzies (Holdings) plc — 235
Merck, Sharp & Dohme Ltd — 236
Metal Box plc — 238
Montague L Meyer plc — 240
Midland Bank plc — 244
National Bus Co — 249
National Coal Board — 251
Newey & Eyre Group Ltd — 258
Edmund Nuttall Group of Cos — 263
Pannell Kerr Forster — 263
Peat Marwick Mitchell & Co — 267
Pedigree Petfoods — 269
Plessey — 273
Police Service in England & Wales — 275
Post Office — 276
Prison Service — 279
Richmond Fellowship Therapeutic
Communities — 297
Royal Air Force — 301
Royal Navy, Royal Marines & WRNS — 305
Systime Ltd — 331
Thomson McLintock & Co — 341
Touche Ross & Co — 350
Trading Standards Officers — 349
TSB Group — 351
Unigate plc — 357
Union International plc — 358
United Biscuits (UK) plc — 358
Watney Mann & Truman Brewers Ltd — 367
YMCA — 373

GREATER LONDON

AE Group — 69
AGB Research Group — 70
Alfa-Laval Co Ltd — 72
Analysts Schlumberger — 73
Arthur Andersen & Co — 74
Arthur Andersen & Co Management
Consultancy Division — 74
Armitage & Norton — 76
Arthur Young McClelland Moores & Co — 79
Association of Cost & Executive
Accountants — 379
Baker Rooke — 85
John Baker, Sons & Bell — 83
Bank of Credit & Commerce International
SA — 86
Bank of Scotland — 87
Beecham Pharmaceuticals — 90
Beecham Products — 91
Benton & Bowles Ltd — 92
BIS Applied Systems Ltd — 96
BIS Software Ltd — 96
Boase Massimi Pollitt — 97
BOC Ltd — 98
Boots Co plc — 99
Bowater Organisation — 100
Brebner, Allen & Trapp — 101
Brewer & Co — 102
Brian Ingram Associates — 102
British Airways — 104
British Linen Bank Ltd — 107
Brown & Root (UK) Ltd — 117
John Brown Engineers & Constructors Ltd — 116
Burmah Oil plc — 118
Leo Burnett Ltd — 120
Buzzacott & Co — 121
CAP Group Ltd — 123
Casson Beckman — 125
Clark Pixley — 129
Clerical Medical & General Life Assurance
Society — 131
Conoco Group in the UK — 137
Coopers & Lybrand — 140
Coopers & Lybrand Associates Ltd — 141
Richard Costain plc — 142
Crosfield Electronics Ltd — 145
Data Logic Ltd — 149
Davy McKee (London) Ltd — 151
Dearden Farrow — 152
Dept of Industry (Science Group) — 154
Endsleigh Insurance Services — 159
Engineering Careers Information Service — 24
Equity & Law Life Assurance Society plc — 160
Ernst & Whinney — 161
Esso Group of Cos — 163
Fairey Hydraulics Ltd — 165
Finnie Ross Allfields — 168
Fraser Keen — 171
Fraser Williams — 171
Friends' Provident Life Office — 173
Fryer Whitehill & Co — 174
Gallaher Ltd — 175
General Electric Co plc — 177
Gestetner — 181
Getty Oil (Britain) Ltd — 183
Greater London Council — 185
Habitat — 188
Hacker Young — 189
Hambros Bank Ltd — 190
HAT Accountancy Training Syndicate — 191
Haymarket Publishing Group — 193
Help the Aged — 194
Hughes Allen Payne Stone — 198
Hymans, Robertson & Co — 198
Ilford Ltd — 200
Imperial Brewing & Leisure Ltd — 201

Incorporated Society of Valuers &
Auctioneers — 379
Institute of Chartered Accountants of
Scotland — 381
Institute of Chartered Secretaries &
Administrators — 382
Institution of Electrical Engineers — 204
Johnson Matthey Group — 208
MW Kellogg Ltd — 211
Kidsons — 213
Knight Frank & Rutley — 214
Knill Padgham & Grande — 214
Lloyds Bank plc — 219
Logica Group — 220
London Fire Brigade — 222
London Transport — 222
Longcrofts — 223
McDermott Engineering London — 226
Mallinson-Denny Ltd — 227
Matthew Hall Group — 234
McDonald's Golden Arches Restaurants
Ltd — 226
Merrill Lynch International — 237
Metal Box plc — 238
Micro Focus Ltd — 241
Midland Bank plc — 244
Mobil Oil Co Ltd — 247
Morgan Brown & Haynes — 249
Motorola Ltd — 247
Murray Noble — 249
National Mutual Life Association of
Australasia Ltd — 252
National Westminster Bank plc — 257
Norris Gilbert Stern & Co — 259
Pearl Assurance plc — 265
Phillips & Drew — 272
Providence Capitol Life Assurance Co Ltd — 284
Provident Life Association of London Ltd — 284
Prudential Assurance Co Ltd — 285
Racal Electronics plc — 288
Research Bureau Ltd — 291
Reuters — 292
RHM (Ranks Hovis McDougall plc) — 293
Robson Rhodes — 298
NM Rothschild & Sons Ltd — 299
Rowe & Pitman — 300
Rowland Nevill & Co — 301
Save & Prosper Group — 306
J Henry Schroder Wagg & Co Ltd — 307
Scicon — 310
Security Pacific National Bank — 315
Miss Selfridge Ltd — 318
Selfridges Ltd — 319
SGRD Ltd — 320
SIA Computer Services — 321
Silver Altman & Co — 321
Smallfield Fitzhugh Tillet & Co — 322
Software Sciences — 323
Spicer & Pegler — 325
SPL International — 326
Stanley A Spofforth & Co — 327
Standard Telephones & Cables plc — 328
Stewart Wrightson — 330
Stoy Hayward & Co — 331
Sun Life Assurance Co of Canada — 334
Tandy Corporation (Branch UK) — 335
Thomson McLintock & Co — 341
THORN EMI plc — 343
Thornton Baker — 346
TI Group plc — 347
Touche Ross & Co — 350
Trower, Still & Keeling — 351
UK Atomic Energy Authority — 360
Unilever — 355
United Biscuits (UK) plc — 358
Vetco Offshore Ltd — 362

VNU Business Publications BV 365
Waitrose Ltd 365
R Watson & Sons 367
Wellcome Foundation Ltd 369
Williams & Glyn's Bank plc 20
Wilson Green Gibbs 373

SOUTH EAST
AE Group 69
Amersham International plc 72
John Baker, Sons & Bell 83
Beecham Products 91
Bowater Organisation 100
Brebner, Allen & Trapp 101
British Airports 104
John Brown Engineers & Constructors Ltd 116
Burmah Oil plc 118
BXL Plastics Ltd 122
Richard Costain plc 142
Cubie Wood & Co Ltd 146
Data Logic Ltd 149
Dearden Farrow 152
Dept of Industry (Science Group) 154
Engineering Careers Information Service 24
Fenwick Ltd 166
Ferranti plc 167
Fraser Williams 171
Friends' Provident Life Office 173
Fryer Whitehill & Co 174
Gallaher Ltd 175
General Electric Co plc 177
Geophysical Service International 180
Getty Oil (Britain) Ltd 183
Habitat 188
Haines Watts 189
HAT Accountancy Training Syndicate 191
Help the Aged 194
Horizon Exploration Ltd 195
Hughes Allen Payne Stone 198
Imperial Brewing & Leisure Ltd 201
Institute of Chartered Accountants of
  Scotland 381
Institute of Chartered Secretaries &
  Administrators 382
International Computers Ltd 206
Johnson Matthey Group 208
Kennedy & Donkin 211
Kyle Stewart Group 215
Lex Service Group plc 216
Longcrofts 223
McDonald's Golden Arches Restaurants
  Ltd 226
Metal Box plc 238
Midland Bank plc 244
Mobil Oil Co Ltd 247
National Maritime Institute 251
National Provident Institution 254
National Westminster Bank plc 257
Pearl Assurance plc 265
Pedigree Petfoods 269
Phillips & Drew 272
Prime Computer (UK) Ltd 438
Providence Capitol Life Assurance Co Ltd 284
Provident Life Association of London Ltd 284
Racal Electronics plc 288
RHM (Ranks Hovis McDougall plc) 293
Royal Corps of Naval Constructors 303
Schlumberger Measurement & Control
  (UK) Ltd 309
Miss Selfridge Ltd 318
Jefferson Smurfit Group 322
Spicer & Pegler 325
SPL International 326
Standard Telephones & Cables plc 328
Staveley Industries plc 329
Stewart Wrightson 330

Tandy Corporation (Branch UK) 335
THORN EMI plc 343
Thornton Baker 346
Touche Ross & Co 350
Unilever 355
VNU Business Publications BV 365
Waitrose Ltd 365
Western Geophysical Co of America 371

Beds
Arthur Young McClelland Moores & Co 79
Coopers & Lybrand 140
Geophysical Service International 180
Microwave Associates Ltd 243
Prime Computer (UK) Ltd 438
Software Sciences 323
Texas Instruments Ltd 338
Unilever Research 355

Berks
Bestobell plc 93
British Standards Institution 113
CAP Group Ltd 123
Coopers & Lybrand 140
Ferranti plc 167
Finnie Ross Allfields 168
Mars Group Services 230
Mars Ltd (Confectionery Division) 230
Mars Money Systems 233
Meteorological Office 239
Micro Consultants Group 243
Quantel Ltd 287

Bucks
Armitage & Norton 76
Equity & Law Life Assurance Society plc 160
Ford Motor Co Ltd 169
Instron Ltd 205

E Sussex
Taylor Instrument Ltd Analytics Division 336

Essex
Beecham Pharmaceuticals 90
Cossor Electronics Ltd 142
Ford Motor Co Ltd 169
Hambros Bank Ltd 190
Knill Padgham & Grande 214
May & Baker Ltd 235
Phillips & Drew 272
Save & Prosper Group 306
Standard Telecommunication Laboratories 328

Hants
Arthur Young McClelland Moores & Co 79
John Brown Engineers & Constructors Ltd 116
Coopers & Lybrand 140
Esso Group of Cos 163
Ford Motor Co Ltd 169
IBM United Kingdom Ltd 199
Motorola Ltd 247
Powell Duffryn Systems Ltd 278
Software Sciences 323

Herts
British Aerospace-Dynamics Group 103
CASE Computer & Systems Engineering
  plc 126
Compeda Ltd 135
Computer Machinery Company (CMC) Ltd 133
Computer Technology Ltd 136
Crosfield Electronics Ltd 145
Fishburn Printing Ink Co Ltd 168
Foseco Minsep Group 169
Fraser Williams 171
Hawker Siddeley Dynamics Engineering
  Ltd 192

Institution of Electrical Engineers 204
ITT-IDEC 207
Merck, Sharp & Dohme Ltd 236
Taylor Instrument Ltd 335
Wellcome Foundation Ltd 369

IoW
Westland plc 372

Kent
Abbott Laboratories Ltd 68
C & S Antennas 145
Coopers & Lybrand 140
Mallinson-Denny Ltd 227
National Provident Institution 254
Pfizer Ltd 271
Seismograph Service Ltd 317
Touche Ross & Co 350
Wellcome Foundation Ltd 369

Oxon
Esso Group of Cos 163
Nielsen Business Services 259
SPL International 326
UK Atomic Energy Authority 360

Surrey
Air Products plc 70
Beecham Pharmaceuticals 90
Brewer & Co 102
Crown Life 143
Easams 58
Geophysical Service International 180
Hughes Microelectronics Ltd 197
Imperial Life Assurance Co of Canada 203
Knill Padgham & Grande 214
Logica Group 220
Mallinson-Denny Ltd 227
PMA Consultants Ltd 274
Stewart Wrightson 330
Timex Corporation 349
James Walker Group of Cos 366
R Watson & Sons 367

W Sussex
APV Co Ltd 75
Beecham Pharmaceuticals 90
Eurotherm International 164
Kidsons 213
Ricardo Consulting Engineers 297

SOUTH WEST
AE Group 69
Arthur Andersen & Co 74
Baker Rooke 85
Burmah Oil plc 118
C & J Clark Ltd 128
Clerical Medical & General Life Assurance
  Society 131
Richard Costain plc 142
Endsleigh Insurance Services 159
Engineering Careers Information Service 24
Fraser Williams 171
Fryer Whitehill & Co 174
Government Communications HQ 183
Help the Aged 194
Imperial Brewing & Leisure Ltd 201
Institute of Chartered Accountants of
  Scotland 381
Institute of Chartered Secretaries &
  Administrators 382
Lex Service Group plc 216
Longcrofts 223
Metal Box plc 238
Midland Bank plc 244
National Westminster Bank plc 257
Pearl Assurance plc 265

Pedigree Petfoods 269
Racal Electronics plc 288
RHM (Ranks Hovis McDougall plc) 293
Royal Corps of Naval Constructors 303
Schlumberger Measurement & Control (UK) Ltd 309
Miss Selfridge Ltd 318
Spicer & Pegler 325
Tandy Corporation (Branch UK) 335
THORN EMI plc 343
Thornton Baker 346
Touche Ross & Co 350
Unilever 355
United Biscuits (UK) plc 358

Avon
Arthur Young McClelland Moores & Co 79
British Aerospace-Dynamics Group 103
Clerical Medical & General Life Assurance Society 131
Coopers & Lybrand 140
Fairey Hydraulics Ltd 165
Fraser Williams 171
Kidsons 213
Mallinson-Denny Ltd 227
Sun Life Assurance plc 332
Touche Ross & Co 350
Westland plc 372

Channel Islands
Arthur Young McClelland Moores & Co 79
Touche Ross & Co 350

Devon
Coopers & Lybrand 140
Mallinson-Denny Ltd 227
Robson Rhodes 298
Texas Instruments Ltd 338
Touche Ross & Co 350

Dorset
UK Atomic Energy Authority 360

Glos
Dowty Group Ltd 159
Government Communications HQ 183
Joint Technical Language Service 209

Som
Arthur Young McClelland Moores & Co 79
Mallinson-Denny Ltd 227
Westland plc 372

Wilts
Logica Group 220
Micro Focus Ltd 241
Raychem 291
UK Provident 353

WALES
Associated British Foods plc 80
Association of Certified Accountants 378
Bradford & Bingley Building Society 101
British Gas Corporation 106
British Steel Corporation 115
British Transport Police 36
Civil Service 127
Coopers & Lybrand 140
Richard Costain plc 142
Robert M Douglas Holdings plc 155
Dowty Group Ltd 159
Dunlop 157
Endsleigh Insurance Services 159
Engineering Careers Information Service 24
Ferranti plc 167
French Kier Construction Ltd 172
Gallaher Ltd 175

Habitat 188
Help the Aged 194
IBM United Kingdom Ltd 199
Industrial & Commercial Finance Corporation Ltd 204
Institute of Chartered Accountants of Scotland 381
Institute of Chartered Secretaries & Administrators 382
Institute of Cost & Management Accountants 383
Institute of Marketing 385
Mars Ltd (Confectionery Division) 230
Metal Box plc 238
Midland Bank plc 244
National Bus Co 249
National Coal Board 251
National Westminster Bank plc 257
Newey & Eyre Group Ltd 258
Pannell Kerr Forster 263
Pearl Assurance plc 265
Peat Marwick Mitchell & Co 267
Pedigree Petfoods 269
Post Office 276
Prison Service 279
RHM (Ranks Hovis McDougall plc) 293
Richmond Fellowship Therapeutic Communities 297
Spicer & Pegler 325
Standard Telephones & Cables plc 328
THORN EMI plc 343
Thornton Baker 346
Touche Ross & Co 350
Trading Standards Officers 349
TSB Group 351
YMCA 373

Clwyd
Union International plc 358

Dyfed
Esso Group of Cos 163

Gwent
Ferranti plc 167
Touche Ross & Co 350

M Glamorgan
Amersham International plc 72

S Glamorgan
Coopers & Lybrand 140
Dow Corning Ltd 155
Ford Motor Co Ltd 169
Mallinson-Denny Ltd 227
Touche Ross & Co 350

W Glamorgan
Ford Motor Co Ltd 169
Touche Ross & Co 350

MIDLANDS
AE Group 69
Arthur Andersen & Co 74
Aurora Holdings plc 81
Baker Rooke 85
Bank of Credit & Commerce International SA 86
Bowater Organisation 100
British Linen Bank Ltd 107
British Steel Corporation 115
Burmah Oil plc 118
BXL Plastics Ltd 122
Clark Pixley 129
Richard Costain plc 142
Data Logic Ltd 149
Dunlop 157

Endsleigh Insurance Services 159
Engineering Careers Information Service 24
Equity & Law Life Assurance Society plc 160
Fraser Williams 171
Fryer Whitehill & Co 174
General Electric Co plc 177
Guest Keen & Nettlefolds plc 187
Habitat 188
Haines Watts 189
Help the Aged 194
Institute of Chartered Accountants of Scotland 381
Institute of Chartered Secretaries & Administrators 382
International Computers Ltd 206
Johnson Matthey Group 208
Kyle Stewart Group 215
Lex Service Group plc 216
McDonald's Golden Arches Restaurants Ltd 220
Metal Box plc 238
Midland Bank plc 244
National Westminster Bank plc 257
Northern Foods plc 260
Pearl Assurance plc 265
Pedigree Petfoods 269
Quinton Hazell plc 287
Racal Electronics plc 288
RHM (Ranks Hovis McDougall plc) 293
Miss Selfridge Ltd 318
Shand Group 320
Jefferson Smurfit Group 322
Spicer & Pegler 325
SPL International 326
Staveley Industries plc 329
Tandy Corporation (Branch UK) 335
THORN EMI plc 343
Thornton Baker 346
TI Group plc 340
Touche Ross & Co 350
Unilever 355
United Biscuits (UK) plc 358
Yorkshire Bank plc 374

Derby
NEI International Combustion Ltd 20

Leics
Armitage & Norton 76
Brush Electrical Machines Ltd 114
Coopers & Lybrand 140
Leicestershire County Council 42
Mallinson-Denny Ltd 227
Mars Group Services 230
National Nuclear Corporation Ltd 25
Touche Ross & Co 350

Lincs
Baker Perkins Group of Cos 84
British Sugar plc 11
Coles Cranes Ltd 13
Conoco Group in the UK 13

Northants
Coopers & Lybrand 140
Ford Motor Co Ltd 16
Lummus Co Ltd 22

Notts
Arthur Young McClelland Moores & Co 79
Boots Co plc 9
Coopers & Lybrand 140
Kidsons 213
Scicon 31

Salop
British Sugar plc 11

fs

er Perkins Group of Cos 84
helin Tyre plc 241

Midlands

hur Young McClelland Moores & Co 79
ish Sugar plc 115
pers & Lybrand 140
vty Group Ltd 159
ity & Law Life Assurance Society plc 160
eco Minsep Group 169
ser Williams 171
amazoo Business Systems 211
sons 213
linson-Denny Ltd 227
ss Computer Systems Ltd 278
son Rhodes 298
Thompson Ltd 342
che Ross & Co 350
trose Ltd 365
st Midlands Fire Service 370

rwicks

tware Sciences 323

ST ANGLIA

water Organisation 100
wn & Root (UK) Ltd 117
hard Costain plc 142
gineering Careers Information Service 24
neral Electric Co plc 177
p the Aged 194
ghes Allen Payne Stone 198
titute of Chartered Accountants of Scotland 381
titute of Chartered Secretaries & Administrators 382
er-Scan Laboratories Ltd 215
Donald's Golden Arches Restaurants Ltd 226
tal Box plc 238
dland Bank plc 244
tional Westminster Bank plc 257
arl Assurance plc 265
digree Petfoods 269
M (Ranks Hovis McDougall plc) 293
ss Selfridge Ltd 318
cer & Pegler 325
ndard Telephones & Cables plc 328
ornton Baker 346
Group plc 347
ilever 355
ited Biscuits (UK) plc 358

mbs

ker Perkins Group of Cos 84
tish Sugar plc 115
a-Geigy Plastics & Additives Co 126
er-Scan Laboratories Ltd 215
rkins Engines Ltd 270

rfolk

tish Sugar plc 115
opers & Lybrand 140
rdline Surveys 177
dsons 213
allinson-Denny Ltd 227
ay & Baker Ltd 235
rwich Union Insurance Group 262

ffolk

itish Sugar plc 115
rdline Surveys 177
dsons 213

NORTH EAST

AE Group 69
Arthur Andersen & Co 74
Aurora Holdings plc 81
Bank of Credit & Commerce International SA 86
Bowater Organisation 100
British Steel Corporation 115
BXL Plastics Ltd 122
Richard Costain plc 142
Cummins Engine Co Ltd 147
Dunlop 157
Endsleigh Insurance Services 159
Engineering Careers Information Service 24
Fenwick Ltd 166
Fraser Williams 171
Gallaher Ltd 175
General Electric Co plc 177
Habitat 188
Help the Aged 194
Holset Engineering Co Ltd 195
Imperial Brewing & Leisure Ltd 201
Institute of Chartered Accountants of Scotland 381
Institute of Chartered Secretaries & Administrators 382
Lishman Sidwell Campbell & Price 218
Metal Box plc 238
Midland Bank plc 244
National Westminster Bank plc 257
Northern Foods plc 260
Pearl Assurance plc 265
Pedigree Petfoods 269
RHM (Ranks Hovis McDougall plc) 293
Miss Selfridge Ltd 318
Shand Group 320
Spicer & Pegler 325
SPL International 326
Tandy Corporation (Branch UK) 335
THORN EMI plc 343
Thornton Baker 346
Unilever 355
United Biscuits (UK) plc 358
Yorkshire Bank plc 374

Cleveland

Coopers & Lybrand 140
Davy McKee Ltd 150

Durham

Coopers & Lybrand 140
Moores Furniture Group 248

Humberside

Conoco Group in the UK 137
Kidsons 213
Mallinson-Denny Ltd 227

N Yorks

Lishman Sidwell Campbell & Price 218
Moores Furniture Group 248

S Yorks

Coopers & Lybrand 140
Finnie Ross Allfields 168
Fraser Williams 171

W Yorks

Armitage & Norton 76
Arthur Young McClelland Moores & Co 79
Baker Perkins Group of Cos 84
Baker Rooke 85
Coopers & Lybrand 140
Finnie Ross Allfields 168
Fraser Williams 171
Hickson & Welch Ltd 194
Kidsons 213

Robson Rhodes 298
Touche Ross & Co 350

Tyne & Wear

Arthur Young McClelland Moores & Co 79
Baker Perkins Group of Cos 84
British Ship Research Association 111
Coles Cranes Ltd 133
Mallinson-Denny Ltd 227
Timex Corporation 349
Touche Ross & Co 350
Victor Products (Wallsend) plc 363

NORTH WEST

Arthur Andersen & Co 74
Aurora Holdings plc 81
Bank of Credit & Commerce International SA 86
British Nuclear Fuels Ltd 109
Burmah Oil plc 118
BXL Plastics Ltd 122
Clark Pixley 129
Richard Costain plc 142
Dunlop 157
Endsleigh Insurance Services 159
Engineering Careers Information Service 24
Ferranti plc 167
Fraser Williams 171
Gallaher Ltd 175
General Electric Co plc 177
Habitat 188
Haines Watts 189
Help the Aged 194
Institute of Chartered Accountants of Scotland 381
Institute of Chartered Secretaries & Administrators 382
International Computers Ltd 206
Kennedy & Donkin 211
Lex Service Group plc 216
McDonald's Golden Arches Restaurants Ltd 226
Metal Box plc 238
Midland Bank plc 244
National Westminster Bank plc 257
Northern Foods plc 260
Pearl Assurance plc 265
Pedigree Petfoods 269
Quinton Hazell plc 287
RHM (Ranks Hovis McDougall plc) 293
Miss Selfridge Ltd 318
Shand Group 320
Jefferson Smurfit Group 322
Spicer & Pegler 325
SPL International 326
Staveley Industries plc 329
Tandy Corporation (Branch UK) 335
THORN EMI plc 343
Thornton Baker 346
TI Group plc 347
Unilever 355
United Biscuits (UK) plc 358
Yorkshire Bank plc 374

Cheshire

Arthur Young McClelland Moores & Co 79
British Nuclear Fuels Ltd 109
Daresbury Laboratory 148
Ferranti plc 167
Ilford Ltd 200
National Nuclear Corporation Ltd 253
Software Sciences 323
UK Atomic Energy Authority 360
VG Isotopes Ltd 362
Wellcome Foundation Ltd 369

Cumbria

British Nuclear Fuels Ltd	109
C & J Clark Ltd	128
Mallinson-Denny Ltd	227
UK Atomic Energy Authority	360
James Walker Group of Cos	366

Gtr Manchester

Armitage & Norton	76
Arthur Young McClelland Moores & Co	79
CAP Group Ltd	123
Ciba-Geigy Plastics & Additives Co	126
Co-operative Insurance Society Ltd	139
Coopers & Lybrand	140
Ferranti plc	167
Fraser Williams	171
Hawker Siddeley Dynamics Engineering Ltd	192
Kidsons	213
Mallinson-Denny Ltd	227
Milliken Industrials Ltd	245
Robson Rhodes	298
Scapa Group plc	310
SPL International	326
Touche Ross & Co	350
United Biscuits (UK) plc	358
Williams & Glyn's Bank plc	20

IoM

Coopers & Lybrand	140

Lancs

Armitage & Norton	76
Arthur Young McClelland Moores & Co	79
British Aerospace-Dynamics Group	103
British Nuclear Fuels Ltd	109
Coles Cranes Ltd	133
Michelin Tyre plc	241
National Nuclear Corporation Ltd	253
Pilkington Brothers plc	272
Scapa Group plc	310
UK Atomic Energy Authority	360

Merseyside

Arthur Young McClelland Moores & Co	79
Coopers & Lybrand	140
Fishburn Printing Ink Co Ltd	168
Ford Motor Co Ltd	169
Fraser Williams	171
Kidsons	213
Lever Brothers Ltd	216
Littlewoods Organisation plc	218
Mallinson-Denny Ltd	227
Pilkington Brothers plc	272
ER Squibb & Sons plc	328
Touche Ross & Co	350
Unilever Research	355

NORTHERN IRELAND

Accountancy & Financial Management in the Public Sector	68
Association of Certified Accountants	378
BHS (British Home Stores) plc	94
BXL Plastics Ltd	122
Chartered Institute of Public Finance & Accountancy	379
Civil Service	127
Cleanaway	130
Coopers & Lybrand	140
Engineering Careers Information Service	24
French Kier Construction Ltd	172
Gallaher Ltd	175
General Electric Co plc	177
IBM United Kingdom Ltd	199
Institute of Chartered Accountants of Scotland	381
Institute of Chartered Secretaries & Administrators	382
Institute of Cost & Management Accountants	383
Institute of Marketing	385
Institute of Purchasing & Supply	385
Metal Box plc	238
Newey & Eyre Group Ltd	258
Northern Foods plc	260
Pannell Kerr Forster	263
Post Office	276
Royal Navy, Royal Marines & WRNS	305
Miss Selfridge Ltd	318
Spicer & Pegler	325
Standard Telephones & Cables plc	328
Thomson McLintock & Co	341
TSB Group	351
YMCA	373

Antrim

Michelin Tyre plc	241

Down

Michelin Tyre plc	241

SCOTLAND

AE Group	69
Arthur Andersen & Co	74
Armitage & Norton	76
Associated British Foods plc	80
Association of Certified Accountants	378
Aurora Holdings plc	81
Babcock International plc	82
Bank of Credit & Commerce International SA	86
Bank of Scotland	87
BHS (British Home Stores) plc	94
BICC plc	94
Bradford & Bingley Building Society	101
British Airports	104
British Gas Corporation	106
British Shipbuilders	112
British Steel Corporation	115
British Transport Police	36
Brown & Root (UK) Ltd	117
BXL Plastics Ltd	122
Civil Service	127
Clark Pixley	129
Clydesdale Bank plc	132
Richard Costain plc	142
Dept of Industry (Science Group)	154
Robert M Douglas Holdings plc	155
Endsleigh Insurance Services	159
Engineering Careers Information Service	24
Ferranti plc	167
Fraser Williams	171
French Kier Construction Ltd	172
Gallaher Ltd	175
General Electric Co plc	177
Geoservices	180
Habitat	188
Help the Aged	194
IBM United Kingdom Ltd	199
Industrial & Commercial Finance Corporation Ltd	204
Institute of Chartered Accountants of Scotland	381
Institute of Chartered Secretaries & Administrators	382
Institute of Cost & Management Accountants	383
Institute of Marketing	385
Institute of Purchasing & Supply	385
International Computers Ltd	206
Marley Group	229
Mars Ltd (Confectionery Division)	230

John Menzies (Holdings) plc
Metal Box plc
Mobil Oil Co Ltd
National Coal Board
National Semiconductor
Newey & Eyre Group Ltd
Edmund Nuttall Group of Cos
Pannell Kerr Forster
Peat Marwick Mitchell & Co
Post Office
Racal Electronics plc
RHM (Ranks Hovis McDougall plc)
Richmond Fellowship Therapeutic Communities
Royal Corps of Naval Constructors
Royal Navy, Royal Marines & WRNS
Scottish Equitable Life Assurance Society
Scottish Provident Institution
Scottish Special Housing Association
Scottish Widows' Fund & Life Assurance Society
Miss Selfridge Ltd
Jefferson Smurfit Group
Spicer & Pegler
Tandy Corporation (Branch UK)
Teaching Profession (Scotland)
Thomson McLintock & Co
THORN EMI plc
Thornton Baker
TI Group plc
Touche Ross & Co
Trading Standards Officers
TSB Group
United Biscuits (UK) plc
Vetco Offshore Ltd
Weir Pumps Ltd
YMCA

Border

Teaching Profession (Scotland)

Central Region

Ferranti plc
Teaching Profession (Scotland)

Grampian

Analysts Schlumberger
Arthur Young McClelland Moores & Co
British National Oil Corporation
Conoco Group in the UK
Gardline Surveys
Mallinson-Denny Ltd
Michelin Tyre plc
Scicon
Teaching Profession (Scotland)
Vetco Offshore Ltd

Dumfries & Galloway

British Nuclear Fuels Ltd
Teaching Profession (Scotland)

Fife

Arthur Young McClelland Moores & Co
Hughes Microelectronics Ltd
Mallinson-Denny Ltd
Teaching Profession (Scotland)

Highland

Mallinson-Denny Ltd
Teaching Profession (Scotland)
UK Atomic Energy Authority

Lothian

Arthur Young McClelland Moores & Co
British Linen Bank Ltd
Coopers & Lybrand
Teaching Profession (Scotland)

uche Ross & Co	350
Watson & Sons	367

rathclyde

thur Young McClelland Moores & Co	79
arr & Stroud	89
eecham Pharmaceuticals	90
ritish Linen Bank Ltd	107
ritish National Oil Corporation	107
iba-Geigy Plastics & Additives Co	126
leanaway	130
oopers & Lybrand	140
nnie Ross Allfields	168
aser Williams	171
ymans, Robertson & Co	198
allinson-Denny Ltd	227
otorola Ltd	247
ational Semiconductor	255
eaching Profession (Scotland)	337
ouche Ross & Co	350

ayside

thur Young McClelland Moores & Co	79
ichelin Tyre plc	241
CR (Manufacturing) Ltd	258
eaching Profession (Scotland)	337
mex Corporation	349

EPUBLIC OF IRELAND

thur Young McClelland Moores & Co	79
ssociated British Foods plc	80
HS (British Home Stores) plc	94
oopers & Lybrand	140
stitute of Chartered Secretaries & Administrators	382

Institute of Cost & Management Accountants	383
FJC Lilley plc	217
Metal Box plc	238
Pannell Kerr Forster	263
Jefferson Smurfit Group	322
Touche Ross & Co	350
R Watson & Sons	367

OVERSEAS

Analysts Schlumberger	73
Anglo American Corporation of South Africa Ltd	388
Association of Certified Accountants	378
Babcock International plc	82
Barclays Bank plc Group	88
Bowater Organisation	100
John Brown Engineers & Constructors Ltd	116
Compeda Ltd	135
Consolidated Gold Fields plc	388
Dowell Schlumberger	389
Exploration Logging	165
Flopetrol International SA	390
Gardline Surveys	177
General Electric Co plc	177
General Mining Union Corp Ltd (Gencor)	391
Geophysical Service International	180
Geoservices	180
Hong Kong Administrative Class	392
Horizon Exploration Ltd	195
Institute of Chartered Accountants in England & Wales	380
Institute of Marketing	385
Johannesburg Consolidated Investment Co Ltd	393

Kennedy & Donkin	211
FJC Lilley plc	217
Lloyds Bank International	394
Lloyds Bank plc	219
Logica Group	220
Metal Box plc	238
Micro Focus Ltd	241
National Mutual Life Association of Australasia Ltd	252
NEI Overseas Ltd	395
Richmond Fellowship Therapeutic Communities	297
NM Rothschild & Sons Ltd	299
Royal Air Force	301
Royal Electrical & Mechanical Engineers	304
Royal Hong Kong Police Force	395
Royal Navy, Royal Marines & WRNS	305
Schlumberger Wireline Logging	396
Security Pacific National Bank	315
Seiscom Delta United	316
Seismograph Service Ltd	317
Software Sciences	323
South African Civil Service	397
Taylor Woodrow International Ltd	336
Touche Ross & Co	350
Trower, Still & Keeling	351
Union International plc	358
United Biscuits (UK) plc	358
Vetco Offshore Ltd	362
Voluntary Service Overseas	62
R Watson & Sons	367
Western Geophysical Co of America	371
YMCA	373
Zambia Consolidated Copper Mines Ltd	398

Advertisers

Advertisers are listed alphabetically with page references to their entries.

Abbott Laboratories Ltd 68
Accountancy & Financial Management in the Public Sector 68
AE Group 69
AGB Research Group 70
Air Products plc 70
Alfa-Laval Co Ltd 72
Amersham International plc 72
Analysts Schlumberger 73, 428
Arthur Andersen & Co 74
Arthur Andersen & Co Management Consultancy Division 74
Anglo American Corporation of South Africa Ltd 388
APV Co Ltd 75
Armitage & Norton 76
Regular Army 77
Arthur Young McClelland Moores & Co 79
Associated British Foods plc 80
Association of Certified Accountants 376, 378
Association of Cost & Executive Accountants 379
Aurora Holdings plc 81
Babcock International plc 82
John Baker, Sons & Bell 83
Baker Perkins Group of Cos 84
Baker Rooke 85
Balfour Beatty Ltd 86
Bank of Credit & Commerce International SA 86
Bank of Scotland 87
Barclays Bank plc Group 88
Barr & Stroud 89
Beecham Pharmaceuticals 90
Beecham Products 91
Benton & Bowles Ltd 92
Bestobell plc 93
BHS (British Home Stores) plc 28, 94
BICC plc 94
Binder Hamlyn 95
BIS Applied Systems Ltd 96
BIS Software Ltd 96
Boase Massimi Pollitt 97
BOC Ltd 98
Boehringer Corporation (London) Ltd 98
Boots Co plc 99
Bowater Organisation 100
CT Bowring & Co Ltd 100
Bradford & Bingley Building Society 101
Brebner, Allen & Trapp 101
Brewer & Co 102
Brian Ingram Associates 102
British Aerospace-Dynamics Group 103
British Airports 104
British Airways 104
British Gas Corporation 106
British Linen Bank Ltd 107
British National Oil Corporation 6, 107
British Nuclear Fuels Ltd 109
British Rail 111
British Ship Research Association 111
British Shipbuilders 112
British Standards Institution 113
British Steel Corporation 115
British Sugar plc 115
British Transport Police 36
Britoil 116
John Brown Engineers & Constructors Ltd 116
Brown & Root (UK) Ltd 117
Brush Electrical Machines Ltd 118

Burmah Oil plc 118
Leo Burnett Ltd 120
Buzzacott & Co 121
BXL Plastics Ltd 122
Cadbury Schweppes 122
CAP Group Ltd 123
CASE Computer & Systems Engineering plc 126
Casson Beckman 125
Chartered Institute of Public Finance & Accountancy 379
Ciba-Geigy Plastics & Additives Co 126
Civil Service 32, 66, 127
C & J Clark Ltd 128
Clark Pixley 129
Cleanaway 130
Clerical Medical & General Life Assurance Society 131
Clydesdale Bank plc 132
Coles Cranes Ltd 133
Compeda Ltd 135
Computer Machinery Company (CMC) Ltd 133
Computer Technology Ltd 136
Computervision Europe Inc 436
Conoco Group in the UK 137
Conoco (UK) Ltd 137
Conoco Ltd (Humber Refinery) 138
Conoco Ltd (Marketing) 138
Consolidated Gold Fields plc 388
Continental Oil Co Ltd 139
Co-operative Insurance Society Ltd 139
Coopers & Lybrand 10, 140
Coopers & Lybrand Associates Ltd 141
Cossor Electronics Ltd 142
Richard Costain plc 142
Courage Ltd 143
Crosfield Electronics Ltd 145
Crown Life 143
C & S Antennas 145
Cubie Wood & Co Ltd 146
Cummins Engine Co Ltd 147
Daresbury Laboratory 148
Data Logic Ltd 149
Davy McKee Ltd 150
Davy McKee (London) Ltd 151
Dearborn Chemicals Ltd 152
Dearden Farrow 152
Deloitte Haskins & Sells 18, 153
Dept of Industry (Science Group) 154
Robert M Douglas Holdings plc 155
Dow Corning Ltd 155
Dowell Schlumberger 14, 389
Dowty Group Ltd 159
Dunlop 157
Easams 58
Endsleigh Insurance Services 159
Engineering Careers Information Service 24, 48
Equity & Law Life Assurance Society plc 160
Ernst & Whinney 161
Esso Group of Cos 163
Eurotherm International 164
Exploration Logging 165
Fairey Hydraulics Ltd 165
Fenwick Ltd 166
Ferranti plc 167
Financial Training 12
Fine Fare 446
Finnie Ross Allfields 168, 422
Fishburn Printing Ink Co Ltd 168

Flopetrol International SA 39
Ford Motor Co Ltd 26, 16
Foseco Minsep Group 16
Four Square 17
Fraser Keen 17
Fraser Williams 17
French Kier Construction Ltd 17
Friends' Provident Life Office 17
Fryer Whitehill & Co 17
Gallaher Ltd 17
Gardline Surveys 17
General Electric Co plc 17
General Mining Union Corp Ltd (Gencor) 39
General Motors Ltd 17
Geophysical Service International 18
Geoservices 18
Gestetner 18
Getty Oil (Britain) Ltd 18
Government Communications HQ 18
Graduate Appointments 45
Greater London Council 18
Guardian Royal Exchange Assurance plc 18
Guest Keen & Nettlefolds plc 18
Habitat 18
Hacker Young 18
Haines Watts 19
Hambros Bank Ltd 19
HAT Accountancy Training Syndicate 19
Hawker Siddeley Dynamics Engineering Ltd 19
Haymarket Publishing Group 19
Help the Aged 19
Hickson & Welch Ltd 19
Holset Engineering Co Ltd 19
Hong Kong Administrative Class 39
Horizon Exploration Ltd 19
Hughes Allen Payne Stone 19
Hughes Microelectronics Ltd 19
Hymans, Robertson & Co 19
IBM United Kingdom Ltd 19
Ilford Ltd 20
Imperial Brewing & Leisure Ltd 20
Imperial Life Assurance Co of Canada 20
Incorporated Society of Valuers & Auctioneers 37
Industrial & Commercial Finance Corporation Ltd 20
Institute of Chartered Accountants in England & Wales 38
Institute of Chartered Accountants of Scotland 38
Institute of Chartered Secretaries & Administrators 38
Institute of Cost & Management Accountants 38
Institute of Marketing 38
Institute of Purchasing & Supply 38
Institution of Electrical Engineers 20
Instron Ltd 20
NEI International Combustion Ltd 20
International Computers Ltd 20
ITT-IDEC 20
Johannesburg Consolidated Investment Co Ltd 39
Johnson Matthey Group 20
Joint Technical Language Service 20
Kalamazoo Business Systems 21
MW Kellogg Ltd 21
Kennedy & Donkin 21
Kidsons 21

ight Frank & Rutley 214
nill Padgham & Grande 214
ile Stewart Group 215
nsdowne Appointments Register 452
ser-Scan Laboratories Ltd 215
icestershire County Council 424
ver Brothers Ltd 216
x Service Group plc 216
C Lilley plc 217
shman Sidwell Campbell & Price 218
ttlewoods Organisation plc 218
oyds Bank International 394
oyds Bank plc 219
agica Group 220
ondon Fire Brigade 222
ondon Transport 222
ongcrofts 223
ucas Industries plc 224
ummus Co Ltd 225
cDermott Engineering London 226
cDonald's Golden Arches Restaurants
  Ltd 226
allinson-Denny Ltd 227
arks & Spencer plc 228
arley Group 229
ars Group Services 230
ars Ltd (Confectionery Division) 230
ars Money Systems 233
atthew Hall Group 234
lay & Baker Ltd 235, 460
ohn Menzies (Holdings) plc 235
erck, Sharp & Dohme Ltd 236
errill Lynch International 237
etal Box plc 238
leteorological Office 239
lontague L Meyer plc 240
lichelin Tyre plc 241
licro Consultants Group 243
licro Focus Ltd 241
icrowave Associates Ltd 243
lidland Bank plc 244
lilliken Industrials Ltd 245
lobil Oil Co Ltd 247
loores Furniture Group 248
lorgan Brown & Haynes 249
lotorola Ltd 247
lurray Noble 249
lational Bus Co 249
lational Coal Board 251
lational Maritime Institute 251
lational Mutual Life Association of
  Australasia Ltd 252
lational Nuclear Corporation Ltd 253
lational Provident Institution 254
lational Semiconductor 255
lational Westminster Bank plc 257
lCR (Manufacturing) Ltd 258
lewey & Eyre Group Ltd 258
lielsen Business Services 259
lorris Gilbert Stern & Co 259
lorthern Engineering Industries plc 260
lorthern Foods plc 260
lorthern Ireland Civil Service 261
lorwich Union Insurance Group 262
Edmund Nuttall Group of Cos 263

NEI Overseas Ltd 395
Pannell Kerr Forster 263
Partco Europe 265
Pearl Assurance plc 265
Peat Marwick Mitchell & Co 267
Pedigree Petfoods 269
Perkins Engines Ltd 270
Pfizer Ltd 271
Phillips & Drew 272
Pilkington Brothers plc 272
Plessey 273
PMA Consultants Ltd 274
Police Service in England & Wales 275, 432
Post Office 276
Powell Duffryn Systems Ltd 278
Press Computer Systems Ltd 278
Prime Computer (UK) Ltd 438
Prison Service 279
Protech International 442
Providence Capitol Life Assurance Co Ltd 284
Provident Life Association of London Ltd 284
Prudential Assurance Co Ltd 285
Quantel Ltd 287
Quinton Hazell plc 287
Racal Electronics plc 288
Raychem 291
Recruitment Business 46
Research Bureau Ltd 291
Reuters 292
RHM (Ranks Hovis McDougall plc) 293
Ricardo Consulting Engineers 297
Richmond Fellowship Therapeutic
  Communities 297
Rio Tinto Zinc Corporation plc 295
Robson Rhodes 298
NM Rothschild & Sons Ltd 299
Rowe & Pitman 300
Rowland Nevill & Co 301
Royal Air Force 301
Royal Corps of Naval Constructors 303
Royal Electrical & Mechanical Engineers 304
Royal Hong Kong Police Force 395
Royal Insurance 50
Royal Navy, Royal Marines & WRNS 305
Save & Prosper Group 306
Scapa Group plc 310
Schlumberger Measurement & Control (UK)
  Ltd 309
Schlumberger Wireline Logging 396, ibc
J Henry Schroder Wagg & Co Ltd 307
Scicon 310
Scientific Civil Service 311
Scottish Equitable Life Assurance Society 313
Scottish Provident Institution 314
Scottish Special Housing Association 314
Scottish Widows' Fund & Life Assurance
  Society 315
Security Pacific National Bank 315
Seiscom Delta United 316
Seismograph Service Ltd 317, 456
Miss Selfridge Ltd 318
Selfridges Ltd 319
SGRD Ltd 320
Shand Group 320
SIA Computer Services 321

Silver Altman & Co 321
Smallfield Fitzhugh Tillet & Co 322
Jefferson Smurfit Group 322
Software Sciences 323
South African Civil Service 397
Spicer & Pegler 325
SPL International 326
Stanley A Spofforth & Co 327
ER Squibb & Sons plc 328
Standard Telecommunication Laboratories 22, 328
Standard Telephones & Cables plc 328
Staveley Industries plc 329
Stephens Associates 46
Stewart Wrightson 330
Stoy Hayward & Co 331
Sun Life Assurance plc 332
Sun Life Assurance Co of Canada 334
Systime Ltd 331
Tandy Corporation (Branch UK) 335
Taylor Instrument Ltd 335
Taylor Instrument Ltd Analytics Division 336
Taylor Woodrow International Ltd 336
Teaching Profession (Scotland) 337
Texas Instruments Ltd 338
NEI Thompson Ltd 342
Thomson McLintock & Co 341
THORN EMI plc 343
Thornton Baker 346
TI Group plc 8, 347
Timex Corporation 349
Touche Ross & Co ifc, 350
Trading Standards Officers 349
Trower, Still & Keeling 351
TSB Group 351
UK Atomic Energy Authority 360
UK Provident 353
Unigate plc 357
Unilever 355
Unilever Research 355
Union International plc 358
United Biscuits (UK) plc 358, 430
Vetco Offshore Ltd 362
VG Isotopes Ltd 362
Vickers Shipbuilding & Engineering Ltd 363
Victor Products (Wallsend) plc 363
VNU Business Publications BV 365, 434
Vocational Guidance Association 44
Voluntary Service Overseas 62
Vosper Thornycroft (UK) Ltd 365
Waitrose Ltd 365
James Walker Group of Cos 366
Watney Mann & Truman Brewers Ltd 367
R Watson & Sons 367
Weir Pumps Ltd 368
Wellcome Foundation Ltd 369
West Midlands Fire Service 370
Western Geophysical Co of America 371
Westland plc 372
Williams & Glyn's Bank plc 20
Wilson Green Gibbs 373
YMCA 373
Yorkshire Bank plc 374
Zambia Consolidated Copper Mines Ltd 398

NOTES

NOTES

NOTES

NOTES

NOTES

NOTES

NOTES